KU-227-531

CONTENTS

Leatherhead Food RA
PUBLISHING

FOOD CRAVINGS AND ADDICTION

Edited by
Marion M. Hetherington

Published by
Leatherhead Publishing
a division of
LFRA Limited
Randalls Road, Leatherhead, Surrey KT22 7RY, UK

First Edition 2001
ISBN No: 0 905748 18 2

Printed and bound in the UK by IBT Global, 1B Barking Business Centre, 25 Thames Road, Barking, London IG11 0JP

CONTRIBUTORS

Dr Antonio Cepeda-Benito and
  Dr David Gleaves
TEXAS A&M UNIVERSITY
Department of Psychology
College Station
TX 77843-4235
USA

Professor Roy A. Wise
Behavioral Neuroscience Branch
Intramural Research Program
National Institute on Drug Abuse
5500 Nathan Shock Drive
Baltimore
MD 21224
USA

Dr Blake A. Gosnell
Neuropsychiatric Research Institute
P.O. Box 1415
Fargo
ND 58107
USA

Dr Dean D. Krahn
Department of Veterans Affairs
William S. Middleton Memorial Veterans
  Hospital
2500 Overlook Terrace
Madison
WI 53705
USA

Dr Tim C. Kirkham and Dr Claire M. Williams
Department of Psychology
University of Reading
Whiteknights
Reading
RG6 6AL
UK

Dr Suzanne Higgs
School of Psychology
University of Birmingham
Edgbaston
Birmingham
B15 2TT
UK

Professor Steven J. Cooper
Department of Psychology
Eleanor Rathbone Building
Bedford Street South
Liverpool
L69 7ZA
UK

Dr Martin R. Yeomans
Department of Experimental Psychology
University of Sussex
Brighton
Sussex
BN1 9QA
UK

Dr Debra A. Zellner
Department of Psychology
Montclair State University
Upper Montclair
New Jersey 07043
USA

Ms Erin M. Edwards
Department of Behavioral Science
C1747, Postal Code H181
Pennsylvania State College of Medicine
500 University Drive
Hershey
PA 17033
USA

Dr Edward Leigh Gibson
Health Behaviour Unit
Department of Epidemiology and Public
    Health
Royal Free and University College Medical
    School
University College London
2-16 Torrington Place
London WC1E 6BT
UK

Professor Anne Murcott
Sociology
South Bank University
103 Borough Road
London SE1 0AA
UK

Dr Leslie Gofton
Department of Sociology and Social Policy
University of Newcastle Upon Tyne
Claremont Road
Newcastle Upon Tyne
NE1 7RU
UK

Professor David Benton
Department of Psychology
University of Wales, Swansea
Singleton Park
Swansea SA2 8PP
UK

Dr Marion M. Hetherington
Department of Psychology
University of Dundee
Dundee
Scotland DD1 4NH
UK

Dr Hendrik J. Smit and Dr Peter J. Rogers
Department of Experimental Psychology
University of Bristol
8 Woodland Road
Bristol BS8 1TN
UK

Dr Debra J. Bowen
Fred Hutchinson Cancer Research Center
1100 Fairview Ave N.
Seattle
WA 98109
USA

Dr Susan Crystal
Lombardi Cancer Center
Cancer Control
2233 Wisconsin Ave
Suite 317
Washington
DC 20007
USA

Dr Louise Dye
School of Psychology
University of Leeds
Leeds
LS2 9JT
UK

Dr Suzette Evans
Department of Psychiatry
College of Physicians and Surgeons of
    Columbia University
The New York State Psychiatric Institute
1051 Riverside Drive
Unit 66
New York
NY 10032
USA

Professor Richard Hammersley
Health and Social Services Institute
University of Essex
Colchester
CO4 3SQ
UK

Professor Keith Matthews, Mr Alasdair
    Rooney and Dr Richard Day
Department of Psychiatry
University of Dundee
Dundee DD1 9SY
UK

Dr Marie Reid
Health and Social Services Institute
University of Essex
Colchester
CO4 3SQ
UK

Dr France Bellisle
Hôtel-Dieu
INSERM U341
1 place du Parvis Notre-Dame
75181 Paris
Cedex 04
France

Dr Michael Green
School of Life and Health Sciences
Aston University
Aston Triangle
Birmingham
B4 7ET
UK

Professor A Jansen
Maastricht University
Dept. of Experimental Psychology
PO Box 616
6200 MD Maastricht
The Netherlands

Dr Kelly A. Gendall and
    Professor Peter R. Joyce
Department of Psychological Medicine
Christchurch School of Medicine
P.O. Box 4345
Christchurch
New Zealand

Dr G. Terence Wilson and
    Ms Janet Latner
Rutgers The State University of New Jersey
Graduate School of Applied and
    Professional Psychology
152 Frelinghuysen Road
Piscataway
NJ 08854
USA

PREFACE

Food craving, defined as a strong desire for a particular food, is an extremely common, everyday experience for many people. Interest in food cravings and food addiction has increased dramatically over the last decade, with the press eager to present food cravings, particularly in pregnancy, as weird and wonderful urges for strange combinations of foods or even non-food items. Similarly, there is a general acceptance in the media of chocolate addiction or "chocoholism" in which preoccupation with securing chocolate or the intake of very large quantities of chocolate is regularly portrayed. Behind this rather sensationalist interest has been a serious, scientific analysis of the origins of food cravings and addiction, along with sociological, psychological and biological explanations of their emergence. Some have accounted for the phenomenon of food cravings using straightforward homeostatic principles, suggesting that cravings represent a direct expression of a need for a particular nutritive substance; thus, for example, cravings for salty foods are explained by a need for salt. The popular press accepts and promotes this simple association. However in well-nourished, healthy individuals, eating and food choice are only loosely coupled to strict physiological needs. In contrast, it is clear from empirical investigations that the concept of food cravings is complex and cannot neatly be explained merely with reference to nutritional deficiency.

The overall aim of this book is to examine the nature, aetiology, development and experience of food cravings and how these might relate to addiction and overeating. The concept of craving as applied to eating is explored in depth and whether there is a legitimate generalisation of food cravings to food addiction is carefully considered. The book has been divided into seven sections. The first section provides an overview and critique of food cravings research, including theories, definitions and measurement of food cravings. The second section outlines the neural circuitry involved in the anticipation of positive outcomes associated with eating. It provides an account of the neurobiology of desire, neuropharmacology of pleasure and appetite, and in particular the involvement of opioid, dopaminergic and endocannabinoid systems in food reward and hyperphagia. The third section examines behavioural models of craving using learning theory and specifically the role of associative conditioning in the development of food cravings. The fourth is devoted entirely to chocolate, since this is the food most commonly craved by consumers, occupying a very special place in the Anglo-American diet, and has been linked to addiction through both pharmacological and psychological explanations. Section five examines the relationship between cravings and hormonal status across the menstrual cycle and during pregnancy, since it is often observed that cravings and aversions emerge during pregnancy and that the frequency and intensity of cravings increase premenstrually, especially in women who experience premenstrual depression. Section six further highlights the link between mood state and appetite by considering concepts of craving and addiction as they relate to simple carbohydrates and alcohol; addiction to the chilli burn; how appetite changes in depression and with antidepressant medication; and the effects of food and food components on cognitive function and mood. The final section explores the relationship between cravings, dieting and eating disorders. Caloric restriction is frequently identified as a precursor to the development of food cravings; in turn, food cravings may trigger episodes of binge eating; and links between cravings, bingeing and the addiction-like qualities of eating disorders are often made. Thus, section seven addresses the role of dietary restriction and food cravings in binge eating, and whether eating disorders constitute a type of addiction.

My hope is that this book will be of interest and value to a variety of readers in both industry and academia, and to students from a range of disciplines as well as clinicians working with patients presenting with food cravings, food addiction or binge eating. I also anticipate that journalists and members of the public will use this book as a resource to answer questions about the nature and experience of food cravings and food addiction. The book offers the reader a near comprehensive account of food cravings and addiction; the underlying neurochemistry of food reward and desire; behavioural explanations of the development of food cravings; the impact of hormonal status on cravings; the relationship of food cravings to general constructs of addiction and mood modulation; and the link between dieting, cravings, food addiction and eating disorders.

I am extremely grateful to the distinguished authors of this book who have submitted promptly and with good humour. Victoria Emerton, my commissioning editor has been a faithful liaison and offered excellent assistance with all aspects of publication. I would like to acknowledge the support and friendship of my colleague Professor Wolfgang Langhans at the Swiss Federal Institute of Technology in Zürich, who hosted me during my sabbatical so that I could edit this volume and who provided a very apposite and inspirational environment in which to write my chapter. A word of thanks is due to Mr Alan Grant, Information Services Librarian at the University of Dundee, for his help in obtaining old, rare and obscure references. Finally, I would like to thank my husband Dr Martin Regan for his continuous intellectual and emotional support and for ensuring an unlimited supply of chocolate!

Marion M. Hetherington, D.Phil.
Editor

Department of Psychology
University of Dundee
Dundee
DD1 4HN
Scotland

1. OVERVIEW

1.1. A CRITIQUE OF FOOD CRAVINGS RESEARCH: THEORY, MEASUREMENT, AND FOOD INTAKE

Antonio Cepeda-Benito and David H. Gleaves

1.1.1 Relevance of Cravings Research

Cravings are subjective motivational states that, in theory, promote substance seeking and ingestive behaviours. Most theories of drug addiction attribute a causal role of cravings to the maintenance of compulsive drug use, the great difficulties addicts have in achieving abstinence, and the high rates of relapse following sustained drug abstinence (1). Drug cravings are so significant that most current state-of-the-art and experimental drug-treatment programmes include intervention components to prevent craving-related relapses (2).

Nicotine-replacement therapies are often advertised as 'craving reducing' tools that allow smokers to cope with the difficulties of quitting cigarettes (3). Bupropion and other antidepressants appear to be effective in the treatments of cocaine and nicotine addictions, in part, through their craving reducing properties (4-6, *cf* 7). Agonist maintenance for opiate addicts, which consists of the controlled use of long-acting synthetic opiates, is prescribed with the goals of preventing opiate withdrawal, blocking the effects of other opiates, and decreasing opiate cravings (8). (Unfortunately, research also shows that high-dose methadone maintenance may increase rather than decrease cravings for heroin (9).) It is also believed that opiate antagonists may increase the effectiveness of alcohol treatments by reducing cravings for alcohol and blocking the reinforcing effects of alcohol (10).

In cognitive-behavioural treatments, relapse prevention efforts consist to a large extent in teaching patients to monitor and control cravings (8). The so called 'cue-exposure' treatments are based on the hypothesis that experiencing cravings without self-administering drugs, or without losing control over self-administration, will extinguish or diminish the intensity of drug cravings and increase treatment effectiveness (11-13).

Similar to the hypothesised causal relationship between drug cravings and compulsive drug use, the construct of food cravings has been important for theories and treatments of eating disorders. Food cravings have been linked to binge eating in bulimia, early dropout from weight-loss treatments, over-eating in obese individuals, and the life-time prevalence of bulimia nervosa (14). The effectiveness of pharmacotherapy in reducing compulsive or binge eating has been attributed to the possibility that serotonin-enhancing drugs either block or reduce food cravings (15). Similar to drug-addiction treatments, some cognitive-behavioural interventions for binge eating also target cravings through cue-exposure and response-prevention methods (16).

Additionally, a great deal of food-craving research has been motivated by investigations of the mechanisms that control appetite, feeding behaviour, and the experience of food cravings. Most of these research efforts could be described as attempts to explain whether and how food cravings are related to a variety of physiological and psychological variables (hormonal activity, nutrition deficiencies and nutrition selection, feeding-related changes in neurobiology, cognitive and mood states and associated neurobiology, and feeding-related behaviours). There have been numerous studies - for example, investigating or reviewing the associations of food cravings and consumption of sweets with menstrual-related changes (17), endogenous opioid peptides (18), and depression (19).

1.1.2   Theories of Cravings

Tiffany (1) noted that researchers attribute the genesis of drug cravings to the negative reinforcing or the positive reinforcing properties of drugs or to both. Similarly, Weingarten and Elston (20) classified drug and food cravings into two broad categories: abstinence- and expectation-generated cravings. We will organise hypotheses about the origins and functionality of cravings under three labels: homeostasis-based, incentive, and cognitive.

1.1.2.1   *Homeostasis-based hypotheses of cravings*

Homeostasis-based models of drug dependence assume that addicts use drugs to avoid or escape the physiological and psychological distress that results from the homeostatic imbalance produced by the sudden withdrawal of a drug regime. That is, cravings represent the desire to obtain the specific drug effects that will restore homeostatic balance in a drug-depleted drug-dependent organism. Thus, drug use that results from cravings generated by homeostatic imbalances or aversive states is maintained by schedules of negative reinforcement (21).

Conditioned homeostatic models of drug dependence posit that contextual cues that reliably accompany drug self-administration begin to elicit conditioned responses in the form of drug-withdrawal effects (22), or drug-opposite effects (23), or behavioural disturbances (24). These conditioned responses, which in theory have the function of counteracting drug effects to restore homeostasis, may produce homeostatic imbalances in the drug-free organism (24) or 'announce' an impending homeostatic imbalance in anticipation of drug use (25). Detected homeostatic imbalances encourage consummatory behaviours through a negative feedback mechanism (26). On the other hand, 'expected' homeostatic disturbances could result in feedforward-regulation or anticipatory behavioural adjustments aimed at coping with impending homeostatic imbalances (25).

Homeostatic imbalances produced by drug withdrawal or conditioned homeostasis-restoring responses are aversive and strongly associated with negative mood states. Thus, some cognitive-behavioural theories of drug addiction predict that negative mood states may become conditioned stimuli capable of eliciting drug cravings that activate either aversion-avoidance motivational networks (27) or the expectation that drug consumption will reduce negative affect (28). For example, opiates can alleviate distress caused by social isolation or the loss of a loved one (21). Theories that attribute the genesis of cravings to negative affect could also be conceptualised as homeostasis-based theories to the extent that distress or depressive states can be conceptualised as detected homeostatic imbalances.

Homeostasis models of food cravings assume that biological deficiencies or altered states in nutrition, hormone regulation, or neural activity produce the desire for specific types of food that, once ingested, can induce chemical changes to restore homeostasis. Wurtman, for example, posited that carbohydrate craving is a homeostatic mechanism to compensate for declines in brain serotonin in premenstrual depressed women, some obese individuals, and people suffering from seasonal affective disorder (29). That is, foods rich in carbohydrates indirectly increase serotonin by causing a relative increase in plasma tryptophan (the precursor of serotonin) and, subsequently, brain tryptophan uptake. Thus, consumption of foods high in carbohydrates and low in protein is negatively reinforced because the behaviour results in an escape from depressive states.

Some homeostasis-based hypotheses of food cravings emphasise that restrictive dieting may result in biological imbalances that create a physiological drive to eat (e.g. Nisbett's weight set point theory (30)). (Section 7.1). Within these models, nutritional deprivation leads to food cravings and subsequently to loss of control over eating (31-32).

Borrowing from theories of drug addiction, some authors have also theorised that food cravings can become conditioned responses triggered by environmental cues associated with food consumption, and that this cue reactivity results in compensatory or anticipatory homeostasis-restoring responses (33). Also, given the reported associations between negative affective states (e.g. negative mood, anxiety) and binge eating, researchers have hypothesised that negative affect can elicit conditioned cravings (34).

1.1.2.2   Incentive hypotheses of cravings

Incentive hypotheses of cravings are based on the positive-reinforcement contingencies associated with drug use and food consumption. That is, people have cravings for specific drugs or foods because they have learned that the consumption of specific substances 'feels good.' These theories may emphasise the 'pleasurable', pharmacological effects of drugs, or the 'pleasant' taste and texture, or even mood-enhancement effects of foods. Like homeostasis-based hypotheses, incentive hypotheses may highlight either or both neurobiological processes and psychological constructs. Wise (21) indicated that both positive reinforcement and the memory of reinforcement are biological events resulting from dopaminergic activation in the brain, with the memory for reinforcement being the biological substrate of reward-associated cravings.

Incentive hypotheses also rely heavily on classical conditioning to explain cravings. That is, these theories predict that external and internal cues associated with the rewarding effects of drugs or food become conditioned stimuli that elicit memories or expectancies for the pleasurable effects that follow consummatory behaviours. Positive affect, small priming drug doses or 'appetisers', seeing drug-associated stimuli or smelling a tasty food, for example, may elicit a desire for the drug or food (27,28,34).

1.1.2.3   The cognitive theory of cravings

Tiffany (1) presented a unique theory of cravings based on the principles of automatic and non-automatic cognitive processing. This model, although originally developed to explain drug cravings and drug use in addicts, has now been applied to food cravings and binge eating (35). The cognitive model downplays but does not deny the role of cravings in consummatory behaviours. That is, Tiffany asserts that craving is not necessary for drug use. Using the notion that, with sufficient practice, performance on a task can become automatic (36), Tiffany suggests that drug-use behaviour in the addict is largely controlled by automatic processes. The model proposes that the procedures for carrying out these automatised skills are stored in long-term memory in the form of action schemata, which control the initiation and co-ordination of drug-use behaviour.

The model posits that craving is supported by non-automatic processes activated in parallel with drug-use action schemata. As with other forms of non-automatic functioning, the cognitive processes controlling craving are seen as slow, dependent upon intention, flexible, cognitively effortful, and restricted by limited cognitive capacity. Non-automatic processing is required either when automatic processes cannot produce the intended responses or when the individual attempts to inhibit automatic processing (37). Therefore, craving is presumed to arise either when an environmental condition impedes the completion of drug use (e.g. when a smoker runs out of cigarettes) or when the addict attempts to avoid drug use (e.g. a smoker tries to quit).

Thus, Tiffany differentiated between 'abstinence-avoidance urges' (or cravings that arise from difficulties an individual may encounter in completing consummatory behaviours), and 'abstinence-promotion urges' (or cravings that arise from self-imposed restrictions upon behaviours). Hypothetically, abstinence-promotion and abstinence-avoidance cravings differ not only functionally but also subjectively. For example, a heavy smoker who runs out of cigarettes may become frustrated, especially if contextual circumstances indicate the prospect that finding cigarettes is rather grim (e.g. "If I don't have a cigarette soon I'm going to go crazy"). On the other hand, an ex-smoker watching others smoke may engage in cognitive-restructuring to avoid yielding to the craving (e.g. "If I smoke my clothes will smell bad").

1.1.3 Definition and Measurement of Cravings

Perhaps the most controversial aspect of food-craving research is the fundamental issue of defining cravings. The experience of a craving has often been conceptualised as an 'irresistible demand' for a substance. This view most likely originated from the observation that alcoholics and other addicts continued to engage in compulsive drug use despite their repeated attempts at sobriety, the reasoning being that an uncontrollable desire must be behind the self-destructive behaviour of the addict (38).

However, food cravings are not necessarily pathological, and many individuals simply describe cravings as a yearning, desire, or longing for a specific substance (39). Also, Weingarten and Elston administered a questionnaire to over 1,000 male and female college students and found that 68% of men and 97% of women reported that they had experienced cravings (40). Cravings were defined as an intense desire to eat a specific food. In a prospective investigation of non-clinical women, Hill and Heaton-Brown concluded that food cravings are commonplace experiences not associated with physiological or psychological abnormalities (41). Nonetheless, and not surprisingly, it should be noted that using different definitions of cravings may have a substantial effect on the estimated prevalence of food cravings (42), and thus the associations that might be found between cravings, eating behaviours and specific populations.

1.1.3.1   Cravings measured as consumption

The conceptualisation of craving as an irresistible or uncontrollable desire implies a causal link and strong correlation between cravings and consumption, at least in situations in which there are not insurmountable barriers preventing access to the craved substance. Thus, the use of food-consumption measures to index levels of craving assumes that, other things being equal, consumption-related behaviours should be greater in the presence than in the absence of cravings. Although frequency, amount, and speed of consumption could be valid indices of cravings, defining cravings merely as degree of consumption can be circular (20,39), and ignores the fact that cravings do not necessarily lead to substance-seeking behaviours (1). Additionally, measuring cravings solely as changes in consumption downplays the psychological, social, cultural, ideographic, and situational factors that also control ingestive behaviours, and may interact with cravings to predict consumption.

1.1.3.2   Variability in the definition of cravings

Reading the research literature, it is obvious that many authors conceptualise the functionality of eating as more than providing fuel for the body. For instance, food cravings have been linked to negative affect (17), sensory, environmental, and cognitive food-associated stimuli (43,44), as well as to guilt and stress (45). That is, some researchers theorise that eating the craved food is an attempt to cope with negative psychological states. Moreover, others have suggested that food cravings are cue-elicited expectations for the pleasurable sensations (e.g. the sweetness, texture, and aroma of chocolate) that accompany the consumption of the desired substance (20). That is, eating is used to feel 'good.'

Although many authors have expressed their dissatisfaction with the unscientific and imprecise definition and measurement of food cravings in investigations of craving, there have been few sound attempts to conceptualise scientifically and assess the construct (14). The measurement of food cravings has been mostly limited to asking participants whether or not and with what intensity cravings are experienced, with the definition of craving varying widely across investigations. To name only a few, intensity of cravings has been variously measured as degree of desirability of certain foods (46), degree of agreement with statements of having 'cravings' (47), overall strength of a 'craving' (41-43,48,49), strength of a 'craving' from 'slight ideation of a food or a substance' to 'an overwhelming desire to consume the craved item' (50), or even as scores on hunger and eating disinhibition measures (51).

We have already noted that craving is an ambiguous term that usually, but not always, denotes an intense and specific desire for a substance. Some individuals define cravings as mere desires for a food or drug, whereas others claim that a craving could be any desire for anything (39). We would like to add that the word craving is not a universal term. For example, in Spanish, the closest equivalent for the word craving is 'antojo'. The word antojos is used to describe food-specific desires during pregnancy. Alternatively, antojo may be used in some situations to describe a whim. That is, antojo is very often used to name behaviours and actions that are motivated by capriciousness rather than by need. Thus, it is difficult to know what it is being measured when we simply ask people about whether or not, and how often, they have 'cravings' or 'antojos'. We find even more troublesome the great variability in the definition of cravings across different groups of investigators. That is, if all studies simply asked about 'cravings' without providing an operational definition for the term, the source of measurement error would at least be consistent across studies. However, when the definition of craving varies along degree of inclusiveness, from 'any food desire' to 'an intense food desire that cannot be resisted', one must even question if the same construct is being measured.

We recently identified four substantial efforts to improve the definition and measurement of cravings (14). Weingarten and Elston (40) investigated the prevalence of cravings among college students. These authors asked about food cravings, feelings associated with cravings, whether edibles other than the craved food would satisfy specific cravings, and how often cravings led to seeking and eating the desired food. Hill and Heaton-Brown (41) included questions to detect what contextual and sensory cues (e.g. time of the day, smell, taste), feelings (e.g. happy, nervous, bored) and intensities of hunger were associated with cravings. Mahaluf *et al.* (52) interviewed Chilean pregnant women and reported six distinct features of cravings: (i) pregnancy-dependent cravings; (ii) a sense of urgency; (iii) problems delaying the craving; (iv) the need to eat big amounts of food; (v) a sense of special satisfaction after eating the desired food; and (vi) and indisposition if the craving could not be satisfied. Recently, Gendall *et al.* (42) developed a craving questionnaire that combined and refined several of the dimensions assessed by the questionnaires described above. (See also section 7.3).

However, we did not find any published information on the psychometric properties of any of the above questionnaires. We also thought that the content of any of these measures by themselves was not sufficiently broad to assess many of the craving dimensions proposed in the literature. Thus, we developed two multidemensional craving questionnaires in the hope that they would facilitate future investigations of food cravings. We describe below some aspects of the development, validation, and cross-validation of English and Spanish versions of the questionnaires. [For a more detailed description of the questionnaires, psychometric characteristics and item content, see 14 and 53].

1.1.3.3   Development and Psychometric Properties of the Food Cravings Questionnaire - Trait (FCQ-T) and the Food Cravings Questionnaire - State (FCQ-S)

We developed two different instruments because we thought it was important to be able to measure how cravings are typically manifested in any given individual or specific populations (e.g. 'chocolate addicts'), as well as to assess cravings as a psychological state in specific situations (e.g. stressful events, after food deprivation). Items for the questionnaires were generated from previous multidimensional instruments of drug cravings (54-56), and other authors' conceptualisations of food cravings (40,47,48,57-60).

Both the English and the Spanish versions of the two questionnaires were administered to undergraduate male and female students from the USA and Spain, respectively. The psychometric properties of the two instruments were promising, with the FCQ-T (9 factors, 39 items) and the FCQ-S (5 factors, 15 items) showing excellent internal consistency in both US and Spanish populations. Confirmatory factor analyses (CFA) demonstrated a good fit and discriminant validity (of the factors) for both instruments in both languages. We also examined 3-week test-retest reliability, conducted a cross-validation study of the factor structure (using CFA), and carried out a study of convergent and discriminative validity with the English versions. Consistent with the expectation that the FCQ-S should measure state-dependent cravings, the test-retest reliability for FCQ-S was considerably lower than that of the FCQ-T, which was excellent. In the cross-validation study (again using CFA), the nine (FCQ-T) and five factor (FCQ-S) solutions obtained in our initial study also fit the data well. There was also the clear presence of a single second-order factor, suggesting the presence of a unifying construct (food craving) with multiple dimensions (see Figs 1.1.1 and 1.1.2).

To further test the construct validity of the FCQ-T and the FCQ-S, we took measurements across two satiety conditions: before eating and after eating breakfast following a 12-h food deprivation period. We also examined the relationship between the two questionnaires and a trait measure of eating behaviours, the Three Factor Eating Questionnaire (TFEQ, 61,62). Because the FCQ-T should measure trait rather than state cravings, we hypothesised that the degree of satiety would have a weak impact on the FCQ-T scales. Consistent with homeostatic theories, we predicted that completing the questionnaires after food deprivation would result in greater levels of state cravings (FCQ-S) than completing the questionnaires immediately after eating breakfast. We also predicted that the FCQ-T factors would be more strongly related to the disinhibition and hunger dimensions of the TFEQ than to the cognitive restraint dimension. Furthermore, we hypothesised that the TFEQ scales would not be as strongly associated with the FCQ-S scales as the FCQ-T scales. The results supported all of our predictions. We realise that we used a non-clinical population to investigate two measures we hope eventually will be useful in eating disorders research. Nonetheless, our results were congruent with the notion that food cravings, although at one level being a cohesive construct, can be conceptualised as a multidimensional construct.

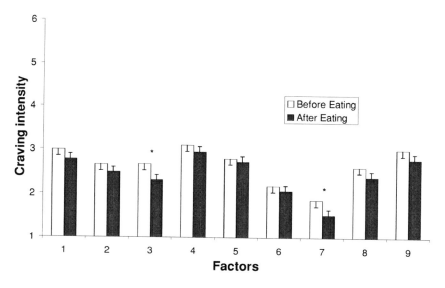

Fig. 1.1.1. Food Craving Questionnaire - Trait. Each bar represents the mean item-score (six-point scale) within each factor in the Before Eating (empty bars) and After Eating conditions (solid bars). The factors were: 1 = an intention and planning to consume food; 2 = anticipation of positive reinforcement that may result from eating; 3 = anticipation of relief from negative states and feelings as a result of eating; 4 = lack of control over eating; 5 = thoughts or preoccupation with food; 6 = craving as a physiological state; 7 = emotions that may be experienced before or during food cravings or eating; 8 = cues that may trigger food cravings; and 9 = guilt that may be experienced as a result of cravings and/or giving into them. * Statistically significant differences between conditions.

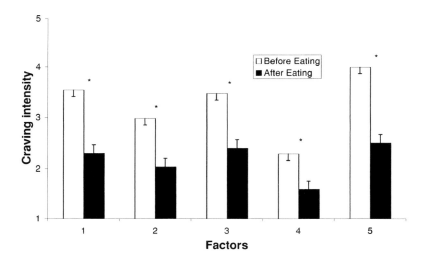

*Fig. 1.1.2. Food Craving Questionnaire - State. Each bar represents the mean item-score (five-point scale) within each factor in the Before Eating (empty bars) and After Eating conditions (solid bars). The factors were: 1 = an intense desire to eat; 2 = anticipation of positive reinforcement that may result from eating; 3 = anticipation of relief from negative states and feelings as a result of eating; 4 = thoughts of preoccupation with food and lack of control over eating; and 5 = craving as a physiological state. * Statistically significant differences between conditions.*

1.1.4   Food Intake and Cravings

Regardless of the specific definition, all theories of cravings predict that, at least in some situations, cravings will promote substance seeking and eating-related behaviours. Therefore, examining the effect of cravings on eating behaviours is obviously the most relevant way of testing the validity of the construct.

1.1.4.1   Animal studies

Researchers who use animal data to make inferences about the aetiology of food cravings (63), or the role of cravings in drug seeking behaviours (28) should keep in mind that cravings are subjective phenomena (20). On the other hand, after conceding that animal research cannot tell us whether the rat 'craves' a substance in question, it would be foolish to deny that animal models of feeding and drug addiction can make important contributions to the understanding of the biological and learning mechanisms that control ingestive behaviours.

Mercer and Holder provided a good illustration of how animal and human data can be integrated to develop theories and hypotheses regarding the aetiology of cravings and the role of cravings in feeding behaviour (18). In their review, these authors found that endogenous opioid peptides (EOPs) altered food intake in animals by modifying the palatability of foods. For example, in rats, the antagonist naloxone suppresses the ingestion of a preferred 10% sucrose solution but not of a less preferred 20% sucrose solution (64), whereas morphine increases the preference for saccharin (65). They conclude that both the consumption of highly palatable foods and food deprivation alter EOP activity. In reviewing human research, they point out that altered EOP levels, intensified food cravings, and increased food intake co-occur in various clinical conditions (e.g. pregnancy, depression). Thus, based on the empirical animal data that causally link EOP activity to palatability changes, and human data that correlate EOP activity, cravings, and consumption, Mercer and Holder concluded that changes in EOPs might elicit food cravings that modulate food intake (18). (See also sections 2.2 and 2.5.)

The point we stress is that animal data can be very useful in theory generation and hypothesis testing. In fact, it would be fairly accurate to say that homeostasis and incentive theories of cravings are based to a large extent on animal data.

1.1.4.2 *Manipulation of cravings in human research*

Relatively few laboratory-based investigations have used consumption-related measures to index drug cravings. The behavioural measures have varied considerably across studies, ranging from effort to obtain a substance, to speed of consumption, to duration of consumption, to choice of substance and to latency to use. (For a review, see 66.)

Parenthetically, there have been many studies that have investigated the effects of diets, menstrual cycles, mood, and cue reactivity on either food cravings or food intake. However, relatively few investigations have measured both food cravings and food intake. Likewise, studies of the therapeutic effectiveness of pharmacological agents for the treatment of clinical conditions have rarely measured the treatment's effect on cravings.

Regarding the manipulation of food cravings, researchers have typically used pharmacological, dietary, or cue-exposure methods to measure the impact of food cravings on food consumption. In studies using pharmacological methods, participants from specific clinical populations (e.g. those with obesity, bulimia, premenstrual dysphoric disorder) take a drug with hypothesised craving-reducing properties (e.g. serotonin-enhancing antidepressants), and researchers then monitor food consumption or related measures (e.g. food selection, weight, bingeing episodes, caloric intake). Some investigators have measured within-subject changes in food cravings and food consumption, whereas others have relied on comparing cravers and non-cravers. A strength of pharmacological investigations of food cravings is that they have typically included placebo, double-blind, and randomised control trials (51,67-71).

Researchers have found that serotonin-enhancing drugs reduce (a) carbohydrate intake among obese individuals self-identified as carbohydrate cravers (69-71), and (b) urges to binge, food cravings and binge episodes among bulimia nervosa patients (68). On the other hand, ingestion of L-tryptophan, the amino acid precursor of serotonin, did not change food cravings and food intake for either depressed or non-depressed participants (67).

The use of naloxone, an opioid antagonist, resulted in reduced cravings (defined as hunger and eating disinhibition) and reduced body weight in clinical subjects undergoing tricyclic-antidepresant treatment (51). Conversely, the prediction that the benzodiazepine alprazolam would decrease food cravings and food intake by improving mood among women with premenstrual dysphoric disorder was not supported (46). In this study,

Alprazolam did not improve mood, and the authors did not report conducting any analyses to examine the direct effects of Alprazolam on cravings. The results of the study were that, premenstrually but not postmenstrually, Alprazolam increased intake of fatty foods and decreased intake of carbohydrate-only foods in a dose-dependent manner. (See also section 5.3).

Three studies have examined the effects of meal composition on food cravings. In the first investigation, obese patients were randomly assigned to either a balanced, low-calorie diet (1,000-1,200 kcal/day) or a macronutrient-restricted, very-low-calorie diet (400 kcal/day). Subjects in both treatments showed significant decreases in cravings for all types of food, with the craving changes being particularly pronounced in the very-low-calorie diet participants (48). In a different study, meal composition also altered cravings in a group of nine women self-identified as experiencing very intense cravings. Protein-rich meals increased cravings for sweet, carbohydrate-rich foods more than carbohydrate-rich and mixed meals did (72). A third study examined the situational determinants of lapses in obese subjects with Type II diabetes who were randomly assigned to a balanced low-calorie diet or to a very-low-calorie diet. For participants in the low-calorie group, negative emotion was the typical trigger of lapses. For participants in the very-low-calorie group, food availability and cravings were the primary triggers of lapses (73).

Two experiments examined both craving reactivity and food-intake reactivity to either food cues or thoughts about food. In one experiment, participants were divided into 'restrained' and 'non-restrained' eaters, exposed to food-related cues or thoughts about foods, and then given the opportunity to eat or sample a variety of foods. Compared with non-restrained eaters, restrained eaters craved more and consumed more food after pre-exposure to food cues than after pre-exposure to neutral cues (43). In the second study, self-identified 'chocolate addicts' showed greater excitement, anxiety, frustration, guilt, restlessness, depression, craving, salivation, and chocolate consumption after pre-exposure to chocolate cues than control subjects. Regarding trait characteristics, chocolate addicts scored higher in hunger, eating disinhibition, depression, and other measures associated with eating disorder psychopathology than control subjects (49).

1.1.4.3 *Correlational investigations*

1.1.4.3.1 *Prospective studies*

We found six prospective investigations that monitored food cravings and food intake using self-report diaries. As a whole, these six studies sought information from a variety of female populations ranging from 'healthy', to obese, to 'chocolate-addicted', to very intense and frequent cravers, and to women diagnosed with binge eating disorder. The studies also varied methodologically regarding both the point at which the subjects needed to complete their diaries and the specific information they included in the diaries. In terms of when the diaries were completed, the instructions varied quite a bit. For example, some subjects were asked to complete food diaries once every night (47,50), whereas others had to complete the diaries at the exact time that the food-craving was experienced (41,74), or even at random times throughout the day (74).

Regarding the measurement of consumption-related behaviours, one study asked for self-estimates of whether more, less, or about the same amount of food was consumed in comparison with what the person typically ate (50). Six studies requested a description of the type and amount of food consumed (47,48,60,72-74), but actual estimations of amount consumed, or caloric intake, were calculated differently across studies.

Overall, cravers and non-cravers did not tend to differ on dietary intake (44-60), although, not surprisingly, self-identified 'chocolate-addicts' reported greater chocolate cravings and greater chocolate consumption than comparison groups (47). A group of investigators found that food intake and craving reports increased premenstrually, with subjects 'succumbing' to cravings on 66% of the days on which cravings were reported. However, these authors also reported a small correlation (r = .26) between craving intensity and food intake (50). Cravings and feelings of poor eating control predicted binge episodes for both women diagnosed with binge-eating disorder and non-clinical controls (74).

Some of these studies also investigated the question of whether dietary restraint increased cravings, as well as the relationship between mood, cravings, and food intake. For both of these questions the data were somewhat inconclusive. Two studies found that dietary restraint decreased cravings (48,50) and one found no significant differences in dietary restraint between groups of cravers and non-cravers (44). Regarding emotional states, obese women self-identified as high cravers were more likely to report feeling bored than obese, low-craving women; and feeling bored predicted the probabilty of craving sweets for both groups (60). Women self-identified as cravers characterised food cravings as 'mood-improving' experiences (41), and reported greater levels of boredom, anxiety (44) and depression (47) than non-cravers. Moreover, poor mood predicted binge episodes among women with binge eating disorder but not among matched controls (74). Conversely, neither overall mood ratings of female undergraduates (50) nor 15 different emotional states measured in high- and low-craving obese women (60) predicted cravings.

1.1.4.3.2   Retrospective studies

We found only five studies that investigated retrospectively the relationship between cravings and food intake. Two of these found clear positive associations between craving and food intake. Of these investigations, one used a structured interview to compare eating-related behaviours between obese women seeking treatment and normal weight women. In contrast with normal weight women, overweight women were characterised by their propensity to: (a) yield to chocolate and sweet cravings; (b) eat more during the weekend than during regular week days; (c) feel incapable of resisting food cues; and (d) engage in automatic eating (75). The second study investigated differences in nutrient intake among depressed and non-depressed women. Depressed participants reported greater intensity of carbohydrate cravings and increased ingestion of sweet carbohydrates than non-depressed women (76).

Three studies showed either conflicting or no relationships between cravings and food intake. In an investigation of food aversions and cravings during pregnancy, cravings for salty foods increased from pre-pregnancy to pregnancy. However, actual salt intake decreased from pre-pregnancy to pregnancy for a subgroup of women who suffered from severe morning sickness, but remained unchanged for women without severe morning sickness. That is, salt cravings and salt consumption did not change or were inversely associated with one another (77). In a study of self-identified 'chocolate addicts', participants that craved chocolate more intensely than other foods reported giving in to cravings 86.5% of the time. However, intensity of cravings was not related to amount of chocolate consumed. Moreover, although about half of the 'chocolate addicts' thought that dieting increased cravings, dieters and non-dieters did not differ on reported chocolate intake and craving (78). Finally, in a study of male and female college students, dieters and non-dieters did not differ in the frequency with which they experienced cravings, but cravings led to consumption of the craved food about 85% of the time (40).

1.1.5   Summary and Recommendations

First, a cautionary note is necessary. The heterogeneity of the populations studied, variables measured, and methodologies employed make the integration of results across studies rather difficult. Nonetheless, the data from experimental investigations tentatively support the hypothesis that changes in food cravings correlate with isodirectional changes in food intake and other eating-related behaviours. The data from prospective and retrospective correlational studies are not so clear, with different studies showing positive, negative or no relationship between food cravings and food consumption.

We noted an interesting contrast between experimental and correlational findings. In cue-reactivity studies, restrained eaters reported greater cravings and food intake in reaction to food cues than unrestrained eaters (43). Conversely, in correlational studies, dietary restriction either decreased cravings (48,50) or was unrelated to cravings and food consumption (44). We believe that the answer to such deceptively paradoxical findings lies in the failure to differentiate between successful and unsuccessful dieters (79). Careful examination of the measures used to measure restraint in the two cue-reactivity studies (43) suggests that subjects showing greater craving reactivity to food cues were restrained eaters with a high tendency towards disinhibition. In the correlational studies, restrained eaters were either successful dieters (48) or probably a mixture of successful and unsuccessful dieters (41). It has been suggested that this confound can be easily resolved by differentiating between restraint and tendencies to overeat (79).

We were somewhat surprised that we could not find laboratory-based studies investigating the effect of mood manipulations on cravings and food consumption. Tiffany and colleagues have developed a series of situational scripts that, when imagined, produce positive, negative, or neutral mood states in the laboratory. These investigators have found that both positive and negative mood scripts increase self-reported cravings to smoke. Moreover, smoking urge scripts devoid of mood content selectively increased self-reported negative mood (80-84). We believe that this methodology could be easily adapted to test causal relationships between emotional states, food cravings, and food consumption. Such investigations would be an important complement to the correlational prospective investigations we reviewed above, which suggest that, for some women, emotional states might predict cravings.

Finally, we also feel that using a multifactorial, psychometrically sound tool to measure cravings might be advantageous over the use of single-item, and necessarily single-construct instruments. For example, a sound craving questionnaire could help eating disorder researchers know the reliability with which they measure the construct, if craving profiles differ across populations (e.g. clinical and non-clinical), or what craving dimensions are most important in predicting treatment outcome among, for example, bulimia nervosa patients. Investigators would also be in a better position to investigate the origins and functionality of food cravings. For instance, are cravings elicited by environmental or emotional cues? Does the conceptualisation of drug cravings as effortful cognitive processes generalise to food cravings?

In conclusion, the construct of food cravings has drawn considerable attention from a wide variety of researchers wanting to learn about the motivational processes underlying eating-related behaviours and/or the relationship between food cravings and specific medical/clinical conditions (e.g. premenstrual dysphoric disorder, pregnancy, depression). The heterogeneity of approaches and increased research activity have the potential of rapidly advancing our understanding of food cravings. However, without a clear definition of food cravings and theoretically congruent assessment methods, the integration of knowledge across disciplines will be difficult.

1.1.6   References

1.   Tiffany S. A cognitive model of drug urges and drug-use behaviour: Role of automatic and nonautomatic processes. *Psychological Review*, 1990, 97(2), 147-68.

2.   Swift R.M. Medications and alcohol craving. *Alcohol Research and Health*, 1999, 23(3), 207-13.

3.   Cepeda-Benito A. A meta analytical review of the efficacy of nicotine chewing gum in smoking treatment programs. *Journal of Consulting and Clinical Psychology*, 1993, 61( ), 822-30.

4.   Harazin J., Berigan T. The use of buproprion in reducing cravings after cessation of cocaine use. *Substance Abuse*, 1995, 16(3), 181-2.

5.   Hollister L.E., Krajewski K., Rustin T., Gillespie H. Drugs for cocaine dependence: Not easy. *Archives of General Psychiatry*, 1992, 49(11), 905-6.

6.   Hurt R.D., Sachs D.P.L, Glover E.D., Offord K.P., Johnston J.A., Dale L.C., Khayrallah M.A., Schroeder D.R., Glover P.N., Sullivan C.R., Croghan I.T., Sullivan P.M. A comparison of sustained-release bupropion and placebo for smoking cessation. *New England Journal of Medicine*, 1997, 337(17), 1195-202.

7.   Shiffman S., Johnston J.A., Khayrallah M., Elash C.A., Gwaltney C.J., Paty J.A., Gnys M., Evoniuk G., DeVeaugh-Geiss J. The effect of bupropion on nicotine craving and withdrawal. *Psychopharmacology*, 2000, 148(1), 33-40.

8. National Institute on Drug Abuse. *Principles of Drug Addiction Treatment: A Research-Based Guide*. Washington DC, HIH Publication No. 99-4180. 1999.

9. de Vos J.W., van Wilgenburg H., van den Brink W., Kaplan C.D., De Vries M.W. Patterns of craving and pharmacokinetics in long-term opiate addicts in methadone maintenance therapy. *Addiction Research*, 1996, 3(4), 285-95.

10. Anton R.F., Moak D.H., Waid R., Latham P.K., Malcolm R.J., Dias J.K. Naltrexone and cognitive behavioural therapy for the treatment of outpatient alcoholics: Results of a placebo-controlled trial. *American Journal of Psychiatry*, 1999, 156(11), 1758-64.

11. Staiger P.K., Greeley J.D., Wallace S.D. Alcohol exposure therapy: Generalisation and changes in responsivity. *Drug and Alcohol Dependence*, 1999, 57(1), 29-40.

12. McCusker C.G., Brown K. Cue-exposure to alcohol-associated stimuli reduces autonomic reactivity, but not craving and anxiety, in dependent drinkers. *Alcohol and Alcoholism*, 1995, 30(3), 319-27.

13. Sitharthan T., Sitharthan G., Hough M.J., Kavanagh D.J. Cue exposure in moderation drinking: A comparison with cognitive-behaviour therapy. *Journal of Consulting and Clinical Psychology*, 1997, 65(5), 878-82.

14. Cepeda-Benito A., Gleaves D.H., Williams T.L., Erath S.T. The development and validation of the state and trait food cravings questionnaires. *Behaviour Therapy*, 2000, 31 (1), 151-73.

15. Fluoxetine Bulimia Nervosa Collaborative Study Group. Fluoxetine in the treatment of bulimia nervosa: A multicenter, placebo-controlled, double-blind trial. *Archives of General Psychiatry*, 1992, 49(2), 139-47.

16. Bulik C.M., Epstein L.H., Kaye W. Treatment of laxative abuse in a female with bulimia nervosa using an operant extinction paradigm. *Journal of Substance Abuse*, 1990, 2(3), 381-8.

17. Dye L., Warner P., Bancroft J. Food craving during the menstrual cycle and its relationship to stress, happiness of relationship and depression: A preliminary enquiry. *Journal of Affective Disorders*, 1995, 34(3), 157-64.

18. Mercer M.E., Holder M.D. Food cravings, endogenous opioid peptides, and food intake: A review. *Appetite*, 1997, 29(3), 325-52.

19. Buffenstein R., Poppitt S.D., McDevitt R.M., Prentice A.M. Food intake and the menstrual cycle: A retrospective analysis, with implications for appetite research. *Physiology and Behaviour*, 1995, 58(6), 1067-77.

20. Weingarten H.P., Elston D. The phenomenology of food cravings. *Appetite*, 1990, 15(3), 231-46.

21. Wise R.A. The neurobiology of craving: Implications for the understanding and treatment of addiction. *Journal of Abnormal Psychology*, 1988, 97(2), May, 118-32.

22. Wikler A. Sources of reinforcement for drug using behaviour: A theoretical formulation. *Pharmacology and the Future of Man. Proceedings of the 5th International Congress of Pharmacology*, 1972, 1, 18-30.

23. Siegel S. Classical conditioning, drug tolerance and drug dependence, in *Research Advances in Alcohol and drug Problems*. Eds Israel Y., Glasser F.B., Kalant H., Popham R.E., Schmidt W., Smart R.G. New York, Plenum Press. 1983, 7, 207-46.

24. Poulos C.X., Cappell H. Homeostatic theory of drug tolerance: A general model of physiological adaptation. *Psychological Review*, 1991, 98(3), 390-408.

25. Ramsay D.S., Seeley R.J., Bolles R.C., Woods S.C. Ingestive homeostasis: The primacy of learning, in *Why We Eat What We Eat: The Psychology of Eating*. Ed. Capaldi E.D.Washington, DC. American Psychological Association. 1996, 11-27.

26. Cannon W.B. *The Wisdom of the Body*. New York, W.W. Norton. 1932.

27. Baker T.B., Morse E., Sherman J.E. The motivation to use drugs: A psychobiological analysis of urges, in *The Nebraska Symposium on motivation: Alcohol use and abuse*. Ed. Rivers P.C. Lincoln, University of Nebraska Press. 1987, 257-323.

28. Niaura R.S., Rohsenow D.J., Binkoff J.A., Monti P.M., Pedraza M., Abrams D.B. Relevance of cue reactivity to understanding alcohol and smoking relapse. *Journal of Abnormal Psychology*, 1988, 197(2), 133-52.

29. Wurtman J.J. Carbohydrate craving, mood changes, and obesity. *Journal of Clinical Psychiatry*, 1988, 49(Supplement), 37-9.

30. Nisbett R. Hunger, obesity, and the ventromedial hypothalamus. *Psychological Review*, 1972, 79(6), 433-53.

31. Slade P.D. Towards a functional analysis of anorexia nervosa and bulimia nervosa. *British Journal of Clinical Psychology*, 1982, 21(3), 167-79.

32. McManus F., Waller G. A functional analysis of binge-eating. *Clinical Psychology Review*, 1995, 15, 845-63.

33. Karhunem L.J., Lappalainen R.I., Tammela L., Turpeinen A.K., Cusitupa M.I.J. Subjective and physiological cephalic phase responses to food in obese binge-eating women. *International Journal of Eating Disorders*, 1997, 21(4), 321-8.

34. Jansen A. A learning model of binge eating: Cue reactivity and cue exposure. *Behaviour Research and Therapy*, 1998, 36(3), 257-72.

35. Green M.W., Rogers P.J., Elliman N.A. Dietary restraint and addictive behaviours: The generalizability of Tiffany's cue reactivity model. *International Journal of Eating Disorders*, 2000, 27, 419-27.

36. Logan G.D. Toward an instance theory of automatization. *Psychological Review*, 1988, 95(4), 492-527.

37. Norman D.A., Shallice T. Attention to action: Willed and automatic control of behaviour, in *Consciousness and Self-Regulation: Advances in Research Theory*. Eds Davidson R.J., Schwartz G.E., Shapiro D. New York, Plenum Press. 1985, 4, 2-18.

38. World Health Organization. The "craving" for alcohol: Report of the WHO Expert Committee on Mental Health and on Alcohol. *Quarterly Journal of Studies on Alcohol*, 1955, 16(1), 33-66.

39. Kozlowski L.T., Mann R.E., Wilkinson D.A., Poulos C.X. "Cravings" are ambiguous: Ask about urges or desires. *Addictive Behaviours*, 1989, 14, 443-5.

40. Weingarten H., Elston D. Food cravings in a college population. *Appetite*, 1991, 17, 167-75.

41. Hill A.J., Heaton-Brown L. The experience of food craving: A prospective investigation in healthy women. *Journal of Psychosomatic Research*, 1994, 38, 801-14.

42. Gendall K.A., Joyce P.R., Sullivan P.F. Impact of definition on prevalence of food cravings in a random sample of young women. *Appetite*, 1997, 28, 63-72.

43. Fedoroff I.C., Polivy J., Herman C.P. The effect of pre-exposure to food cues on the eating behaviour of restrained and unrestrained eaters. *Appetite*, 1997, 28(1), 33-47.

44. Hill A.J., Weaver C.F., Blundell J.E. Food craving, dietary restraint and mood. *Appetite*, 1991, 17(3), 187-97.

45. Benton D., Greenfield K., Morgan M. The development of the attitudes to chocolate questionnaire. *Personality and Individual Differences*, 1998, 24(4), 513-20.

46. Evans S.M., Foltin R.W., Fischman M.W. Food "cravings" and the acute effects of alprazolam on food intake in women with premenstrual dysphoric disorder. *Appetite*, 1999, 32(3), 331-49.

47. Macdiarmid J.I., Hetherington M.M. Mood modulation by food: An exploration of affect and cravings in "chocolate addicts." *British Journal of Clinical Psychology*, 1995, 34(1), 129-38.

48. Harvey J., Wing R.R., Mullen M. Effects on food cravings of a very low-calorie diet or a balanced, low-calorie diet. *Appetite*, 1993, 21(2), 105-15.

49. Tuomisto T., Hetherington M.M., Morris M.-F., Tuomisto M., Turjanmaa V., Lappalainen R. Psychological and physiological characteristics of sweet food "addiction." *International Journal of Eating Disorders*, 1999, 25(2), 169-75.

50. Cohen I.T., Sherwin B.B., Fleming A.S. Food cravings, mood, and the menstrual cycle. *Hormones and Behaviour*, 1987, 21(4), 457-70.

51. Zimmermann U., Rechlin T., Plaskacewicz G.J., Barocka A., Wildt L., Kaschka W.P. Effect of naltrexone on weight gain and food craving induced by tricyclic antidepressants and lithium: An open study. *Biological Psychiatry*, 1997, 41(6), 747-9.

52. Mahaluf J.Z., Nader A.N., Correa E.D., Vargas J.V. Craving in pregnancy. Initial definition. *Revista de Psiquiatria Clinica*, 1991, 28, 118-25.

53. Cepeda-Benito A., Gleaves D.H., Fernandez M.C., Vila J., Reynoso J. The development and validation of Spanish versions of the state and trait food cravings questionnaires. *Behaviour Research and Therapy*, 2000, 38, 71-84.

54. Singleton E., Tiffany S.T., Henningfield J.E. The development of an alcohol craving questionnaire. *Unpublished Manuscript.* 1994

55. Tiffany S.T., Drobes D.J. The development and initial validation of a questionnaire of smoking urges. *British Journal of Addiction*, 1991, 86, 1467-76.

56. Tiffany S.T., Singleton E., Haertzen C.A., Henningfield J.E. The development of a cocaine craving questionnaire. *Drug and Alcohol Dependence*, 1993, 34, 19-28.

57. Michener W., Rozin P. Pharmacological versus sensory factors in the satiation of chocololate craving. *Physiology and Behaviour*, 1994, 56, 419-22.

58. Overduin J., Jansen A. Food cue reactivity in fasting and non-fasting subjects. *European Eating Disorders Review*, 1996, 4, 249-59.

59. Rodin J., Mancuso J., Granger J., Nelbach E. Food cravings in relation to body mass index, restraint and estradiol levels: A repeated measures study in healthy women. *Appetite*, 1991, 17, 177-85.

60. Schlundt D.G., Virts K.L., Sbrocco T., Pope-Cordle J., Hill J.O. A sequential behavioural analysis of craving sweets in obese women. *Addictive Behaviours*, 1993, 18(1), 67-80.

61. Stunkard A.J., Messik S. The Three-Factor Eating Questionnaire to measure dietary restraint, disinhibition and hunger. *Journal of Psychosomatic Research*, 1985, 29, 71-83.

62. Stunkard A.J., Messik S. *Eating Inventory Manual.* San Antonio, Hardcourt Brace and Company. 1988.

63. Locke K.W., Fielding S. Enhancement of salt intake by choline chloride. *Physiology and Behaviour*, 1994, 55(6), 1039-96.

64. Kirkham T.C., Cooper S.J. Naloxone attenuation of sham feeding is modified by manipulation of sucrose concentration. *Physiology and Behaviour*, 1988, 44(4-5), 491-4.

65. Lynch W.C., Libby L. Naloxone suppresses intake of highly preferred saccharin solutions in food deprived and sated rats. *Life Sciences*, 1983, 33(19), 1909-14.

66. Drummond D.C., Tiffany S.T., Glautier S., Remington B. *Addictive Behaviour: Cue Exposure Theory and Practice.* Chichester, John Wiley and Sons. 1995.

67. Russ M.J., Ackerman S.H., Banayschwartz M., Shindledecker R.D., Smith G.P. L-tryptophan does not affect food intake during recovery from depression. *International Journal of Eating Disorders,* 1991, 10(5), 539-46.

68. Solyom L., Solyom C., Ledwidge B. Trazodone treatment of bulimia nervosa. *Journal of Clinical Psychopharmacology,* 1989, 9(4), 287-90.

69. Wurtman J., Wurtman R., Berry E., Gleason R., Goldberg H., Mcdermott J., Kahne M., Tsay R. Dexfenfluramine, fluoxetine, and weight loss among female carbohydrate cravers. *Neuropsychopharmacology,* 1993, 9(3), 201-10.

70. Wurtman J.J., Wurtman R.J., Growdon J.H., Henry P., Lipscomb A., Zeisel S.H. Carbohydrate craving in obese people: Suppression by treatments affecting serotonergic transmission. *International Journal of Eating Disorders,* 1981, 1(1), 2-15.

71. Wurtman J., Wurtman R., Reynolds S., Tsay R., Chew B. Fenfluramine suppresses snack intake among carbohydrate cravers but not among noncarbohydrate cravers. *International Journal of Eating Disorders,* 1987, 6(6), 687-99.

72. Gendall K.A., Joyce P.R., Abbott R.M. The effects of meal composition on subsequent craving and binge eating. *Addictive Behaviours,* 1999, 24(3), 305-15.

73. Wing R.R, Shiffman S., Drapkin R.G., Grilo C.M., Mcdermott M. Moderate versus restrictive diets: Implications for relapse. *Behaviour Therapy,* 1995, 26(1), 5-24.

74. Greeno C.G., Wing R.R., Shiffman S. Binge antecedents in obese women with and without binge eating disorder. *Journal of Consulting and Clinical Psychology,* 2000, 68(1), 95-102.

75. Bjoervell H., Roennberg S., Roessner S. Eating patterns described by a group of treatment seeking overweight women and normal weight women. *Scandinavian Journal of Behaviour Therapy,* 1985,14(4), 147-56.

76. Christensen L., Somers S. Comparison of nutrient intake among depressed and nondepressed individuals. *International Journal of Eating Disorders,* 1996, 20(1), 105-9.

77.   Crystal S.R., Bowen D.J., Bernstein I.L. Morning sickness and salt intake, food cravings, and food aversions. *Physiology and Behaviour*, 1999, 67(2), 181-7.

78.   Hetherington M.M., Macdiarmid J.I. "Chocolate addiction": A preliminary study of its description and its relationship to problem eating. *Appetite*, 1993, 21(3), 233-46.

79.   van Strien T. The concurrent validity of a classification of dieters with low versus high susceptibility toward failure of restraint. *Addictive Behaviours*, 1997, 22 (5), 587-97.

80.   Cepeda-Benito A., Tiffany S.T. The use of a dual-task procedure for the assessment of cognitive effort associated with cigarette craving. *Psychopharmacology*, 1996, 127(2), 155-63.

81.   Elash C.A., Tiffany S.T., Vrana S.R. The manipulation of smoking urges and affect through a brief imagery procedure: Self-report, psychophysiological, and startle probe responses. *Experimental and Clinical Psychopharmacology*, 1995, 3(2), 156-62.

82.   Maude-Griffin P., Tiffany S.T. Production of smoking urges through imagery: The impact of affect and smoking abstinence. *Experimental and Clinical Psychopharmacology*, 1996, 4(2), 198-208.

83.   Tiffany S.T., Drobes D.J. Imagery and smoking urges: The manipulation of affective content. *Addictive Behaviours*, 1990, 15(6), 531-9.

84.   Tiffany S.T., Hakenwerth D.M. The production of smoking urges through an imagery manipulation: Psychophysiological and verbal manifestations. *Addictive Behaviours*, 1991, 16(6), 389-400.

2. NEUROBIOLOGY OF CRAVINGS

2.1. NEURAL CIRCUITRY OF DESIRE

Roy A. Wise

2.1.1   Introduction

The sources of desire are multiple and not yet well understood, and desire is not yet well defined. The most obvious objects of desire are the things that we pursue; the sexually experienced male pursues the sexually receptive female, and the hungry animal pursues food. Some such approach responses are unconditioned; we approach novel stimuli if they are not too intense, we approach heat sources when we are cold and cold places when we are hot; hummingbirds approach red objects and orioles orange ones, and many species appear to show an unconditioned approach to species-specific olfactory stimuli. Unconditioned desire for these things is evident only when the things themselves enter our sensory fields.

Most desires are not unconditioned, however; most things that we pursue are those that we have experienced and enjoyed in the past. These objects of desire are objects of memory. For example, the addict is said to "chase the remembered high." Another example occurs when an adult human relationship breaks up and there is the fleeting desire to contact a remembered sweetheart. The desire for things remembered can be as fuzzy as the memory; the stimulus for such desire is not always obvious, but it is always memory-dependent.

Some desires involve things we have only heard about. Desire for travel to exotic lands, desire for membership in secret societies, desire for the 1941 Inglenook cabernet sauvignon or the 1862 patented single-lever corkscrew of Abraham Russel, desire for weightlessness in space, desire to sight the Abominable Snowman or the Loch Ness Monster - in all but a few initial cases, these are desires that are established through human communication. Much of our adolescent sexual desire is also desire for things discussed but not yet experienced.

We are beginning to learn about the neural circuitry of desire from brain imaging studies involving human subjects. What parts of our brains are active when our minds are filled with desire? The few reported studies of this type suggest that the parts of our brains that are activated during desire are the parts of our brain that are activated when we experience various rewards (1-3); thus the neural circuitry of desire appears to be common with at least a portion of the neural circuitry of reward. The present chapter deals primarily with current knowledge of the neural circuitry of reward. It draws heavily on studies of the laboratory rat. What we learn from the rat about the neural circuitry of desire is limited to the desires that can be inferred from what the rat approaches or works for. These are largely desires for rewards remembered and the strongest of such rewards are the laboratory rewards of drugs of abuse and direct electrical brain stimulation. While the human desires for rewards imagined presumably involve much of the same basic neural circuitry, they almost certainly involve additional circuitry - at least the circuitry of language.

2.1.2   Rewards as Things Approached

Whereas plants are usually rooted to their food supply, depend largely on insects and birds for reproductive fertilisation, and have passive defences against predators (noxious tastes, thorns, alkaloid poisons), animals search out their food and sexual partners and flee from those enemies they don't choose to fight. Thus the brain that distinguishes higher animals from plants is largely an organ of locomotion, whether it be locomotion toward an incentive or locomotion away from a source of stress. Theodore Schneirla has argued forcefully that the only empirical, objective terms applicable to all motivated behaviour in all animals are the terms 'approach', 'withdrawal', and their derivatives (4). The environmental stimuli we approach - and can, therefore, be assumed to be objects of desire - are the things we label more familiarly as 'rewards'; the things from which we withdraw are the things we label 'punishers.' Schneirla argued that the brain mechanisms of approach and avoidance are the core neural substrates of motivation.

Pavlov identified basic reflexes of approach and withdrawal as the 'orienting' or 'investigative' reflexes on the one hand and the 'defensive' reflexes on the other (5). Pavlov termed the more specific reflexes 'adaptive reflexes'; they adapt the organism to the specific conditions of the environment. These include salivation in response to food, pupillary dilation in response to low light, and pupillary constriction in response to bright light. His more general reflexes - the investigatory reflexes and the defensive reflexes - are more related to whether we like or dislike a sensory input (6). This, in turn, is determined by the intensity of a stimulus rather than by its other particulars (7). These reflexes involve the general sensitivity of the animal to the environment, and they are not restricted to the sense modality of the specific stimulus that has attracted the subject's attention. The defensive reflexes serve to withdraw the organism from, and desensitize it to stimuli, and they are reactions to stimuli that are too intense. The defensive reflexes include pupillary constriction that reduces visual acuity (this reflex overrides, to a degree, the adaptive reflex that adjusts pupillary dilation to the level of ambient light), changes in galvanic skin response that reduce touch sensitivity, contraction of the arteries to the head and dilation of those to the muscles, and physical withdrawal from the offensive stimulus (7).

The investigatory reflexes have the opposite effects; they serve to sensitise and expose the subject further to novel stimuli of low or moderate intensity. They include pupillary dilation, sensitising changes in galvanic skin response, and dilation of the arteries to the head with constriction of those to the muscles (7). They also include head and eye movements toward the stimulus and are followed by approach. Pavlov's investigatory and defensive reflexes are the elemental units of approach and withdrawal. As Pavlov and his disciples noted and Schneirla subsequently underlined, the same intense source of stimulation that elicits defensive reflexes will elicit investigatory reflexes and approach responses if its intensity is sufficiently reduced. Approach and the investigatory reflexes are elicited by rewards and reward-associated stimuli, while withdrawal and the defensive reflexes are elicited by punishers. It is the rewards we approach that we can most safely assume to be objects of desire.

2.1.3 Brain Stimulation Reward

Much of our knowledge of the brain mechanisms of approach and withdrawal comes from studies of the effects of direct electrical stimulation of specific brain regions. In the early 1950s, Olds and Milner discovered that rats would approach areas of their environment where they had received direct electrical stimulation of the septal area (8). Heath, at about the same time, discovered that humans found such stimulation pleasurable (9) and would work for it (10). Olds and Milner showed that rats would lever-press compulsively for such stimulation and Olds went on to identify a variety of subcortical structures in which stimulation was rewarding (11). Olds and Heath each proposed multi-structure circuitry that they believed to participate in reward function. Subsequent investigators have identified additional structures in which stimulation is rewarding; these structures range from regions of the medulla to regions of the neocortex (12). It remains to be determined how many of these structures contribute to a common motivational circuitry, but patients that have experienced stimulation in the rostral origins of the medial forebrain bundle, in an area roughly corresponding to the nucleus accumbens, report that it is pleasurable and that they desire its repetition (13). Presumably, other rewards that activate this circuitry are similarly desired. A good deal of work has been done to characterise this circuitry and to determine if it is activated by the more normal pleasures of life.

Olds and colleagues discovered that drugs affecting catecholamine neurotransmission modulated the effectiveness of brain stimulation reward (14). Catecholamine antagonists reduce willingness to work for rewarding stimulation, whereas drugs that augment catecholamine function do the opposite. Stein suggested that noradrenaline, then the only known catecholamine neurotransmitter, was the chemical messenger of reward circuitry (15). He suggested noradrenergic fibres from the nucleus locus coeruleus as a central element in the substrate of reward, the element on which amphetamine exerts its habit-forming actions (16). When it was discovered the brain dopamine was a neurotransmitter in its own right, and not merely a metabolic precursor of noradrenaline, attention turned to the possibility that dopamine-containing neurons played a role in reward function. The development of selective antagonists for noradrenaline and dopamine neurotransmission made it possible to contrast the roles of the two transmitters.

2.1.4   Dopamine Antagonists and Brain Stimulation Reward

The early prototypical catecholamine antagonist was chlorpromazine; it blocked both noradrenaline and dopamine receptors and it attenuated responding for brain stimulation reward (14). In the early 1970s, more selective agents - α- and β-noradrenergic antagonists and dopamine antagonists - became available. Both classes attenuated responding for brain stimulation reward, but it was dopamine antagonists that appeared to block the rewarding impact of the stimulation; the effects of adrenergic antagonists appeared to impair the performance capacity of the animal (17). The reward-attenuating effects of dopamine antagonists were reflected in two animal models: the extinction model and the curve-shift model.

In the extinction model, attention was paid to the temporal pattern of responding for brain stimulation reward following treatments with selective catecholamine receptor blockers. Whereas animals tested with selective noradrenergic blockers showed depressed responding from the opening seconds of the test session, animals tested with selective dopamine blockers began responding at normal rates but did not continue to do so after receiving normal levels of stimulation (18,19). In the words of a colleague, the dopamine blocker pimozide appeared to "take the jolts out of the volts." At the doses tested, the dopamine blocker did not block the animal's ability to lever-press; thus, presumably, it blocked the animal's desire to do so.

Results from the curve-shift model support this interpretation. In the curve-shift model, the number of stimulation pulses per lever-press (a direct ratio measure of reward strength) necessary to maintain responding is determined. The animal does not lever-press when the number of pulses in each earned reward is too small. When a sufficient number of pulses per reward is given, on the other hand, the animal responds at a maximal rate. At intermediate pulses per reward, response rate increases as an approximately linear function of reward strength. The function relating the rate of responding to the number of stimulation pulses in a reward is analogous to a dose-response curve in pharmacology. Drugs that antagonise the rewarding effect of the stimulation shift the curve to the right (20), while drugs that impair co-ordination or strength, on the other hand, shift the asymptote of maximum response rate down (21). Dopamine antagonists shift the curve to the right, increasing the amount of stimulation needed to motivate the animal. They can do so at moderate doses that do not cause any downward shift that would signal significant motoric impairment (22,23).

Whereas the rightward shift caused by dopamine antagonists is interpreted to reflect antagonism of reward function and a reduction of desire for a given level of stimulation, treatments that cause a leftward shift have the opposite significance. Drugs that are rewarding in their own right, such as amphetamine, cocaine, heroin, and nicotine, each shift the curve to the left, acting as synergists that reduce the number of stimulation pulses necessary to maintain lever-pressing (24). As would be expected from the dynamics of synergists and antagonists in dose-response analysis of drug effects, a rewarding drug that shifts the curve a given number of log units to the left can offset precisely the effects of a reward antagonist that shifts the curve the same number of log units to the right (25). With one unexplained exception (clonidine), the drugs that shift the curve to the right are dopamine or opioid antagonists. The drugs that shift the curve to the left are drugs that augment dopamine neurotransmission in one way or another (26). These dopamine-augmenting drugs include cocaine (which blocks inactivation of spontaneously released dopamine), amphetamine (which induces synaptic dopamine release), nicotine (which stimulates dopamine cells to 'fire'), and morphine and heroin (which disinhibit dopaminergic cell firing). Each of these drugs can be seen as augmenting the desirability of a given level of brain stimulation.

2.1.5   Dopamine Antagonists and Drug Reward

Amphetamine, cocaine, nicotine, morphine, and heroin are, of course, powerfully rewarding (and, in experienced users, desirable) in their own right. The rewarding effects of amphetamine, cocaine, and nicotine are antagonised by dopamine receptor blockers and by lesions of the dopamine system. Morphine and heroin reward are blocked in some but not all cases by dopamine antagonists and dopamine lesions (27); these opiates have two sites of potential action in reward circuitry - one site "downstream" and one site "upstream" from the dopaminergic link in the circuitry (28). That is, morphine and heroin can act at opiate receptors on cells that synapse on dopaminergic neurons and also at opiate receptors on the cells that receive synapses from dopaminergic neurons.

In each case, the site at which a drug is rewarding in its own right is a site at which it also potentiates brain stimulation reward. In the case of opiates, for example, mu and delta opioids can each enhance brain stimulation reward when they are injected near the dopamine cell bodies of the ventral tegmental area (29). These drugs are also rewarding when injected into this region in the absence of brain stimulation reward (30). The mu agonist [D-Ala^2, N-Me-Phe^4-Gly^5-ol]-enkephalin (DAMGO) is 100X more effective than the delta agonist [D-pen^2, D-Pen^5]-enkephalin (DPDPE) in this regard. DAMGO and DPDPE injections in this region each cause elevations of dopamine level at the terminals of the dopamine projections to nucleus accumbens. In this action as well, the mu agonist is 100 times more effective than the delta agonist (31). Thus the capacity of these drugs to elevate brain dopamine is proportional to their ability to serve as rewards in their own right, to summate with the rewarding effects of brain stimulation, and to activate the mesolimbic dopamine system (see also sections 2.3 and 2.4). The dopamine antagonists block the post-synaptic effects of the elevated dopamine block or attenuate desire for these rewarding and reward-enhancing drugs (32-35).

2.1.6   Dopamine Antagonists and Food Reward

The brain mechanisms capable of mediating addiction evolved long before the invention of the syringe, the harnessing of fire, or the development of barrels, corks and bottles that we use to store alcohol beyond the period of normal fermentation. Thus the mechanisms of addiction antedated, by millions of years, the phenomenon of addiction. Addiction is a recent, human artifact; addiction can occur in lower animals, but only with human intervention. Drugs are addictive when they are capable of activating the primitive brain mechanisms by which more natural rewards establish and control adaptive foraging and ingestion habits. Unfortunately, some drugs are able to activate these mechanisms more strongly and more rapidly than can the normal pleasures of life. It is for this reason that addictive drugs are able to establish maladaptive drug-seeking behaviour. Inasmuch as brain dopamine systems play a role in natural motivations such as hunger and thirst, dopamine antagonists block natural rewards such as food and water in addition to the laboratory rewards of brain stimulation and addictive drugs. However, inasmuch as dopamine depletion was initially identified with the motoric symptoms of Parkinson's disease, dopamine was initially identified with motor function. Special paradigms and careful analysis were needed to determine that dopamine antagonists attenuate the ability of food reward to maintain feeding and food-seeking and do not simply impair the ability of the animal to perform the required response. As was the case with brain stimulation reward, however, dopamine antagonists proved to disrupt the maintenance of responding for food reward at doses that did not significantly disrupt initial responding (36). That is, dopamine antagonists were shown to attenuate the desire for food and not just the ability to procure it and eat it.

In both free-feeding and lever-pressing tasks, animals treated with dopamine blockers begin but do not sustain the behaviours from which we infer the desire for food. Animals trained to lever-press for food initiate responding but do not sustain it despite the fact that they continue to earn the expected food pellets (36). At first, the animals eat the earned pellets, but in time they cease to do so. After they cease to eat the pellets, they still continue, for a time, to earn them. Finally, they stop earning the pellets as well. The extinction of the lever-pressing habit appears to reflect a loss of desire for food that develops as the animals taste the food in the dopamine-blocked condition.

The first time the animals are tested under conditions of dopamine blockade, they respond quite normally for several minutes before losing interest in the food they earn. If they are retrained in the drug-free condition for 2 days and then they are tested a second time under dopamine blockade, the earned food sustains responding only about half as long. With subsequent repetitions of retraining and retesting, the animals sustain responding for progressively shorter durations on drug treatment days. It is as if they learn with experience that there is no payoff for persevering on those days when they have been treated with dopamine antagonists. Just as dopamine antagonists reduce the desire for normally rewarding brain stimulation, so do they reduce the desire for normally rewarding food.

The important thing to note, however, is that the desire for stimulation or food is lost only after the animals experience the stimulation or the food in the dopamine-blocked condition. The primary effect of dopamine antagonists is to make the normal reward non-rewarding, not to blunt initial desire for the reward remembered. It is as if the loss of desire is secondary to the animal learning that the stimulation no longer feels good or that the food no longer tastes good. That is, it is only when the memory of the reward is degraded through experience with degraded reward that the desire itself is lost. In a similar manner, dopamine antagonists block the rewarding effects of water for thirsty animals, leading, subsequently, to the lack of desire for water despite severe dehydration (37). Desire for food and water is quickly rekindled, of course, as soon as animals happen to eat or receive water in the drug-free condition.

The conclusion that dopamine antagonists make normal rewards non-rewarding was nicely confirmed in studies of Ettenberg and Camp (38,39), where animals were tested in drug-free and reward-free sessions following training under various regimens. In these studies, hungry or thirsty animals were trained to run down a 6-foot straight alley for food or water reward. The animals were given one training trial per day, and groups were trained in each of three conditions. One group was given its normal (food or water) reward at the end of the alley on every training day. One group was rewarded on only half of the training days, finding no reward on the intervening days. The third group was rewarded with food or water on every training day, but was treated with the dopamine antagonist haloperidol on half these days. Following 15 days of such training, the animals were tested for 21 days, one trial per day, under conditions where they were never again rewarded or given the dopamine antagonist. Inasmuch as these animals were motivated only by the reward remembered, the responding in the test sessions was free from any possible contamination by drug-induced motoric impairment.

All animals ran quickly to the end of the alley on the first day of the non-rewarded extinction trials. On successive days, however, animals in each group took progressively longer to reach and enter the goal box. However, the behaviour deteriorated most quickly in the animals that were trained to expect reward every day and were never given the dopamine antagonist. The animals that had received reward only on 50% of trials during training extinguished at a much slower rate; they continued to run longer and ran more quickly than animals trained with normal reward on every trial. This is the well-known 'partial reinforcement extinction effect'; animals trained with only partial reinforcement persist longer under conditions of extinction. The animals that had been trained under haloperidol on 50% of trials also continued to run longer and faster than the animals trained under full reward. The animals trained with intermittent haloperidol performed just like the animals trained with intermittent reward. Thus the animals that had been trained under haloperidol on 50% of training trials performed in extinction as if they had earned no food on 50% of training trials; that is, they performed as if the food was essentially worthless on the haloperidol training days. Blocking the rewarding effects of food is not the same as blocking the desire for food, of course; the animals with food reward blocked on half the training days showed stronger and longer evidence of desire during the non-rewarded extinction testing. However, this anomaly is peculiar to partial reinforcement conditions; the desire for food or water is lost if the experience of food or water becomes consistently non-rewarding. Indeed, desire for a given food - chocolate, say, or ice cream - would never develop if the rewarding properties of that food were somehow blocked. In the case of food, this can be done at the sensory level, as in conditions of taste insensitivity due to zinc deficiency (40), or at the central level, as in conditions of dopamine blockade (41).

2.1.7   Dopamine Fluctuations and Reward

The obvious hypothesis as to why dopamine-blocked animals behave as if food or brain stimulation is not normally rewarding is that the rewards cause - and depend on - dopamine neurotransmission. That is: (i) they must cause dopamine release or block dopamine's inactivation, and (ii) the resulting increase in dopamine levels at nucleus accumbens dopamine receptors must play a critical role in reward function. It was a decade after postulation that various rewards elevated nucleus accumbens dopamine levels before this hypothesis was tested directly. By perfusing artificial cerebrospinal fluid through a microdialysis probe, we can now extract traces of brain chemicals from local regions in the brain. Microdialysis studies have confirmed that food reward (42), sex reward (43), brain stimulation reward (44), and a variety of drug rewards (26) all elevate extracellular dopamine levels in nucleus accumbens. Generally speaking, the relative effectiveness of these rewards is proportional to the speed and extent that they elevate extracellular dopamine levels.

Among the most likely natural pleasures of rodent life - the 'pleasures of the flesh' - are food and sex. These rewards tend to elevate brain dopamine levels modestly. Exposure to a receptive female tends to double the extracellular dopamine levels of sexually experienced male rats (45), while exposure to food reward tends to elevate nucleus accumbens dopamine levels by 30-80% (42,46). The addictive drugs amphetamine, heroin, and cocaine, in contrast, tend to elevate nucleus accumbens dopamine concentration to 300-500% and higher (26). Moreover, animals allowed to lever-press for these drugs press frequently enough to maintain their dopamine levels at two to four times normal (47-49). That is, experienced animals that control their opiate or psychomotor stimulant intake respond frequently enough to keep their nucleus accumbens dopamine concentrations well above the range that is normally reached in response to natural rewards such as food or sex. This would appear to explain the power of drugs of abuse; they allow animals to maintain dopamine levels in excess of what can be achieved by more natural rewards that are less avidly sought.

What, then, is the correlate of desire? Rats with free access to food will take cocaine to the point of death by starvation (50). For drug rewards, at least, desire appears to be strongest for the things that elevate brain dopamine most strongly and most rapidly. In animals experienced with the rewarding effects of heroin, cocaine, or amphetamine, a state of desire can be inferred from drug-seeking behavior that usually starts as soon as the animal, after a drug-free period, is allowed access to the drug. Partial elevation of dopamine levels - provoked by an experimenter-administered 'taste' of a drug the animal has previously been trained with (51) - increases the probability of drug-seeking (shortens the latency to initiate a binge of drug self-administration), and thus increases the neural correlate of desire.

2.1.8   Drug Satiety

Current data suggest that drug-associated desire is satisfied in drug-experienced animals when dopamine levels are sufficiently elevated (47-49). While rats will usually lever-press for the next drug injection when dopamine levels fall to a mere 200% of normal, the probability is very low that they will do so when dopamine levels are 300% or 400% of normal (52). Animals that could drive their dopamine levels to 2000% of normal with intravenous amphetamine do not do so. Experienced rats working for intravenous amphetamine wait tens of minutes after each injection before responding for the next, allowing the greater portion of the last injection to be metabolised before responding for another. The pattern of temporally spaced responding must be learned, however, and the form the learning takes suggests that the period of non-responding between injections is a true state of satiety. With experience, the animals learn to regulate their dopamine levels just above the point that can be reached with food or sex. It would appear that desire for the drug slowly fades as the animal learns about the drug's lack of effectiveness during periods of elevated dopamine levels.

2.1.9   Combination of Drug Reward and Brain Stimulation Reward

Is all desire satisfied when dopamine levels are sufficiently elevated by amphetamine or cocaine? It would not appear so. When rats are allowed to lever-press for intravenous injections of 0.25 mg/kg of d-amphetamine sulfate, they maintain their dopamine levels above 200% of normal, responding about once every half-hour, whenever their blood amphetamine levels fall to about 0.2 µg/ml (53). No drug seeking is seen for periods of about half an hour between injections. However, while the desire for more amphetamine is sated so long as dopamine levels are elevated to about double their normal values, the desire for more brain stimulation is not. If given the opportunity to press a second lever for rewarding hypothalamic brain stimulation, the animals will press this lever several hundred times between pauses to press the drug lever. Indeed, the desire for brain stimulation appears to be enhanced by this condition; animals respond more for the same amount of brain stimulation when they are intoxicated to satiating levels with amphetamine (54). Thus there is more to the satisfaction of desire than simply the activation of the dopamine system, and there is more to the rewarding effects of brain stimulation than the simple elevation of brain dopamine levels. The nature of the additional reward that can be produced by brain stimulation under these conditions is not known.

2.1.10   Opioid Antagonists and Reward

Dopamine is but one of 50 or more neurotransmitters or neuromodulators that act in the synapses of the brain. Among the others are the endogenous opioid peptides with their actions at various opioid receptors (55-57). Opiate antagonists, by blocking access of opiates to the endogenous opioid receptors, block the rewarding - as well as the other - effects of opiates (see also sections 2.2 and 2.5). The opiate antagonist naloxone also decreases the rewarding effects of food (58) and at least some forms of rewarding brain stimulation (59). Opiates stimulate feeding when administered into the ventral tegmental area (60), where they act to inhibit GABA-containing neurons that normally hold the dopamine system under inhibitory control (61). It would appear that endogenous opioid mechanisms (62) may contribute to the regulation of feeding, at least in part, through their interaction with the mesolimbic dopamine system that is important for opiate reward (63). The GABAergic neurons that synapse on the dopamine system contribute but a subset to the inputs to the dopamine system, and they are part of a feedback loop that originates in the nucleus accumbens. There are several other inputs to the ventral tegmental dopamine-containing neurons; the transmitters include norepinephrine, serotonin, glutamate, and acetylcholine. Thus the brain circuitry of reward involves many potential links and chemical messengers (64).

2.1.11   Priming and Incentive Motivation

Prior experience with a reward is usually required before that reward becomes desired. Once we have had experience with a reward, a 'taste' of that reward - like the taste of a salted peanut or a glimpse of exposed flesh - becomes a potent priming stimulus for approach behavior and the desire that accompanies or precedes it. Lesser but also effective provocations of desire are stimuli in the environment that have become associated, through Pavlovian conditioning, with primary rewards. Desire that is induced by sensory exposure to a primary reward or an associated conditioned stimulus is termed 'incentive motivation' (65). Incentive exposure is a powerful stimulus for desire, and one of the most effective ways to provoke re-initiation of motivated behavior is to 'prime' a subject with an incentive motivational stimulus.

In the case of drug reward and brain stimulation, the most effective incentive tends to be a free 'taste' of the reward itself (66,67). Experimenters routinely 'prime' their subjects with a free stimulation or free injection in order to trigger immediate initiation of self-stimulation or intravenous drug self-administration. The incentive motivational effectiveness of priming is the basis for an animal model of relapse to drug taking (68). In this model, the animal is first trained to perform some task such as lever-pressing for intravenous drug injections, and then the habit is extinguished by allowing the animal to continue responding without reward. When the animal has been sufficiently non-rewarded to have given up attending to the lever, the experimenter can then probe to see what stimuli will cause the animal to re-initiate the response despite the fact that it continues to go unrewarded. In the case of intravenous cocaine- or heroin-trained responding, various forms of stress are effective in this relapse paradigm (69). However, the most effective stimuli for reinstating the response pattern are the training drug or drugs that, like the training drug, activate the dopamine system (51,70-72).

2.1.12 Conditioned Reinforcers

While primary incentives are the most effective stimuli for priming motivated behaviour patterns, it is incentive-associated stimuli - such as, for humans, currency - that usually draw us through our environment and entice us to the objects of our desire. In the case of brain stimulation reward and intravenous drug reward, it is only conditioned stimuli - stimuli with little incentive value of their own prior to being associated with a primary reward - that do so. Laboratory animals, at least, cannot see, hear, smell, feel, or taste the stimulation that is delivered by wire or the drug that is delivered by catheter. They approach the lever or a reward-associated portion of the environment; they do not approach the drug or the stimulation itself. The effects of conditioned motivational stimuli - stimuli that have become associated with primary rewards - can be viewed in two ways.

First, reward-associated stimuli can be seen as conditioned reinforcers. These stimuli can, through association with primary reward, become sufficiently rewarding to establish new response habits. Again, human currency is the best example; we learn many new behaviours when the immediate reward, money, is only indirectly related to primary rewards such as food and shelter from cold. Second, conditioned reinforcers can be seen as incentive motivational properties. Because of their association with past reward, they become incentives that excite us and attract us through the environment. A good example of incentive motivational arousal is the frantic tail-wagging and prancing of a previously resting dog that is suddenly asked - having previously learned the significance of these words - "Do you want to go for a walk?" Desire may have existed in latent form before the incentive-motivational sentence was uttered, but now desire is raw and, presumably, stronger. If the dog had been sleeping before the sentence was uttered, we might suppose desire to have been absent until the words called it forth. Incentive stimuli also lead us to goal objects. Rats learn first the turns in a maze that are closest to the goal box. Presumably this is because the association with primary reward is stronger through proximity. As earlier and earlier landmarks become associated with reward, these landmarks come to control the animal's behaviour at each successive choice-point in the maze.

The neurobiology of conditioned reinforcement is not completely understood, but it is dependent in major part on the functions of dopamine in nucleus accumbens. Amphetamine injections into the nucleus accumbens enhance the behavioural effectiveness of conditioned reinforcers, and lesions of nucleus accumbens block this effect (73,74). Thus brain dopamine would appear to play a part in the desire not only for food, sex, and previously experienced drugs of abuse, but also for stimuli associated with these more primary rewards.

However, several investigators have looked for, and few have found, conditioned release of dopamine. One promising possibility is that drug-associated stimuli cause dopamine release in some but not all projection areas of the mesolimbic dopamine system. Di Chiara and colleagues have reported that drug-associated stimuli cause dopamine release in the core but not the shell area of nucleus accumbens (and also in the medial prefrontal cortex) (46). This is somewhat surprising, as it is thought to be preferential release of dopamine in the shell rather than the core region of nucleus accumbens that plays the major role in primary drug reward (75,76). Nonetheless, release in the core and not the shell might explain why so many investigators have found no effect of reward-associated stimuli on dopamine release; probe placements have frequently been aimed at or near the shell rather than in the centre of the core.

If drug-associated stimuli do indeed activate portions of the meso-corticolimbic dopamine system, how might they do so? Current attention focuses on three cortical structures that interact with the nucleus accumbens: the medial prefrontal cortex, the amygdala, and the hippocampus (52). These structures are associated with such functions as working memory and decision making, emotional learning, and context or place learning, respectively.

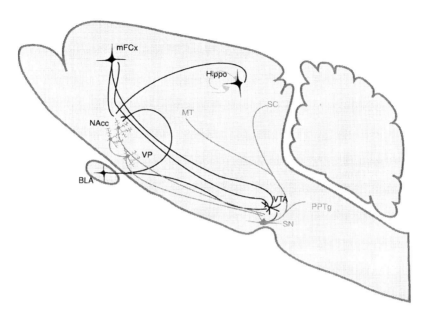

Fig. 2.1.1. Schematic diagram of reward-associated input and output systems of nucleus accumbens. Nucleus accumbens receives excitatory amino acid inputs from the medial prefrontal cortex (mFCx), hippocampus (Hippo), and, from a more lateral plane, the basolateral amygdala (BLA). It receives dopaminergic input from the ventral tegmental area (VTA). Medial prefrontal cortex and basolateral amygdala also send excitatory amino acid input to the ventral tegmental area, though not exclusively to the dopaminergic neurons there. Nucleus accumbens sends GABAergic outputs to the ventral pallidum (VP) and to the ventral tegmental region; GABAergic outputs of the ventral pallidum also descend to the ventral tegmental region. Some of the GABAergic fibres descending to the ventral tegmental area synapse on dopaminergic cells, while others synapse on GABAergic cells that project to distal targets-the medial thalamus (MT), superior colliculus (SC) and pedunculo-pontine tegmental nucleus (PPTg), but also send collaterals to their dopaminergic neighbours. The medial thalamus feeds back (or forward) to the medial prefrontal cortex and the pedunculo-pontine tegmental nucleus feeds back (or forward) to the ventral tegmental area and nucleus accumbens. These are but some of the ways in which activation of reward-related structures feed back upon one another in complex recurrent loops.

The medial prefrontal cortex, the amygdala, and the hippocampus send excitatory amino acid containing projections to the nucleus accumbens, and at least two of them - the medial prefrontal cortex and the amygdala - send excitatory amino acid projections to the ventral tegmental area as well (Fig. 2.1.1). Stimulation of medial prefrontal cortex causes dopamine release in nucleus accumbens, and it appears to do so by activating the dopamine-containing cells of nucleus accumbens (77,78). Stimulation of the hippocampus also activates the ventral tegmental dopamine-containing neurons (79). The amygdala presumably has the capacity to do so as well. Thus structures that are known to play roles compatible with detection of motivationally significant conditioned stimuli have connections that should allow them to alert the nucleus accumbens, either directly or by elevating brain dopamine into the effective range for priming the animal.

2.1.13   Summary

We have little firm knowledge about the neural circuitry of desire. A good deal is known, however, about the neural circuitry activated by the rewards that constitute the principal objects of desire. Food and sexual rewards activate the mesolimbic dopamine system; they do so by pathways that are not yet characterized. The mesolimbic dopamine system is also activated by the laboratory rewards of direct electrical stimulation and intravenous psychomotor stimulants. These laboratory rewards activate the system more strongly than do food or sex, and they appear to be more strongly desired by animals that have had chronic exposure to them. This may explain why food and social interaction are often forsaken when addictive drugs are offered as a freely available alternative. The mesolimbic dopamine system is a centrally situated and widely projecting system involved variously in arousal, reward, anticipation of reward, and other aspects of motivated behavior. It has sub-systems and multiple inputs, each of which remains to be fully characterised. This system offers a heuristic starting point for attempts to understand the neural circuitry of a wide range of human and lower animal desires.

2.1.14   References

1.   Childress A.R., Mozley P.D., McElgin W., Fitzgerald J., Reivich M., O'Brien C.P. Limbic activation during cue-induced cocaine craving. *American Journal of Psychiatry*, 1999, 156, 11-8.

2.   Grant S., London E.D., Newlin D.B., Villemagne V.L., Liu X., Contoreggi C., Phillips R.L., Kimes A.S., Margolin A. Activation of memory circuits during cue-elicited cocaine craving. *Proceedings of the National Academy of Sciences (U.S.A.)*, 1996, 93, 12040-5.

3.   Breiter H.C., Rosen B.R. Functional magnetic resonance imaging of brain reward circuitry in the human. *Annals of the New York Academy of Science*, 1999, 877, 523-47.

4.   Schneirla T.C. An evolutionary and developmental theory of biphasic processes underlying approach and withdrawal, in *Nebraska Symposium on Motivation*. Ed. Jones M.R. Lincoln, University of Nebraska Press. 1959, 1-42.

5.   Pavlov I.P. *Conditioned Reflexes*. Oxford, Oxford University Press. 1927.

6.   Hess E.H. The role of pupil size in communication. *Scientific American*, 1975, 233, 110-9.

7.   Sokolov Y.N. *Perception and the conditioned reflex*. Oxford, Pergamon. 1963.

8.   Olds J., Milner P.M. Positive reinforcement produced by electrical stimulation of septal area and other regions of rat brain. *Journal of Comparative and Physiological Psychology*, 1954, 47, 419-27.

9.   Heath R.G. *Studies in Schizophrenia*. Cambridge, Harvard University Press. 1954.

10.   Heath R.G. Intracranial self-stimulation in man. *Science*, 1963, 140, 394-6.

11.   Olds M.E., Olds J. Approach-avoidance analysis of rat diencephalon. *Journal of Comparative Neurology*, 1963, 120, 259-95.

12.   Phillips A.G. Brain reward circuitry: A case for separate systems. *Brain Research Bulletin*, 1984, 12, 195-201.

13.   Heath R.G. Pleasure and brain activity in man. *Journal of Nervous and Mental Disorders*, 1972, 154, 3-18.

14. Olds J., Travis R.P. Effects of chlorpromazine, meprobamate, pentobarbital and morphine on self-stimulation. *Journal of Pharmacology and Experimental Therapeutics*, 1960, 128, 397-404.

15. Stein L. Chemistry of reward and punishment, in *Proceedings of the American College of Neuropsychopharmacology*. Ed. Efron D.H. Washington, DC, U.S. Government Printing Office. 1968, 105-23.

16. Stein L., Wise C.D. Amphetamine and noradrenergic reward pathways, in *Frontiers in Catecholamine Research*. Eds Usdin E., Snyder S.H. New York, Pergamon Press. 1973, 963-8.

17. Wise R.A. Catecholamine theories of reward: A critical review. *Brain Research*, 1978, 152, 215-47.

18. Fouriezos G., Wise R.A. Pimozide-induced extinction of intracranial self-stimulation: response patterns rule out motor or performance deficits. *Brain Research*, 1976, 103, 377-80.

19. Fouriezos G., Hansson P., Wise R.A. Neuroleptic-induced attenuation of brain stimulation reward in rats. *Journal of Comparative and Physiological Psychology*, 1978, 92, 661-71.

20. Edmonds D.E., Stellar J.R., Gallistel C.R. Parametric analysis of brain stimulation reward in the rat: II. Temporal summation in the reward system. *Journal of Comparative and Physiological Psychology*, 1974, 87, 860-9.

21. Edmonds D.E., Gallistel C.R. Parametric analysis of brain stimulation reward in the rat: III. Effect of performance variables on the reward summation function. *Journal of Comparative and Physiological Psychology*, 1974, 87, 876-83.

22. Gallistel C.R., Boytim M., Gomita Y., Klebanoff L. Does pimozide block the reinforcing effect of brain stimulation? *Pharmacology Biochemistry and Behavior*, 1982, 17, 769-81.

23. Franklin K.B.J. Catecholamines and self-stimulation: Reward and performance effects dissociated. *Pharmacology Biochemistry and Behavior*, 1978, 9, 813-20.

24. Wise R.A. Addictive drugs and brain stimulation reward. *Annual Review of Neuroscience*, 1996, 19, 319-40.

25. Gallistel C.R., Freyd G. Quantitative determination of the effects of catecholaminergic agonists and antagonists on the rewarding efficacy of brain stimulation. *Pharmacology Biochemistry and Behavior,* 1987, 26, 731-41.

26. Di Chiara G., Imperato A. Drugs abused by humans preferentially increase synaptic dopamine concentrations in the mesolimbic system of freely moving rats. *Proceedings of the National Academy of Sciences (U.S.A.),* 1988, 85, 5274-8.

27. Bozarth M.A., Wise R.A. Involvement of the ventral tegmental dopamine system in opioid and psychomotor stimulant reinforcement, in *Problems of Drug Dependence 1985.* Ed. Harris L.S. Washington, D.C., U.S. Government Printing Office. 1986, 190-6.

28. Kalivas P.W., Widerlov E., Stanley D., Breese G., Prange A.J. Enkephalin action on the mesolimbic system: A dopamine-dependent and a dopamine-independent increase in locomotor activity. *Journal of Pharmacology and Experimental Therapeutics,* 1983, 227, 229-37.

29. Jenck F., Gratton A., Wise R.A. Opioid receptor subtypes associated with ventral tegmental facilitation of lateral hypothalamic brain stimulation reward. *Brain Research,* 1987, 423, 34-8.

30. Devine D.P., Wise R.A. Self-administration of morphine, DAMGO, and DPDPE into the ventral tegmental area of rats. *Journal of Neuroscience,* 1994, 14, 1978-84.

31. Devine D.P., Leone P., Pocock D., Wise R.A. Differential involvement of ventral tegmental mu, delta, and kappa opioid receptors in modulation of basal mesolimbic dopamine release: *In vivo* microdialysis studies. *Journal of Pharmacology and Experimental Therapeutics,* 1993, 266, 1236-46.

32. Yokel R.A., Wise R.A. Increased lever-pressing for amphetamine after pimozide in rats: Implications for a dopamine theory of reward. *Science,* 1975, 187, 547-9.

33. de Wit H., Wise R.A. Blockade of cocaine reinforcement in rats with the dopamine receptor blocker pimozide but not with the noradrenergic blockers phentolamine or phenoxybenzamine. *Canadian Journal of Psychology,* 1977, 31, 195-203.

34. Corrigall W.A., Franklin K.B.J., Coen K.M., Clarke P. The mesolimbic dopaminergic system is implicated in the reinforcing effects of nicotine. *Psychopharmacology*, 1992, 107, 285-9.

35. Spyraki C., Fibiger H.C., Phillips A.G. Attenuation of heroin reward in rats by disruption of the mesolimbic dopamine system. *Psychopharmacology*, 1983, 79, 278-83.

36. Wise R.A., Spindler J., deWit H., Gerber G.J. Neuroleptic-induced "anhedonia" in rats: Pimozide blocks the reward quality of food. *Science*, 1978, 201, 262-4.

37. Gerber G.J., Sing J., Wise R.A. Pimozide attenuates lever pressing for water reinforcement in rats. *Pharmacology, Biochemistry and Behavior*, 1981, 14, 201-5.

38. Ettenberg A., Camp C.H. Haloperidol induces a partial reinforcement extinction effect in rats: Implications for a dopamine involvement in food reward. *Pharmacology Biochemistry and Behavior*, 1986, 25, 813-21.

39. Ettenberg A., Camp C.H. A partial reinforcement extinction effect in water-reinforced rats intermittently treated with haloperidol. *Pharmacology Biochemistry and Behavior*, 1986, 25, 1231-5.

40. Heyneman C.A. Zinc deficiency and taste disorders. *Annals of Pharmacotherapy*, 1996, 30, 186-7.

41. Wise R.A., Schwartz H.V. Pimozide attenuates acquisition of lever pressing for food in rats. *Pharmacology, Biochemistry and Behavior*, 1981, 15, 655-6.

42. Hernandez L., Hoebel B.G. Food reward and cocaine increase extracellular dopamine in the nucleus accumbens as measured by microdialysis. *Life Sciences*, 1988, 42, 1705-12.

43. Pfaus J.G., Damsma G., Nomikos G.G., Wenkstern D.G., Blaha C.D., Phillips A.G., Fibiger H.C. Sexual behavior enhances central dopamine transmission in the male rat. *Brain Research*, 1990, 530, 345-8.

44. Bauco P., Rivest R., Wise R.A. Extracellular nucleus accumbens dopamine and metabolite levels during earned and unearned lateral hypothalamic brain stimulation. *Society for Neuroscience Abstracts*, 1994, 20, 823.

45. Fiorino D.F., Coury A., Phillips A.G. Dynamic changes in nucleus accumbens dopamine efflux during the Coolidge effect in male rats. *Journal of Neuroscience*, 1997, 17, 4849-55.

46. Bassareo V., Di Chiara G. Differential influence of associative and nonassociative learning mechanisms on the responsiveness of prefrontal and accumbal dopamine transmission to food stimuli in rats fed ad libitum. *Journal of Neuroscience*, 1997, 17, 851-61.

47. Wise R.A. *In vivo* estimates of extracellular dopamine and dopamine metabolite levels during intravenous cocaine or heroin self-administration. *Seminars in the Neurosciences*, 1993, 5, 337-42.

48. Wise R.A., Newton P., Leeb K., Burnette B., Pocock P., Justice J.B. Fluctuations in nucleus accumbens dopamine concentration during intravenous cocaine self-administration in rats. *Psychopharmacology*, 1995, 120, 10-20.

49. Ranaldi R., Pocock D., Zereik R., Wise R.A. Dopamine fluctuations in the nucleus accumbens during maintenance, extinction, and reinstatement of intravenous D-amphetamine self-administration. *Journal of Neuroscience*, 1999, 19, 4102-9.

50. Bozarth M.A., Wise R.A. Toxicity associated with long-term intravenous heroin and cocaine self-administration in the rat. *Journal of the American Medical Association*, 1985, 254, 81-3.

51. Gerber G.J., Stretch R. Drug-induced reinstatement of extinguished self-administration behavior in monkeys. *Pharmacology Biochemistry and Behavior*, 1975, 3, 1055-61.

52. Wise R.A. Cognitive factors in addiction and nucleus accumbens function: Some hints from rodent models. *Psychobiology*, 1999, 27, 300-10.

53. Yokel R.A., Pickens R. Drug level of *d*- and *l*-amphetamine during intravenous self-administration. *Psychopharmacologia*, 1974, 34, 255-64.

54. Wise R.A., Yokel R.A., Hansson P., Gerber G.J. Concurrent intracranial self-stimulation and amphetamine self-administration in rats. *Pharmacology Biochemistry and Behavior*, 1977, 7, 459-61.

55. Simon E.J., Hiller J.M. The opiate receptors. *Annual Review of Pharmacology and Toxicology*, 1978, 18, 371-94.

56.   Snyder S.H. The opiate receptor and morphine-like peptides in the brain. *American Journal of Psychiatry*, 1978, 135, 645-52.

57.   Zadina J.E., Hackler L., Ge L.J., Kastin A.J. A potent and selective endogenous agonist for the mu-opiate receptor. *Nature*, 1997, 386, 499-502.

58.   Wise R.A., Raptis L. Effects of naloxone and pimozide on initiation and maintenance measures of free feeding. *Brain Research*, 1986, 368, 62-8.

59.   Trujillo K.A., Belluzzi J.D., Stein L. Opiate antagonists and self-stimulation: extinction-like response patterns suggest selective reward deficit. *Brain Research*, 1989, 492, 15-28.

60.   Noel M.B., Wise R.A. Ventral tegmental injections of morphine but not U-50, 488H enhance feeding in food-deprived rats. *Brain Research*, 1993, 632, 68-73.

61.   Johnson S.W., North R.A. Opioids excite dopamine neurons by hyperpolarization of local interneurons. *Journal of Neuroscience*, 1992, 12, 483-8.

62.   Noel M.B., Wise R.A. Ventral tegmental injections of a selective μ or ∂ opioid enhance feeding in food-deprived rats. *Brain Research*, 1995, 673, 304-12.

63.   Wise R.A. Opiate reward: Sites and substrates. *Neuroscience and Biobehavioral Reviews*, 1989, 13, 129-33.

64.   Wise R.A. Neurobiology of addiction. *Current Opinion in Neurobiology*, 1996, 6, 243-51.

65.   Bindra D. Neuropsychological interpretation of the effects of drive and incentive-motivation on general activity and instrumental behavior. *Psychological Review*, 1968, 75, 1-22.

66.   Gallistel C.R. The incentive of brain-stimulation reward. *Journal of Comparative and Physiological Psychology*, 1969, 69, 713-21.

67.   Pickens R., Harris W.C. Self-administration of d-amphetamine by rats. *Psychopharmacologia*, 1968, 12, 158-63.

68.   Stewart J., de Wit H. Reinstatement of drug-taking behavior as a method of assessing incentive motivational properties of drugs, in *Methods of Assessing the Reinforcing Properties of Abused Drugs*. Ed. Bozarth M.A. New York, Springer Verlag. 1987, 211-27.

69. Shaham Y., Stewart J. Stress reinstates heroin-seeking in drug-free animals: an effect mimicking heroin, not withdrawal. *Psychopharmacology*, 1995, 119, 334-41.

70. de Wit H., Stewart J. Reinstatement of cocaine-reinforced responding in the rat. *Psychopharmacology*, 1981, 75, 134-43.

71. de Wit H., Stewart J. Drug reinstatement of heroin-reinforced responding in the rat. *Psychopharmacology*, 1983, 79, 29-31.

72. Wise R.A., Murray A., Bozarth M.A. Bromocriptine self-administration and bromocriptine-reinstatement of cocaine-trained and heroin-trained lever-pressing in rats. *Psychopharmacology*, 1990, 100, 355-60.

73. Taylor J.R., Robbins T.W. Enhanced behavioural control by conditioned reinforcers produced by intracerebral injections of d-amphetamine in the rat. *Psychopharmacology*, 1984, 84, 405-12.

74. Taylor J.R., Robbins T.W. 6-hydroxydopamine lesions of the nucleus accumbens, but not of the caudate nucleus, attenuate enhanced responding with conditioned reinforcement produced by intra-accumbens amphetamine. *Psychopharmacology*, 1986, 90, 310-7.

75. Pontieri F.E., Tanda G., Di Chiara G. Intravenous cocaine, morphine, and amphetamine preferentially increase extracellular dopamine in the "shell" as compared with the "core" of the rat nucleus accumbens. *Proceedings of the National Academy of Sciences (U.S.A.)*, 1995, 92, 12304-8.

76. Carlezon W.A., Jr., Wise R.A. Rewarding actions of phencyclidine and related drugs in nucleus accumbens shell and frontal cortex. *Journal of Neuroscience*, 1996, 16, 3112-22.

77. Karreman M., Moghaddam B. The prefrontal cortex regulates the basal release of dopamine in the limbic striatum: An effect mediated by ventral tegmental area. *Journal of Neurochemistry*, 1996, 66, 589-98.

78. Taber M.T., Das S., Fibiger H.C. Cortical regulation of subcortical dopamine release: Mediation via the ventral tegmental area. *Journal of Neurochemistry*, 1995, 65, 1407-10.

79. Legault M., Rompré P.-P., Wise R.A. Chemical stimulation of the ventral hippocampus elevates nucleus accumbens dopamine by activating

dopaminergic neurons of the ventral tegmental area. *Journal of Neuroscience,* 2000, 20, 1635-42.

2.2. OPIOIDS, PLEASURE AND FOOD INTAKE

Blake Gosnell, PhD and Dean D. Krahn, M.D.

2.2.1   Introduction

The title of this chapter is a deceptively simple one - deceptive simply because each of the words involved is actually a label for a complex concept. For example, the class of compounds known as opioids includes a large number of compounds that, among many other actions, change food intake. Whether this is a central or a critical action of opioids is not clear. Also, the role of pleasure in food intake and in the motivation of human behaviour in general, has been debated for thousands of years. The measurement of pleasure in animals as well as in humans is also highly controversial. The title is also deceptively simple because the listing of the three words together suggests that there is an important and well-understood relationship between these three concepts. However, our understanding of the nature and importance of the relationship between these three concepts is still evolving. In part, the reason that our understanding of these relationships is not more advanced is that there are still relatively few studies that measure or vary all three factors. We will review some studies that examine the relationships between two of these factors, but will focus most of our attention on studies that address all three variables. We will first review the data available from studies using laboratory animals. Next, we will review the relevant human studies. Finally, we will point out the areas of controversy and where, in our opinion, future studies are most obviously needed.

2.2.2   Opioids and Food Intake: Animal Studies

It has been known for many years that substances acting at opioid receptors, such as morphine, can influence food intake. This effect was made much more interesting by the discovery of endogenous opioids and opioid receptors, since it suggested a possible role for opioids in the regulation of feeding and appetite. In this section we will briefly outline the effects of exogenous opioid agonists and antagonists on food intake, discuss the brain areas thought to be involved, and then discuss in more detail those studies that suggest that opioids play a role in mediating palatability.

2.2.2.1 Receptor types and sites of action

Quite a few studies have demonstrated that opioids cause an increase in the amount of food consumed and that opioid antagonists typically cause a decrease in intake. Three main classes of opioid receptors have been identified: mu, delta and kappa. Mu receptor agonists such as morphine and DAMGO, delta agonists such as DPDPE and DSLET, and kappa agonists such as U-50,488H and tifluadom, have been found to stimulate food intake (1). Opioid antagonists such as naloxone and naltrexone have been shown repeatedly to cause a reduction of intake in a number of conditions and in a number of species, including humans. Several reviews covering various aspects of opioids and feeding have been published (1-5).

The effect of opioid agonists and antagonists on ingestive behaviour is thought to be mediated via an action in the brain. One line of evidence for a central site of action is that forms of naloxone that do not easily enter the brain from the circulation are not nearly as effective at reducing fluid intake as those that do enter the brain (6,7). Microinjection studies also indicate a central site of action. Changes in food intake have been observed after direct microinjection of opioid agonists or antagonists into the lateral ventricles and into a number of specific brain sites, including the paraventricular and ventromedial nuclei of the hypothalamus, the ventral tegmental area, the amygdala, the nucleus accumbens, and the nucleus of the solitary tract (8-14). Some differences have been noted across injection sites regarding the relative effectiveness of mu, delta and kappa opioid receptor agonists (1). Finally, central injections of antibodies to opioid peptides, or antisense compounds directed against opioid receptors, have effects consistent with a role for central opioids in the regulation of feeding (15,16).

2.2.2.2   Opioid effects on diet selection

Several studies have examined the effects of opioids on macronutrient selection. When rats were provided with separate sources of fat, carbohydrate and protein, Marks-Kaufman and Kanarek observed that naloxone caused a relatively larger reduction in the intake of fat than in the intake of carbohydrate or protein (17). Conversely, acute injections of morphine preferentially stimulated fat intake or fat and protein intake (9,18). With repeated daily injections of morphine, a preferential increase in fat intake developed during the course of the treatment period (19,20). On the other hand, continuous infusions of morphine caused only a transient increase in fat intake and a decrease in carbohydrate intake (21). Systemic injections of the opioid agonist butorphanol tartrate, as well as injections of the mu agonist DAMGO into the nucleus accumbens, also caused a preferential or selective stimulation of fat intake (22,23). In contrast, Gosnell *et al.* reported that the major effect of morphine on diet selection depended on the baseline preferences of the rats: in rats characterised beforehand as fat-preferrers, morphine had the greatest stimulatory effect on fat intake, whereas in rats characterised as carbohydrate-preferrers, carbohydrate intake was most affected (24). They concluded that the effect of morphine was to enhance the intake of the preferred diet rather than to enhance the intake of dietary fat. Evans and Vaccarino drew a similar conclusion based on studies in which morphine was microinjected into the nucleus accumbens of rats that had been selectively deprived of either protein or carbohydrate (25).

Glass and colleagues found that in food-deprived rats given a choice between a high-fat and a high-carbohydrate diet, naloxone was more effective in reducing the intake of the preferred diet compared with the non-preferred diet (26). This observation was somewhat supported by the findings of Koch and Bodnar, who found that a significant amount of the variance in response to central injections of naltrexone in food-deprived rats could be explained by baseline preferences for fat and carbohydrate (27). However, they also noted some conditions under which the effects of opioid antagonists were independent of baseline preferences. Welch *et al.* found that, even after adjusting for baseline preferences, morphine caused a preferential increase in fat intake (28). Thus it appears that opioids may cause a relative increase in fat preference under some conditions, and that pre-existing preferences may modulate this effect. It is possible that mixed results on this issue are due in part to the fact that systemic or intracerebroventricular injections may act on multiple structures with different influences on macronutrient selection. This possibility was addressed by Glass *et al.*, who measured diet selection after microinjections of naltrexone into either the amygdala or the paraventricular hypothalamic nucleus (PVN) (29). They found that PVN injections of naltrexone caused a reduction of both a high-fat and a high-carbohydrate diet, whereas injections into the amygdala caused a reduction in intake of the preferred diet. They suggest that the PVN is more associated with postingestive functions (e.g. energy balance), while the amygdala is more closely associated with affective processing.

In studies in which rats were given a choice between standard rat chow and a palatable alternative diet, mixed results have been obtained. File reported that, when rats were given a choice between lab chow and chocolate chips, naloxone reduced chow intake to 41–48% of control, but completely blocked the intake of chocolate chips (30). Similarly, Cooper and Turkish found that, when a choice between chow and chocolate-coated cookies was presented, naltrexone reduced intake of the cookies and actually increased the intake of chow (31). However, Giraudo *et al.* did not observe this effect (a selective decrease in the intake of the more palatable food) in a similarly designed study with naloxone (32). They did find, however, that, in rats given a choice between chow and a less palatable high-fibre diet, naloxone had a more potent effect on chow intake. Differences in the length of the deprivation period prior to the test, as well as the length of the test session itself, may have contributed to differences in the observed effect of naloxone in this study and that by Cooper and Turkish with naltrexone (31).

2.2.2.3 *Opioid antagonist effects on diets varying in palatability*

A second approach to studying whether opioids influence the palatability (or pleasure experienced when foods are ingested or tasted) of foods is to measure the effectiveness of opioid antagonists in reducing the intakes of foods varying in palatability or under conditions in which the role of palatability is manipulated. Segall and Margules studied the effects of naloxone on the intake of a juice solution by rats in the hungry vs. non-deprived states (33). They found that naloxone was more effective in reducing juice intake in the non-deprived condition (in which it is assumed that palatability plays a major role in controlling intake) than when rats were maintained on a food-restriction schedule, and argued that naloxone reduced the reinforcing qualities of the juice. Apfelbaum and Mandenoff measured the effect of naltrexone in rats maintained on a regular chow diet and in rats given chow plus an array of palatable foods (34). They found opioid blockade to be much more effective at reducing the hyperphagia induced by the palatable food than in reducing intake in the chow condition. Similarly, Levine and colleagues concluded that naloxone blocks the portion of food intake that may be attributable to sweet taste (35). Food-deprived rats consume more food when given a sweetened chow than when given standard chow. When naloxone was administered, intake of the sweetened chow was similar to that of untreated rats given unsweetened chow. In a follow-up study, it was found that, in food-restricted rats, naloxone was much more effective in reducing the intake of a sucrose-based diet than it was when less-preferred cornstarch- or polycose-based diets were available (36).

2.2.2.4   Opioid antagonist effects on palatable fluid intake

Additional support for the idea that opioids play a role in mediating the rewarding aspects of food or fluids comes from studies in which opioid antagonists were found to alter the intake of palatable fluids. In studies in which both water and a palatable saccharin solution were provided, opioid antagonists have been shown to cause a preferential decrease in the intake of the saccharin solution (37-40). Interestingly, the antagonist naltrexone was found to cause a selective decrease in saccharin intake and in conditioned anticipatory behaviour in the environment paired with saccharin access (41). The effect of naloxone on intake is not limited to sweet solutions, as it has also been shown for sodium chloride solutions (42). Kirkham and Cooper reported that the reductions in sucrose intake observed after injections of naloxone were similar to those observed after reductions in the concentration of the sucrose (43). In rats prepared with gastric fistulas, such that stomach contents are drained before they can pass to the intestine, naloxone caused a reduction in sucrose solution intake (43,44). These findings are consistent with the interpretation that the antagonist reduced the palatability of the solution. The finding that opioid receptor-deficient mice have a reduced saccharin preference also reinforces the view that opioids may be involved in mediating palatability (45).

Most of the studies mentioned above utilised a water deprivation schedule to promote drinking during the test period. It could be argued, therefore, that the results reflect, to some degree, an influence of naloxone on thirst and/or water balance. Indeed, there are reports of naloxone causing a reduction in water intake (7,46). However, even in studies in which no deprivation is used, opioid antagonist treatment has been shown to reduce the intake of palatable fluids. In the non-deprived condition, it is presumed that the intake of a flavoured solution is driven primarily by the palatability of the fluid; water intake is generally minimal. Thus, rats will readily consume sucrose or saccharin solutions and will avoid quinine solutions. Opioid antagonists have been shown to reduce this palatability-induced intake after systemic and intracerebroventricular injections as well as after microinjections into the nucleus accumbens (47-50).

2.2.2.5   Opioid agonist effects on palatable fluid intake

As noted above, opioid agonists have an effect on intake that is the opposite of that of opioid antagonists, i.e. an increased intake. This effect has been demonstrated with standard lab chow as well as with more palatable foods and fluids. In chronically water-restricted rats, the preference for saccharin over water was increased by systemic morphine injections (51). This effect was also observed when the alternative to water was a solution containing sodium chloride or ethanol (52,53). Thus, the effect of morphine is not limited to sweet tastes. When mu or delta agonists were injected into the lateral ventricles of non-thirsty rats, there was an increased intake of saccharin or sodium chloride solution (54-56). This also occurred when rats were required to press a lever to obtain saccharin solution (57). Agonists at mu, delta and kappa receptors were observed to increase the intake of sucrose solution, although in most cases the effects were dependent on sucrose concentration (58).

Results from studies in which opioid agonists were microinjected into the nucleus accumbens (N. Acc.) also indicate an effect on palatability. The nucleus accumbens receives a dopaminergic projection from the ventral tegmental area, and this dopaminergic system is thought to be important in mediating some aspects of drug reward. Injections of selective mu or delta opioid receptor agonists into the N. Acc. caused an increase in the intake of sucrose solution in non-deprived rats (59). This pattern is somewhat similar to that observed for food intake or feeding behaviour after injections into the N. Acc. and the ventral tegmental area (10,13,60-62). A role for mu but not kappa receptors in the N. Acc. in mediating palatability-induced intake is also supported by studies in which selective opioid antagonists were microinjected (49,50). As mentioned above, this pattern of apparent receptor involvement (mu and delta, but not kappa) was also obtained in measures of saccharin or saline intake after intracerebroventricular (icv) injections of selective opioid agonists (54-57). Mu and delta agonists are generally more effective than kappa agonists in several types of measures that are thought to be relevant to brain reward systems, including drug self-administration, conditioned place preference, and the stimulation of dopamine release in the nucleus accumbens (63–67). The possibility that mu and delta opioid receptor-selective compounds affect intake by influencing palatability, therefore, is congruent with the demonstrated ability of these types of compounds to activate the mesolimbic dopaminergic system. It has been suggested that the feeding effects of kappa agonists are not dependent on this system (61). A more detailed comparison of the feeding effects of mu vs. kappa agonists can be found in a review by Nencini (68).

Although the preceding discussion implies that mu and delta opioid receptors may play a more central role in feeding reward than kappa receptors, a few studies indicate that the kappa opioid system may also have an effect on food reward. As noted above, selective kappa agonists have been shown to stimulate food intake (69,70). Injections of kappa antagonists into the paraventricular nucleus of the hypothalamus or the lateral ventricle have been shown to reduce the intake of sucrose solution by non-deprived rats (48,71), and systemic injection of the selective kappa agonist U50,488H facilitated sucrose intake (72). Intracerebroventricular injections of the kappa antagonist nor-binaltorphimine or antibodies to dynorphin A (an endogenous kappa-preferential peptide) elevate the threshold for stimulation-induced feeding (73). In light of the differences between mu and kappa agonists in their effects on the mesolimbic dopaminergic system, additional research will be necessary to clarify the role of kappa receptors in modifying food reward.

2.2.2.6   *Opioids and non-ingestive measures of palatability*

Most of the studies reviewed above in support of a role for opioids in mediating the rewarding aspects of feeding involve measures of intake of various foods or fluids. A few studies that do not have "amount consumed" as the primary dependent variable also support such a role for opioids. These include studies with the taste reactivity technique and studies of neuronal activation after chronic or acute ingestion of palatable foods.

The taste reactivity technique involves measurement of aversive and hedonic reactions to the intra-oral infusion of a substance (74). A treatment that enhances the palatability of a substance would be expected to increase the frequency or duration of hedonic responses and/or decrease the frequency or duration of aversive responses. It has been shown that morphine does increase hedonic responses to sucrose when given subcutaneously, intracerebroventricularly, or microinjected into the nucleus accumbens (75–78). Morphine also reduced the number of aversive responses to the intra-oral infusion of a bitter quinine solution (79). Taste reactivity studies, then, are consistent with the idea that opioids influence palatability.

Another approach to studying the mechanisms by which opioids influence intake is to examine the neural structures activated when a palatable food is ingested. An increase in Fos protein, typically measured with immunoreactive techniques, is frequently used as an index of cellular activation (80). Park and Carr found that the ingestion of a palatable food, or being placed in an environment paired with a palatable food, caused an increase in Fos-like immunoreactivity (FLI) in several areas of the rat brain, including several that are thought to be involved in reward, such as the lateral hypothalamus, the N. Acc. and the ventral tegmental area (81). Naltrexone injections also increased FLI in some areas, notably in the central nucleus of the amygdala and bed nucleus of the stria terminalis, but blocked the increases produced by the meal (or meal-paired environment). Interestingly, in a subsequent study, these investigators attributed the activation of cells in the bed nucleus to kappa receptor antagonism and the activation of cells in central amygdala to combined kappa and mu receptor antagonism (82). These effects provide some indication of the areas upon which naloxone may act to reduce food reward. Pomonis and colleagues also studied the effects of ingestion of a palatable substance on FLI (83). They found that, when rats were given a 10% sucrose solution as their only fluid for 3 weeks, there was an increase in FLI in the N. Acc., bed nucleus of the stria terminalis, central nucleus of the amygdala (ACe), the caudate-putamen, and the lateral parabrachial nucleus. Naloxone treatment caused an increase in FLI in some nuclei within the hypothalamus and in the ACe. Most importantly, the effect of naloxone on FLI in the ACe was enhanced in rats maintained on sucrose. This enhancement was interpreted as an indication of an increased opioid tone in the amygdala produced by sucrose ingestion.

In summary, studies using laboratory animals have consistently shown that opioid agonists cause increased food intake and opioid antagonists cause decreased food intake. Studies designed to test the effects of opioid agonists or antagonists in paradigms varying or measuring preference or palatability have, in large part, shown that opioids are particularly involved in the ingestion thought to be caused by palatability. Moreover, the specific sites and receptors involved in the ingestion of preferred or palatable foods are being mapped out. Overall, the animal studies support the theory that opioids are significant factors in the mechanism mediating food choice and pleasure from food.

2.2.3   Relevant Studies in Humans

The early discovery that opiate antagonists decreased food intake in laboratory animals quickly led to multiple studies of the effects of opiate antagonists on the food intake and weight of humans. de Zwaan and Mitchell (84) reviewed these early studies in normal weight and obese humans. In most studies, the treatment of normal-weight or obese humans with opiate antagonists leads to an acute decrease of food intake. The decrease in energy intake induced by an opiate antagonist for a test meal was consistently in the 20-29% range in normal-weight and obese subjects. However, three 8-week trials in which naltrexone (in doses ranging from 50-300 mg/day) was used to treat obesity showed little support for the use of this long-acting, oral opiate antagonist for the induction of weight loss (85-87). Two trials showed no significant weight loss effect (86,87), while one study showed a small but significant weight loss only in female subjects (85). The minimal or absent weight loss effect plus the elevations in liver function tests seen in studies using higher dosages of naltrexone effectively dampened enthusiasm for these agents in obesity treatment. Unfortunately, these longer-term studies were not designed to determine the mechanism by which obese humans adapt to the effects of naltrexone on food intake.

However, the animal studies cited earlier showed that opiate antagonists are particularly important in mediating food intake apparently motivated by sensory- or ingestion-related pleasure. The belief that the endogenous peptides are important in pleasure-based eating depends, to a large degree, on the validity of food choice, post-satiation feeding, and taste reactivity paradigms. Obviously, it is not possible to ask animals directly about their motivations for food intake in these paradigms. The ability of human subjects to report on their subjective, internal experiences of pleasure during food tasting and intake as well as their individual preferences for various foods makes human experimentation critical for the understanding of the relationship of opioids, pleasure, and food intake. However, human experimentation is fraught with difficulties as well. While one can use exclusion criteria to attempt to homogenise groups for study, human subjects bring remarkably different experiences to "the table" of the feeding laboratory. It is also not clear how the degree of liking a food is linked to the ingestion of that food for a given human in the laboratory situation. It seems likely that a human could eat the same amount of the same food for either pleasure or non-pleasure reasons depending on difficult-to-control factors such as mood, stress, idiosyncratic experiences with a particular food, length of time since last meal, frequency of intake of the particular food, or other unknown factors. In fact, a number of studies have shown differences in effects on amount ingested vs pleasantness of taste. Finally, the process of monitoring food choice over weeks, months, or years is very difficult and very costly in humans.

There are relatively few studies of human subjects that assess pleasure or preference and food tasting or ingestion in humans who are being randomly assigned to treatments with opioid agonists/antagonists and/or placebo. Those that have been done focus on short-term in-laboratory feeding behavior and are of unknown generalisability to the "real" world. Fantino et al. (88) reported that a single morning dose of naltrexone (60 mg) resulted in a decrement in pleasantness ratings for sweet but not salty solutions in eight normal volunteers. Bertino et al. (89) demonstrated that naltrexone blocked the phenomenon of sweet and salty tastes becoming increasingly pleasant as time since last meal lengthens. Moreover, naltrexone also decreased food intake and hunger in the 18 normal subjects tested in this study. The findings from these two studies suggest that opiate antagonism decreases the pleasure of normally pleasant tastants and that this effect might be linked to actual acute decreases in food intake. It should be noted, however, that Hetherington et al. (90) failed to demonstrate a decrease in either pleasantness or food intake in response to naltrexone.

The finding that naltrexone decreased pleasantness of tastes thought to be routinely pleasant, such as sweet sugar solutions, led to the use of more sophisticated paradigms to test the effects of opiate antagonists. Yeomans and Wright (91) reported that nalmefene relatively selectively decreased the normal subjects' intake of the most preferred foods that were available for a lunch test meal. Our group (92,93) extended the findings regarding the effects of opiate antagonists on taste and food intake by studying female subjects with and without binge eating behaviour; testing the effects of intravenous naloxone on the pleasantness and intensity of mixtures of sugar and dairy fats; testing the effects of intravenous naloxone on the intake of preferred foods from food groups including sweet, low-fat; sweet, high-fat; low-sweet, low-fat; and low-sweet, high-fat; and testing the effects of the opiate agonist butorphanol on hedonics and ingestion. As predicted, intravenous naloxone decreased the pleasantness of tastants across a range of sucrose and fat concentrations (Fig. 2.2.1). The naloxone treatment also decreased the amount of food ingested by both binge eating and non-binge eating women. Naloxone-induced reductions in intake of sweet, high-fat foods were greater than the reductions for the other food groups (Table 2.2.I). When binge eaters were treated acutely with intravenous naloxone, their intake of highly preferred foods was very similar to that of naloxone-treated non-binge eaters. It is possible that the specificity shown in these studies for sweet, high-fat foods was due to a paradigm that used only highly preferred foods so that any specificity related to sweetness and richness could be detected. Mitchell and colleagues (94) also showed that intravenous naloxone decreased the size of binge episodes in bulimic women while cholecystokinin infusions did not. Yeomans and Gray have done two studies of the acute effects of naloxone on the ingestion and gustatory hedonic responses of normal male subjects. In one study (95), naltrexone reduced the pleasantness of the taste of foods, with sweetened, fatty and high-protein foods affected the most. In the other study (96), naltrexone was shown to decrease not only the pleasantness of food intake, but also the positive linear component of food intake reflecting the initial stimulation of appetite by palatable foods. Thus, acute tests of opiate blockade result in decreased pleasantness of highly preferred foods, which are often sweet, high-fat foods. Likewise, opiate blockade can decrease intake of these foods in most acute studies. Moreover, opiate blockade seems to change these characteristics of ingestion in normal men and women and binge-eating women. It is important to note that the observed reduction in palatability of specific tastes caused by opioid antagonism does not appear to be due simply to a reduced ability to detect, taste or discriminate the stimuli. Naloxone reduced the preference for sugar/fat mixtures without affecting evaluations of sweetness or fat content (92-93). Similarly, naltrexone caused a slight reduction in preference for sucrose solutions without affecting detection or recognition thresholds (97). Naltrexone reduced the rated pleasantness of some but not all foods without affecting the evaluations of sweetness or saltiness (95). Thus, opioid receptor blockade appears to affect hedonic rather than sensory evaluation of foods.

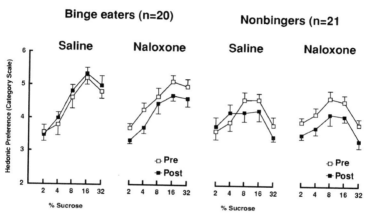

Fig. 2.2.1. Hedonic preference profiles of binge eaters and non-bingers before and after drug infusions shown as a function of sugar content separately for each drug type. The data, averaged across stimulus fat content, are $\bar{x} \pm SEM$.

Reproduced with kind permission from Drewnowski A., Krahn D.D., Demitrack M.A., Nairn K., Gosnell B.A. Naloxone, an opiate blocker, reduces the consumption of sweet high-fat foods in obese and lean female binge eaters. American Journal of Clinical Nutrition, 1995, 61, 1206-12. © American Journal of Clinical Nutrition. American Society for Clinical Nutrition.

It appears that naltrexone would be a good agent for treating individuals who suffered from a disorder characterised by excessive liking and ingestion of certain foods that were highly palatable to them. The first people who were identified as likely beneficiaries of the hypothesised benefits of naltrexone were patients with bulimia nervosa. Not only were they characterised by binges on foods that are thought by most to be highly palatable, but bulimic subjects had decreased their binge size and their intake of highly palatable foods in studies (92–94). Despite these propitious findings, the most rigorous tests of naltrexone in the treatment of bulimia have been uniformly negative (98–100). While some open-label studies of high-dose naltrexone indicated that opiate blockade might be helpful in treating binge eating episodes (101), three double-blind trials of naltrexone have failed to show any significant benefit to naltrexone treatment (98-100). Also, despite the fact that naltrexone has now been used in the case of many thousands of alcoholics attempting to maintain sobriety, there are very few, if any, reports of changes in food intake in these patients.

TABLE 2.2.I
Energy intakes of binge eaters and non-bingers in each food category as a function of drug infusion[1]

	Saline kJ	Naloxone kJ
Binge eaters		
Category 1: low sugar/low fat	406 ± 351	335 ± 494
Category 2: low sugar/high fat	891 ± 866	619 ± 870
Category 3: high sugar/low fat	469 ± 377	280 ± 297
Category 4: high sugar/high fat	1025 ± 979	481 ± 736[2]
Total	2791 ± 1766	1715 ± 1653[2]
Non-bingers		
Category 1: low sugar/low fat	435 ± 272	393 ± 285
Category 2: low sugar/high fat	828 ± 628	590 ± 477
Category 3: high sugar/low fat	264 ± 280	251 ± 234
Category 4: high sugar/high fat	569 ± 536	586 ± 766
Total	2096 ± 1067	1820 ± 1197

[1] $\bar{x} \pm SD$

[2] Significantly different from saline, $P < 0.01$

Reproduced with kind permission from Drewnowski A., Krahn D.D., Demitrack M.A., Nairn K., Gosnell B.A. Naloxone, an opiate blocker, reduces the consumption of sweet high-fat foods in obese and lean female binge eaters. American Journal of Clinical Nutrition, *1995, 61, 1206-12. © American Journal of Clinical Nutrition. American Society for Clinical Nutrition.*

What might explain the fact that opiate blockade appears so well-suited to the treatment of binge eating of highly palatable foods when tested acutely, but has been so ineffective in chronic tests of efficacy as an appetite suppressant in obese and bulimic humans? Perhaps opioid mechanisms are but one of many redundant systems of eating control. Therefore, one might need to block multiple mechanisms to create a significant effect on the eating of adult humans. It is also feasible that the opioid mechanisms affected by naloxone or naltrexone adapt rapidly to blockade with increased numbers of opioid receptors rendering ineffective previously effective opiate blockade. The acute effects of opiate blockade may be maintained over time, but the effect on meal size wanes quickly. It is possible that opioid mechanisms are critical to the development of food preferences, but are not potent in creating permanent changes of preferences in adults. Similarly, opioid mechanisms are potentially critical in defining (early in the disorder) which foods will become binge foods of choice for a bulimic, but are not highly involved in the maintenance of the behaviour. Finally, it is possible that we have been testing naltrexone in rather ill-defined populations (i.e. all obese or all bulimic subjects). It is certainly conceivable that only a minority of obese or binge-eating subjects have a significant problem with "over enjoyment" of particular foods. Recent findings by Mitchell et al. (102) do indicate significant differences in the extent of enjoyment of foods during binges across subtypes of binge-eating subjects.

Is there any role for opiate blockade in the treatment of abnormal human eating behavior? At this point, one would have to say that the effects of opioid blockade on palatability and intake in the laboratory are an interesting finding in search of a clinically relevant phenomenon. Certainly, opiate blockade is not a simple treatment for either obesity or bulimia nervosa. It is conceivable that there are subsets of obese or binge-eating patients who will be sensitive to opiate blockade. Perhaps the subset of patients identified by Mitchell et al. (102) as enjoying their binge foods more would also be more sensitive to naltrexone treatment. It is plausible that the effect of naltrexone on food intake or palatability is only acute (unlike the effect of naltrexone on alcohol cravings or hedonics). If the effect is only acute, then perhaps one must develop a way to deliver acutely an opiate blocker when cravings are present or when eating seems likely to go out of control. Finally, it is possible that the phenomenon of opiate blockade resulting in decreased pleasantness of food intake demonstrates that endogenous opioids are critical in normal eating, but are not critical in the pathophysiology of eating disorders or obesity. Given the animal studies showing changes in CNS cellular metabolism as a function of palatable food ingestion, it seems likely that sophisticated imaging studies will eventually clarify whether palatable foods similarly modify human CNS function, whether this effect differs as a function of disordered eating behavior, and whether opioids are involved. Clearly, while initial therapeutic ventures have been disappointing, opioids are part of the control mechanism of eating in humans and will continue to be an important part of the story of the hedonic mechanisms involved in food intake.

2.2.4   References

1. Gosnell B.A., Levine A.S. Stimulation of ingestive behaviour by preferential and selective opioid agonists, in *Drug Receptor Subtypes and Ingestive Behavior*. Eds Cooper S.J., Clifton P.G. London, Academic Press. 1996, 147-66.

2. Morley J.E., Levine A.S., Yim G.K., Lowy M.T. Opioid modulation of appetite. *Neuroscience & Biobehavioral Reviews*, 1983, 7, 281-305.

3. Reid L.D. Endogenous opioid peptides and regulation of drinking and feeding. *American Journal of Clinical Nutrition*, 1985, 42, 1099-132.

4. Cooper S.J., Jackson A., Kirkham T.C., Turkish S. Endorphins, opiates and food intake, in *Endorphins, Opiates and Behavioural Processes*. Eds Rodgers R.J., Cooper S.J. New York, John Wiley and Sons. 1988, 143-86.

5. Bodnar R.J. Opioid receptor subtype antagonists and ingestion, in *Drug Receptor Subtypes and Ingestive Behavior*. Eds Cooper S.J., Clifton P.G. London, Academic Press. 1996, 127-46.

6. Cooper S.J., Turkish S. Effects of naloxone and its quaternary analogue on fluid consumption in water-deprived rats. *Neuropharmacology*, 1983, 22, 797-800.

7. Brown D.R., Holtzman S.G. Opiate antagonists: central sites of action in suppressing water intake of the rat. *Brain Research*, 1981, 221, 432-6.

8. Tepperman F.S., Hirst M. Concerning the specificity of the hypothalamic opiate receptor responsible for food intake in the rat. *Pharmacology, Biochemistry and Behavior*, 1982, 17, 1141-4.

9. Bhakthavatsalam P., Leibowitz S.F. Morphine-elicited feeding: diurnal rhythm, circulating corticosterone and macronutrient selection. *Pharmacology, Biochemistry and Behavior*, 1986, 24, 911-7.

10. Majeed N.H., Przewlocka B., Wedzony K., Przewlocki R. Stimulation of food intake following opioid microinjection into the nucleus accumbens septi in rats. *Peptides*, 1986, 7, 711-6.

11. Gosnell B.A., Morley J.E., Levine A.S. Opioid-induced feeding: localization of sensitive brain sites. *Brain Research*, 1986, 369, 177-84.

12. Stanley B.G., Lanthier D., Leibowitz S.F. Multiple brain sites sensitive to feeding stimulation by opioid agonists: a cannula-mapping study. *Pharmacology, Biochemistry and Behavior*, 1989, 31, 825-32.

13. Noel M.B., Wise R.A. Ventral tegmental injections of a selective μ or δ opioid enhance feeding in food-deprived rats. *Brain Research*, 1995, 673, 304-12.

14. Kotz C.M., Billington C.J., Levine A.S. Opioids in the nucleus of the solitary tract are involved in feeding in the rat. *American Journal of Physiology*, 1997, 272, R1028-R1032.

15. Schulz R., Wilhelm A., Dirlich G. Intracerebral injection of different antibodies against endogenous opioids suggests α-neoendorphin participation in control of feeding behaviour. *Naunyn-Schmiedeberg's Archives of Pharmacology*, 1984, 326, 222-6.

16. Leventhal L., Cole J.L., Rossi G.C., Pan Y.X., Pasternak G.W., Bodnar R.J. Antisense oligodeoxynucleotides against the *MOR*-1 clone alter weight and ingestive responses in rats. *Brain Research*, 1996, 719, 78-84.

17. Marks-Kaufman R., Kanarek R.B. Modifications of nutrient selection induced by naloxone in rats. *Psychopharmacology*, 1981, 74, 321-4.

18. Marks-Kaufman R. Increased fat consumption induced by morphine administration in rats. *Pharmacology, Biochemistry and Behavior*, 1982, 16, 949-55.

19. Ottaviani R., Riley A.L. Effect of chronic morphine administration on the self-selection of macronutrients in the rat. *Nutrition and Behavior*, 1984, 2, 27-36.

20. Marks-Kaufman R., Kanarek R.B. Diet selection following a chronic morphine and naloxone regimen. *Pharmacology, Biochemistry and Behavior*, 1990, 35, 665-9.

21. Gosnell B.A., Krahn D.D. The effects of continuous morphine infusion on diet selection and body weight. *Physiology and Behavior*, 1993, 54, 853-9.

22. Romsos D.R., Gosnell B.A., Morley J.E., Levine A.S. Effects of kappa opiate agonists, cholecystokinin and bombesin on intake of diets varying in carbohydrate-to-fat ratio in rats. *Journal of Nutrition*, 1987, 117, 976-85.

23. Zhang M., Gosnell B.A., Kelley A.E. Intake of high-fat food is selectively enhanced by *mu* opioid receptor stimulation within the nucleus accumbens. *Journal of Pharmacology and Experimental Therapeutics*, 1998, 285, 908-14.

24. Gosnell B.A., Krahn D.D., Majchrzak M.J. The effects of morphine on diet selection are dependent upon baseline diet preferences. *Pharmacology, Biochemistry and Behavior*, 1990, 37, 207-12.

25. Evans K.R., Vaccarino F.J. Amphetamine- and morphine-induced feeding: evidence for involvement of reward mechanisms. *Neuroscience & Biobehavioral Reviews*, 1990, 14, 9-22.

26. Glass M.J., Grace M., Cleary J.P., Billington C.J., Levine A.S. Potency of naloxone's anorectic effect in rats is dependent on diet preference. *American Journal of Physiology*, 1996, 271, R217-R221.

27. Koch J.E., Bodnar R.J. Selective alterations in macronutrient intake of food-deprived or glucoprivic rats by centrally-administered opioid receptor subtype antagonists in rats. *Brain Research*, 1994, 657, 191-201.

28. Welch C.C., Grace M.K., Billington C.J., Levine A.S. Preference and diet type affect macronutrient selection after morphine, NPY, norepinephrine and deprivation. *American Journal of Physiology*, 1994, 266, R426-R433.

29. Glass M.J., Billington C.J., Levine A.S. Naltrexone administered into the central nucleus of amygdala or paraventricular nucleus: neural dissociation of diet and energy. *American Journal of Physiology*, 2000, 279(1), R86-92.

30. File S.E. Effects of benzodiazepines and naloxone on food intake and food preference in the rat. *Appetite*, 1980, 1, 215-24.

31. Cooper S.J., Turkish S. Effects of naltrexone on food preference and concurrent behavioral responses in food-deprived rats. *Pharmacology, Biochemistry and Behavior*, 1989, 33, 17-20.

32. Giraudo S.Q., Grace M.K., Welch C.C., Billington C.J., Levine A.S. Naloxone's anorectic effect is dependent upon the relative palatability of food. *Pharmacology, Biochemistry and Behavior*, 1993, 46, 917-21.

33. Segall M.A., Margules D.L. Central mediation of naloxone-induced anorexia in the ventral tegmental area. *Behavioral Neuroscience*, 1989, 103, 857-64.

34. Apfelbaum M., Mandenoff A. Naltrexone suppresses hyperphagia induced in the rat by a highly palatable diet. *Pharmacology, Biochemistry and Behavior*, 1981, 15, 89-91.

35. Levine A.S., Weldon D.T., Grace M., Cleary J.P., Billington C.J. Naloxone blocks that portion of feeding driven by sweet taste in food-restricted rats. *American Journal of Physiology*, 1995, 268, R248-R252.

36. Weldon D.T., O'Hare E., Cleary J., Billington C.J., Levine A.S. Effect of naloxone on intake of cornstarch, sucrose, and Polycose diets in restricted and nonrestricted rats. *American Journal of Physiology*, 1996, 270, R1183-R1188.

37. Le Magnen J., Marfaing-Jallat P., Miceli D., Devos M. Pain modulating and reward systems: A single brain mechanism? *Pharmacology, Biochemistry and Behavior*, 1980, 12, 729-33.

38. Cooper S.J. Effects of opiate agonists and antagonists on fluid intake and saccharin choice in the rat. *Neuropharmacology*, 1983, 22, 323-8.

39. Siviy S.M., Reid L.D. Endorphinergic modulation of acceptability of putative reinforcers. *Appetite*, 1983, 4, 249-57.

40. Touzani K, Akarid K, Velley L. Modulation of saccharin preference by morphine and naloxone: inversion of drug effects as a function of saccharin concentration. *Pharmacology, Biochemistry and Behavior*, 1991, 38, 37-41.

41. Chow B.L.C., Sellers E.M., Tomkins D.M. Effect of naltrexone and its derivatives, nalmefene and naltrindole, on conditioned anticipatory behavior and saccharin intake in rats. *Behavioural Pharmacology*, 1997, 8, 725-35.

42. Cooper S.J., Gilbert D.B. Naloxone suppresses fluid consumption in tests of choice between sodium chloride solutions and water in male and female water-deprived rats. *Psychopharmacology*, 1984, 84, 362-7.

43. Kirkham T.C., Cooper S.J. Naloxone attenuation of sham feeding is modified by manipulation of sucrose concentration. *Physiology and Behavior*, 1988, 44, 491-4.

44. Rockwood G.A., Reid L.D. Naloxone modifies sugar-water intake in rats drinking with open gastric fistulas. *Physiology and Behavior*, 1982, 29, 1175-8.

45. Yirmiya R., Lieblich I., Liebeskind J.C. Reduced saccharin preference in CXBK (opioid receptor-deficient) mice. *Brain Research*, 1988, 438, 339-42.

46. Cooper S.J., Holtzman S.G. Patterns of drinking in the rat following the administration of opiate antagonists. *Pharmacology, Biochemistry and Behavior*, 1983, 19, 505-11.

47. Lynch W.C. Opiate blockade inhibits saccharin intake and blocks normal preference acquisition. *Pharmacology, Biochemistry and Behavior*, 1986, 24, 833-6.

48. Beczkowska I.W., Bowen W.D., Bodnar R.J. Central opioid receptor subtype antagonists differentially alter sucrose and deprivation-induced water intake in rats. *Brain Research*, 1992, 589, 291-301.

49. Bodnar R.J., Glass M.J., Ragnauth A., Cooper M.L. General, μ and κ opioid antagonists in the nucleus accumbens alter food intake under deprivation, glucoprivic and palatable conditions. *Brain Research*, 1995, 700, 205-12.

50. Kelley A.E., Bless E.P., Swanson C.J. Investigation of the effects of opiate antagonists infused into the nucleus accumbens on feeding and sucrose drinking in rats. *Journal of Pharmacology and Experimental Therapeutics*, 1996, 278, 1499-507.

51. Calcagnetti D.J., Reid L.D. Morphine and acceptability of putative reinforcers. *Pharmacology, Biochemistry and Behavior*, 1983, 18, 567-9.

52. Bertino M., Abelson M.L., Marglin S.H., Neuman R., Burkhardt C.A., Reid L.D. A small dose of morphine increases intake of and preference for isotonic saline among rats. *Pharmacology, Biochemistry and Behavior*, 1988, 29, 617-23.

53. Stromberg M.F., Meister S., Volpicelli J.R., Ulm R.R. Morphine enhances selection of both sucrose and ethanol in a two-bottle test. *Alcohol*, 1997, 14, 55-62.

54. Gosnell B.A., Majchrzak M.J. Centrally administered opioid peptides stimulate saccharin intake in nondeprived rats. *Pharmacology, Biochemistry and Behavior*, 1989, 33, 805-10.

55. Gosnell B.A., Majchrzak M.J. Effects of a selective mu opioid receptor agonist and naloxone on the intake of sodium chloride solutions. *Psychopharmacology*, 1990, 100, 66-71.

56. Gosnell B.A., Majchrzak M.J., Krahn D.D. Effects of preferential delta and kappa opioid receptor agonists on the intake of hypotonic saline. *Physiology and Behavior*, 1990, 47, 601-3.

57. Gosnell B.A., Patel C.K. Centrally administered μ- and δ-opioid agonists increase operant responding for saccharin. *Pharmacology, Biochemistry and Behavior*, 1993, 45, 979-82.

58. Ruegg H., Yu W.-Z., Bodnar R.J. Opioid-receptor subtype agonist-induced enhancements of sucrose intake are dependent upon sucrose concentration. *Physiology and Behavior*, 1997, 62, 121-8.

59. Zhang M., Kelley A.E. Opiate antagonists microinjected into the nucleus accumbens enhance sucrose drinking in rats. *Psychopharmacology*, 1997, 132, 350-60.

60. Bakshi V.P., Kelley A.E. Feeding induced by opioid stimulation of the ventral striatum: role of opiate receptor subtypes. *Journal of Pharmacology and Experimental Therapeutics*, 1993, 265, 1253-60.

61. Noel M.B., Wise R.A. Ventral tegmental injections of morphine but not U-50, 488H enhance feeding in food-deprived rats. *Brain Research*, 1993, 632, 68-73.

62. Badiani A., Leone P., Noel M.B., Stewart J. Ventral tegmental area opioid mechanisms and modulation of ingestive behavior. *Brain Research*, 1995, 670, 264-76.

63. Hoffman D.C. The use of place conditioning in studying the neuropharmacology of drug reinforcement. *Brain Research Bulletin*, 1989, 23, 373-87.

64. Spanagel R., Herz A., Shippenberg T.S. The effects of opioid peptides on dopamine release in the nucleus accumbens: an in vivo microdialysis study. *Journal of Neurochemistry*, 1990, 55, 1734-40.

65.   Self D.W., Stein L. Receptor subtypes in opioid and stimulant reward. *Pharmacology & Toxicology*, 1992, 70, 87-94.

66.   Devine D.P., Leone P., Pocock D., Wise R.A. Differential involvement of ventral tegmental *mu*, *delta* and *kappa* opioid receptors in modulation of basal mesolimbic dopamine release: *in vivo* microdialysis studies. *Journal of Pharmacology and Experimental Therapeutics*, 1993, 266, 1236-46.

67.   Van Ree J.M., Gerrits M.A.F.M., Vanderschuren L.J.M.J. Opioids, reward and addiction: an encounter of biology, psychology and medicine. *Pharmacological Reviews*, 1999, 51, 341-96.

68.   Nencini P. Sensitization to the ingestive effects of opioids, in *Drug Receptor Subtypes and Ingestive Behavior*. Eds Cooper S.J., Clifton P.G. London, Academic Press. 1996, 193-218.

69.   Cooper S.J., Jackson A., Kirkham T.C. Endorphins and food intake: *Kappa* opioid receptor agonists and hyperphagia. *Pharmacology, Biochemistry and Behavior*, 1985, 23, 889-901.

70.   Morley J.E., Levine A.S., Kneip J., Grace M., Zeugner H., Shearman G.T. The κ opioid receptor and food intake. *European Journal of Pharmacology*, 1985, 112, 17-25.

71.   Koch J.E., Glass M.J., Cooper M.L., Bodnar R.J. Alterations in deprivation, glucoprivic and sucrose intake following general, mu and kappa opioid antagonists in the hypothalamic paraventricular nucleus of rats. *Neuroscience*, 1995, 66, 951-7.

72.   Lynch W.C., Burns G. Opioid effects on intake of sweet solutions depend both on prior drug experience and on prior ingestive experience. *Appetite*, 1990, 15, 23-32.

73.   Carr K.D. Opioid receptor subtypes and stimulation-induced feeding, in *Drug Receptor Subtypes and Ingestive Behavior*. Eds Cooper S.J., Clifton P.G. London, Academic Press. 1996, 167-91.

74.   Grill H.J., Norgren R. The taste reactivity test: I. Mimetic responses to gustatory stimuli in neurologically normal rats. *Brain Research*, 1978, 143, 263-79.

75.   Doyle T.G., Berridge K.C., Gosnell B.A. Morphine enhances hedonic taste palatability in rats. *Pharmacology, Biochemistry and Behavior*, 1993, 46, 745-9.

76. Rideout H.J., Parker L.A. Morphine enhancement of sucrose palatability: analysis by the taste reactivity test. *Pharmacology, Biochemistry and Behavior*, 1996, 53, 731-4.

77. Pecina S., Berridge K.C. Central enhancement of taste pleasure by intraventricular morphine. *Neurobiology*, 1995, 3, 269-80.

78. Pecina S., Berridge K.C. Opioid site in nucleus accumbens shell mediates eating and hedonic 'liking' for food: map based on microinjection Fos plumes. *Brain Research*, 2000, 863, 71-86.

79. Clarke S.N., Parker L.A. Morphine-induced modification of quinine palatability: effects of multiple morphine-quinine trials. *Pharmacology, Biochemistry and Behavior*, 1995, 51, 505-8.

80. Sheng M., Greenberg M.E. The regulation and function of c-*fos* and other immediate early genes in the nervous system. *Neuron*, 1990, 4, 477-85.

81. Park T.H., Carr K.D. Neuroanatomical patterns of Fos-like immunoreactivity induced by a palatable meal and meal-paired environment in saline- and naltrexone-treated rats. *Brain Research*, 1998, 805-169-180.

82. Carr K.D., Kutchukidze N., Park T.H. Differential effects of mu and kappa opioid antagonists on fos-like immunoreactivity in extended amygdala. *Brain Research*, 1999, 822, 34-42.

83. Pomonis J.D., Jewett D.C., Kotz C.M., Briggs J.E., Billington C.J., Levine A.S. Sucrose consumption increases naloxone-induced cFos-immunoreactivity in limbic forebrain. *American Journal of Physiology*, 2000, 278(3), R712-9.

84. de Zwaan M., Mitchell J.E. Opiate antagonists and eating behavior in humans: a review. *Journal of Clinical Pharmacology*, 1992, 32, 1060-72.

85. Atkinson R.L., Berke L.K., Drake C.R., Bibbs M.L., Williams F.L., Kaiser D.L. Effects of long-term treatment with naltrexone on body weight in obesity. *Clinical Pharmacology Therapy*, 1985, 38, 419-22.

86. Malcolm R., O'Neil P.M., Von J.M., Dickerson P.C. Naltrexone and dysphoria: a double-blind placebo controlled trial. *Biological Psychiatry*, 1987, 22, 710-6.

87. Mitchell J.E., Morley J.E., Levine A.S., Hatsukami D., Gannon M., Pfohl D. High-dose naltrexone treatment and dietary counseling for obesity. *Biological Psychiatry*, 1987, 22, 35-42.

88.   Fantino M., Hosotte J., Apfelbaum M. An opioid antagonist, naltrexone, reduces preference for sucrose in humans. *American Physiological Society*, 1986, R91-R96.

89.   Bertino M., Beauchamp G.K., Engelman K. Naltrexone, an opioid blocker, alters taste perception and nutrient intake in humans. *American Physiological Society*, 1991, R59-R63.

90.   Hetherington M.M., Vervaet N., Blass E., Rolls B.J. Failure of naltrexone to affect the pleasantness or intake of food. *Pharmacology Biochemistry & Behavior*, 1991, 40, 185-90.

91.   Yeomans M.R., Wright P. Lower pleasantness of palatable foods in nalmefene-treated human volunteers. *Appetite*, 1991, 16(3), 249-59.

92.   Drewnowski A., Krahn D.D., Demitrack M.A., Nairn K., Gosnell B.A. Taste responses and preferences for sweet-high-fat foods: evidence for opioid involvement. *Physiology and Behavior*, 1992, 51, 371-9.

93.   Drewnowski A., Krahn D.D., Demitrack M.A., Nairn K., Gosnell B.A. Naloxone, an opiate blocker, reduces the consumption of sweet high-fat foods in obese and lean female binge eaters. *American Journal of Clinical Nutrition*, 1995, 61, 1206-12.

94.   Mitchell J.E., Laine D.E., Morley J.E., Levine A.S. Naloxone but not CCK-8 may attenuate binge-eating behavior in patients with the bulimia syndrome. *Biological Psychiatry*, 1986, 21, 1399-406.

95.   Yeomans M.R., Gray R.W. Selective effects of naltrexone on food pleasantness and intake. *Physiology and Behavior*, 1996, 60(2), 439-46.

96.   Yeomans M.R., Gray R.W. Effects of naltrexone on food intake and changes in subjective appetite during eating: evidence for opioid involvement in the appetizer effect. *Physiology & Behavior*, 1997, 62(1), 15-21.

97.   Arbisi P.A., Billington C.J., Levine A.S. The effect of naltrexone on taste detection and recognition threshold. *Appetite*, 1999, 32, 241-9.

98.   Mitchell J.E., Christenson G., Jennings J., Huber M., Thomas B., Pomeroy C., Morley J. A placebo-controlled, double-blind crossover study of naltrexone hydrochloride in outpatients with normal weight bulimia. *Journal of Clinical Psychopharmacology*, 1988, 9(2), 94-7.

99. Igoin-Apfelbaum L., Apfelbaum M. Naltrexone and bulimic symptoms. *Lancet*, 1987, 1087-8.

100. Alger S.A., Schwalberg M.D., Bigaoutte J.M., Michalek A.V., Howard L.J. Effect of a tricyclic antidepressant and opiate antagonist on binge-eating behavior in normoweight bulimic and obese, binge-eating subjects. *American Journal of Clinical Nutrition*, 1991, 53, 865-71.

101. Jonas J.M., Gold M.S. Treatment of bulimia with the opiate antagonist naltrexone: preliminary data and theoretical implications, in *Psychobiology of Bulimia*. Eds Hudson J.I., Pope H.G. Washington, D.C., American Psychological Association Press. 1987.

102. Mitchell J.E., Mussell M.P., Peterson C.B., Crow S., Wonderlich S.A., Crosby R.D., Davis T., Weller C. Hedonics of binge eating in women with bulimia nervosa and binge eating disorder. International Journal of Eating Disorders, 1999, 26(2), 165-70.

Dr Krahn's work was supported in part by funds from the Department of Veterans Affairs Medical Research Service Merit Review Program.

Dr Gosnell's work is supported in part by funds from the National Institute on Drug Abuse.

2.3. ENDOCANNABINOIDS: NEUROMODULATORS OF FOOD CRAVING?

Tim C. Kirkham and Claire M. Williams

2.3.1 Introduction

Many neurochemical systems have been implicated in the physiological and psychological processes that control ingestive behaviour. Occasionally, individual transmitters or hormones are postulated to mediate specific appetites or cravings for particular kinds of food. Such linkages are usually serendipitous, occurring only after the extensive behavioural and pharmacological analyses that follow the discovery of each new family of neuromodulators or receptors.

In this chapter we will discuss a much rarer sequence of events: the discovery of a neurochemical-receptor system for which a probable involvement in appetite regulation is predicted by knowledge of drug actions obtained over thousands of years of human experience. Specifically, we shall review the behavioural effects of pharmacologically active cannabinoid compounds derived from the plant *Cannabis sativa* (marijuana), and their relationship to the biological role of the newly discovered, endogenous cannabinoid systems present within the central nervous system.

2.3.2 *Cannabis sativa* and the Exogenous Cannabinoids

Cultivation of *Cannabis sativa* (Indian hemp) began in prehistoric times, probably more than 10,000 years ago, in the central Asian plains. Since the earliest written records, the plant has been utilised for ritual and medicinal purposes as well as being grown on a massive scale to obtain fibres for the manufacture of textiles and rope. Cannabis has long been known to have a number of pharmacological actions, which underlie its past widespread medicinal use and account for its modern recreational abuse.

Surprisingly, Western medical science took little notice of the pharmacological properties of cannabis, its use in Europe being centred upon cultivation for the production of hemp fibre. Not until the mid-19th century, with the work of O'Shaughnessy in Britain (1) and Moreau in France, did the respective medicinal and psychological actions of cannabis preparations come to a wider audience (2). Even then, advances in medicinal chemistry in the late 19th and early 20th centuries meant that new drugs, such as barbiturates, heroin and cocaine, soon superseded the medicinal use of cannabis.

Accordingly, research into characterising the active pharmacological principle contained within cannabis preparations took a rather leisurely pace compared, for example, with the rate of research into opiates. In fact, it was not until 1964 that Gaoni and Mechoulam isolated delta-9-tetrahydrocannabinol (THC) and a group of related organic, 'cannabinoid' molecules in hashish (3). The chemical structure of THC was subsequently elucidated and shown to be the main psychoactive ingredient of cannabis, capable of mimicking the effects of cannabis when administered to rhesus monkeys (4).

2.3.3   Cannabinoid Receptors and Endogenous Cannabinoids

In the past decade or so, researchers have successfully demonstrated that cannabinoids exert their principal pharmacological actions through specific, G-protein linked, cell-surface receptors (5-7). At least two cannabinoid receptors have been identified and their genes cloned. These receptors are classified as 'central-type' CB1, and are widely distributed within the central nervous system (CNS) and a number of peripheral tissues, and the 'peripheral-type' CB2 receptor, which is not significantly expressed in the CNS.

Cannabinoids exhibit a wide range of brain-mediated effects, which include (in rodents) decreased movement, hypothermia, analgesia, and memory disruption (8). In humans, cannabinoids cause short-term memory deficits, a sense of time dilation, enhanced sensation, and higher-order cognitive impairments (9). Most researchers agree that these behavioural effects are mediated by brain cannabinoid receptors. Cannabinoid binding sites are very widely distributed throughout the mammalian CNS (10-12), and cannabinoid receptor density is extremely high compared with other G-protein-coupled receptors in the brain (13). But, despite their wide distribution, the brain regional localization of cannabinoid receptors and receptor-activated G-proteins corresponds well with the known behavioural effects of these compounds (14).

Naturally, the existence of specific receptor sites mediating the effects of exogenous, plant-derived cannabinoids implied that there should also be endogenous ligands for these receptors – ligands that compounds like THC mimic to produce their various effects. Studies attempting to test this hypothesis had already commenced in the late 1980s, but proved to be inconclusive, leading to the isolation of various water-soluble brain components whose chemical structure and pharmacological activity could not be assessed (15). The idea that an endogenous cannabimimetic compound might be, like THC, a lipophilic molecule and not necessarily a peptide, proved a successful lead for the isolation and complete characterisation of the first endocannabinoid (16). This compound was named *anandamide*, from "ananda", the Sanskrit word for bliss.

The identification of a second cannabinoid receptor in immune cells, and the observation that anandamide, like THC, behaved only as a weak agonist at these receptors led to a search for additional active endogenous ligands selective for the CB2 cannabinoid receptor. 2-Arachidonoylglycerol (2-AG), an arachidonic acid derivative, was first isolated from canine gut (17) and then later in rat brain (18). Although it exhibits a lower affinity for CB1 receptors than anandamide, evidence suggests that it is present in the brain at higher levels than anandamide; moreover, it is a full agonist at CB1 receptors (18).

2.3.4   Cannabinoids and Appetite

Marijuana or hashish intoxication in humans has long been associated with an increase in appetite. Anecdotal evidence and early clinical data supporting this phenomenon has been in existence for many years. Indeed, references to appetite-stimulant properties can be found as far back as AD 300 (19). In a more modern context, O'Shaughnessy, writing in 1838 (1), observed of cannabis intoxication:

"The state is at once recognised by the strange balancing gait of the patients; a constant rubbing of the hands; perpetual giggling; and a propensity to caress and chafe the feet of all bystanders of whatever rank. The eye wears an expression of cunning and merriment which can scarcely be mistaken. In a few cases, the patients are violent, in many highly aphrodisiac; *in all that I have seen, voraciously hungry.*"

Modern folklore amongst cannabis users also provides convincing evidence of the power of the drug to induce a particularly powerful impulse to eat – and to over-consume; an effect commonly referred to as 'the munchies'. However, detailed scientific confirmation of cannabis-induced hyperphagia was not obtained until the late 20th century (20-23), when the identification of the exogenous cannabinoids suggested therapeutic applications for THC and related compounds in the alleviation of appetite loss associated with disease states. Despite this interest, and the subsequent licensing of THC for clinical use as an appetite stimulant, there has been no comprehensive, systematic characterisation of cannabinoid effects on feeding. We are still largely dependent on anecdotal sources for our knowledge of cannabinoid effects on eating and appetite.

The literature on cannabinoid effects on eating in animal models is also less than compelling. Until very recently, and in contrast to the human studies, the most common findings have been either a lack of effect of cannabinoids on eating (24,25), or of intake suppression (26-28). With the advent of new developments in cannabinoid pharmacology, there is a clear need to rectify this state of affairs. Certainly, improved or novel cannabinoid therapies targeted at appetite disorders and obesity require adequate pre-clinical animal models.

In the following sections, we will briefly review the effects of cannabinoids on appetite and feeding in humans and laboratory animals.

We will also describe some recent data from our own laboratory that indicate that the feeding effects of exogenous and endogenous cannabinoids can provide some further insight into the biological bases of food craving.

2.3.5   Human Studies

Early anecdotal accounts indicating that marijuana increases appetite and food intake in humans (29-31) have slowly, and rather fitfully, received support from clinical observations and empirical studies (for reviews see (32-34)). In 1941, Adams reported that the increase in food intake following the ingestion of marijuana, might be an "…'invariable characteristic' of the drug…" (35), leading the editor of the Journal of the American Medical Association to suggest cannabis administration as a promising treatment for appetite loss (36). However, the first systematic studies did not take place until the 1970s.

Hollister (37) examined the effects of single oral doses of marijuana on food intake, hunger and appetite in normal, overnight-fasted or unfasted volunteers. Intake of milk shakes increased significantly in unfasted subjects after cannabis, but hunger ratings showed only non-significant increases. In 1971, Abel reported that inhalation of two cannabis cigarettes (of unknown potency) significantly increased the consumption of marshmallows over control levels - from an average of 3.8 to 45.6.

Greenberg et al. (21) examined body weight and caloric intake in marijuana smokers before, during, and after 21 days of marijuana smoking under research ward conditions. Marijuana cigarettes were supplied by the National Institute of Mental Health (NIMH) and were assayed as containing approximately 1.8-2.3% THC. The study ran for 31 days and consisted of three phases: a 5-day, pre-drug baseline; a 21-day period during which marijuana was available, and a 5-day, post-drug phase. The type and amount of food eaten per day were recorded and caloric intake calculated.

Subjects defined as 'heavy marijuana users' showed a significant increase in caloric intake and body weight in the early stages of the drug-treatment phase. Daily caloric intake rose from a pre-drug level of 3,200 (± 200) kcal, to peak in the first few days of treatment at 3,900 (± 300) kcal.

Subsequently, caloric intake declined somewhat, but remained elevated above baseline levels at 3,300 (± 200) kcal per day. Accompanying the hyperphagia was a persistent body weight increase, averaging 2.3 kg across the entire drug phase. During the post-drug phase, both body weight and caloric intake decreased significantly; subjects losing an average of 1.8 kg, and decreasing their daily caloric intake to 2,100 (± 200) kcal. Despite these changes, the author could not ascertain any marked change in eating patterns between the successive stages of the study.

In the 1980s, Foltin and colleagues expanded on these findings by using more naturalistic settings and more systematic analyses of changes in eating behaviour (22,23). In their 1986 study, volunteer subjects were tested in a residential laboratory for periods of up to 25 days. Marijuana cigarettes were supplied by the National Institute of Drug Abuse (NIDA) and contained either 0% or 1.84% (w/w) THC. Each test day comprised three phases: a private work period, a performance task and a period of social access. Marijuana or placebo cigarettes were smoked prior to private work periods and during the social access phases.

Average daily intake under placebo conditions increased from 2,780 (± 130) kcal to 3,340 (± 160) kcal under active marijuana treatment. Analysis of intake revealed little or no difference in food consumption during private work periods, but marijuana markedly increased intake during social access. Under control conditions, subjects consumed an average of 1,000 kcal, while marijuana administration significantly increased consumption to 2,500 kcal.

This phenomenon was further analysed by breaking down food intake into one of three categories: 'snacks', 'meals', or 'snacks with meals'. The consumption of snack items was consistently and significantly increased by marijuana. Snack intake increased by 63% under drug treatment compared with placebo, with no difference between placebo and marijuana conditions for the other two categories. Similarly, the number of eating episodes was significantly increased by marijuana treatment.

Subsequently, Foltin *et al.* (23) demonstrated that the effect of smoked marijuana in increasing snack food intake could be principally attributed to an increase in the intake of sweet solid items such as candy bars, cookies and chocolate, rather than sweet fluid, or savoury solid items. This characteristic of THC administration (although not the same magnitude of hyperphagia) was later corroborated in a study by Mattes *et al.* (38): small increases in caloric intake following acute cannabinoid treatment were derived principally from an increase in snack consumption, rather than any self-selected meal. Mattes also examined the influence of satiety status on THC effects (comparing subjects who were fasted overnight with those provided with a standard breakfast), but found no obvious interaction.

The evidence we have reviewed so far is rather inconclusive, given the very variable - and often insubstantial - effects of cannabinoid treatment on eating and appetite-related variables. Nevertheless, these limitations have not deflected clinicians from assessing THC treatments for their potential efficacy in the treatment of clinical syndromes affecting food consumption. Indeed, commercial preparations of THC, manufactured under the trade name Marinol (dronabinol; 2.5 or 5.0 mg THC in a sesame seed oil vehicle) have been licensed for clinical use.

In a single-case report, Sacks and colleagues (39) examined the effect of THC on food intake during a highly emetigenic chemotherapy regimen. Treatment with Marinol alone (THC, 5 mg, three times daily) had little effect on intake, but greatly attenuated the severe reduction in daily caloric intake produced by chemotherapy (intake + Marinol =1,453 kcal; without Marinol = 764 kcal). Contrary to the findings of Foltin and Mattes (23,38), this difference was attributed largely to an increase in calories derived from fat. No changes in appetite ratings were seen.

In a more comprehensive survey, Beal *et al.* (40) evaluated the effects of Marinol in 139 patients with AIDS-related appetite and weight loss. Marinol (2.5 mg, bi-daily) improved appetite and mood, decreased nausea and stabilised weight, although the onset of beneficial effects did not appear until 2 – 4 weeks after treatment began. The mean increase in appetite ratings over the trial was 37% after Marinol, compared with 17% after placebo. Again, no data are available for effects on specific macronutrient or flavour preferences.

2.3.6   Animal Studies

In general, the literature on cannabinoids and feeding in animals is characterised by its sparse and inconsistent nature. Very few studies have analysed the behavioural actions of exogenous cannabinoids in detail, and the majority of research was published over 20 years ago. Surprisingly, the most common findings have been a lack of effect, or intake suppression, following cannabinoid administration. Such failures to observe hyperphagia can mostly be ascribed to the use of single doses of cannabinoids that were either too low to exert any effect, or too high - resulting in a number of behavioural consequences (sedation, ataxia, etc), which are incompatible with the expression of feeding behaviour.

Glick and Milloy (41) did demonstrate hyperphagia in rats following 1.0 mg/kg i.p. THC. However, the reported increase was rather modest (less than 2 g over 2 hours), probably reflecting high baselines due to the fact that the animals were already highly motivated to eat following 24-hour food and water deprivation. Doubling the dose significantly suppressed both food and water intake.

Brown *et al.* (42) used more naturalistic methods, such as nocturnal testing and non-deprived rats, together with lower doses of THC (0.25 or 0.4 mg/kg, p.o.). However, while significant, short-term increases in chow intake were obtained, the sizes of those increases were actually very small (< 1 g over 1 hour). In a second experiment, these authors reported that both THC doses increased intake of a 0.8M sucrose solution. But again, the increases were relatively small (1 hour intakes were 20.6, 26.4 and 26.8 ml for vehicle, 0.25 and 0.4 mg/kg THC, respectively).

What appears to have been the first comprehensive dose-response analysis of THC hyperphagia in rats was reported by us in 1998 (43)[1]. Adapting the mode of administration employed by Brown *et al.* (42), we added the use of a pre-feed meal to ensure low baseline intakes and hopefully maximise our ability to detect cannabinoid-induced increases in food consumption. At the beginning of the dark period, rats were thoroughly

---

[1] Our studies were conducted in accordance with the UK Animals (Scientific Experiments) Act, 1986.

sated by the provision of 40 g of a palatable wet mash pre-feed, which most animals consumed in its entirety over a 2-hour period. Rats were subsequently treated orally with THC in sesame oil. After a further hour, the animals were given unrestricted access to their normal maintenance diet. As can be seen in Fig. 2.3.1, a wide range of THC doses were able to stimulate a degree of hyperphagia far greater than any previously reported with this drug.

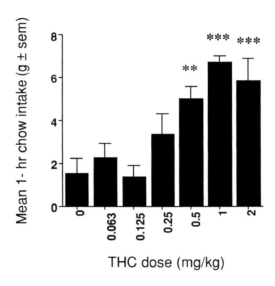

Fig. 2.3.1. Orally administered Δ^9-THC (the principal psychoactive ingredient of marijuana) exerts a profound hyperphagic action in satiated rats. These animals had already eaten the equivalent of their normal daily food intake in a pre-test, wet mash meal, yet were still stimulated to eat by the drug.

The most marked hyperphagic effect was obtained by a 1.0 mg/kg dose, which produced a greater than four-fold increase in consumption over 1 hour. After administration of the highest dose, non-specific behavioural effects of the drug were evident, such as impaired motor co-ordination.

Our next step was to ascertain whether these effects were specifically mediated by central CB1 receptors. Using the same test conditions as before, we tested the ability of the selective CB1 receptor antagonist SR141716 or a selective antagonist of the peripheral type, CB2, receptor antagonist SR144258 to block the hyperphagic effects of THC. As Figs 2.3.2 and 2.3.3 illustrate, the feeding stimulation induced by THC was significantly attenuated by SR141716, but not by SR144258. These results strongly indicate a central, cannabinoid-specific mediation of THC-induced overconsumption.

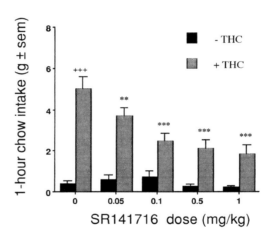

*Fig. 2.3.2. The hyperphagia produced by THC (1.0 mg/kg) is attenuated by the specific CB1 receptor antagonist SR14716. Solid bars show the effect of SR141716 alone; hatched bars show the effects of THC alone, or in combination with increasing doses of the antagonist (+: significant difference between the vehicle-vehicle and THC-vehicle treatments; *significant attenuation of THC hyperphagia).*

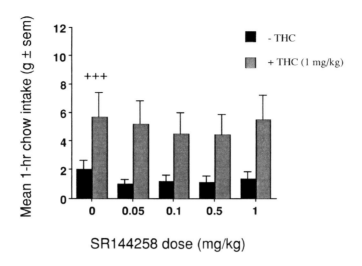

Fig. 2.3.3. The hyperphagic effect of THC is unaffected by SR144258, an antagonist which is selective for the peripheral type CB2 cannabinoid receptor. Since CB1 blockade (Fig. 2.3.2) does reverse THC effects, cannabinoid hyperphagia appears to mediated by receptors in the brain.

It is also noteworthy that the considerable degree of hyperphagia observed in this study is comparable to – and probably exceeds - the overconsumption induced by central administration of neuropeptide Y (44,45), a peptide that is widely regarded as playing a major role in the control of ingestive behaviour. Given the state of satiation of our animals, the remarkable potency of THC provides a very convincing case for involvement of the endocannabinoid systems in the normal regulation of feeding.

Having identified conditions that could reliably demonstrate the hyperphagic effects of exogenous cannabinoids, we went on to examine the potential for endogenous cannabinoids to exert similar actions (46). Only one test of anandamide effects on eating had previously been published (47). In that case, no obvious feeding effects were observed, despite clear changes in a number of other physiological and behavioural parameters.

Although less dramatic than the effects of THC in terms of magnitude, we successfully obtained significant hyperphagia with anandamide, over a range of peripherally administered doses (Fig. 2.3.4).

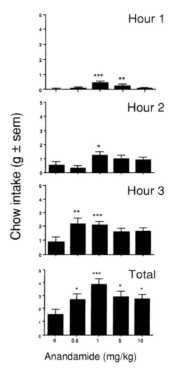

Fig. 2.3.4. In pre-fed rats, subcutaneous injection of the endocannabinoid, anandamide, produces significant overeating. The effects are modest in comparison with THC, but have a much longer duration. Over 3 hours, the most effective dose of anandamide more than doubled the amount eaten. The nature of these effects may reflect augmentation of naturally occurring, appetite-related endocannabinoid rhythms. Thus, the degree of hyperphagia corresponds to the likelihood and extent of eating seen under control conditions.
Reproduced with kind permission of Springer-Verlag from Williams C.M., Rogers P.J., Kirkham T.C. Hyperphagia in pre-fed rats following oral Δ-9-THC. Physiology & Behaviour, 1998, 65, Fig. 1, p316. © Springer-Verlag.

Anandamide hyperphagia was entirely prevented by pre-treatment with SR141716, while SR144258 was without effect (Figs 2.3.5 and 2.3.6), indicating that anandamide hyperphagia is mediated by central CB1 receptors. These combined results thus provide the first clear indications that endogenous cannabinoid systems may play a normal role in the physiological regulation of appetite. Importantly, this effect has recently been replicated in mice, under somewhat different test conditions. Hao and colleagues (48) reported that a very low dose of peripherally injected anandamide (0.001 mg/kg, i.p.) in schedule fed mice produced significant increases in food intake on each of six successive treatment days.

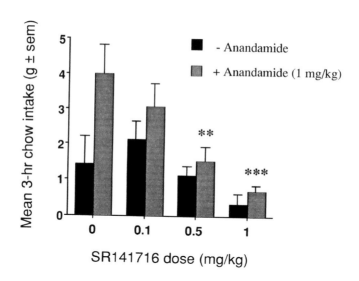

Fig. 2.3.5. Anandamide hyperphagia is dose-dependently reversed by CB1 blockade with the selective antagonist, SR141716, implicating central cannabinoid receptors in the phenomenon. The reversal is far more complete than observed with THC.

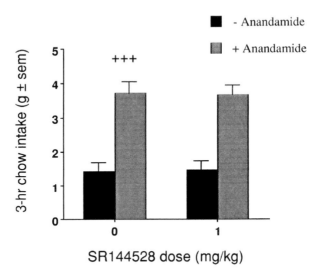

Fig. 2.3.6. Anandamide (1.0 mg/kg) hyperphagia is unaffected by a peripheral-type cannabinoid (CB2) receptor antagonist. As in the case of THC, anandamide's actions on feeding are mediated via CB1 receptors localised within the brain.

2.3.7   Mode of Action of Cannabinoids on Appetite

The nature of our results suggests that there is some involvement of endocannabinoids in feeding regulation, and indicates that the use of exogenous cannabinoids, such as THC, could usefully add to the armoury of tools to treat appetite disorders. However, the studies described above give only limited insights into the effects of cannabinoids on feeding, and, as already noted, the evidence is predominantly limited to exogenous cannabinoids. Although it is surprising that assumed knowledge concerning cannabinoid effects on feeding is unmatched by actual empirical evidence, it is disquieting that clinical treatments and current theorizing are based on a few, mostly trivial, and un-replicated findings.

While the available data do not convincingly support any single mechanism whereby appetite is enhanced by cannabinoids, there is a wide acceptance and general propagation of the notion that cannabinoids such as THC promote the consumption of palatable, sweet, snack-type foods (see above). This has encouraged the view that cannabinoids may provoke over-consumption by amplifying the orosensory reward – or palatability – of foods (49).

The classification of marijuana and hashish as drugs of abuse links cannabinoids, at least semantically, with drugs such as cocaine and heroin, which are known to activate directly reward pathways in the brain. There is compelling evidence from both *in vivo* and *in vitro* studies to suggest that exogenous cannabinoids can also exert significant influences on these brain reward systems (for an extensive review of these studies, see (50)).

In relation to feeding, Trojniar and Wise (51) showed that THC had a facilitatory effect on feeding induced by electrical stimulation of the lateral hypothalamus. Such intra-cranial electrical stimulation is regarded as being rewarding, effectively activating circuits that may normally mediate the appetitive and consummatory aspects of natural rewards, such as food and sex. Importantly, THC treatment also led to a reduction in the latency to begin eating - a phenomenon we will return to later.

Endocannabinoids were first directly implicated in food reward by examination of the effects of CB1 blockade on feeding. Arnone and colleagues reported that, in rats and marmosets SR141716 selectively attenuated the consumption of palatable ingesta (49,52), while having little or no effect on bland food intake (of the kind normally provided to laboratory animals for their general maintenance). These workers suggested that such preferential effects of CB1 blockade indicated important tonic endocannabinoid activity underlying food reward. Thus, cannabinoid agonists could increase food intake by rendering foods more palatable, while antagonists might tend to diminish the hedonic value of foods, and hence reduce consumption.

With these findings as our starting point, we undertook a number of studies to address the cannabinoid-reward hypothesis and, more generally, to pursue a more comprehensive behavioural characterisation of cannabinoid effects.

2.3.8   Endocannabinoids and Food Reward

We first tested the cannabinoid-reward hypothesis by measuring the effects of SR141716 in the sucrose sham-feeding paradigm. In this model, rats ingest palatable sucrose solutions, which are subsequently recovered directly from the stomach via an open gastric fistula[2]. Under these circumstances, normal satiation mechanisms are minimised and ingestion is motivated exclusively by food palatability (53). In the absence of normal satiety, sham-feeding rats will consume many times the amount of sucrose ingested by intact, normally feeding rats. The gastric sham-feeding model is especially sensitive to manipulations that alter the level of orosensory reward - whether that is simple manipulation of the sensory properties of the test food, or some pharmacological treatment. Since sucrose sham-feeding is generated and maintained by the orosensory reward of the solution, then, if endogenous cannabinoids mediate this reward, sham-feeding should be disrupted by CB1 blockade. Specifically, SR141716 would be expected to suppress sham-feeding in a manner that mimics the effects of sucrose dilution (54,55).

Much to our surprise, SR141716 failed to induce any attenuation of sucrose sham feeding (Fig. 2.3.7). Doses of the antagonist, an order of magnitude greater than those required to block anandamide-induced feeding (46) or to suppress sucrose drinking in intact animals (49), were entirely without effect. This failure of CB1 blockade to influence ingestion motivated primarily by food palatability implies a less than critical role for endogenous CB1 ligands in orosensory reward. Moreover, the lack of effect of SR141716 in this paradigm is in marked contrast to the suppressive effects of opioid antagonists on this behaviour; effects were instrumental in consolidating endogenous opioid involvement in food reward. For example, we have previously demonstrated that not only do opioid receptor

---

[2] When the tube is sealed externally, animals are able to ingest and absorb nutrients normally.

antagonists reduce sucrose sham-feeding, but their effects mimic the changes in ingestion produced by diluting the concentration, and hence the palatability, of the sucrose. Additionally, attenuation of sham-feeding by opioid antagonists can be reversed by increasing the palatability of the sucrose during a sham-feeding test (54-56).

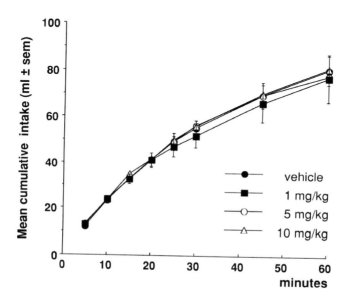

Fig. 2.3.7. Rats with open gastric fistulae ingest large volumes of a highly palatable (0.44M) sucrose solution. This behaviour is maintained by the rewarding properties of the sucrose. Even very high doses of the CB1 antagonist SR141716 failed to attenuate sham feeding, discounting endocannabinoid mediation of the immediate reward derived from the orosensory properties of ingesta.

The failure of SR141716 to attenuate sham feeding provides strong evidence against significant endogenous cannabinoid activity within the pathways that maintain sucrose ingestion. In other words, endocannabinoids do not seem to be primarily involved in food reward during ingestion. This possibility does not, however, entirely preclude involvement of endocannabinoids in some other aspect of feeding-related reward processes. We might instead examine appetitive aspects of feeding motivation, related to the anticipation or craving for food.

2.3.9   Evidence for Endocannabinoid Involvement in Craving

As we mentioned earlier, links between the pharmacological actions of exogenous cannabinoids and reward processes are well established. More particularly, cannabinoids have been found to influence mesolimbic dopaminergic neurons. These neurons, arising in the ventral tegmental area (VTA) and projecting to the nucleus accumbens, have long been associated with reward (57) (see also section 2.1). Natural rewards - including food, together with many drugs of abuse, have been found to stimulate dopamine release from terminals in the nucleus accumbens. Initially, the mesolimbic pathways were considered to be the final common pathway mediating reward, and particularly the pleasure associated with consummatory behaviour. However, recent developments have led researchers to emphasise a specific role for these pathways in incentive rather than consummatory reward processes (58,59). Incentive motivation, according to these accounts, refers to the generation of emotional arousal and behavioural activation in response to stimuli that predict reward (be it food or cocaine). Authors such as Berridge (60) and Panksepp (58) have, respectively, associated dopamine with 'wanting' (as opposed to 'liking') or 'seeking' behaviour – or in other terms, food craving.

Ingestion of food causes dopamine release in the nucleus accumbens, especially after deprivation, or if the food is novel or palatable. It is noteworthy, therefore, that exogenous cannabinoids have been found to stimulate dopamine release in this region of rat brain (50), and particularly in the shell subregion of the nucleus accumbens (61). Furthermore, these changes in dopamine release can be observed at doses of THC that we have found to produce significant hyperphagia (43,62).

Other data indicate that various behavioural effects of CB1 agonists can be modified by dopamine receptor antagonists (63,64), and that cross-tolerance can occur between CB agonists and dopamine agonists (65). Additionally, CB1 receptors have been found to be co-localised, and to interact with dopamine D1 and D2 receptors (12,66). Overall, there is growing support for functional relationships between endocannabinoid and dopaminergic activity in the brain. Therefore, it is entirely feasible that brain dopaminergic systems implicated in general incentive processes and drug craving could also be involved in the feeding effects of cannabinoids.

Although no direct experimental evidence yet links cannabinoid hyperphagia with alterations in dopamine function, there are some reports - mostly related to work with drugs of abuse - that do provide behavioural evidence of cannabinoid links with incentive processes.

Some interesting studies by McGregor and his colleagues (67) have pointed directly to a role for endocannabinoids in the processes that orient animals toward reinforcers and energise appetitive, seeking behaviour. These workers have adopted an operant, lick-based, progressive ratio paradigm as a model of craving. In this model, rats are required to complete a progressively greater number of responses (licks at a spout) to obtain successive reinforcements of small volumes (0.1 ml) of some liquid (typically alcohol or sucrose solutions). The ratio at which animals cease to respond (the 'break point') is taken as an index of the degree of craving for the specific reinforcer.

Using this technique, Gallate and McGregor (67) were able to confirm earlier reports that CB1 blockade with SR141716 would reduce ethanol intake in rats (49,68). Moreover, the antagonist produced a dramatic dose-related reduction in break point to obtain beer reinforcers. Subsequently, the same group found that the CB1 agonist CP 55,940 would increase break points in rats licking for beer or sucrose solutions. These effects, which were reversed by SR141716 (69), strongly implicate endocannabinoid systems in the processes underlying the motivation to obtain and ingest palatable ingesta.

Returning to feeding behaviour, we have also obtained evidence to support such a role of endocannabinoids in incentive motivation. Using an open field apparatus, we observed the behaviour of satiated rats following administration of THC and anandamide. Under our specific test conditions, a palatable wet mash meal was provided prior to drug administration;

vehicle-treated rats exhibited very little interest in food over the course of a 45-minute test. In most cases, animals failed to engage in eating at all. However, after both exogenous and endogenous cannabinoid treatments, feeding replaced exploratory ambulation as the predominant behaviour. Figure 2.3.8 illustrates the changes in frequency and distribution of eating episodes after each treatment.

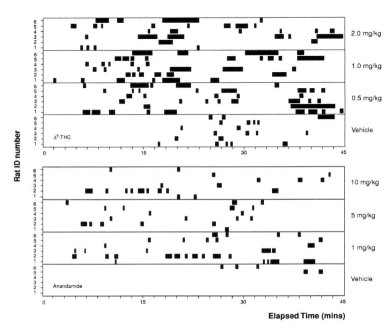

Fig. 2.3.8. These charts represent the occurrence of all eating by two groups of pre-satiated rats, observed in an open field arena following administration of THC or anandamide. For each drug, behavioural traces are presented for six rats (numbered 1-6), so that it is easy to compare an individual's behaviour under each treatment. After vehicle, exploratory behaviours predominate, with little if any eating. Both exogenous and endogenous cannabinoids promote eating: reducing latencies and inducing a pattern of feeding that is very similar to that seen under control conditions in the home cage.

What is especially clear from these data is the rapidity with which animals began to eat after cannabinoid injection. In other words, the cannabinoids induce a marked reduction in eating latency in rats that, under control conditions, would be notably disinclined to engage in feeding. A similar effect of THC to reduce eating latency was reported by Trojniar and Wise in their experiments on eating induced by electrical stimulation of the lateral hypothalamus (51).

Another feature of these data that should be emphasised is that the pattern of behaviour displayed by THC- and anandamide-treated rats in the open field very closely matches that typically seen in untreated rats feeding freely in their home cages. We have interpreted these findings as evidence that stimulation of CB1 receptors increases the salience of food and the motivation to eat. Like Gallate's break-point data (67,69), our observational analyses again implicate endocannabinoids in the motivational processes that lead to the initiation of feeding - or what could be described as food craving.

A similar interpretation can be given to data we have obtained with a more naturalistic, continuous meal-pattern-monitoring technique. Using pre-satiated rats, we have looked at moment-to-moment changes in feeding behaviour in the home cage following peripheral injection of anandamide. As Fig. 2.3.9 summarises, the principal action of anandamide under these conditions is to reduce the latency to the first meal very markedly. Under control conditions, animals did not take a meal until the fourth hour of the test. By contrast, after anandamide treatment, rats had consumed two meals over the same period, the first occurring after approximately 2 hours. This effect is again consistent with a general increase of incentive motivation. Viewed in conjunction with the apparent lack of effect of SR141716 on the intra-meal factors maintaining sham feeding, our observational results and meal pattern data tend to support a specific endocannabinoid involvement in inter-meal motivational processes.

Further support for this notion comes from an experiment examining interactions between food deprivation and the anorectic potency of SR141716. In our laboratory, we have generally failed to find any reliable immediate effect on intake in short-term tests with acute SR141716 treatments. This lack of effect is in sharp contrast to the effects reported by Arnone *et al.* (49). In the search for an explanation for this disparity, we noted that Arnone's group obtained antagonist-induced intake suppression in schedule-fed rats; rats allowed to feed for only a few hours a day, and eating much less than our *ad libitum* fed rats routinely eat over 24 hours. We suspected that the imposition of food deprivation might somehow potentiate the effects of the CB1 antagonist. Accordingly, we conducted a single-dose pilot study with SR141716 administered to rats that had been food-deprived for 18 hours. What we found in this instance was a weak, but significant suppression of food intake in a 1-hour test.

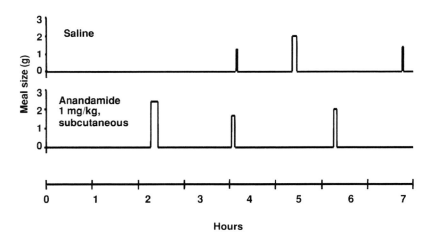

Fig. 2.3.9. These diagrams summarise the feeding effects of anandamide administered to ten pre-satiated rats feeding in their home cage during the dark phase. Each vertical bar represents a single meal (the height and width of the bar respectively indicating meal size and duration). As in Fig. 2.3.8, the action of anandamide to potentiate feeding is apparent: after anandamide, rats eat considerably earlier and more frequently than under control conditions.

More detailed analyses of the interaction between deprivation level and SR141716 potency are in progress, but our results are in line with the notion that endocannabinoid activity is related to the appetitive aspects of feeding motivation. A parsimonious explanation for enhanced anorectic potency of a CB1 antagonist in deprived animals would be that deprivation induces, or enhances, endocannabinoid activity. Clearly, if SR141716 acts as a competitive antagonist at CB1 receptors, the behavioural effects of CB1 blockade will become apparent only if there is cannabinoid release and receptor stimulation. The greater the level of cannabinoid activity, the greater will be the behavioural consequences of SR141716 treatment.

Some indirect evidence for a link between deprivation and endocannabinoid activity is provided by a recent report by Hao *et al.* (48). Doses of anandamide that provoked overeating in mice were found to reverse several of the changes in brain neurotransmitter level and turnover induced by food restriction alone. Such data are particularly complicated to unravel and require substantial development. We hope, in the near future, to provide more straightforward evidence of deprivation- or feeding-related changes in endocannabinoids, by measuring regional levels of anandamide and 2-AG in the brains of rats subjected to varying deprivation levels, and at different times during and after feeding.

Currently, we hypothesise that endogenous cannabinoid activity rises during intermeal intervals to reach some critical level, at which point further eating is stimulated. According to this model, the longer the time that has elapsed since the last meal, the greater will be the activity in relevant endocannabinoid circuits and the higher the likelihood of eating. Such a pattern might help explain the greater potency of SR141716 in food-deprived animals. We might also assume that there are natural rhythms in such activity which are correlated with normal patterns of meal taking, so that the optimal demonstration of agonist or antagonist effects on feeding will be obtained by carefully synchronising drug administration with these endogenous cycles. Given our discussion of cannabinoid influences on dopaminergic systems modulating food salience, we might reasonably predict that endocannabinoids would interact significantly with mesolimbic dopamine. It will be important, therefore, to assess the extent to which feeding effects of CB1 ligands can be affected by treatments modifying dopamine function.

2.3.10   Links between Endocannabinoid and Opioidergic Reward Systems

Although our analyses are in their preliminary stages, the meal pattern analysis reported above suggests that there may be a secondary action of anandamide. In addition to the marked effects on eating latency, there may be a tendency for agonist administration to increase the size and/or duration of meals. If this latter effect can be confirmed, it would suggest that endocannabinoid actions might not, after all, be restricted solely to inter-meal processes. Whatever the case, we do have evidence to suggest that any influence on intra-meal factors may be indirect, and mediated through interactions with other important neurochemical systems. Specifically, we have found convincing evidence for an interaction between cannabinoids and endogenous opioids.

Opioids are firmly implicated in the mediation of food reward, not least by the ability of opioid receptor agonists and antagonists to, respectively, increase or reduce food intake. These effects have been shown to involve changes in the hedonic evaluation of foods (for reviews, see (70,71) and section 2.5). For example, opioid antagonists are reported by human volunteers to reduce the perceived palatability of previously preferred foods and fluids. Consequently, opioid manipulations primarily affect the duration of meals and are most apparent in tests with palatable foods.

Opioids are intimately linked to central reward pathways. For example, in the accumbens, dopamine neurons synapse with encephalinergic neurons, which are critical to the expression of reward- or incentive-related behaviours (50). In the ventral tegmental area, opioids are thought to remove mesolimbic dopaminergic neurons from GABA-mediated inhibition (59).

Evidence has accumulated to support overlapping endogenous opioid and endocannabinoid mechanisms in relation to a wide range of physiological processes (72), including reward and appetite. For example, Gardner *et al.* (73) reported that enhancement of brain-stimulation reward by THC was blocked by the general opioid receptor antagonist, naloxone. Importantly, the facilitation by THC of feeding induced by stimulation of the lateral hypothalamus is also blocked by naloxone (51). Finally, Gallate *et al.* (69) found that the facilitatory effects of a CB agonist on responding for palatable solutions were reversed by both a CB1 antagonist and naloxone. Such findings imply that cannabinoids modulate the motivation to ingest via actions on both cannabinoid and opioid systems.

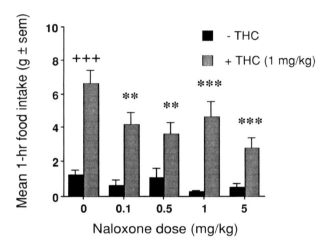

Fig. 2.3.10. The hyperphagic effect of THC is attenuated by the general opioid receptor antagonist naloxone. Note that, when given alone (solid bars), only the highest doses of naloxone show any tendency to reduce intake. However, even sub-anorectic naloxone doses significantly reverse the feeding effects of THC.

We initially addressed this possibility by attempting to block the hyperphagic actions of THC with naloxone. Figure 2.3.10 illustrates that, predominantly sub-anorectic doses of naloxone will very effectively block cannabinoid-induced over-consumption of chow in pre-satiated rats.

Subsequently, we examined whether combined administration of the CB1 antagonist SR141716 with naloxone could provide further evidence of some co-operative interaction between cannabinoid and opioid systems. We chose a range of doses of each antagonist that, alone, are capable of reversing the actions of agonists at their respective binding sites but exert no significant effect on chow intake. As can be seen in Fig. 2.3.11, neither naloxone alone nor SR141716 alone produced any reliable effects on food intake. However, when given in combination, every dose of SR141716 potentiated the effects of all doses of naloxone. Significant intake suppression occurred with every combination of the two drugs, relative to the vehicle-vehicle, SR141716-vehicle or vehicle-naloxone conditions.

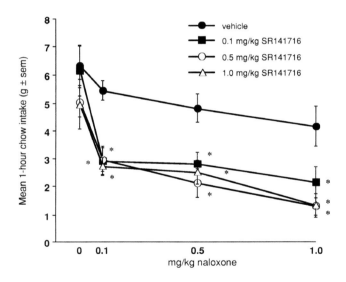

Fig. 2.3.11. Subanorectic doses of the opioid antagonist naloxone and the CB1 antagonist, SR141716, were given alone or in combination to non-deprived rats. The graph illustrates how doses of each drug that were ineffective independently interacted synergistically to suppress food intake. Asterisks indicate a significant difference between each drug combination and the vehicle-vehicle control.

These data seem to indicate a synergistic action of opioid and cannabinoid receptor antagonists, and go a long way to support an important functional relationship between cannabinoid and opioid systems in the normal regulation of appetite. These findings may have particular importance in the light of a recent proposal that a cannabinoid receptor subtype may exist that is differentially linked to opioid systems (74). A further possibility is that these combinatorial effects reflect similar actions on ventral tegmental dopamine neurons. These neurons are under the inhibitory influence of GABAergic neurons in the ventral tegmental area (VTA). Endogenous opioids act to increase dopamine release in the accumbens by disinhibiting GABA neurons in the VTA (75). Additionally, many of the neurons that express CB1 receptors are GABAergic, and the effect of CB1 agonists on these cells is again to reduce the release of GABA (76). The marked effects of combined administration of opioid and cannabinoid receptor blockers might thus be explained in terms of enhanced GABAergic inhibition of mesolimbic dopamine activity. Obviously, a wide range of detailed pharmacological analyses is required to test these speculative accounts.

2.3.11   Central Administration of Endocannabinoids

To date, our cumulative findings seem to support a link between cannabinoids and eating motivation – whether mediated via direct activation of incentive processes, or through some indirect action on orosensory reward. What remains to be demonstrated are the specific central nervous system targets mediating these actions. As noted earlier, CB1 receptors are expressed throughout the brain, and the number of potential targets is extensive. However, one particular brain region has been increasingly linked to feeding and reward processes: the nucleus accumbens, and especially the shell sub-region of this nucleus.

As part of an ongoing series of mapping studies, we have begun to examine the effects of endogenous cannabinoids injected directly into the shell region of the accumbens. So far, we have obtained pilot data showing that a wide range of CB1 agonists can induce feeding in this region. Figure 2.3.12 shows our most recent finding: hyperphagia obtained with bi-lateral infusion of 2-arachidonyl glycerol (2-AG). This endocannabinoid occurs at much higher concentrations in brain than anandamide, and has not previously been shown to increase food intake.

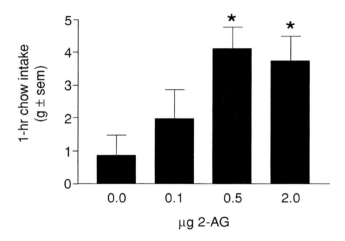

Fig. 2.3.12. Bilateral, nucleus accumbens injections of the endogenous cannabinoid 2-arachidonylglycerol (2-AG) significantly increase the short term food intake of non-deprived, spontaneously feeding rats

Unlike our previous studies, 2-AG was administered at the onset of the dark phase of the daily cycle (rats are predominantly nocturnal) to freely feeding rats, with no pre-feed. 2-AG clearly exerted a potent hyperphagic action under these conditions. This effect thus provides compelling evidence for a natural role of this endocannabinoid in appetite regulation and, since the accumbens has proved to be a sensitive target, our data further strengthen the link between endocannabinoids and the motivational processes outlined above.

2.3.12   Concluding Remarks

The historical association between the effects of exogenous cannabinoids and appetite gave a strong lead in suggesting possible physiological roles for the newly discovered endocannabinoid systems. Indeed, one of these compounds, Δ^9-THC, can induce a degree of over-eating that far exceeds that produced by most other hyperphagic pharmacological manipulations. Although this research is still in its infancy, different groups have already obtained convincing evidence that the endocannabinoids anandamide and 2-AG contribute to the normal mechanisms regulating appetite since both of these agents induce hyperphagia. Crucially, the behavioural adjustments induced by exogenous or endogenous cannabinoids suggest that endocannabinoid systems are involved in the processes that drive us to eat. Animals work harder to obtain food after CB1 stimulation, and eat earlier and more frequently when food is freely available. Agonists at CB1 receptors thus seem to actively provoke feeding, rather than merely prolonging eating that has been initiated through other mechanisms.

In support of these hypotheses, we have seen that blockade of CB1 receptors reduces the willingness of laboratory animals to work for ingesta, but does not necessarily alter the progress of eating when food is readily available. In fact, we have presented evidence to suggest that endocannabinoid activity is not crucial to the maintenance of ingestion, particularly ingestion maintained by palatability. However, we have also seen evidence of synergy between the effects of CB1 and opioid receptor antagonists, where combined administration exerts a greater anorectic effect than when either antagonist is administered alone.

The demonstration of interactions between endogenous cannabinoid and opioid systems suggests that, in addition to making food stimuli more salient, cannabinoid administration may also indirectly amplify the hedonic evaluation of foods. We have proposed that these combined actions on appetitive and consummatory aspects of feeding motivation may reflect modulation of classical, dopaminergic reward pathways. Finally, our demonstration that the nucleus accumbens shell supports the hyperphagic actions of an endogenous ligand for CB1 receptors provides confirmation of endocannabinoid involvement in the critical motivational processes that modulate appetite and guide feeding behaviour.

Overall, research in this area provides a convincing body of data to support the involvement of endocannabinoids in feeding, particularly in relation to food seeking or craving. Given the early stage of development of these studies, we look forward to many more exciting advances, and the consolidation of endocannabinoids as key components of appetite regulatory mechanisms.

2.3.13   References

1. O'Shaughnessy W.B. On the preparations of the Indian Hemp or Gunjah. *Transactions of the Medical and Physical Society of Bengal (1830-1840)*, 1838, 421-61.

2. Peters H., Nahas G.G. A brief history of four millenia (B.C. 2000-A.D. 1974), in *Marijuana and Medicine*. Eds Nahas G.G., Sutin K.M., Harvey D.J., Agurell S. Totowa N.J., Humana Press. 1999, 3-7.

3. Gaoni Y., Mechoulam R. Isolation, structure and partial synthesis of an active constituent of hashish. *Journal of the American Chemical Society*, 1964, 86, 1646.

4. Mechoulam R., Shani A., Edery H., Grunfield Y. Chemical basis of hashish activity. *Science*, 1970, 169, 611.

5. Devane W.A., Dysarz F.A., Johnson M.R., Melvin L.S., Howlett A.C. Determination and characterisation of a cannabinoid receptor in rat brain. *Molecular Pharmacology*, 1988, 34, 605-13.

6. Matsuda L.A., Lolait S.J., Brownstein M.J., Young A.C., Bonner T.I. Structure of a cannabinoid receptor and functional expression of the cloned cDNA. *Nature*, 1990, 346, 561-4.

7. Munro S., Thomas K.L., Abu-Shaar M. Molecular characterisation of a peripheral receptor for cannabinoids. *Nature*, 1993, 365, 61-5.

8. Dewey W.L. Cannabinoid pharmacology. *Pharmacological Reviews*, 1986, 38, 151-78.

9. Hollister L.E. Health aspects of cannabis. *Pharmacological Reviews*, 1986, 38, 1-20.

10. Herkenham M., Lynn A.B., Johnson M.R., Melvin L.S., De Costa B.R., Rice K.C. Characterisation and localisation of cannabinoid receptors in rat brain: A

quantitative in vitro autoradiographic study. *Journal of Neuroscience*, 1991, 11, 563-83.

11.   Mailleux P., Vanderhaeghen J.-J. Distribution of neuronal cannabinoid receptor in the adult rat brain: A comparative receptor binding radioautography and in situ hybridisation histochemistry. *Neuroscience*, 1992, 48, 655-68.

12.   Glass M., Dragunow M., Faull R.L.M. Cannabinoid receptors in the human brain: A detailed anatomical and quantitative autoradiographic study in the fetal, neonatal and adult human brain. *Neuroscience*, 1997, 77, 299-318.

13.   Herkenham M., Lynn A.B., Little M.D., Johnson M.R., Melvin L.S., De Costa B.R., Rice K.C. Cannabinoid receptor localisation in brain. *Proceedings of the National Academy of Science (USA)*, 1990, 87, 1932-6.

14.   Breivogel C.S., Sim L.J., Childers S.R. Regional differences in cannabinoid receptor/G-protein coupling in rat brain. *Journal of Pharmacology & Experimental Therapeutics*, 1997, 282, 1632-42.

15.   Evans D.M., Lake J.T., Johnson M.R., Howlett A.C. Endogenous cannabinoid receptor binding activity released from rat brain slices by depolarisation. *Journal of Pharmacology & Experimental Therapeutics*, 1994, 268, 1271-7.

16.   Devane W.A., Hanus L., Breuer A., Pertwee R.G., Stevenson L.A., Griffin G., Gibson D., Mandelbaum A., Etinger A., Mechoulam R. Isolation of a brain constituent that binds to the cannabinoid receptor. *Science*, 1992, 258, 1946-9.

17.   Mechoulam R., Ben-Shabat S., Hanus L., Ligumsky M., Kaminski N.E., Schatz A.R., Gopher A., Almog S., Martin B.R., Compton D.R., Pertwee R.G., Griffin G., Bayewitch M., Barg J., Vogel Z. Identification of an endogenous 2-monoglyceride, present in canine gut, that binds to cannabinoid receptors. *Biochemical Pharmacology*, 1995, 50, 83-90.

18.   Stella N., Schweitzer P., Piomelli D. A second endogenous cannabinoid that modulates long-term potentiation. *Nature*, 1997, 388, 773-8.

19.   Chopra R.N., Chopra G.S. The present position of hemp-drug addiction in India. *Indian Medical Research Memoirs*, 1939, 31, 1-119.

20.   Abel E.L. Effects of marijuana on the solution of anagrams, memory and appetite. *Nature*, 1971, 231, 260-1.

21.   Greenberg I., Kuehnle J., Mendelson J.H., Bernstein J.G. Effects of marijuana use on body weight and caloric intake in humans. *Psychopharmacology*, 1976, 49, 79-84.

22.   Foltin R.W., Brady J.V., Fischman M.W. Behavioural analysis of marijuana effects on food intake in humans. *Pharmacology Biochemistry & Behaviour*, 1986, 25, 577-82.

23.   Foltin R.W., Fischman M.W., Byrne M.F. Effects of smoked marijuana on food intake and body weight of humans living in a residential laboratory. *Appetite*, 1988, 11, 1-14.

24.   Sjoden P.-O., Jarbe T.U.C., Henriksson B.G. Influence of tetrahydrocannabinols (Δ-8-THC and Δ-9-THC) on body weight, food and water intake in rats. *Pharmacology Biochemistry & Behaviour*, 1973, 1, 395-9.

25.   Graceffo T.J., Robinson J.K. Delta-9-tetrahydrocannabinol (THC) fails to stimulate consumption of a highly palatable food in the rat. *Life Sciences*, 1998, 62, 85-8.

26.   Jarbe T.U.C., Henriksson B.G. Acute effects of two tetrahydrocannabinols (Δ-9-THC and Δ-8-THC) on water intake in water-deprived rats: implications for behavioural studies on marijuana compounds. *Psychopharmacologia*, 1973, 30, 315-22.

27.   Sofia R.D., Barry H. Acute and chronic effects of Δ-9-tetrahydrocannabinol on food intake by rats. *Psychopharmacologia*, 1974, 39, 213-22.

28.   Sofia R.D., Knobloch L.C. Comparative effects of various naturally occurring cannabinoids on food, sucrose and water consumption by rats. *Pharmacology Biochemistry & Behaviour*, 1976, 4, 591-9.

29.   Haines L., Green W. Marijuana use patterns. *British Journal of Addiction*, 1970, 65, 347-62.

30.   Tart C. Marijuana intoxication: Common experiences. *Nature*, 1970, 226, 701-4.

31.   Halikas J.A., Goodwin D.W., Guze S.B. Marijuana effects. A survey of regular users. *Journal of the American Medical Association*, 1971, 217, 692-4.

32.   Gilbert C.J., Ohly K.V., Rosner G., Peters W.P. Randomised, double-blind comparison of a prochloperazine-based versus a metoclopramide-based

antiemetic regimen in patients undergoing autologous bone-marrow transplantation. *Cancer*, 1995, 76, 2330-7.

33. Chlebowski R.T., Palomares M.R., Lillington L., Grosvenor M. Recent implication of weight loss in lung cancer management. *Nutrition*, 1996, 12, S43-S47.

34. Schwartz R.H., Voth E.A., Sheridan M.J. Marijuana to prevent nausea and vomiting in cancer patients: A survey of clinical oncologists. *Southern Medical Journal*, 1997, 90, 167-72.

35. Adams R. Marijuana (1941-1942). *Harvard Lectures*, 1941, 37, 169-95.

36. Grinspoon L., Bakalar J.B. *Marijuana, the forbidden medicine*. London, Yale University Press. 1997.

37. Hollister L.E. Hunger and appetite after single doses of marijuana, alcohol and dextroamphetamine. *Clinical Pharmacology & Therapeutics*, 1971, 12, 45-9.

38. Mattes R.D., Engelman K., Shaw L.M., Elsohly M.A. Cannabinoids and appetite stimulation. *Pharmacology Biochemistry & Behaviour*, 1994, 49, 187-95.

39. Sacks N., Hutcheson J.R., Watts J.M., Webb R.E. Case report: the effect of tetrahydrocannabinol on food intake during chemotherapy. *Journal of the American College of Nutrition*, 1990, 9, 630-2.

40. Beal J.E., Olson R., Laubenstein L., Morales J.O., Bellman P., Yangco B., Lefkowitz L., Plasse T.F., Shepard K.V. Dronabinol as a treatment for anorexia associated with weight loss in patients with AIDS. *Journal of Pain & Symptom Management*, 1995, 10, 89-97.

41. Glick S.D., Milloy S. Increased and decreased eating following THC administration. *Psychonomic Science*, 1972, 29, 6.

42. Brown J.E., Kassouny M., Cross J.K. Kinetic studies of food intake and sucrose solution preference by rats treated with low doses of delta-9-tetrahydrocannabinol. *Behavioral Biology*, 1977, 20, 104-10.

43. Williams C.M., Rogers P.J., Kirkham T.C. Hyperphagia in pre-fed rats following oral Δ-9-THC. *Physiology & Behaviour*, 1998, 65, 343-6.

44. Clark J.T., Kalra P.S., Crowley W.R., Kalra S.P. Neuropeptide Y and human pancreatic polypeptide stimulate feeding behaviour in rats. *Endocrinology*, 1984, 115, 427-9.

45. Corp E.S., Melville L.D., Greenberg D., Gibbs J., Smith G.P. Effect of fourth ventricular neuropeptide Y and peptide YY on ingestive and other behaviours. *American Journal of Physiology*, 1990, 259 (Regulatory Integrative and Comparative Physiology 28), R317-R323.

46. Williams C.M., Kirkham T.C. Anandamide induces overeating: mediation by central cannabinoid receptors. *Psychopharmacology*, 1999, 143, 315-7.

47. Crawley J.N., Corwin R.L., Robinson J.K., Felder C.C., Devane W.A., Axelrod J.A. Anandamide, an endogenous ligand of the cannabinoid receptor, induces hypomotility and hypothermia in vivo in rodents. *Pharmacology Biochemistry & Behaviour*, 1993, 46, 967-72.

48. Hao S., Avraham Y., Mechoulam R., Berry E.M. Low dose anandamide affects food intake, cognitive function, neurotransmitter and corticosterone levels in diet-restricted mice. *European Journal of Pharmacology*, 2000, 392, 147-56.

49. Arnone M., Maruani J., Chaperon F., Thiebot M.H., Poncelet M., Soubrié P., LeFur G. Selective inhibition of sucrose and ethanol intake by SR141716, an antagonist of central cannabinoid (CB1) receptors. *Psychopharmacology*, 1997, 132, 104-6.

50. Gardner E.L., Vorel S.R. Cannabinoid transmission and reward-related events. *Neurobiology of Disease*, 1998, 5, 502-33.

51. Trojniar W., Wise R.A. Facilitory effect of Δ-9-tetrahydrocannabinol on hypothalamically-induced feeding. *Psychopharmacology*, 1991, 103, 172-6.

52. Simiand J., Keane M., Keane P.E., Soubrie P. SR141716, a CB1 cannabinoid receptor antagonist, selectively reduces sweet food intake in marmoset. *Behavioural Pharmacology*, 1998, 9, 179-81.

53. Weingarten H.P., Watson S.D. Sham feeding as a procedure for assessing the influence of diet palatability on food intake. *Physiology & Behaviour*, 1982, 28, 401-7.

54. Kirkham T.C., Cooper S.J. Naloxone attenuation of sham feeding is modified by manipulation of sucrose concentration. *Physiology & Behaviour*, 1988, 44, 491-4.

55. Kirkham T.C. Enhanced anorectic potency of naloxone in rats sham feeding 30% sucrose: reversal by repeated naloxone administration. *Physiology & Behaviour*, 1990, 47, 419-26.

56. Leventhal L., Kirkham T.C., Cole J.L., Bodnar R.J. Selective actions of central mu and kappa opioid antagonists upon sucrose intake in sham-feeding rats. *Brain Research*, 1995, 685, 205-10.

57. Wise R.A. The brain and reward, in *The Neuropharmacological Basis of Reward*. Eds Liebman J.A., Cooper S.J. Oxford, Clarendon Press. 1989, 377-424.

58. Ikemoto S., Panksepp J. The role of nucleus accumbens dopamine in motivated behavior: a unifying interpretation with special reference to reward-seeking. *Brain Research Reviews*, 1999, 31, 6-41.

59. Spanagel R., Weiss F. The dopamine hypothesis of reward: past and current status. *Trends in Neurosciences*, 1999, 22(11), 521-7.

60. Berridge K. Food reward: brain substrates of wanting and liking. *Neuroscience and Biobehavioral Reviews*, 1995, 20, 1-25.

61. Tanda G., Pontieri F.E., DiChiara G. Cannabinoid and heroin activation of mesolimbic dopamine transmission by a common mu 1 opioid receptor mechanism. *Science*, 1997, 276, 2048-50.

62. Gardner E.L. Cannabinoid interaction with brain reward systems - the neurobiological basis of cannabinoid abuse, in *Marijuana/Cannabinoids: Neurobiology and Neurophysiology*. Eds Murphy L.L., Bartke A. New York, CRC Press. 1992, 275–335.

63. Souilhac J., Poncelet M., Rinaldi-Carmona M., Le Fur G., Soubrie P. Intrastriatal injection of cannabinoid receptor agonists induced turning behavior in mice. *Pharmacology Biochemistry and Behavior*, 1995, 51, 3–7.

64. Sanudo-Pena M.C., Tsou K., Delay E.R., Hohman A.G., Force M., Walker J.M. Endogenous cannabinoids as an aversive or counter-rewarding system in the rat. *Neuroscience Letters*, 1997, 223, 125–8.

65. Rodriguez de Fonseca F., Martn Calderon J.L., Mechoulam R., Navarro M. Repeated stimulation of D1 dopamine receptors enhances (-)-11-hydroxy-delta-8-tetrahydrocannabinol-dimethyl-heptyl-induced catalepsy in male rats. *Neuroreport*, 1994, 5, 761–5.

66. Bidaut-Russell M., Howlett A.C. Cannabinoid receptor regulated cAMP accumulation in the rat striatum. *Journal of Neurochemistry*, 1991, 57, 1769–73.

67. Gallate J.E., McGregor I.S. The motivation for beer in rats: effects of ritanserin, naloxone and SR141716. *Psychopharmacology*, 1999, 142, 302-8.

68. Colombo G., Agabio R., Diaz G., Lobina C., Reali R., Gessa G.L. Appetite suppression and weight loss after the cannabinoid antagonist SR141716. *Life Sciences*, 1998, 63, PL113-PL117.

69. Gallate J.E., Saharov T., Mallet P.E., McGregor I.S. Increased motivation for beer in rats following administration of a cannabinoid CB1 receptor agonist. *European Journal of Pharmacology*, 1999, 370, 233-40.

70. Kirkham T.C., Cooper S.J. Opioid peptides in relation to the treatment of obesity and bulimia, in *Peptides: A Target for New Drug Development*. Eds Bloom S.R., Burnstock G. London, IBC. 1991, 28–44.

71. Cooper S.J., Kirkham T.C. Opioid mechanisms in the control of food consumption and taste preferences, in *Handbook of Experimental Pharmacology*. Eds Herz A., Akil H., Simon E.J. Berlin, Springer–Verlag. 1993, 104 (2), 239–63.

72. Fuentes J.A., RuizGayo M., Manzanares J., Vela G., Reche I., Corchero J. Cannabinoids as potential new analgesics. *Life Sciences*, 1999, 65, 675-85.

73. Gardner E.L., Paredes W., Smith D., Donner A., Milling C., Cohen D., Morrison D. Facilitation of brain stimulation reward by Δ-9-tetrahydrocannabinol. *Psychopharmacology*, 1988, 96, 142-4.

74. Welch S.P., Eads E.M. Synergistic interactions of endogenous opioids and cannabinoid systems. *Brain Research*, 1999, 848, 183-90.

75. Johnson S.W., North R.A. Opioids excite dopamine neurons by hyperpolarization of local interneurons. *Journal of Neuroscience*, 1992, 12, 483-8.

76. Marsicano G., Lutz B. Expression of the cannabinoid receptor CB1 in distinct neuronal subpopulations in the adult mouse forebrain. *European Jouranal of Neuroscience*, 1999, 11, 4213-25.

2.4. FOOD CRAVINGS AND THE NEUROPHARMACOLOGY OF FOOD REWARD

Suzanne Higgs and Steven John Cooper

2.4.1 Introduction

Food is obviously essential to our being and so it is perhaps not surprising that mechanisms have evolved to encourage the consumption of sufficient energy and nutrients to ensure survival. For example, food is rewarding, meaning that it increases the occurrence of behaviour associated with its presentation. Put a hungry rat in a Skinner box and it will quickly learn to press a lever in order to obtain food. The same applies to humans, who will perform various operant behaviours, including lever pressing, for food reward. For some researchers, food reward, along with the reward associated with other reinforcing stimuli (for example, drugs of abuse), is thought to be linked with the subjective feeling of pleasure (1,2). Few people would deny that eating can be an intensely pleasurable experience and it is often presumed that the ability of food to induce a positive affective state is responsible for its rewarding effects. This hedonistic aspect of eating is reflected in the term palatability, which is used to refer to the sensory-affective response of an organism to a foodstuff (although see refs 3 and 4 for alternative definitions).

In fact, much of the work conducted on the rewarding properties of food, as distinct from its nutritive functions, has centred on this concept of palatability. Ingenious tests of palatability have been devised that isolate orosensory factors from other confounding variables, such as those affecting the ability of the animal to generate appropriate behaviours, e.g. fatigue, motor incapacitation and/or other variables relating more specifically to the control of ingestive behaviour, such as postingestive factors. This has allowed the neuropharmacological basis of food reward to be investigated through examination of the effect of various drug or lesion manipulations in such tests. More recently, the effect of drug manipulations on ingestive behaviour in human subjects has begun to be investigated, and provides an important comparison for the available animal data.

Much attention has focused on the benzodiazepine/GABA and endogenous opioid systems. The mesocorticolimbic dopamine system has also been implicated in the mediation of food reward. Early studies on the role of dopamine in reward employed traditional operant techniques rather than specific tests of palatability, but were nevertheless interpreted within the framework of hedonics. Wise and colleagues (5) found that the dopamine antagonist pimozide affected food rewarded lever pressing in a manner similar to extinction (omission of reward). This effect was reported as neuroleptic-induced anhedonia or loss of pleasure, since it was assumed that the reduction in rewarded behaviour observed was accompanied by an attenuation of subjective pleasure. The role of dopamine in mediating the rewarding properties not only of food, but also of other reinforcers such as sex, drugs of abuse and brain stimulation has since been extensively investigated and hotly debated. Dopaminergic systems are known to be important for sensorimotor function, and it has been argued that compromised movement may suffice to explain some reward-like effects (6). Despite this, there is much evidence to suggest that dopaminergic systems are involved in reward processes in a way that cannot be explained purely in terms of sensorimotor deficits. However, the specific relationship between dopamine and pleasure has recently been challenged, leading to the suggestion that this aspect of reward may be dissociable from other processes determining the motivating properties of incentive stimuli such as food.

The principal aim of this chapter is to review the experimental evidence concerning the neurochemical basis of food reward and relate these findings to recent ideas about the nature of reward. We do not intend to provide a general overview of the neuropharmacology of appetite (for a more comprehensive review, see ref. 7) but rather focus in particular on the effects of benzodiazepines, opiates and dopamine on feeding behaviour in both animals and humans, and explore the suggestion that these drugs influence ingestion via a modulation of reward processes. Finally, we discuss the implications of such research for our understanding of food cravings and addictions.

2.4.2   Benzodiazepines

Benzodiazepines are synthetic therapeutic compounds that act in the central nervous system to modify the action of the inhibitory neurotransmitter gamma amino butyric acid (GABA) (8). They are well known for their anti-anxiety and sedative properties, but also have robust effects on feeding behaviour. The first report of a benzodiazepine affecting food intake was by Randall and colleagues (9), who showed that chlordiazepoxide (CDP) (a benzodiazepine agonist) increased food consumption in rats and dogs. Although this result was largely ignored at the time, a body of evidence has since been gathered to suggest that benzodiazepines are some of the most potent pharmacological stimulators of food intake. Dramatic increases in consumption have been reported for a whole range of benzodiazepine agonists (10). Moreover, the effect has been documented across a range of different species, including the cat (11), the rabbit (12), the non-human primate (13) and the pigeon (14). More recently, the hyperphagic effects of benzodiazepines have also been confirmed in humans (15-17).

2.4.2.1   Benzodiazepines and palatability

Initial explanations of benzodiazepine-induced hyperphagia suggested that it was due to a reduction in food neophobia (18). This account was relatively short-lived since it failed to explain how CDP increased consumption of a familiar but not novel food in food-deprived rats (19). Later, explanations focused on the direct effects of these compounds on appetite, suggesting variously that benzodiazepines suppressed satiety (20), mimicked hunger (21), or stimulated appetite (22). However, within a few years, evidence was accumulated by Cooper and colleagues to suggest that modulation of palatability was a likely mechanism (23). Importantly, it was shown that benzodiazepine administration brings about large increases in food intake in rats that have been pre-fed (24), indicating that inhibition of postingestive satiety signals is not a crucial factor. There then followed systematic investigation of the effects of benzodiazepines in a range of behavioural tests designed to measure palatability. The outcome was consistent positive evidence in support of the assertion that benzodiazepines are prototypic palatability-enhancing drugs. Evidence from some of these tests is reviewed below.

2.4.2.1.1 Taste preference

Dissociation of generalised/non-specific increases in ingestive behaviour from enhancement of those responses specifically related to the evaluation of taste can be achieved by two-bottle preference testing. In this paradigm, water-deprived rats are given a simultaneous choice between drinking a sapid solution such as saccharin, or consuming plain water. Saccharin is preferentially consumed even though the animals are thirsty and therefore consume some water. Augmentation of taste preferences by benzodiazepines is a robust phenomenon. A selective increase in the consumption of saccharin over water has been demonstrated following administration of the benzodiazepine agonist clonazepam (25). Similar results have also been reported for the agonists CDP (26), abecarnil (27), and the partial agonists bretazenil and Ro 17-1812 (28). Benzodiazepine potentiation of taste preferences is not limited to sweet taste either, because the above agonists have been shown to increase intake of a 0.9% NaCl solution without affecting water consumption in a two-choice test (27,29).

In addition to agonists and antagonists, there exists another category of benzodiazepine drugs known as "inverse agonists". These compounds produce pharmacological and behavioural effects that are the opposite of those caused by classical agonists (30). Examples of such reverse modulation can be observed at other receptor sites, but benzodiazepine inverse agonists are probably the best-characterised (see ref. 31 for a review). It has been shown that benzodiazepine inverse agonists possess anorectic as opposed to hyperphagic properties (32,33). They also block sweet taste preferences, suggesting that *bidirectional* control of palatability can be achieved via drug action at benzodiazepine receptors (34,35).

2.4.2.1.2   Taste reactivity

Analysis of the distinctive facial reactions elicited in response to basic taste stimuli (e.g. sucrose, salt, quinine, and citric acid solutions) is known as taste reactivity testing. This method does not rely on an animal's ability to ingest fluids and can be used to determine affective reactions to tastes. Similar expressions can be observed in human infants (36) and apes (37). However, most pharmacological studies have been conducted using rats (38,39). The procedure involves infusion of small amounts of tastants directly into the mouth of a rat via a chronically implanted intraoral cannula. This is followed by observer categorisation of the responses as either positively hedonic (e.g. tongue protrusions and mouthing movements) or aversive (e.g. gapes and headshakes) (40).

Benzodiazepines were the first drugs to be evaluated in the taste reactivity test. Berridge and Treit (41) found that CDP enhanced the positive hedonic reactions to sucrose without affecting aversive reactions. This result has since been confirmed many times (42-46), and is consistent with the suggestion that benzodiazepines enhance positive hedonic reactions to taste stimuli.

2.4.2.1.3   Licking microstructure

A powerful method that can reveal much about the effects of drug treatments on ingestive behaviour is microstructural analysis of licking behaviour. This kind of analysis has the benefit that the occurrence of individual licks can be recorded accurately using automated lickometer systems, giving a high temporal resolution. Importantly, the measurement of individual licks also provides a direct metric of the behaviour that is actually used by an animal to ingest fluids. Licking in rats is highly stereotyped in nature, consisting of fast rhythmic tongue protrusions (47). Davis and his colleagues have shown that manipulation of orosensory and postingestive factors produces distinctive effects on these licking patterns. For example, the initial rate of licking and duration of bouts or clusters of licks increase as a function of sugar concentration and so provide measures of the palatability of ingested fluids (48,49). Other microstructural variables are more sensitive to motoric manipulations. Stellar and Hill (47) have also shown that rats lick at a constant rate of about 6-7 licks per second. This intra-bout lick rate is affected by moving the drinking spout progressively further away from the animal but not by altering sucrose concentration (49). Recent data from our laboratory suggests that benzodiazepines have two distinct effects on licking microstructure. We found that the benzodiazepine agonist midazolam selectively increased the initial rate of licking in brief contact taste tests via an increase in mean bout duration (50,51). Specific benzodiazepine receptor mediation of this effect was confirmed when the increase in mean bout duration was blocked by administration of the selective antagonist flumazenil (50). A drug-induced suppression of the usually constant intra-bout lick rate was also observed. The effect of midazolam on mean bout duration mimics the effect of increasing concentration and is consistent with an enhancement of palatability, while the reduction in intrabout lick rate is consistent with the muscle relaxant properties of this drug. In keeping with the idea of bidirectional control of palatability is the demonstration that the inverse agonist Ro 15-4513 decreases the initial lick rate and the mean duration of bouts (51,52). It also seems that benzodiazepine alterations in licking behaviour go beyond sweet taste stimuli such as sucrose and saccharin and apply to maltodextrin and fat emulsions as well (51,52).

2.4.2.1.4   Human studies

It is only relatively recently that the effects of benzodiazepines on food intake in human subjects have been examined. This is despite the fact that benzodiazepines are probably some of the most frequently prescribed drugs for conditions such as sleep disorders and anxiety. Earlier clinical reports had noted weight gain in some patients taking benzodiazepines as anti-anxiety treatments (53), but a hyperphagic effect was not demonstrated under experimental conditions until much later (15). Subsequently, Haney et al. (16) investigated the phenomenon further, and showed that the short-acting benzodiazepine agonist, alprazolam, increased food intake in normal-weight male volunteers living in a residential laboratory. This was apparently due to an increase in the number of eating episodes during the evening and was not associated with anxiety reduction (which is entirely consistent with the general proposal that the hyperphagic effects of benzodiazepine can be dissociated from their tranquillising actions). Interestingly, alprazolam has also been shown to enhance food intake premenstrually in women with pre-menstrual syndrome (17) (see section 5.3). However, these studies did not directly examine the proposal that benzodiazepines affect palatability responses in humans. Therefore, although the hyperphagic effect of benzodiazepines in humans is consistent with an enhancement of palatability, the underlying mechanism responsible for the effects of benzodiazepines on human ingestion remains an open question.

2.4.2.1.5   Neural substrate

The potential central sites of action of benzodiazepines on food intake and palatability have recently begun to be examined. The focus for these studies has been structures in the brainstem. Berridge (42) showed that hedonic enhancement by CDP measured by the taste reactivity test could be demonstrated in the decerebrate rat. In this model, a brain transection is made that effectively isolates the brainstem from forebrain structures. The above result indicates that the important neural circuitry mediating the effects of CDP on affective responding resides in the lower brainstem. Further evidence in support of this suggestion was provided by Pecina and Berridge, who showed that injection of the benzodiazepine agonist diazepam into the 4th ventricle of the brainstem also increased hedonic reactions to a 7% sucrose solution (54). We tested the possibility that brainstem structures are involved in the hyperphagic effects of benzodiazepines by performing 4th ventricle injections of midazolam and examining the effect on consumption of a palatable diet. Midazolam dose-dependently increased consumption of the diet, and this effect was blocked by pre-treatment with the benzodiazepine antagonist flumazenil (55). The parabrachial nucleus (PBN) of the pons was further highlighted as a candidate for the mediation of the above effect following the demonstration that direct injections of midazolam into this nucleus also dose-dependently increased food intake in non-deprived rats (56). Since the PBN is the second relay in the taste pathway, action at benzodiazepine receptors in this area is also consistent with an explanation of benzodiazepine-induced hyperphagia in terms of modulation of taste palatability.

2.4.3   Opioid Peptides

Opioid agonists, such as morphine, increase food intake under a variety of experimental conditions (57-60), while opioid antagonists, such as naloxone, decrease consumption (61-64). It has been suggested that the underlying mechanism responsible for these changes in intake is a modulation of palatability (65). The role of opioids in pleasurable aspects of food intake is reviewed fully elsewhere in this volume (see section 2.5). Here, we would like to draw the reader's attention briefly to the similarities between the effects of opioids and benzodiazepines in palatability tests. Like benzodiazepines, opioid agonists enhance taste acceptance and preference (66,67). Antagonists, on the other hand, reduce or abolish sweet and salt taste preferences (68-71). Opioid antagonists also reduce sucrose sham feeding in satiated rats (72-75). Finally, there is evidence that morphine enhances positive hedonic responses elicited by intraoral infusions of sucrose (76-78), and that the antagonist naltrexone diminishes them (79). These data are consistent with the idea that endogenous opioids are involved in the positive hedonic evaluation of taste stimuli. Interestingly, Yeomans *et al.* (80) (see also section 2.5) found that the antagonist nalmefene reduced food intake in human volunteers but had no effect on subjective ratings of hunger and satiety. In contrast, the drug did seem to reduce consumption of those food items rated as particularly palatable (81). Furthermore, naltrexone was also subsequently shown to reduce the rated pleasantness of palatable foods (82,83). Therefore, the human data are also supportive of a role for endogenous opioids in palatability (see section 2.2).

In contrast to the available data for benzodiazepines, recent evidence suggests that the site of action of opioids on palatability may be located in the forebrain. Injection of morphine into the nucleus accumbens has been shown to increase positive hedonic reactions to oral sucrose (84). This result is consistent with previous demonstrations of the effectiveness of accumbens injections of opioid agonists in stimulating food intake (85,86).

2.4.4   Benzodiazepine-Opioid Interactions

The parallels between the effects of opioids and of benzodiazepines on ingestion suggest that there may be an interaction between them. Affective responses may be influenced by benzodiazepines, which in turn results in the release of opioid peptides. Three lines of evidence are consistent with this proposal. First, benzodiazepine agonists modulate the release of endogenous encephalins in the brain (87,88). Second, benzodiazepine-induced hyperphagia is blocked by pre-treatment with opioid antagonists (89-91). Third, we have shown that midazolam-induced enhancement of licking behaviour in the rat is dependent upon endogenous opioid activity (50). Using the brief contact licking test, we found that naloxone blocked the increase in total number of licks and mean bout duration brought about by midazolam, but failed to reverse the drug-induced suppression of lick rate. These data suggest that opioids are involved in the palatability effects of benzodiazepines but may not be important for their muscle relaxant effects. A role for the PBN in mediating benzodiazepine/opioid interactions is an interesting possibility that deserves further investigation. For example, analysis of the distribution of both mu and kappa types of opioid receptor shows that they are localised in the PBN (92). In addition, Carr and colleagues (93) have shown that feeding elicited by electrical stimulation of the lateral hypothalamus can be affected by injection of naloxone into the PBN.

2.4.5   Dopamine

The effects of dopamine antagonists on food intake have been appreciated for some time. It is generally accepted that these compounds reduce intake of solid food and sucrose solutions (94-96) and disrupt operant responding for food (5,97). There is not the space here to discuss the extensive literature on dopaminergic contributions to ingestion and so the reader is referred to other recent reviews (98,99). However, as noted in the Introduction, it was suggested some time ago that dopamine antagonism might block the reward quality of food (58). Formally presented as the "anhedonia" hypothesis by Wise in 1982 (1), this idea has had a controversial history. Initial objections focused on alternative explanations of the effects of dopamine antagonists in terms of drug-induced movement impairments. Others took issue with the specific suggestion that dopamine has a role in mediating palatability. Below we provide a brief overview of investigations into the role of dopamine in food reward.

2.4.5.1   Dopamine and food reward

2.4.5.1.1   Taste preference

The effect of dopamine antagonists on taste preference has been investigated in a series of experiments by Willner and colleagues (100). Towell *et al.* (101) found that the preference for sucrose over water was reduced by pimozide. A motor deficit could not fully explain the reduction in sucrose intake in this experiment because the same animals actually increased their water intake. These authors also excluded the possibility that the reduced preference might be due to an alteration in the perceived intensity of sucrose because pimozide did not affect the threshold for sweetness detection in conditioned discrimination tasks (100). Using a different approach, Hsaio and Smith (102) complemented the results from Willner's laboratory by demonstrating that the dopamine D2 antagonist raclopride reduced drug-free conditioned preferences. Rats were trained to drink two novel flavours presented in a 10% sucrose solution. One flavour was paired with an injection of raclopride while on alternate days the other equally preferred flavour was paired with a vehicle control injection. After the conditioning period, the rats were offered a straight choice between the two flavours in the absence of drug (this removed the possibility that the direct effects of the drug could have influenced responding). Preference for the flavour that had been paired with raclopride was decreased, suggesting that the drug had reduced the positive rewarding effect of sucrose. More recently, in further support of this suggestion, both the D1 antagonist SCH23390 and the D2 antagonist raclopride have been shown to block the expression of conditioned flavour preferences under sham feeding conditions (103).

2.4.5.1.2   Sham feeding

The sham feeding paradigm provides a means of studying the effect of oropharyngeal factors on the consumption of palatable fluids. In this preparation, the aim is to eliminate postingestional factors by allowing ingested material to drain out of the stomach via a chronically implanted gastric fistula. Such fistulated animals display a pronounced satiety deficit, and it has been proposed that the technique provides a measure of palatability (104). The work of Smith and colleagues has shown that, under various conditions, dopamine antagonism reduces intake in rats with gastric fistulas. Geary and Smith (105) first observed that a low dose of pimozide decreased sucrose intake in sham feeding rats. This finding was then explored in more detail by Schneider, who showed that either dopamine D1 or dopamine D2 antagonism was sufficient to decrease sham intake of a 10% sucrose solution (106,107). These effects were dose-related and appeared to be selective for sucrose (although at larger doses sham drinking of water was also affected). An account of the drug effect in terms of a motoric deficit was rejected because microstructural analysis showed that lick rate was not disrupted. Instead, the pattern of licking was similar to that seen following a reduction in sucrose concentration. The authors concluded that dopamine blockade attenuated the positive reinforcing aspects of sucrose drinking. Further evidence to support a role for dopamine in mediating the rewarding properties of ingested solutions comes from finding that blockade of dopamine D2 receptors reduces sham feeding of a concentrated salt solution in sodium-depleted rats (108).

2.4.5.1.3   Taste reactivity

In contrast to the effects of dopamine antagonists in taste preference and sham feeding tests, results from taste reactivity testing have been inconsistent and subject to much debate. Berridge and colleagues found that lesions of the dopamine system made with the neurotoxin

6-hydroxydopamine rendered rats aphagic but had no effect on the pattern of taste reactivity responses elicited to an infused sucrose solution (109). Direct pharmacological manipulation of dopamine neurotransmission using either a dopamine agonist (apomorphine) or antagonist (haloperidol) similarly failed to alter taste reactivity responding (45). These authors concluded that hedonic evaluation of foodstuffs is not dependent upon dopaminergic neurotransmission. Given the evidence outlined above, which is apparently supportive of the involvement of dopamine in food palatability, this was a controversial stance - one that also seemed at odds with data from another laboratory demonstrating both attenuated positive hedonic reactions and enhancement of aversive reactions to sucrose following dopamine blockade with pimozide (110,111). However, in an unusual move, collaboration between the two groups was undertaken to try to resolve the issue (112). This study suggested, firstly, that the previously reported reduced palatability following dopamine antagonism (110) might have been an artifact of the duration of testing. In the collaborative venture, only responses elicited towards the end of the period were diminished and this was considered representative more of progressive sensorimotor deficit rather than of reduced palatability. Second, data reanalysis suggested that the previous report of enhanced aversiveness in response to pimozide (111) was due to drug-induced reductions in locomotor activity that resulted in a sampling bias.

2.4.5.1.4   Human studies

An increasing amount of evidence suggests that substantial weight gain is often associated with chronic administration of antipsychotic drugs (113). Although the primary effect of these drugs is to block dopamine receptors, the implication of neuroleptic-induced weight gain for the role of dopamine in food reward is difficult to determine. This is because the mechanism underlying such weight gain remains unclear and may relate to additional non-dopaminergic actions of neuroleptics such as metabolic and endocrine effects (114). Nevertheless, there is still some evidence for changes in hedonic evaluation of sweet-tasting stimuli in patients with Parkinson's disease. These individuals have reduced dopamine function due to degeneration of dopamine-containing neurones in the substantia nigra. Travers *et al.* (115) found enhanced preference for higher concentrations of sucrose solutions in these patients, suggesting a possible role for dopamine palatability. However, further investigation of the specific nature of this effect is required before any strong conclusions can be drawn.

2.4.6   Wanting and Liking

Berridge (116) has interpreted the lack of effect of dopamine in the taste reactivity test as significant. Based on this, and other evidence (117,118), he has suggested that food reward is a more complex phenomenon than previously supposed. According to Berridge, food reward is not a unitary psychological process but a collection of multiple functions that normally integrate to form a whole. Crucial to this argument is the proposal that palatability tests such as sham feeding measure a different aspect of food reward from taste reactivity. For example, Berridge argues that most palatability tests require a voluntary approach and consumption of the food reward, e.g. approach of a licking spout, and so measure the willingness of an animal to eat. This contrasts with taste reactivity, which is not influenced by appetitive factors, because the fluids are delivered involuntarily directly into the mouth. Berridge therefore draws a distinction between taste reactivity, which he argues measures pure affective reactions, and tests such as sham feeding and taste preference that assess both hedonic reactivity and the motivation directed towards food incentives. The fact that dopamine manipulations affect sham feeding but not taste reactivity is taken to mean that food reward is made up of functionally dissociable processes that have separate neural substrates: palatability or hedonics on the one hand and appetite or the disposition to eat on the other. This distinction is referred to more colloquially as the difference between "wanting" versus "liking". Activity in dopaminergic systems is thought to underlie "wanting", whereas a separate neural system is involved in determining "liking". Although this aspect of the theory is less fully explored by Berridge, the implication is that it could involve benzodiazepine/opioid systems.

Under normal circumstances, both "liking" and "wanting" are essential components of reward, which is why pleasure is often seen as being synonymous with reward. However, Berridge's theory allows for the possibility that they can be triggered separately. For example, manipulation of dopamine neurotransmission is assumed to alter selectively "wanting" but not "liking". This conceptualisation of food reward appears to account for much of the pharmacological data presented above. It is consistent with the idea that benzodiazepines/opioids may mediate palatability, and explains why dopamine manipulations fail to alter hedonic taste reactivity responding but have robust effects in sham feeding and taste preference. Perhaps most significant for our present purposes, though, it also predicts that some changes in human ingestive behaviour could result from changes in "liking", whereas others could result from changes in "wanting" alone. It is this assertion that may be significant for interpreting the phenomenon of food cravings.

2.4.7   Implications for Food Cravings and Addictions

It is often assumed that food cravings are related to the pleasure derived from consuming certain foodstuffs, and it is this intense "liking" that leads to the desire to eat. While this may be true in some instances (119), in many cases, consumption of craved foods can actually lead to increased negative feelings rather than inducing pleasurable states. For example, Macdiarmid and Hetherington (120) have shown that self-identified chocolate "addicts" feel more guilty and depressed after eating chocolate than controls. Berridge's theory provides an alternative to the pleasure interpretation of food cravings because it suggests that cravings could result from changes in "wanting" as opposed to "liking". Such an account would explain why individuals might experience cravings in the absence of any pleasurable effects of food, as seems to be the case for some chocolate "addicts". The importance of this analysis lies in its implications for the control and treatment of food cravings. Successful management of cravings will require a full understanding of the contributing factors. For example, if heightened "wanting" is the major determinant of cravings, then the use of therapies that blunt the hedonic impact of foods are unlikely to be useful clinically. Interestingly, the same may apply to other behaviours characterised by severe cravings, such as drug addiction. It has been suggested that the cravings experienced by drug addicts are also due to excessive "wanting" resulting from sensitisation of brain dopamine systems by psychostimulant drugs (121). The implication here is that drug and food cravings may share similar underlying mechanisms. Therefore, further investigation of neuropharmacology of both food and drug reward may prove to be useful in improving the management of both drug and food addictions.

2.4.8   Conclusions

This chapter has highlighted the role of benzodiazepines, endogenous opioids, and dopamine in the mediation of food reward. Examination of the effects of benzodiazepine and opioid drugs in many different tests of palatability in animals and humans has provided a firm basis for the assertion that these compounds alter ingestive behaviour via changes in the hedonic evaluation or "liking" of food stimuli. A strong case for the involvement of dopamine in food reward has also been presented, although the evidence indicates that this may occur via modulation of a different process, which has been referred to by Berridge and colleagues as "wanting". These studies have opened the possibility that food cravings could result in neurochemical changes in either system (benzodiazepine/opioid-mediated "liking" or dopamine-mediated "wanting"). It has been argued that the absence of pleasurable reactions upon consumption of highly craved foods in some individuals is supportive of exaggerated "wanting" being a likely mechanism. This suggests that investigation of the specific role of dopamine in food cravings may yield some important advances in the management of such cravings and that continued study of the neuropharmacology of food reward should provide further valuable insight into the nature of psychological mechanisms governing what we choose to eat.

2.4.9 References

1.   Wise R.A. Neuroleptics and operant behavior: the anhedonia hypothesis. *Behavioral Brain Sciences*, 1982, 5, 39-87.

2.   Di Chiara G., North R.A. Neurobiology of opiate abuse. *Trends In Pharmacological Sciences*, 1992, 13, 185-93.

3.   Kissileff H.R. Quantitative relationship between palatability and food intake in man, in *Interaction of the Chemical Sense with Nutrition*. Eds Kare M., Brand J.G. New York, Academic Press. 1986, 293-317.

4.   Grill H.J., Berridge K.C. Taste reactivity as a measure of the neural control of palatability. *Progress in Psychobiology and Physiological Psychology*, 1985, 11, 1-61.

5.   Wise R.A., Spindler J., de Wit H., Gerber G.J. Neuroleptic-induced "anhedonia" in rats: pimozide blocks the reward quality of food. *Science*, 1978, 201, 262-4.

6.   Salamone J.D., Cousins M.S., Snyder B.J.B. Behavioural functions of nucleus accumbens dopamine: Empirical and conceptual problems with the anhedonia hypothesis. *Neuroscience and Biobehavioural Reviews*, 1997, 21, 341-59.

7.   Cooper S.J., Clifton P.G. *Drug receptor subtypes and ingestive behaviour*. London, Academic Press. 1996.

8.   Ticku M.K. Drug modulation of GABA-A mediated transmission. *Seminars in the Neurosciences*, 1991, 3, 211-8.

9.   Randall L.O., Dodd R.R., Felblum S., Heise G.A., Keith E.F., Bagdon R.E. The psychosedative properties of methainodiazepoxide. *Journal of Pharmacology and Experimental Therapeutics*, 1960, 129, 163-71.

10. Cooper S.J. Benzodiazepine receptor mediated enhancement and inhibition of taste reactivity, food choice and intake. *Annals of the New York Academy of Science*, 1989, 575, 321-37.

11. Fratta W., Mereu G., Chessa P., Paglietti E., Gessa G. Benzodiazepine induced voraciousness in cats and inhibition of amphetamine-induced anorexia. *Life Sciences*, 1976, 18, 1156-66.

12. Mansbach R.S., Stanley J.A., Barrett J.E. Ro 15-4513 and β-CCE selectively eliminate diazepam-induced feeding in the rabbit. *Pharmacology, Biochemistry and Behavior*, 1984, 20, 763-6.

13. Foltin R.W., Ellis S., Schuster C.R. Specific antagonism by Ro 15-1788 of benzodiazepine-induced increases in food intake in rhesus monkeys. *Pharmacology, Biochemistry and Behavior*, 1985, 23, 249-52.

14. Cooper S.J., Posados Andrews A. Food and water intake in the non-deprived pigeon after chlordiazepoxide administration. *Psychopharmacology*, 1979, 65, 99-101.

15. Kelly T.H., Foltin R.W., King L. Behavioral-response to diazepam in a residential laboratory. *Biological Psychiatry*, 1992, 31(8), 808-22.

16. Haney M., Comer S.D., Fischman M.W., Foltin R.W. Alprazolam increases food intake in humans. *Psychopharmacology*, 1997, 132, 311-4.

17. Evans S.M., Foltin R.W., Fischman M.W. Food "cravings" and the acute effects of alprazolam on food intake in women with premenstrual dysphoric disorder. *Appetite*, 1999, 32(3), 331-49.

18. Poschel B.P.H. A simple and effective screen for benzodiazepine-like drugs. *Psychopharmacologia*, 1971, 19, 193 198.

19. Cooper S.J., Crummy Y.M.T. Enhanced choice of familiar food in a food preference test after chlordiazepoxide injections. *Psychopharmacology*, 1978, 59, 51-6.

20. Margules D.L., Stein L. Neuroleptics v. tranquilizers: evidence from animal studies and site of action, in *Neuropsychopharmacology*. Eds Brill H., Cole J.O., Deniker P., Hippius H., Bradley P.B. Amsterdam, Excerpta Medica Foundation. 1967, 108-20.

21. Wise R.A., Dawson V. Diazepam-induced eating and lever pressing for food in sated rats. *Journal of Comparative and Physiological Psychology*, 1974, 86, 930-41.

22. Cooper S.J. Benzodiazepines as appetite enhancing compounds. *Appetite*, 1980, 1, 7-19.

23. Cooper S.J., Estall L.B. Behavioral pharmacology of food, water and salt intake in relation to drug actions at benzodiazepine receptors. *Neuroscience and Biobehavioral Reviews*, 1985, 9(1), 5-19.

24. Cooper S.J., Barber D.J., Gilbert D.B., Moores W.R. Benzodiazepine receptor ligands and the consumption of a highly palatable diet in non-deprived male rats. *Psychopharmacology*, 1985, 86, 348-55.

25. Cooper S.J., Yerbury R.E. Clonazepam selectively increases saccharin consumption in a two-choice test. *Brain Research*, 1988, 456, 173-6.

26. Parker L.A. Chlordiazepoxide nonspecifically enhances the consumption of a saccharin solution. *Pharmacology Biochemistry and Behavior*, 1991, 38, 375-7.

27. Cooper S.J., Greenwood S.E. The carboline abecarnil, a novel agonist at central benzodiazepine receptors influences saccharin and salt preference in the rat. *Brain Research*, 1992, 599, 144-7.

28. Cooper S.J., Green A.E. The benzodiazepine receptor partial agonists, bretazenil (Ro-16 6028) and Ro-17-1812, affect saccharin preference and quinine aversion in the rat. *Behavioral Pharmacology*, 1993, 4(1), 81-5.

29. Cooper S.J., Barber D.J. The benzodiazepine receptor partial agonist bretazenil and the partial inverse agonist Ro-15-4513 - effects on salt preference and aversion in the rat. *Brain Research*, 1993, 612(1-2), 313-8.

30. Braestrup C., Nielson M., Honore T., Jensen L.H., Peterson E.N. Benzodiazepine receptor ligands with positive and negative efficacy. *Neuropharmacology*, 1983, 22, 1451-7.

31. Sarter M., Nutt D.J., Lister R.G. *Benzodiazepine receptor inverse agonists*. New York, Wiley-Liss. 1995.

32. Cooper S.J. Bidirectional control of palatable food-consumption through a common benzodiazepine receptor - theory and evidence. *Brain Research Bulletin*, 1985, 15(4), 397-410.

33. Cooper S.J., Yerbury R.E. Midazolam induced hyperphagia and FG 7142-induced anorexia: behavioural characteristics in the rat. *Pharmacology Biochemistry and Behavior*, 1986, 25, 99-106.

34. Cooper S.J. Effects of the β-carboline FG 7142 on saccharin preference and quinine aversion in water deprived rats. *Neuropharmacology*, 1986, 25, 213-6.

35.   Kirkham T.C., Cooper S.J. CGS 8216, a novel anorectic agent reduces saccharin consumption in the rat. *Pharmacology Biochemistry and Behavior,* 1986, 25, 341-5.

36.   Steiner J.E., Glaser D. Differential behavioral-responses to taste stimuli in non-human primates. *Journal of Human Evolution,* 1984, 13(8), 709-23.

37.   Steiner J.E. Human facial expressions in response to taste and smell stimulation. *Advances in Child Developmental Behavior,* 1979, 13, 257-95.

38.   Grill H.J., Norgren R. The taste reactivity test. 1. Mimetic responses to gustatory stimuli in neurologically normal rats. *Brain Research,* 1978, 143, 263-79.

39.   Grill H.J., Norgren R. The taste reactivity test. 2. Mimetic responses to gustatory stimuli in chronic thalamic and chronic decerebrate rats. *Brain Research,* 1978, 143, 281-97.

40.   Grill H.J., Spector A.C., Schwartz G.J., Kaplan J.M., Flynn F.W. Evaluating taste effects on ingestive behavior, in *Feeding and Drinking.* Eds Toates F.M., Rowland N.E. Amsterdam, Elsevier. 1987, 151-89.

41.   Berridge K.C., Treit D. Chlordiazepoxide directly enhances positive ingestive reactions in rats. *Pharmacology Biochemistry and Behavior,* 1986, 24, 217-21.

42.   Berridge K.C. Brain-stem systems mediate the enhancement of palatability by chlordiazepoxide. *Brain Research,* 1988, 447(2), 262-83.

43.   Gray R.W., Cooper S.J. Benzodiazepines and palatability: taste reactivity in normal ingestion. *Physiology & Behavior,* 1995, 58, 8753-859.

44.   Treit D., Berridge K.C., Schultz C.E. The direct enhancement of palatability by chlordiazepoxide is antagonized by Ro 15-1788 and CGS 8216. *Pharmacology Biochemistry and Behavior,* 1987, 26, 709-14.

45.   Treit D., Berridge K.C. A comparison of benzodiazepine, serotonin, and dopamine agents in the taste-reactivity paradigm. *Pharmacology Biochemistry and Behavior,* 1990, 37(3), 451-6.

46.   Berridge K.C., Pecina S. Benzodiazepines, appetite and taste palatability. *Neuroscience and Biobehavioral Reviews,* 1995, 19, 121-31.

47.   Stellar E., Hill J.H. The rat's rate of drinking as a function of water deprivation. *Journal of Comparative and Physiological Psychology,* 1952, 5, 96-102.

48.   Davis J.D. The effectiveness of some sugars in stimulating licking behaviour in the rat. *Physiology & Behavior*, 1973, 11, 39-45.

49.   Davis J.D., Smith G.P. Analysis of the microstructure of the rhythmic tongue movements of rats ingesting maltose and sucrose solutions. *Behavioral Neuroscience*, 1992, 106, 217-28.

50.   Higgs S., Cooper S.J. Midazolam induced rapid changes in licking behaviour: Evidence for involvement of endogenous opioid peptides. *Psychopharmacology*, 1997, 131, 278-86.

51.   Higgs S., Cooper S.J. Effects of benzodiazepine receptor ligands on the ingestion of sucrose, intralipid, and maltodextrin: An investigation using a microstructural analysis of licking behavior in a brief contact test. *Behavioral Neuroscience*, 1998, 112, 447-57.

52.   Higgs S., Cooper S.J. Effects of the benzodiazepine receptor inverse agonist Ro 15-4513 on the ingestion of sucrose and sodium saccharin solutions: A microstructural analysis of licking behavior. *Behavioral Neuroscience*, 1996, 110, 559-66.

53.   Greenblatt D.J., Shader R.I. Drug therapy. Benzodiazepines. *New England Journal of Medicine*, 1974, 291, 1239-43.

54.   Pecina S., Berridge K.C. Brainstem mediates diazepam enhancement of palatability and feeding: microinjections into fourth ventricle versus lateral ventricle. *Brain Research*, 1996, 727(1-2), 22-30.

55.   Higgs S., Cooper S.J. Increased food intake following injection of the benzodiazepine receptor agonist midazolam into the IVth ventricle. *Pharmacology Biochemistry and Behavior*, 1996, 55, 81-6.

56.   Higgs S., Cooper S.J. Hyperphagia induced by direct administration of midazolam into the parabrachial nucleus of the rat. *European Journal of Pharmacology*, 1996, 313, 1-9.

57.   Sanger D.J., McCarthy P.S. Differential effects of morphine on food and water intake in food deprived and freely feeding rats. *Psychopharmacology*, 1980, 72, 103-6.

58.   Morley J.E., Levine A.S., Kneip J., Grace M. The role of k opioid receptors in the initiation of feeding. *Life Sciences*, 1982, 31, 2617-26.

59. Gosnell B.A., Levine A.S., Morley J.E. N allylnormetazocine (SKF-10,047): the induction of feeding by a putative sigma agonist. *Pharmacology Biochemistry and Behavior*, 1983, 19, 737-42.

60. Levine A.S., Billington C.J. Opioids: are they regulators of feeding? *Annals of the New York Academy of Sciences*, 1989, 575, 194-209.

61. Holtzman S.G. Behavioural effects of separate and combined administration of naloxone and d-amphetamine. *Journal of Pharmacology and Experimental Therapeutics*, 1974, 189, 51-60.

62. Cooper S.J. Naloxone: effects on food and water consumption in the non deprived and deprived rat. *Psychopharmacology*, 1980, 71, 1-6.

63. Apfelbaum M., Mandenoff A. Naltrexone suppresses hyperphagia induced in the rat by a highly palatable diet. *Pharmacology Biochemistry and Behavior*, 1981, 15, 89-91.

64. Levine A.S., Murrey S.S., Kneip J., Grace M., Morley J.E. Flavour enhances the dipsogenic effect of naloxone. *Physiology & Behavior*, 1982, 28, 23-5.

65. Cooper S.J., Kirkham T.C. Opioid mechanisms in the control of food consumption and taste preferences, in *Handbook of Experimental Pharmacology*. Ed. Herz A. Berlin, Springer. 1993, 239-62.

66. Bertino M., Abelson M.L. A small dose of morphine increases intake of and preference for isotonic saline amongst rats. *Pharmacology Biochemistry and Behavior*, 1988, 29, 617-23.

67. Calcagnetti D.J., Reid L.D. Morphine and acceptability of putative reinforcers. *Pharmacology Biochemistry and Behavior*, 1983, 18, 567-9.

68. Le Magnen J., Marfaing-Jallat P.D.M., Devos M. Pain modulating and reward systems: a single brain mechanism. *Pharmacology Biochemistry and Behavior*, 1980, 12, 729-33.

69. Cooper S.J. Effects of opiate agonists and antagonists on fluid intake and saccharin choice in the rat. *Neuropharmacology*, 1983, 22, 323-8.

70. Lynch W.C., Libby L. Naloxone suppresses intake of highly palatable preferred saccharin in food deprived and satiated rats. *Life Sciences*, 1983, 33, 1909-24.

71.   Cooper S.J., Gilbert D.B. Naloxone suppresses fluid consumption in tests of choice between sodium chloride solutions and water and male and female rats. *Psychopharmacology*, 1984, 84, 362-7.

72.   Rockwood G.A., Reid L.D. Naloxone modifies sugar-water intake in rats with open gastric fistulas. *Physiology & Behavior*, 1982, 29, 1175-8.

73.   Kirkham T.C., Cooper S.J. Naloxone attenuation of sham feeding is modified by manipulation of sucrose concentration. *Physiology & Behavior*, 1988, 44 (4-5), 491-4.

74.   Kirkham T.C., Cooper S.J. Attenuation of sham feeding by naloxone is stereospecific - evidence for opioid mediation of orosensory reward. *Physiology & Behavior*, 1988, 43(6), 845-7.

75.   Kirkham T.C. Enhanced anorectic potency of naloxone in rats sham feeding 30% sucrose: reversal by repeated naloxone administration. *Physiology & Behavior*, 1990, 47, 419-26.

76.   Doyle T.G., Berridge K.A., Gosnell B.A. Morphine enhances hedonic taste palatability in rats. *Pharmacology Biochemistry and Behavior*, 1993, 46(3), 745-9.

77.   Pecina S., Berridge K.C. Central enhancement of taste pleasure by intraventricular morphine. *Neurobiology*, 1995, 3, 269-80.

78.   Rideout H.J., Parker L.A. Morphine enhancement of sucrose palatability: Analysis by the taste reactivity test. *Pharmacology Biochemistry and Behavior*, 1996, 53(3), 731-4.

79.   Parker L.A., Maier S., Rennie M., Crebolder J. Morphine and naltrexone-induced modification of palatability: analysis by the taste reactivity test. *Behavioural Neuroscience*, 1992, 106, 999-1010.

80.   Yeomans M.R., Wright P., Macleod H.A., Critchley J.A.J.H. Effects of nalmefene on feeding in humans - dissociation of hunger and palatability. *Psychopharmacology*, 1990, 100(3), 426-32.

81.   Yeomans M.R., Wright P. Lower pleasantness of palatable foods in nalmefene-treated human volunteers. *Appetite*, 1991, 16(3), 249-59.

82.   Yeomans M.R., Gray R.W. Effects of naltrexone on food intake and changes in subjective appetite during eating: evidence for opioid involvement in the appetizer effect. *Physiology & Behavior*, 1997, 62(1), 15-21.

83. Yeomans M.R, Gray R.W. Selective effects of naltrexone on food pleasantness and intake. *Physiology & Behavior*, 1996, 60(2), 439-46.

84. Pecina S., Berridge K.C. Opioid site in nucleus accumbens shell mediates eating and hedonic liking for food: map based on microinjection Fos plumes. *Brain Research*, 2000, 863(1-2), 71-86.

85. Bakshi V.P., Kelley A.E. Striatal regulation of morphine-induced hyperphagia - an anatomical mapping study. *Psychopharmacology*, 1993, 111(2), 207-14.

86. Zhang M., Kelley A.E. Opiate agonists microinjected into the nucleus accumbens enhance sucrose drinking in rats. *Psychopharmacology*, 1997, 132(4), 350-60.

87. Duka T., Wuster M., Hertz A. Rapid changes in enkephalin levels in rat striatum and hypothalamus induced by diazepam. *Naunym-Schmiedeberg's Arch Pharmacol.*, 1979, 309, 1-5.

88. Wuster M., Duka T., Hertz A. Diazepam effects on striatal met-enkephalin levels following long term pharmacological manipulations. *Neuropharmacology*, 1980, 19, 501-5.

89. Britton D.R., Britton K.T., Dalton D., Vale W. Effect of naloxone on anticonflict and hyperphagic actions of diazepam. *Life Sciences*, 198, 129, 1297-302.

90. Jackson H.C., Sewell R.D.E. Involvement of endogenous enkephalins in the feeding response to diazepam. *European Journal of Pharmacology*, 1985, 107, 389-91.

91. Stapleton J.M., Lind M.D., Merriman V.J., Reid L.D. Naloxone inhibits diazepam-induced feeding in rats. *Life Sciences*, 1979, 24, 2421-6.

92. Mansour A., Khachaturian H., Lewis M.E., Akil H., Watson S.J. Anatomy of CNS opioid receptors. *Trends in Neurosciences*, 1988, 7, 308-14.

93. Carr K.D., Aleman D.O., Bak T.H., Simon E.J. Effects of parabrachial opioid antagonism on stimulation-induced feeding. *Brain Research*, 1991, 545, 283-6.

94. Rolls E.T., Rolls B.J., Kelly P.H., Shaw S.G., Wood R.J., Dale R. The relative attenuation of self stimulation, eating and drinking produced by dopamine receptor blockade. *Psychopharmacology*, 1974, 38, 216-30.

95. Wise R.A., Colle L.M. Pimozide attenuates free feeding - best scores analysis reveals a motivational deficit. *Psychopharmacology*, 1984, 84(4), 446-51.

96. Wise R.A., Raptis L. Effects of naloxone and pimozide on initiation and maintenance measures of free feeding. *Brain Research*, 1986, 368(1), 62-8.

97. Bailey C.A., Hsiao S., King J.E. Hedonic reactivity to sucrose in rats: modification by pimozide. *Physiology & Behavior*, 1986, 38, 447-52.

98. Terry P. Dopamine receptor subtypes and ingestive behaviour, in *Drug Receptor Subtypes and Ingestive Behaviour*. Eds Cooper S.J., Clifton P.G. London, Academic Press. 1996, 233-66.

99. Terry P., Gilbert D.B., Cooper S.J. Dopamine receptor subtype agonists and feeding behaviour. *Obesity Research*, 1995, 3, 515s-523s.

100. Willner P., Papp M., Phillips G., Maleeh M., Muscat R. Pimozide does not impair sweetness discrimination. *Psychopharmacology*, 1990, 102(2), 278-82.

101. Towell A., Muscat R., Willner P. Effects of pimozide on sucrose consumption and preference. *Psychopharmacology*, 1987, 92(2), 262-4.

102. Hsiao S., Smith G.P. Raclopride reduces sucrose preference in rats. *Pharmacology Biochemistry and Behavior*, 1995, 50(1), 121-5.

103. Wei-Zhen Y., Silva R.M., Sclafani A., Delamater A.R., Bodnar R.J. Pharmacology of flavor preference conditioning in sham feeding rats: Effects of dopamine Receptor antagonists. *Pharmacology, Biochemistry and Behavior*, 2000, 65(4), 635-47.

104. Weingarten H.P., Watson S.D. Sham feeding as a procedure for assessing the influence of diet palatability on food intake. *Psychopharmacology*, 1982, 102, 278-82.

105. Geary N., Smith G.P. Pimozide decreases the positive reinforcing effect of sham fed sucrose in the rat. *Pharmacology Biochemistry and Behavior*, 1985, 22(5), 787-90.

106. Smith G.P., Schneider L.H. Relationships between mesolimbic dopamine function and eating behavior. *Annals of the New York Academy of Science*, 1988, 537, 254-61.

107. Schneider L.H., Gibbs J., Smith G.P. D-2 Selective receptor antagonists suppress sucrose sham feeding in the rat. *Brain Research Bulletin*, 1986, 17(4), 605-11.

108. Roitman M.F., Schafe G.E., Thiele T.E., Bernstein I.L., Dopamine and sodium appetite: antagonists suppress sham drinking of NaCl solutions in the rat. *Behavioural Neuroscience*, 1997, 111(3), 606-11.

109. Berridge K.C., Venier I.L., Robinson T.E. Taste reactivity analysis of 6-hydroxydopamine-induced hyperphagia: implications for arousal and anhedonia hypotheses of dopamine function. *Behavioural Neuroscience*, 1989, 103, 36-45.

110. Leeb K., Parker L., Eikelboom R. Effects of pimozide on the hedonic properties of sucrose - analysis by the taste reactivity test. *Pharmacology Biochemistry and Behavior*, 1991, 39(4), 895-901.

111. Parker L.A., Lopez N. Pimozide enhances the aversiveness of quinine solution. *Pharmacology Biochemistry and Behavior*, 1990, 36(3), 653-9.

112. Pecina S., Berridge K.C., Parker L.A. Pimozide does not shift palatability: Separation of anhedonia from sensorimotor suppression by taste reactivity. *Pharmacology Biochemistry and Behavior*, 1997, 58(3), 801-11.

113. Baptista T. Body weight gain induced by antipsychotic drugs: mechanisms and management. *Acta Pshchiatrica Scandinavia*, 1999, 100(1), 3-16.

114. Baptista T., Reyes D., Hernandez L. Antipsychotic drugs and reproductive hormones: relationship to body weight regulation. *Pharmacology Biochemisty and Behavior*, 1999, 62, 409-17.

115. Travers J.B., Akey L.R, Chen S.C. Taste preferences in parkinsons-disease patients. *Chemical Senses*, 1993, 18(1), 47-55.

116. Berridge K.C. Food reward: Brain substrates of wanting and liking. *Neuroscience and Biobehavioual Reviews*, 1996, 20(1), 1-25.

117. Berridge K.C., Robinson T.E. What is the role of dopamine in reward: hedonic impact, reward learning, or incentive salience? *Brain Research Reviews*, 1998, 28, 309-69.

118. Berridge K.C. Measuring hedonic impact in animals and infants: microstructure of affective taste reactivity patterns. *Neuroscience and Biobehavioural Reviews*, 2000, 24, 173-99.

119. Beauchamp G.K., Bertino M., Burke D., Engelman K. Experimental sodium depletion and salt taste in normal human volunteers. *American Journal of Clinical Nutrition*, 1990, 51(5), 881-9.

120. Macdiarmid J.I., Hetherington M.M. Mood modulation by food: an exploration of affect and cravings in "chocolate addicts". *British Journal of Clinical Psychology*, 1995, 34, 129-38.

121. Robinson T.E., Berridge K.C. The neural basis of drug craving - an incentive sensitization theory of addiction. *Brain Research Reviews*, 1993, 18, 247-91.

2.5. OPIOIDS AND HUMAN INGESTIVE BEHAVIOUR

Martin R. Yeomans

2.5.1   Introduction

The discovery of endogenous opiate-like chemicals in the brain opened up a whole new research area, which has since been critical to current understanding of the neurobiology of a wide range of psychological phenomena, including reward and addiction. As evidence emerged that these endogenous opiates (opioids) were involved in pain control (1) and the neural mechanisms underlying the use of elicit drugs (2), speculation increased about the potential role of these compounds in a wide range of other pleasurable and addictive behaviours. In humans these included evidence of opioid involvement in the pleasure experienced when listening to music (3), data implicating opioids in the positive mood changes produced by excessive exercise (the jogger's high) (4), and speculation about opioid involvement in sexual pleasure (5). There has also been widespread consideration in both the scientific and the general press of opioid involvement in the mechanisms underlying a wide range of behavioural addictions. Once scientists started to explore the effects of drugs that alter opioid function on behaviour, it also became clear that opioids were involved in the control of feeding and drinking. An understanding of the role of these compounds in appetite control is thus an important part of any discussion of food addiction and craving. The present chapter starts by reviewing our current understanding of the role of opioid peptides in normal appetite control in humans (see also section 2.2). The mechanisms underlying these effects are explored, with an emphasis on the potential role of opioid peptides in pleasurable aspects of eating. This is followed by an evaluation of claims that opioid dysfunction may be a component of disordered eating, including discussion of binge eating as an addiction. The chapter ends with evidence for opioid involvement in other addictive aspects of ingestion, with some intriguing data on water intoxication, followed by a discussion of recent developments in our understanding of the role of opioids in alcohol abuse.

2.5.2   Opioids and Eating Behaviour

The most common way of exploring the potential role of any neurochemical in the regulation of a particular behaviour is to examine changes in that behaviour following administration of drugs that either stimulate or block the effects of the relevant neurochemicals. The adoption of this approach in animals has led to clear insights into the role of opioids in appetite control (see sections 2.2 and 2.4), and similar studies have been conducted in humans. However, the scope of the human studies has been limited by the range of drugs that can be administered ethically to humans. Thus, there have been no studies of opiate agonists such as morphine or heroin, since it would be difficult to justify such studies, not only because of the addictive nature of these drugs but also because of their diverse behavioural effects. Equally, animal studies have made use of many selective receptor antagonists that have not yet been approved for use in humans. Pharmacological studies of the role of opioids in human appetite control have therefore been limited mainly to investigations using the general opiate receptor antagonists naloxone (administered intravenously) and naltrexone and nalmefene (both administered orally). These drugs have clear effects on eating behaviour, which imply an important role for opioid peptides in appetite control.

2.5.2.1   *Food intake reduction by opioid antagonists and increase by agonists*

The basic premise of studies using opioid receptor antagonists is that any change in behaviour seen following administration of these drugs is due to blockade of normal opioid function. Thus, specific change in appetite following the administration of these classes of drug could provide powerful evidence for opioid activity in appetite control. Of the nine published double-blind placebo-controlled studies using these drugs that measured food intake in normal subjects, all but one reported significant reductions in overall food intake (Table 2.5.I). The magnitude of these effects has ranged from 14 to 29%, with most studies finding reductions of approximately 20%, which is a surprisingly consistent range of responses given the wide range of drugs, doses and test situations that have been used. This implies that a relatively small but consistent proportion of normal food intake is in some way regulated by the activity of an endogenous opioid.

Of course, the fact that people eat less following administration of a drug that has a wide range of effects on the nervous system and body need not imply a specific effect on appetite. It may instead be the case that reduced eating reflects some non-specific action of these drugs. However, a non-specific action appears to be an unlikely explanation for the effects of opioid antagonists. Thus, although several studies have reported nausea as a side effect of administration of naltrexone (6,7), naltrexone-induced nausea is not seen in all subjects. In the most recent studies, only 19% of subjects felt nauseous after naltrexone administration, compared with 9% in the placebo condition (7,8). Moreover, rated nausea was not a good predictor of reduced intake (6,7). Other drugs that reduce intake, such as naloxone (9,10) and nalmefene (11,12), have not been reported to produce nausea. Other side effects of these drugs have been limited, and again are unlikely explanations for the effects on eating. Thus it seems unlikely that the effects of these drugs on eating are due to a non-specific effect.

In contrast to studies with opiate antagonists, studies using agonists have been rare. The first study (13) compared eating after injections of the mixed opiate agonist/antagonist butorphanol, both alone and with naloxone, and placebo. Butorphanol doubled caloric intake in the 2 hours post-injection relative to placebo, while naloxone partially reversed this effect. The increase in intake was seen with all three macronutrients. However, a second study with butorphanol in normal subjects found no effects on food intake or taste preference (9). Until more studies are reported, no firm conclusions can be drawn about the effects of drugs with opiate-agonist effects.

TABLE 2.5.I
Effects of opiate antagonists on food intake, rated hunger and food pleasantness in normal subjects

Ref.	Subjects	Drug, route and dose	Effects on appetite		
			Food intake	Hunger at start of meal	Rated food pleasantness
72	8 men	Naloxone, IV 18 mg in 4 h	25% decrease	No effect	Not tested
10	12 men	Naloxone, IV 0.8 & 1.6 mg	25% decrease with 1.6 mg	No effect	Not tested
73	7 men	Naloxone IV 2 mg/kg	28% decrease	No effect	Not tested
17	6 men + 2 women	Naltrexone, oral, 60 mg	-	No effect	Decreased
18	11 men + 3 women	Naltrexone, oral 25 mg	-	No effect	Potentiated alliesthesia
12	20 men	Nalmefene, oral 2.5 mg	21% decrease	No effect	Not tested
6	18 men	Naltrexone, oral 50 mg	19% decrease	No effect	Decreased
74	12 men 14 men	Naltrexone, oral 50 mg	No effect 24% increase in ice cream intake	No effect	No effect
11	24 men	Nalmefene, oral 2.5 mg	22% decrease	No effect	Decreased
9	12 women	Naloxone, IV 6 mg + 0.1 mg/kg for 2.5 h	21% decrease	No effect	Decreased
		Butorphanol, IV 1 µg/kg	No effect	No effect	Increased
7	16 men	Naltrexone, oral 50 mg	14% decrease	No effect	Decreased
8	20 men	Naltrexone, oral 50 mg	23% decrease	No effect	Decreased
16	18 women	Naltrexone, oral 50 mg	Not tested	Not tested	Decreased

How then might opioids be involved in appetite regulation? The simplest hypothesis would be that opioids are normally involved in the general desire to eat (or hunger), and that people feel less hungry when opioid receptors are blocked. However, this idea is not supported from these studies. Appetite at the start of a meal (indexed through hunger ratings) has not differed between antagonists and placebo conditions in any study (see Table 2.5.I). It is important here to understand that rated hunger and the motivational construct hunger may not be the same. When asked how hungry they are, subjects are effectively rating how much they wish to eat, which in itself is likely to be a complex interaction between physiological cues related to appetite, alongside contextual cues (14). However, this distinction does not alter the conclusion that opioids are not involved in the general desire to eat, but simply warns against over-interpretation of these sorts of rating data. The conclusion that opioids are not involved in the general desire to eat at the start of a meal also fits with analogous data in animals (15). Thus, an alternative explanation is needed, and current data suggest that opioids may be involved in some aspect of food reward. This conclusion is based mainly on evidence of changes in hedonic evaluations of foods following opioid blockade.

2.5.2.2   Reduction of flavour pleasantness by opioids without alteration in sensory perception

Ten studies have examined effects of opioid antagonists on the rated pleasantness of sucrose solutions (16-18), sweetened milk solutions (9) or actual foods (7,8,11). All but one of these studies found lower rated pleasantness following administration of an opioid antagonist compared with ratings after placebo (see Table 2.5.I). Thus there appears to be a role for opioid receptors in some part of the neural circuitry underlying the expression of hedonic responses to food. One possibility is that opioids are involved in the perception of flavour. However, this seems unlikely since the effects of opioid antagonists on hedonic evaluations were not matched by changes in sensory evaluations. For example, neither the perceived saltiness of soups varying in salt content, nor sweetness of a soft drink varying in sucrose content was altered by naltrexone, but in both cases perceived pleasantness was reduced (6). Likewise, naltrexone did not alter the perceived sweetness or bitterness of sucrose and quinine solutions (19), and the pleasantness of sweetened milk solutions was reduced by naloxone, but neither sweetness nor creaminess was altered (9). This lack of effect of opioid blockade on supra-threshold taste perception was also supported by a lack of change in blandness, sweetness and saltiness ratings for food stimuli following naltrexone (7) and nalmefene (11). Recent research also found no evidence for changes in taste detection or recognition thresholds for the four basic tastes (sweet, sour, bitter and salty), while again finding a small but significant reduction in the rated pleasantness of these stimuli (16). Thus, no study has been able to detect any change in gustatory or olfactory perception either at threshold or supra-threshold levels following opioid blockade. Thus the effect of opioid antagonists on hedonic evaluations of foods and solutions cannot be explained at a sensory level. This implies that the opioid receptors underlying the effects of opioid antagonists on food intake lie outside the neural structures underlying gustatory and olfactory perception.

2.5.2.3   The palatability hypothesis

Since opioid antagonists do not suppress rated appetite (hunger) but do reduce food intake and flavour pleasantness, it has been suggested that opioids may normally be involved in the stimulation of appetite through palatability (20). This idea is consistent with the literature on animal studies, which has highlighted the role of palatability in determining the magnitude of the effects of opioid antagonism on food intake (see section 2.4).

Although ratings of food pleasantness could be taken as a measure of orosensory reward in humans, these ratings are difficult to interpret in an unambiguous way. Thus, some researchers regard these ratings more as a reflection of an individual subject's intention to eat a food than as an independent hedonic evaluation (14). Other researchers have described the pleasantness of a food as a reflection of the need to ingest it (21). Thus in order to evaluate fully the opioid-palatability hypothesis in humans, an alternative measure of orosensory reward is needed. One approach has been to examine in detail changes both in eating rate and the pattern of changes in subjective appetite during meals following manipulations of palatability alone (22). Not surprisingly, increasing the rated palatability of a food increases intake (23). What was perhaps surprising was the finding that hunger ratings increased in the early stages of a meal with palatable, but not neutral, foods. This effect is most apparent when rated hunger within a meal is expressed as a function of food intake. The resulting relationship is best described by a quadratic function, and flavour modulation alters only the linear component of this function (22). The effects of palatability are most evident at the start of a meal, and it is the combined effect of this sensory stimulation of appetite and satiation that determines meal size. This description of meal control is similar to that developed in animal research (24), and makes a useful model for dissociation of different motivational influences on eating (22). The opioid-palatability hypothesis was tested in this model by examining the effects of the opioid antagonist naltrexone on intake, eating rate and changes in subjective appetite (8). If the opioid-palatability hypothesis was correct, then opioid blockade was predicted to reduce intake and to attenuate the stimulation of appetite through palatability. The results of this study strongly suggest that opioids are involved in the stimulation of appetite through palatability since subjects not only ate less after naltrexone (Fig. 2.5.1a), but they also no longer showed any increase in appetite during the early stages of eating (Fig. 2.5.1b). These data thus clearly suggest that opioid release underlies the ability of palatability to stimulate appetite.

2.5.2.4   *Does eating palatable foods release opioid peptides?*

The opioid-palatability hypothesis suggests that the sensory experience of palatable foods can, under certain conditions, lead to release of opioid peptides, which in turn stimulate intake. Consequently, researchers have tested whether higher opioid levels are detectable after palatable foods have been eaten. Most studies have concentrated on one opioid peptide, β-endorphin, primarily because it is present in plasma, and is therefore relatively easy to assay. The earliest relevant study reported that β-endorphin levels were three times higher in obese subjects than in normal subjects (25), and this was confirmed in a follow-up study (26). These results could be interpreted as reflecting heightened β-endorphin levels as a consequence of over-consumption of palatable food. However, other explanations are possible. For example, β-endorphin levels are known to be increased by stress as part of the general stress response, and, although in these studies having a diagnosed affective disorder did not explain the observed results (26), it remains possible that the obese group was more stressed than the controls. A different, if somewhat unconventional, approach was taken by Melchior *et al.* (27). They allowed subjects to select their favourite food from a delicatessen. The food was then eaten on two occasions, once when heated to the correct serving temperature, and once when frozen (ostensibly to remove sensory cues). Beta-endorphin levels increased in the latter condition, contrary to the opioid-palatability hypothesis. However, the β-endorphin response could be explained by the stressful experience of eating a preferred savoury food in a frozen state. An earlier study by the same group had also failed to find any change in β-endorphin in response to consuming a palatable food (28); however, another study by the same group found some evidence for β-endorphin release stimulated by ingestion of a palatable food (29). In that study, ten normal-weight subjects drank two chocolate-flavoured drinks, one sweetened with aspartame and one with sucrose. Beta-endorphin levels were then assayed for 3 hours post-drink, relative to a third day when subjects drank nothing. Beta-endorphin levels were higher throughout the 3 hours post-ingestion after the aspartame relative to control drinks, with the sucrose drink producing an intermediate response. No measure of the relative palatability or sweetness of the two drinks was reported, but, if the aspartame drink was more palatable, this would be good evidence that palatability can induce release of β-endorphin. However, β-endorphin does not appear to be the most likely endogenous compound in appetite control (see section 2.2), and the ambiguous nature of much of these data suggests that further research is needed in this area.

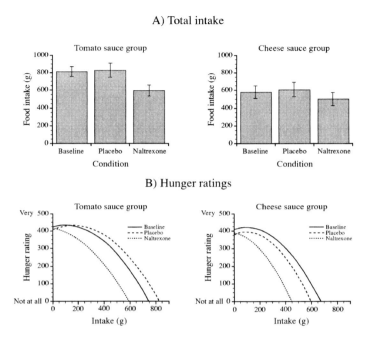

Fig. 2.5.1. Effects of naltrexone on food intake and rated hunger for subjects eating a pasta lunch with cheese or tomato sauce (8)

Incidental evidence that consumption of palatable foods leads to opioid release came from a recent case report (30). In response to increasing evidence of opioid involvement in appetite control, an obese woman was given naltrexone as part of a treatment programme. The woman displayed all the characteristics of opioid withdrawal, and the authors concluded that opioid dysfunction was central to her obesity. However, no other cases have been published despite several long-term trials of opioid antagonists as anti-obesity agents (31-35) (See also section 2.2).

Until we are able to assay brain opioid release while eating in humans, we are unlikely to be able to test the opioid-palatability hypothesis in full. Improvements in brain imaging technology are bringing this possibility closer, but there is still some way to go before definitive studies can be conducted.

2.5.2.5 Is there a specific role for opioids in control of fat and sugar intake?

In addition to a role in the mechanisms underlying the effects of palatability on appetite, there is evidence of a second component to the role of opioids in human ingestion. An intriguing but consistent feature of the effects of opioid antagonists where food choice was included was that intake of non-sweet carbohydrate tended to be spared, whereas intake of fat and protein tended to be reduced. The original studies using this approach were consistent with a palatability-based explanation since it was the most palatable food items that were reduced in intake (11,12), and these happened to be foods that were high in fat and protein. However, when a wide range of snack-type foods was tested, those that were rated as palatable but which were largely non-sweet carbohydrate were almost unaffected by opioid antagonism with naloxone (9). In contrast, intake of those foods that were rich in fat and sugar were greatly reduced. This led to the suggestion that opioids contribute to the control of fat and sugar intake and not to palatability (9). More recent studies lend some support to both arguments: in the most recent study of food choice following naltrexone administration, only intake of fat and protein were reduced (7) and there was no evidence that the rated palatability of the food predicted the magnitude of the reduction in intake. However, intake of sweet items was spared relative to that of other foods in that study, in contradiction to the predictions made by Drewnowski (9). These results may have been in part due to the nature of the eating test. Where sweet items are available in the context of a free-choice buffet meal, subjects maintain their normal habit of eating savoury items first before switching to more dessert-like foods. Under the influence of opioid antagonism, this switch appeared to come earlier, thereby exaggerating the effects of naltrexone on savoury fat/protein-rich foods, and underplaying effects on sweet foods. These data thus confirm the complexity of opioid involvement, and we are still a long way from fully appreciating the significance of opioid involvement in normal appetite control.

2.5.3   Opioids and Disordered Eating

In theory, disruption of any neurochemical that is involved in appetite control could underlie the psychopathological disturbance to appetite seen in eating disorders such as anorexia nervosa, bulimia nervosa and the more recently recognised binge eating disorder. It is thus not surprising that the role of opioid peptides has been explored in relation to all of these disorders, with somewhat mixed results. Since attempts to treat these disorders pharmacologically are described elsewhere (see section 2.2), the present discussion is limited to the evidence for opioid disturbance underlying these disorders rather than any potential therapy.

2.5.3.1   The auto-addiction hypothesis

The idea that disturbance to the opioid systems involved in appetite control might contribute to anorexia nervosa was first developed in the late 1970s (36). These early observations of disordered opioid function in anorexic patients formed the basis for a specific theory of anorexia as a consequence of disordered opioid function (37). For many years it has been known that the longer an individual suffers from anorexia nervosa, the more intractable the disease becomes. Marazzi and Luby (37) formulated their auto-addiction model from this and other features of the disease. In brief, their model suggests three separate roles for opioids in disordered eating. Firstly, the model suggests that initial dieting releases opioids that induce positive mood. This in turn leads, they claim, to an addiction to dieting. Secondly, a separate action of opioids increases the desire to eat to correct the self-induced starvation. Opioids are also heavily implicated in the adaptation to self-starvation, with a variety of effects aimed at reducing energy expenditure. Accordingly, the role of opioids in disordered eating will depend crucially on the relative activity of these three different processes. Persistent anorexic behaviour could be seen as an addiction to the starvation process, whereby the first and third effect of opioids predominate, whereas bulimia is seen in this model as an addiction to the starvation-induced desire to eat. Evidence for opioid dysfunction in anorexia has been found. For example, cerebrospinal fluid (CSF) opioid activity was found to be high in anorexic patients, and these abnormalities normalised when weight was restored (38). In contrast, plasma β-endorphin levels have been found to be raised in anorexic patients in most studies (39,40), but lower in others (41). Thus, opioid activity appears abnormal, and these differences could be explained by an auto-addiction model. However, not all data on opioid disturbance in anorexia are consistent with this model. Krahn *et al.* (42) reported the case history of a young woman with combined problems of heroin abuse and anorexia nervosa. According to the auto-addition model, stabilising this woman's opiate habit by long-term naltrexone therapy should also have led to improvement in her anorexic behaviour. However, the reverse was true: naltrexone blocked heroin addiction (as it should) but exaggerated her anorexia nervosa. When she came off naltrexone, her eating disorder improved but she lapsed back to her heroin habit. Thus her case casts doubt over the auto-addiction model. However, recent studies using naltrexone therapy have reported positive effects on anorexic patients (43,44). Thus it remains possible that opioid dysfunction may underlie some aspects of anorexic behaviour, although whether this reflects the complex role for opioids suggested by the auto-addiction model is unclear.

2.5.3.2 Opioids and binge-eating behaviour

While the case for a role for opioids in anorexia nervosa remains unclear, the case for a role in bulimic behaviour is more compelling. The parallels between eating behaviour in binge eating disorder and bulimia nervosa were highlighted in an important review by Hardy and Waller (45). They emphasised the similarities between binge eating and the diagnostic criteria for substance abuse, and discussed the possibility that opioid dysfunction could underlie addictive binge eating. Evidence in favour of this hypothesis comes from a variety of sources. Firstly, a number of studies have shown abnormal levels of β-endorphin in the plasma or CSF of binge eaters. Most reports suggested that β-endorphin levels in CSF are lower than normal in bulimic patients (46), while plasma levels have also been lower in some studies (47), although higher in others (48). The difference in plasma levels between studies could be explained either by differences between vomiting and non-vomiting patients, with higher levels of β-endorphin in the former as a response to the stress of vomiting, or alternatively it could reflect different sampling points, perhaps with lower β-endorphin levels prior to a binge and higher after. Either way, most published studies do show abnormal β-endorphin levels, in line with the idea of disrupted functioning.

Is binge eating altered by opioid blockade? Studies here have had mixed results. Early studies using open-label designs were promising, with reduced binge size and frequency following naltrexone (49-51). Intravenous naloxone infused double-blind also has a positive effect (52), with a 23% reduction in energy intake, although notably no effect on the time spent bingeing. More recently, a double-blind placebo-controlled study with 100 mg naltrexone extended these findings (53), with 18 of 19 bulimic patients showing improvements in behaviour, including reduced binges and purges, and a reduced ratio of binge to normal eating. Similarly, 100 mg naltrexone reduced binge duration in bulimic patients, and tended to do so also in obese binge eaters (54). In contrast, other double-blind studies have failed to find effects of naltrexone on long-term food intake in bulimic patients (55). (See also section 2.2). Overall, the idea that binge eating behaviour may be at least partly based on some form of eating addiction associated with abnormal opioid function remains possible, but the inconsistencies in the literature to date need to be clarified. As it stands, the idea that binge eating is driven in some way by opioid release remains a plausible and attractive hypothesis. However, the likelihood of any complex disorder being attributable to any single neurochemical dysfunction is unlikely, and further work is needed.

2.5.4   Opioids and Water Intoxication

Although most discussions of addictive components of ingestive behaviour concentrate on aspects of eating, drinking behaviour also exhibits addictive elements under certain conditions. In humans, this is most evident in the case of psychogenic polydipsia. This condition is seen in schizophrenic and other psychiatric patients, and involves excessive water intake to a point where the patient is at risk of self-harm through over-hydration (56). The condition has been described as a compulsive disorder (57), and could be interpreted as an addiction to drinking. In the present context, several recent reports of the effects of opiate antagonists on self-induced water intoxication suggest an opioid action in this behaviour. Starting with a case study (58), Nishikawa and colleagues have provided consistent evidence of a therapeutic benefit following naloxone administration both in open trials (59) and, most recently, double-blind trials (60). In these studies, only some patients showed decreased drinking following naloxone, although these effects were dramatic in certain instances. Why only some patients responded was unclear, but may imply that polydipsia has multiple causes. The ability of naloxone to reduce a behaviour that might be interpreted as water addiction fits well with the idea that opioids play an important role in addictive elements of ingestive behaviour.

2.5.5   Opioids and Alcohol Abuse

Although alcohol intake is not usually discussed as part of ingestive behaviour, recent research on the role of opioid peptides in alcohol abuse are relevant to the present chapter. Most of the interest in opioid function in relation to alcohol abuse stems from a report suggesting that naltrexone reduced relapse rates in recovered alcoholics (61). This initial finding has led to a plethora of successful follow-up studies (62,63), culminating in the approval of the use of naltrexone as a treatment for alcoholism (64-66). What makes these findings relevant here is the mechanism through which naltrexone reduced relapse in recovered alcoholics. Three findings are of particular relevance. Firstly, alcoholics who sampled alcohol experienced fewer hedonic effects than they expected (67). Thus, as with food, naltrexone reduced the hedonic component of ingestion. Secondly, naltrexone reduced the specific urge to drink (62). Thirdly, naltrexone was more effective in patients who had high baseline craving for alcohol (68). Recent models of drug craving are based on the idea that cravings are conditioned responses to drug-associated cues (69). A recent experimental study suggests that naltrexone reduced these cue-elicited cravings for alcohol (70). Together, these results imply that opioid release is involved in the hedonic effects of alcohol, and in urges/cravings to drink. While the hedonic component is consistent with the effects on food pleasantness discussed earlier, the effects on urges are at variance with the lack of effect of naltrexone on the urge to eat indexed through hunger ratings. However, the lack of data on the effects of opiate antagonism on food craving make strong comparisons impossible.

2.5.6   Opioids, Food Craving and Addiction

The evidence summarised in this chapter presents a complicated picture. The idea that opioids underlie food addiction, so often alluded to in the popular press, is clearly unproven. However, the idea that opioid release (at some level) underlies certain addictive aspects of human ingestive behaviour is supported by a variety of evidence. Opioids are clearly implicated in the hedonic evaluation of foods, and it thus follows that over-consumption should lead to greater opioid release. This is consistent with the ability of opioid antagonists to reduce binge size in bulimic and obese patients, and to decrease psychogenic polydipsia and cravings for alcohol. Put together, these disparate findings all point to some association between the oral experiences of eating and drinking and consequent opioid release. However, many of these findings are preliminary, and in some cases contradictory evidence has been published. Surprisingly, no study has actually examined food craving following opioid antagonist administration, and any role for opioids in this respect can only be inferred. There is also an important debate in psychology about the nature of liking and its relationship to motivation in general (i.e. wanting) (71). There is clear evidence that opioids are involved in liking for foods, but whether this changes wanting to eat those foods remains unclear. Until these issues are properly resolved, the exact role for opioids in food craving and addiction will remain unclear.

2.5.7   References

1.   Ramabadran K., Bansinath M. The role of endogenous opioid peptides in the regulation of pain. *Critical Reviews in Neurobiology*, 1990, 6, 13-32.

2.   Bozarth M. Opioids and reinforcement, in *Endorphins, opiates and behavioural processes.* Eds Rodgers R.J., Cooper S.J. Chichester, John Wiley. 1988, 53-75.

3.   Goldstein A. Thrills in response to music and other stimuli. *Physiological Psychology*, 1980, 8, 126-9.

4.   Yeung R.R. The acute effects of exercise on mood state. *Journal of Psychosomatic Research*, 1996, 40, 123-41.

5.   Komisaruk B.R., Whipple B. Vaginal stimulation produced analgesia in rats and women. *Annals of the New York Academy of Sciences*, 1986, 467, 30-9.

6.   Bertino M., Beauchamp G.K., Engelman K. Naltrexone, an opioid blocker, alters taste perception and nutrient intake in humans. *American Journal of Physiology*, 1991, 261, R59-R63.

7.   Yeomans M.R., Gray R.W. Selective effects of naltrexone on food pleasantness and intake. *Physiology and Behavior*, 1996, 60, 439-46.

8.   Yeomans M.R., Gray R.W. Effects of naltrexone on food intake and changes in subjective appetite during eating: evidence for opioid involvement in the appetiser effect. *Physiology and Behavior*, 1997, 62, 15-21.

9.   Drewnowski A., Krahn D.D., Demitrack M.A., Nairn K., Gosnell B.A. Taste responses and preferences for sweet high-fat foods: evidence for opioid involvement. *Physiology and Behavior*, 1992, 51, 371-9.

10.   Trenchard E., Silverstone T. Naloxone reduces the food intake of normal human volunteers. *Appetite*, 1983, 4, 43-50.

11.   Yeomans M.R., Wright P. Lower pleasantness of palatable foods in nalmefene-treated human volunteers. *Appetite*, 1991, 16, 249-59.

12.   Yeomans M.R., Wright P., Macleod H.A., Critchley J.A.J.H. Effects of nalmefene on feeding in humans: dissociation of hunger and palatability. *Psychopharmacology*, 1990, 100, 426-32.

13. Morley J.E., Parker S., Levine A.S. Effect of butorphanol tartrate on food and water consumption in humans. *American Journal of Clinical Nutrition*, 1985, 42, 1175-8.

14. Booth D.A. Cognitive experimental psychology of appetite, in *Eating habits*. Eds Boakes R.A., Burton M.J., Popplewell D.A. Chichester, Wiley. 1987, 175-209.

15. Kirkham T.C., Blundell J.E. Dual action of naloxone on feeding revealed by behavioral analysis - separate effects on initiation and termination of eating. *Appetite*, 1984, 5, 45-52.

16. Arbisi P.A., Billington C.J., Levine A.S. The effect of naltrexone on taste detection and recognition threshold. *Appetite*, 1999, 32, 241-9.

17. Fantino M., Hosotte J., Apfelbaum M. An opioid antagonist, naltrexone, reduces preference for sucrose in humans. *American Journal of Physiology*, 1986, 251, R91-R96.

18. Melchior J.C., Fantino M., Rozen R., Igoin L., Rigaud D., Apfelbaum M. Effects of a low dose of naltrexone on glucose-induced alliesthesia and hunger in humans. *Pharmacology Biochemistry and Behavior*, 1989, 32, 117-21.

19. Gray R.W. *Hedonic factors in food choice*. DPhil, University of Sussex. 1997.

20. Reid L.D. Endogenous opioid peptides and regulation of feeding and drinking. *American Journal of Clinical Nutrition*, 1985, 42, 1099-132.

21. Cabanac M. Physiological role of pleasure. *Science*, 1971, 173, 1103-7.

22. Yeomans M.R. Rating changes over the course of meals: what do they tell us about motivation to eat? *Neuroscience and Biobehavioral Reviews*, 2000, 24, 249-59.

23. Yeomans M.R. Palatability and the microstructure of eating in humans: the appetiser effect. *Appetite*, 1996, 27, 119-33.

24. Davis J.D. The microstructure of ingestive behavior. *Annals of the New York Academy of Sciences*, 1989, 575, 106-21.

25. Facchinetti F., Giovannini C., Barletta C., Petraglia F., Buzzetti R., Burla F., Lazzari R., Genazzani A.R., Scavo D. Hyperendorphinemia in obesity and relationships to affective state. *Physiology and Behavior*, 1986, 36, 937-40.

26. Scavo D., Barletta C., Vagini D., Burla F., Fontana M., Lazzari R. Hyperendorphinemia in obesity is not related to the affective state. *Physiology and Behavior*, 1990, 48, 681-3.

27. Melchior J.C., Rigaud D., Chayvialle J.A., Colas-Linhart N.C., Laforest M.D., Petiet A., Comoy E., Apfelbaum M. Palatability of a meal influences release of beta-endorphin, and of potential regulators of food intake in healthy human subjects. *Appetite*, 1994, 22, 233-44.

28. Melchior J.C., Fantino M., Colas-Linhart N., Rigaud D., Petiet A., Laforest M.D., Fumeron F., Apfelbaum M. Lack of plasmatic beta-endorphin response to a gastronomic meal in healthy humans. *Physiology and Behavior*, 1991, 49, 1217-21.

29. Melchior J.C., Rigaud D., Colas-Linhart N., Petiet A., Girard A., Apfelbaum M. Immunoreactive beta-endorphin increases after an aspartame chocolate drink in healthy subjects. *Physiology and Behavior*, 1991, 50, 941-4.

30. Ibanez-Rojo V., Palanca I., Iruela L.M., Oliveros S.C., Caballero L., Baca E. Naltrexone-induced opiate withdrawal-like syndrome in a non-addict obese woman. *Journal of Drug Development*, 1993, 6, 75-6.

31. Atkinson R.L. Naloxone decreases food intake in obese humans. *Journal of Clinical Endocrinology and Metabolism*, 1982, 55, 196-8.

32. Atkinson R.L., Berke L.K., Drake C.R., Bibbs M.L., Williams F.L., Kaiser D.L. Effects of long-term therapy with naltrexone on body weight in obesity. *Clinical and Pharmacological Therapy*, 1985, 38, 419-22.

33. Maggio C.A., Presta E., Bracco E.F., Vasselli J.R., Kissileff H.R., Pfohl D.N., Hashim S.A. Naltrexone and human eating behaviour: a dose-ranging inpatient trial in moderately obese men. *Brain Research Bulletin*, 1985, 14, 657-61.

34. Mitchell J.E., Morley J.E., Levine A.S., Hatsukami D., Gannon M., Pfohl D. High-dose naltrexone therapy and dietary counseling for obesity. *Biological Psychiatry*, 1987, 22, 35-42.

35. Wolkowitz O.M., Doran A.R., Cohen M.R., Cohen R.M., Wise T.N., Pickar D. Single-dose naloxone acutely reduces eating in obese humans: behavioral and biochemical effects. *Biological Psychiatry*, 1988, 24, 483-7.

36. Huebner H. *Endorphins, eating disorders and other addictive behaviors.* New York, Norton. 1993.

37. Marrazzi M.A., Luby E.D. An auto-addiction model of chronic anorexia nervosa. *International Journal of Eating Disorders*, 1986, 5, 191-208.

38. Kaye W.H., Pickar D., Naber D., Ebert M.H. Cerebrospinal fluid opioid activity in anorexia nervosa. *American Journal of Psychiatry*, 1982, 139, 643-5.

39. Brambilla F., Lampertico M., Sali L., Cavagnini F., Invitti C., Maggioni M., Candolfi C., Panerai A.E., Muller E.E. Clonidine stimulation in anorexia nervosa: growth hormone, cortisol and beta-endorphin responses. *Psychiatry Research*, 1987, 20, 19-31.

40. Tepper R., Weixman A., Apter A., Tyano S., Beyth Y. Elevated plasma immunoreactive β-endorphin in anorexia nervosa. *Clinical Neuropharmacology*, 1992, 15, 387-91.

41. Baranowska B. Are disturbances in opioid and adrenergic systems involved in the hormonal dysfunction of anorexia nervosa. *Psychoneuroendocrinology*, 1990, 15, 371-9.

42. Krahn D.D., DeQuardo J., Gosnell B.A. Opiate addiction and anorexia nervosa: a case report. *International Journal of Eating Disorders*, 1990, 9, 453-6.

43. Iruela L.M., Palanca I., Ibanezrojo V., Lombardia C. Naltrexone induces weight-gain in inpatient treatment of anorexia-nervosa - 4 case-reports. *Journal of Drug Development*, 1994, 6, 123-5.

44. Marrazzi M.A., Bacon J.P., Kinzie J., Luby E.D. Naltrexone use in the treatment of anorexia-nervosa and bulimia-nervosa. *International Clinical Psychopharmacology*, 1995, 10, 163-72.

45. Hardy B.W., Waller D.A. Bulimia and opioids: eating disorder or substance abuse, in *Advances in Eating Disorders*. Ed. JAI Press Inc. 1989, 43-65.

46. Brewerton T.D., Lydiard R.B., Beinfeld M.C., Laraia M., Stuart G., Ballenger J.C. CSF β-endorphin and dynorphin in bulimia nervosa. *American Journal of Psychiatry*, 1992, 149, 1086-90.

47. Waller D.A., Kiser R.S., Hardy B.W., Fuchs I., Feigenbaum L.P., Uauy R. Eating behavior and plasma beta-endorphin in bulimia. *American Journal of Clinical Nutrition*, 1986, 44, 20-3.

48. Fullerton D.T., Swift W.J., Getto C.J., Carlson I.H. Plasma immunoreactive beta-endorphin in bulimics. *Psychological Medicine*, 1986, 16, 59-63.

49. Jonas J.M., Gold M.S. Naltrexone reverses bulimic symptoms. *Lancet*, 1986, 807.

50. Jonas J.M., Gold M.S. Naltrexone treatment of bulimia: clinical and theoretical findings linking eating disorders and substance abuse. *Advances in Alcohol and Substance Abuse*, 1988, 7, 29-37.

51. Jonas J.M., Gold M.S. The use of opiate antagonists in treating bulimia: a study of low-dose versus high-dose naltrexone. *Psychiatry Research*, 1988, 24, 195-9.

52. Mitchell J.E., Laine D.E., Morley J.E., Levine A.S. Naloxone but not CCK-8 may attenuate binge-eating behavior in patients with the bulimic syndrome. *Biological Psychiatry*, 1986, 21, 1399-406.

53. Marrazzi M.A., Kinzie J., Luby E.D. A detailed longitudinal analysis on the use of naltrexone in the treatment of bulimia. *International Clinical Psychopharmacology*, 1995, 10, 173-6.

54. Alger S.A., Schwalberg M.D., Bigauette J.M., Michalek A.V., Howard L.J. Effect of a tricyclic antidepressant and opiate antagonist on binge-eating behaviour in normoweight bulimic and obese, binge-eating subjects. *American Journal of Clinical Nutrition*, 1991, 53, 865-71.

55. Mitchell J.E., Christenson G., Jennings J., Huber M., Thomas B., Pomeroy C., Morley J. A placebo-controlled, double-blind crossover study of naltrexone hydrochloride in outpatients with normal weight bulimia. *Journal of Clinical Psychopharmacology*, 1989, 9, 94-7.

56. Crammer J.L. Drinking, thirst and water intoxication. *British Journal of Psychiatry*, 1991, 159, 83-9.

57. Goldman M.B., Janecek H.M. Is compulsive drinking a compulsive behavior? *Biological Psychiatry*, 1991, 29, 503-5.

58. Nishikawa T., Tsuda A., Tanaka M., Nishikawa M., Koga I., Uchida Y. Naloxone attenuates drinking behaviour in a schizophrenic patient displaying self-induced water intoxication. *Clinical Neuropharmacology*, 1992, 15, 310-4.

59. Nishikawa T., Tsuda A., Tanaka M., Nishikawa M., Koga I., Uchida Y. Decreased polydipsia in schizophrenic patients treated with naloxone. *American Journal of Psychiatry*, 1994, 151, 947.

60. Nishikawa T., Tsuda A., Tanaka M., Nishikawa M., Koga I., Uchida Y. Involvement of the endogenous opioid system in the drinking behavior of schizophrenic patients displaying self-induced water intoxication: a double-blind controlled study with naloxone. *Clinical Neuropharmacology*, 1996, 19, 252-8.

61. Volpicelli J.R., Alterman A.I., Hayasida M., O'Brien C.P. Naltrexone in the treatment of alcohol dependence. *Archives of General Psychiatry*, 1992, 49, 876-80.

62. O'Malley S.S., Jaffe A.J., Chang G., Rode S., Schottenfeld R., Meyer R.E., Rounsaville B. Six month follow-up of naltrexone and psychotherapy for alcohol dependence. *Archives of General Psychiatry*, 1996, 53, 217-44.

63. O'Malley S.S., Jaffe A.J., Chang G., Schottenfeld R.S., Meyer R.E., Rounsaville B. Naltrexone and coping skills therapy for alcohol dependence. *Archives of General Psychiatry*, 1992, 1992, 881-7.

64. Johnson B.A., Ait-Daoud N. Neuropharmacological treatments for alcoholism: scientific basis and clinical findings. *Psychopharmacology*, 2000, 149, 327-44.

65. Spanagel R., Zieglgansberger W. Anti-craving compounds for ethanol: New pharmacological tools to study addictive processes. *Trends in Pharmacological Sciences*, 1997, 18, 54-9.

66. Weinrieb R.M., O'Brien C.P. Naltrexone in the treatment of alcoholism. *Annual Review of Medicine*, 1997, 48, 477-87.

67. Volpicelli J.R., Watson N.T., King A.C., Sherman C.E., O'Brien C.P. Effect of naltrexone on alcohol "high" in alcoholics. *American Journal of Psychiatry*, 1995, 152, 613-315.

68. Jaffe A.J., Rounsaville B., Chang G., Schottenfeld R.S., Meyer R.E., O'Malley S.S. Naltrexone, relapse prevention, and supportive therapy with alcoholics: an analysis of patient treatment matching. *Journal of Consulting and Clinical Psychology*, 1996, 64, 1044-53.

69. Carter B.L., Tiffany S.T. Cue-reactivity and the future of addiction research. *Addiction*, 1999, 94, 349-51.

70. Monti P.M., Rohsenow D.J., Hutchinson K.E., Swift R.M., Mueller T.L., Colby S.M., Brown R.A., Gulliver S.B., Gordon A., Abrams D.B. Natrexone's effects on cue-elicited craving among alcoholics in treatment. *Alcoholism: Clinical and Experimental Research*, 1999, 21, 1386-94.

71. Berridge K.C. Food reward: brain substrates of wanting and liking. *Neuroscience and Biobehavioral Reviews*, 1996, 20, 1-25.

72. Thompson D.A., Welle S.L., Lilavivat U., Penicaud L., Campbell R.G. Opiate receptor blockade in man reduces 2-deoxy-D-glucose-induced food intake but not hunger, thirst, and hypothermia. *Life Sciences*, 1982, 31, 847-52.

73. Cohen M.R., Cohen R.M., Pickar D., Murphy D.L. Naloxone reduces food intake in humans. *Psychosomatic Medicine*, 1985, 47, 132-8.

74. Hetherington M.M., Vervaet N., Blass E., Rolls B.J. Failure of naltrexone to affect the pleasantness or intake of food. *Pharmacology Biochemistry and Behavior*, 1991, 40, 185-90.

3. BEHAVIOURAL MODELS OF CRAVING

3.1. CONDITIONING MODELS OF FOOD CRAVING

Debra A. Zellner and Erin M. Edwards

3.1.1   Introduction

A food craving is an intense desire or yearning for a specific food. Usually, craved foods are high-fat foods. Women tend to crave sweet fat while men crave mostly salty fat (1). A craving is often followed by attempts to obtain the food that is craved. We have descriptions of cravings, people readily report cravings, and many of us have experienced cravings, but we still do not know what cravings are or what causes them.

We do know that the descriptions that people give for food cravings are very similar to those given by drug addicts to describe their drug cravings when in a state of drug need. No matter what type of drug is craved (depressant or stimulant) the description of the craving is the same, usually including a state of arousal, such as excitement, anxiety, and anticipation (2). Similar adjectives have been used by chocolate 'addicts' to describe their state when craving chocolate (3).

One well-studied food craving is that produced by sodium need. The famous case, reported by Wilkins and Richter (4), involved a young boy born without adrenal glands who had a severe salt craving from an early age. When he was admitted to the hospital and put on the standard hospital diet he died. This has led many to believe that cravings are generated by some internal signal from the body, triggered by a physiological need, which notifies the organism of the imbalance or need state that should be addressed. The individual then seeks out the craved item in order to return to homeostasis.

Some cravings might, in fact, work that way. There is evidence that some mineral needs such as that for sodium are the result of some internal signals generated as a result of an imbalance that leads the deprived organism to crave and seek out sodium. Probably the most convincing demonstration of this is the series of studies reported by Krieckhaus and

Wolf (5). In one experiment, rats were trained to bar-press for a sodium chloride solution or plain water in the absence of any sodium need. Then half of each group was sodium-depleted. When tested, the sodium-trained, sodium-depleted rats showed an increased resistance to extinction of the bar-press response, suggesting that, although they had no prior experience of sodium's fulfilling a specific need state, they sought out sodium when deprived. In a further experiment it was demonstrated that the increased resistance to extinction was specific to sodium salt solutions; the same response was not seen for non-sodium salt solutions. These results suggest that an internal need state for sodium may elicit a specific hunger for sodium by some internal mechanism.

So, food cravings may be caused by some physiological imbalance, which causes us to crave foods high in whatever substance we need. One substance that has been hypothesised to be behind many food cravings is serotonin. Many depressed persons and perimenstrual women report cravings for sweet carbohydrates. This observation, coupled with the finding that carbohydrate consumption can increase the concentration of serotonin in the brain (6,7), led to the hypothesis that food cravings may signal a need for more serotonin (8-10). Since low levels of serotonin are known to induce dysphoria (11), we should expect that the experience of carbohydrate cravings would include or be preceded by negative moods. However, many food cravings are experienced in the absence of negative moods (12-15). Neither consuming carbohydrates in response to a craving (15-18) nor in the absence of craving (19) consistently elevates mood. Another problem for this theory is that many foods high in carbohydrates, such as bread and pasta, are rarely craved. Rather, foods high in fat and sweetness, which have high hedonic value, are craved (1).

Endogenous opiates have also been implicated in the production of food cravings (20,21). Because good-tasting foods elicit endogenous opiate release and altered opiate levels occur in many conditions (e.g., obesity, pregnancy, menstruation, depression) associated with food cravings, it has been proposed that these opiate alterations (both increases and decreases) cause cravings (21). But the conditions under which cravings occur do not produce consistent effects on the opiate system. In addition, all liked foods, not just craved ones, produce opiate release. These observations make it unlikely that food cravings are responses to opiate levels.

With the exception of sodium need, there is little evidence for a physiological basis for food cravings. Drug cravings, on the other hand, probably do have some physiological basis since drug withdrawal produces other physiological effects. When drug addicts are in withdrawal they have a physiological need for the drug, which could cause a craving. However, occurrences of cravings and withdrawal effects are not perfectly correlated (22). In fact, sometimes cravings or withdrawal effects occur well after the body no longer has a physiological need for the drug. It is well known that addicts (of any addictive drug) can stop taking the drug and be well past the point where withdrawal effects are present (months or years) and still relapse because they experience a sudden, intense craving. These cravings, following drug detoxification, are not the result of some physiological signal of imbalance but rather the result of conditioning. They occur in response to specific external cues rather than internal mechanisms reflecting need.

Drug conditioning and its role in drug craving have been extensively studied (23-25). It is understood that stimuli that have been associated with drugs or drug use can trigger drug cravings, drug effects and withdrawal. The cravings induced by drug-related cues are described very much like those people experience for food (2,3). We believe that both food and drug cravings are not simply caused by a putative physiological imbalance but are the result of the same type of conditioning and produce the same effect (desire and excitation) in the organism experiencing the craving.

Very little research has been done on the role of conditioning in the production of food cravings. However, there is a fairly extensive body of literature on the role of conditioning in drug craving. We examined the conditioning models of drug craving to determine if they might also apply to food craving.

3.1.2   Pavlovian Models

There are two Pavlovian models that have been proposed to explain drug cravings - the conditioned drive model and the conditioned incentive model.

3.1.2.1 Conditioned drive model

In both versions of the conditioned drive model, some environmental stimulus present during drug administration or drug withdrawal becomes associated with a drug, the drug's effects or the drug's withdrawal effects through Pavlovian conditioning. That is, the environmental stimulus is the CS (conditional stimulus), which starts out as a neutral stimulus and becomes associated with the UCS (unconditional stimulus) of the drug or the drug's effects (see Fig. 3.1.1a).

Conditioned withdrawal. In one version of the conditioned drive model (26,27) environmental stimuli become associated with withdrawal effects of the drug through Pavlovian conditioning. The environmental CS then elicits withdrawal-like effects including cravings. These cravings (and other physiological withdrawal symptoms) act as a drive to obtain drugs, which results in relapse.

Compensatory conditioning. A second version of the conditioned drive model was proposed by Siegel (28). According to his version, environmental CSs become associated with the direct drug effects (UCS) which elicit compensatory or adaptive drug responses to counteract the drug effects. These are the drug compensatory responses (CRs), which resemble withdrawal responses. These CRs include 'neurochemical responses that are interpreted as craving' (28). These cravings and other compensatory CRs cause relapse.

Application of the conditioned drive model to food cravings. In both versions of this model, a specific environmental stimulus (CS) associated with the drug UCS (or drug withdrawal) causes withdrawal-like responses (CRs).These CRs either include or produce cravings for the drug in order to alleviate the conditioned withdrawal effects, which are unpleasant. Both versions see a craving as a drive to procure drugs to correct some need state (withdrawal). Do these theories apply to food craving?

Wikler (26) did apply his theory to food stimuli. He suggested that the CR of salivation to environmental CSs paired with food would be accompanied by a subjective feeling of 'hunger with craving for specific food used in the experiment.' Why for a specific food? His theory, like that of Siegel, postulates that the food-paired stimuli would result in some type of conditioned drive due to food compensatory CRs. Stimuli that signal food delivery would have to result in some responses that would disrupt homeostasis; they would produce a need state. Such stimuli have been shown to result in physiological responses in the organism, such as insulin release, which prepare it for the delivery of food (29). These CRs can produce hunger, but can they produce a specific hunger, that is, a specific craving? This can happen only if the food UCS paired with those environmental stimuli produces specific physiological effects (UCRs). Only then would the environmentally produced CRs be specific enough to result in a craving for a particular food. Only then would they produce some withdrawal response, some physiological need state that only a particular food could alleviate. This drive theory of craving, while possible for drugs, seems unlikely for food. Even the pharmacological effects of a complex and highly craved food such as chocolate are probably not the reason for the craving (1,30). In addition, the pharmacological effects produced by many craved foods are not food-specific (e.g. opioid effects or decreased insulin levels).

This model could be applied to food cravings if the craving was an affective CR. If the food resulted in a very hedonically positive affective experience, the CR could be negative affect, which could be interpreted as a food craving. Unfortunately for this line of reasoning, some evidence suggests that the CR is hedonically positive for hedonically positive UCSs (31). However, there is also some evidence that negative mood states are a component of cravings (3). But that still leaves the question of how the individual knows what food to crave. Many people report that, when a food craving occurs, it is for a particular food and substitution is not possible (18,30). It is doubtful that if the CR is a negative mood state it is food-specific.

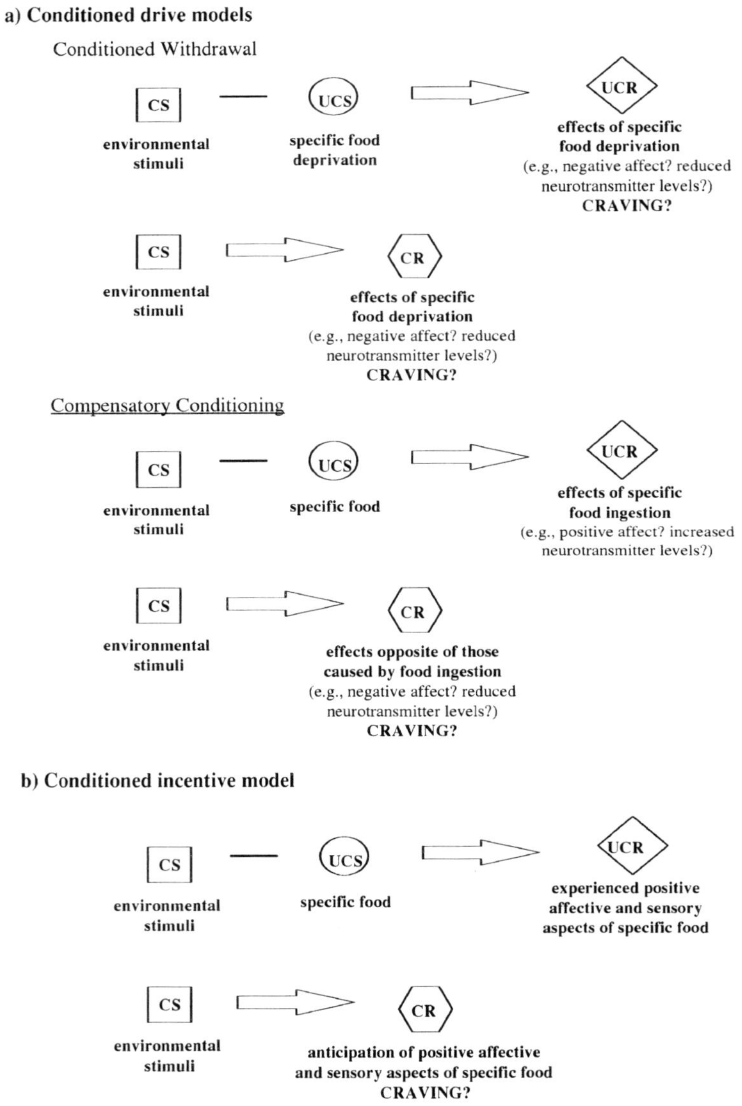

a) Conditioned drive models

Conditioned Withdrawal

Compensatory Conditioning

b) Conditioned incentive model

Fig. 3.1.1. Pavlovian models

3.1.2.2 *Conditioned incentive model*

The second type of Pavlovian model proposes that cravings are the result of a conditioned incentive (24). Advocates of this view note that both drugs of abuse and palatable foods are reinforcing even when an organism is not in a state of need. They postulate that environmental CSs that are paired with a drug come to elicit drug-like CRs. It is those CRs that create a positive motivational state similar to that caused by the drug. This conditioned motivational state results in relapse much as a 'priming' dose of drug can result in relapse in a former addict (see Fig. 3.1.1b).

This model is supported by the finding that addicts cite the desire for euphoria as their most common reason for relapse (32). In addition, rats show a preference for places that have been paired with drugs even when they are not yet addicted or in withdrawal (33,34). Likewise, non-addicted monkeys will lever-press for administration of opiates and cocaine (35). All these results suggest that some positive drug effect, rather than withdrawal, causes drug-taking and relapse.

3.1.2.2.1 *Application of the conditioned incentive model to food craving*

Can this model explain food craving? All that is required is that the environmental stimuli trigger a positive food-like effect. But what would that be? In the case of drugs it could be euphoria or some other reinforcing property of the drug. What would it be in the case of food?

One thing that craved foods do have in common is that they are hedonically positive; they have fairly strong reinforcing properties. Most of the foods are highly caloric and high in fat. We know that the taste of foods paired with calories (36-39) and paired with fat (40,41) become highly liked. The majority of foods craved by women are sweets (1). Sweet foods are innately palatable (42,43) and the taste of foods paired with sweet tastes become liked (44). So, the taste of commonly craved foods should be highly reinforcing. The environmental CS paired with such foods might elicit a similar positive hedonic response, causing the craving. Delamater *et al.* (31) have demonstrated that this does happen. In their experiments, auditory signals paired with infusions of sucrose into rats' mouths later elicited an increase in consummatory mouth movements to an infusion of water. Thus the palatability of water increased in the presence of the sucrose-paired auditory CS. This result supports the idea that an environmental CS paired with a hedonically positive food might elicit hedonically positive CRs. However, in order for the environmental CS to cause a food craving it also has to elicit some response that is food-specific and food-like in order to make the craving food-specific.

Does this mean that the environmental CS elicits a phantom taste of the food associated with it? Probably not. Research on associative learning has suggested that a CS actually elicits a representation of the UCS, which is responded to in a manner similar to the UCS. For example, Jenkins and Moore (45) found that the topography of an auto-shaped pecking response of pigeons on a keylight depended on the reinforcer used. Pigeons reinforced with water pecked with beak closed, but those reinforced with grain pecked with beak open. These match pigeons' consummatory responses for the two substances. The topography of the response was independent of motivational state (food or water deprivation) but dependent on outcome received (food or water). In this case, the keylight paired with the water seemed to cause an expectation of water (producing a water-getting peck) and a keylight paired with grain caused an expectation of grain (producing a grain-getting peck).

More recently, Colwill and Motzkin (46) demonstrated that a food UCS is encoded in detail in a Pavlovian conditioning paradigm. In their first study they paired a tone CS with the delivery of sucrose into a magazine and a light CS with the delivery of a food pellet into the same magazine (vice-versa for half of the rats). After this Pavlovian conditioning had occurred, one of the two UCSs (either the sucrose or food pellets) was devalued by pairing it with an injection of lithium chloride to produce a conditioned taste aversion and reduce its reinforcing properties. Presentations of the CSs during extinction, after devaluation, resulted in fewer magazine-directed behaviours (e.g. inserting the nose into the magazine, approach toward the magazine, etc.) in the presence of the devalued CS. This is similar to results of Stanhope (47), who found reduced pecking to the keylight that had been previously paired with the outcome on which animals had been sated (either water or grain). These studies suggest that exposure to the CS elicits a representation of the UCS to follow.

We believe that something similar is happening in the production of food cravings in humans. There is some evidence that, when a person craves a particular food, the craving is generally preceded by thoughts of the craved food (16,48). These thoughts might be triggered by some environmental CS previously associated with the food. Drug researchers use stimuli associated with drug administration (e.g., the sight of the drug, needles, etc.) to study conditioned drug cravings (22). Similar types of cues have been found to increase food cravings. Cornell *et al.* (49) demonstrated that the sight of a food can increase craving for that food (pizza or ice cream - typical craved foods) in satiated humans. In their Experiment 1, immediately after eating a substantial lunch, participants were asked how much they desired to eat the target foods. They were then presented with either pizza or ice cream. They were told to rate their desire to eat the food again. Participants' desire for the food increased significantly after presentation of the food. A similar increase in the desire to eat chocolate was seen in subjects exposed to the sight of M&M™ candies (50). Thus, seeing (and at least in the case of pizza, smelling) a hedonically positive food can increase the desire to eat that food.

These food cues seem to be more potent in producing cravings in restrained than in unrestrained eaters (51). Because restrained eaters have to ignore internal hunger signals, they may be more sensitive to external food-related cues (52). Federoff *et al.* (51) found that restrained subjects who smelled pizza rated their craving for pizza as higher than both restrained subjects who had not smelled pizza and unrestrained subjects in both conditions. So restrained eaters have cravings that are more easily triggered by food cues.

However, all the external cues discussed so far are those that are products of the food. What of stimuli other than the food itself? There are no such stimuli that always predict the eating of a particular food. The sight of a set table, china and silverware, and mealtimes do not usually elicit cravings. Instead, they might elicit a general desire to eat something (conditioned hunger), but no one food in particular. Cravings for particular foods generally do not occur at mealtimes because at those times a wide variety of foods is eaten and has been eaten in the past. Cravings for particular foods occur at times other than mealtimes (53). For example, for Americans, specific cravings often occur in the evening (54). This is the time when most Americans are at home and a lot of snacking occurs, generally on a small range of snack foods, the very foods they report craving (chocolate, ice cream, chips, pizza, etc.).

One common food craving that could be explained by the conditioned incentive model is the perimenstrual craving for chocolate by some women. The feelings that accompany the onset of menstruation might serve as a CS if chocolate is indulged in at that time and few other times. Because so many women in the populations studied (Americans (55), Canadians (13), and British (48)) are restrained eaters, and to women on a diet chocolate is a forbidden food, few women eat chocolate on a regular basis. They eat it perimenstrually because they have been told that it is OK to do so (they rationalise that they need it then) and because it is more difficult to deprive themselves of something good when they are feeling bad (disinhibition of eating occurs (56,57)). If they eat chocolate predominantly when they are experiencing perimenstrual symptoms, then those symptoms will become CSs, triggering thoughts of and cravings for chocolate (see also section 5.2).

In either type of Pavlovian conditioning model, extinction of the craving should occur if the CS is repeatedly presented without subsequent presentation of the food UCS. Jansen et al. (58) report data that support the idea that, like drug cravings (22), food cravings can be eliminated by severing the CS-UCS connection. In the Jansen et al. (58) study, binge eaters' cravings for binge foods were eliminated by exposing them to contextual cues predicting a binge while they were prevented from eating the top four foods on which they binged. The cues included touching, smelling and even eating a small bite of the binge food. They also had the patient eat the binge food in a place in which eating it would not otherwise occur in order to decrease even further the CS-UCS contingency. This procedure was successful in eliminating binge eating in 100% of patients a year after treatment (other treatments being successful in about one-third of the patients), suggesting that the binge eating was due to the presence of environmental cues associated with the binge foods.

There is additional evidence that food cravings might undergo extinction when the environmental stimuli associated with them are no longer reinforced with the foods. Cravings for high levels of salt (59) and fat (60) decrease when people are put on a low-salt or -fat diet. A decrease in reported cravings has been found for obese people on very low calorie (61) or fasting (no solid foods/low-calorie) diets (62)).

3.1.3   Models with an Instrumental Conditioning Component

Cravings, as we pointed out at the beginning of the chapter, in addition to being a desire or a yearning, also include an action component. An organism experiencing a craving for a food or drug has a desire to consume that food or drug. This elicits action. For example, the smoker in the old Camel cigarette ad. said that he would "walk a mile for a Camel". This indicates that an instrumental conditioning component might be involved with cravings.

3.1.3.1   *Instrumental conditioning model*

One model for cravings is to view them as purely instrumental. In this view, the instrumental response of drug taking or food ingestion is reinforced by the positive, reinforcing aspects of the drug or food. As we discussed earlier, drugs of abuse and craved foods are both perceived as hedonically positive. If drug taking or food ingestion repeatedly occurs in the presence of some environmental stimuli, those stimuli can come to serve as discriminative stimuli. In this view, the discriminative stimulus would signal that a particular response would now be followed by a particular outcome; what is termed S-(R-O) learning (see Fig. 3.1.2a).

Some early results supporting the idea that a discriminative stimulus can result in the anticipation of a particular outcome contingent upon a response were reported by Tinkelpaugh (63). In his study, a monkey was trained to open a box for a banana reinforcer. When the banana was replaced by a lettuce reinforcer, the monkey was clearly dismayed and seemed to search for the banana. From Tinkelpaugh's description it appears that the box signalled to the monkey that opening it would be followed by a specific outcome, the banana.

Recently, even more controlled and compelling studies have provided evidence that discriminative stimuli can provide the organism with somewhat detailed information about the outcome or reinforcer in an instrumental task (64). For example, in an experiment by Colwill and Rescorla (65) rats received a sucrose solution in the presence of one stimulus (light or noise) and food pellets in the presence of the other stimulus for pressing their nose against a panel. Rats were then taught to press a lever for one reinforcer (the sucrose solution or the food pellets) and pull a chain for the other reinforcer. These responses were learned without the light and noise present. In the final phase, both the lever and the chain were present simultaneously and the noise and light were occasionally presented. In the presence of the stimulus previously paired with a particular outcome, the response learned to obtain that outcome, was augmented. That is, if the rat had received sucrose following a light and had then been reinforced for lever pressing with sucrose, lever pressing but not chain pulling was increased in the presence of the light but not the noise. Thus, in this case, the light caused the rat to anticipate the sucrose outcome and enhanced responding for that outcome.

In the food craving case, the environmental stimuli associated with a craved food might cause anticipation of the craved food and its reinforcing effects. This would then increase responding (e.g. seeking, buying, eating) for that craved food. So, in this model, the discriminative stimulus would serve two purposes. It would trigger the craving by eliciting a representation of the craved food (the reinforcer). This is similar to the Pavlovian conditioned incentive model described earlier. It would also initiate the actions that were reinforced in the past to obtain the craved food. This model can thus be recast as a mixed model, combining a Pavlovian and an instrumental component, rather than as purely instrumental (see Fig. 3.1.2a).

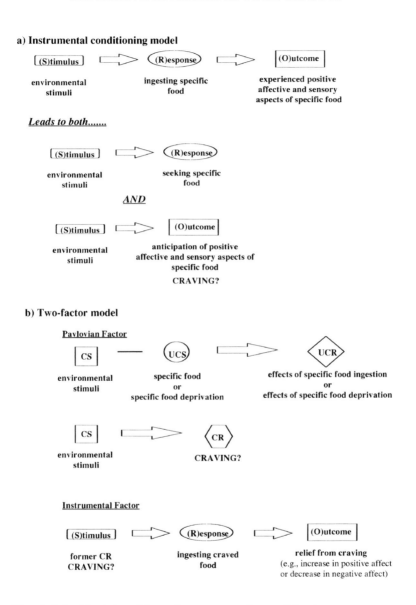

Fig. 3.1.2. Models with an instrumental conditioning component

3.1.3.2   Two-factor model

A model of drug craving involving Pavlovian and instrumental components is based on a two-factor theory (66). In this model, the environmental stimuli (CS) elicit aversive CRs through pairing with the drug. This is the Pavlovian conditioning component, identical to the conditioned drive models discussed above where the CR is a withdrawal response. The instrumental response is then the taking or seeking of the drug in response to the CS in order to escape from the aversive CRs. So, what happens in relapse is that exposure to the environment associated with the drug results in conditioned withdrawal responses, and these result in drug-taking in order to get relief from the conditioned withdrawal.

This model might explain food cravings if the conditioned cravings are aversive. In that case, the Pavlovian component would be the environmental stimulus eliciting a CR, which is an aversive craving for the food. The instrumental component would be the actions taken by the organism to relieve the cravings. This model suggests that cravings are a negative affect state, but, as we discussed previously, it appears that the CRs are instead appetitive for a hedonically positive craved food (31), not negative. In addition, the indulgence of a craving should produce an increase in positive or decrease in negative affect. The findings on the effect of indulging in a craving on mood are mixed. While some studies report that, for most individuals, affect becomes more positive following consumption (48), others report increases in both positive and negative affect (16,18) or an increase in positive affect while indulging and in negative affect following consumption (15).

The two-factor model (see Fig. 3.1.2b) differs from the instrumental model in a manner similar to the way in which the Pavlovian conditioned drive and incentive models differ (see Figs 3.1.1a & b). In the two-factor model, having an image of the craved food is aversive, so that it drives responses that reduce the images (like the conditioned drive model); in the instrumental model, the image of the craved food is a motivator to attain an item of great hedonic value (like the conditioned incentive model). A study by Gibson and Desmond (67) lends support to the idea that the food is a desired outcome by showing that decreasing the reinforcing properties of chocolate decreases craving for chocolate. In their study, chocolate cravers who were required to eat chocolate twice a day for two weeks, only when satiated, reported significantly reduced cravings for chocolate when shown a piece of chocolate and tested sated or hungry. It seems that the sight of chocolate (discriminative stimulus) signalled that consumption would no longer result in a reinforcing outcome. In fact, the chocolate was rated as less pleasant tasting after two weeks of eating it when satiated. The reduction in the reinforcing value of the chocolate reduced both the craving for the chocolate and the anticipated intake. So the devaluation of a food outcome can reduce craving in the presence of the food cue (i.e. the sight of chocolate). It is therefore likely that a cue signalling a food with high hedonic value would increase craving for that food by causing an anticipation of a reinforcing outcome (see also section 3.2).

3.1.3.3   Is an instrumental conditioning component necessary?

Of course, one does not have to resort to an instrumental model of cravings if one believes that the activation of a conditioned incentive is enough to explain the drug- or food-seeking behaviour. According to the incentive motivation model proposed by Bindra (68), stimuli with positive incentive motivational properties, such as food-paired stimuli, will produce approach and consummatory behaviours. Weingarten (69,70) describes his conditioned eating studies in just such a way. In his experiments, an environmental stimulus (tone or light) preceded delivery of food (condensed milk) to a hungry rat. Later, when that rat was satiated and the stimulus previously signalling food was presented, the rat ate. In these studies, Weingarten (69,70) discusses the environmental cue as a CS that is associated with food, such that the cue signalled the delivery of the food, causing consummatory behaviour. However, the consummatory behaviour was not a general consummatory response. The rat did not consume condensed milk continuously present in a bottle in the cage in response to the food-paired signal but only drank condensed milk delivered into the food cup where it was delivered following the CS (69,70). This suggests that the responses are specific and not the result of some general activation to engage in eating. So, if the CS results in activation of incentive motivation, it is a specific motivation to acquire the object whose image was triggered (the UCS) in the place it was acquired during conditioning.

Weingarten (71) proposes that these findings in rats might explain cravings for specific foods in humans. He states that hunger caused by physiological depletion results in a desire to consume food in general but that the consummatory responses caused by food-paired CSs result in a desire for a specific food (i.e. a craving). Unfortunately, his data do not show cravings for specific foods but for food delivered in specific places. So it could be that the environmental stimuli activate a specific response to approach and consume food at a particular place. Such an outcome-specific response requires a model with an instrumental conditioning component. The environmental stimuli act as discriminative stimuli signalling the delivery of a specific food if a specific response is made. To suggest specific consummatory responses is to suggest that the craving is a learned response.

3.1.4   Conclusion

This chapter has described a number of conditioning models with which to conceptualise food cravings, and provided some data that lend support to some models more than others. At this point, the role of learning in cravings is largely speculative and, given the paucity of research on the topic, it would be unwise either to select one model as the one to use or to eliminate any from contention. Clearly, much more research is needed.

However, we can draw some conclusions. It appears that environmental cues associated with a craved food produce a representation of the craved food. This representation includes specifics about what the food is, how good it is, and how to obtain it. The environmentally produced representation leads to a desire to seek and consume the food (the craving), perhaps by causing an increase in incentive motivation or by activation of an instrumental response.

At this point we can be confident that conditioning is strongly involved in the production of food cravings. Although data are accumulating contrary to the view that cravings are the result of some physiological need (1,30), that line of research gets the majority of the attention. Given the strength of the evidence for the role of conditioning in food cravings, more research investigating exactly how conditioning is involved is clearly called for if we are to understand cravings.

3.1.5   References

1. Zellner D.A., Garriga-Trillo A., Rohm E., Centeno S., Parker S. Food liking and craving: A cross-cultural approach. *Appetite*, 1999, 33, 61-70.

2. Merikle E.P. The subjective experience of craving: An exploratory analysis. *Substance Use and Misuse*, 1999, 34(8), 1101-15.

3. Tuomisto T., Hetherington M.M., Morris M.-F., Tuomisto M.T., Turjanmaa V., Lappalainen R. Psychological and physiological characteristics of sweet food "addiction." *International Journal of Eating Disorders*, 1999, 25(2), 169-75.

4. Wilkins L., Richter C.P. A great craving for salt by a child with cortico-adrenal insufficiency. *Journal of the American Medical Association*, 1940, 114, 866-8.

5. Krieckhaus E.E., Wolf G. Acquisition of sodium by rats: Interaction of innate mechanisms and latent learning. *Journal of Comparative and Physiological Psychology*, 1968, 65(2), 197-201.

6. Fernstrom J.D., Wurtman R.J. Brain serotonin content: Increase following ingestion of carbohydrate diet. *Science*, 1971, 174, 1023-5.

7. Fernstrom J.D., Wurtman R.J. Brain serotonin content: Physiological regulation by plasma neutral amino acids. *Science*, 1972, 178, 414-6.

8. Wurtman J.J., Wurtman R.J. Drugs that enhance central serotoninergic transmission diminish elective carbohydrate consumption by rats. *Life Science*, 1979, 24, 895-904.

9. Wurtman R.J., Wurtman J.J. Carbohydrate craving, obesity and brain serotonin. *Appetite*, 1986, 7 (Suppl.), 99-103.

10. Wurtman R.J., Wurtman J.J. Do carbohydrates affect food intake via neurotransmitter activity? *Appetite*, 1988, 11(Suppl.), 42-7.

11. Meltzer H.Y. Role of serotonin in depression. *Annals of the New York Academy of Sciences*, 1990, 600, 486-500.

12. Bancroft J., Cook A., Williamson L. Food craving, mood and the menstrual cycle. *Psychological Medicine*, 1988, 18, 855-60.

13. Cohen I.T., Sherwin B.B., Fleming A.S. Food cravings, mood and the menstrual cycle. *Hormones and Behavior*, 1987, 21, 457-70.

14. Dye L., Warner P., Bancroft J. Food craving during the menstrual cycle and its relationship to stress, happiness of relationship and depression; a preliminary enquiry. *Journal of Affective Disorders*, 1995, 34, 157-64.

15. Hetherington M.M., Macdiarmid J.I. "Chocolate addiction": A preliminary study of its description and its relationship to problem eating. *Appetite*, 1993, 21, 233-46.

16. Hill A.J., Weaver C.F.L., Blundell J.E. Food craving, dietary restraint and mood. *Appetite*, 1991, 17, 187-97.

17. Macdiarmid J.I., Hetherington M.M. Mood modulation by food: An exploration of affect and craving in "chocolate addicts". *British Journal of Clinical Psychology*, 1995, 34, 129-38.

18. Weingarten H.P., Elston D. Food craving in a college population. *Appetite*, 1991, 17, 165-75.

19. Reid M., Hammersley R. Effects of carbohydrate intake on subsequent food intake and mood state. *Physiology and Behavior*, 1995, 58(3), 421-7.

20. Drewnowski A., Krahn D.D., Demitrack M.A., Nairn K, Gosnell B.A. Taste responses and preferences for sweet high-fat foods: Evidence for opioid involvement. *Physiology and Behavior*, 1992, 51, 371-9.

21. Mercer M.E., Holder M.D. Food cravings, endogenous opioid peptides, and food intake: A review. *Appetite*, 1997, 29, 325-52.

22. O'Brien C.P., Childress A.R., McLellan A.T., Ehrman R. A learning model of addiction, in *Addictive States*. Eds O'Brien C.P., Jaffe J.H. New York, Raven Press, Ltd. 1992, 157-77.

23. Rohsenow D.J., Niaura R.S., Childress A.R., Abrams D.B., Monti P.M. Cue reactivity in addictive behaviors: Theoretical and treatment implications. *The International Journal of the Addictions*, 1991, 25(7A and 8A), 957-93.

24.   Stewart J., de Wit H., Eikelboom R. Role of unconditioned and conditioned drug effects in the self-administration of opiates and stimulants. *Psychological Review*, 1984, 91(2), 251-68.

25.   Tiffany S.T. Potential functions of classical conditioning in drug addiction, in *Addictive Behaviour: Cue Exposure Theory and Practice*. Eds Drummond D.C., Tiffany S.T., Glautier S., Remmington B. New York, John Wiley and Sons Ltd. 1995, 47-71.

26.   Wikler A. Recent progress in research of the neurophysiologic basis of morphine addiction. *American Journal of Psychiatry*, 1948, 105, 329-38.

27.   Wikler A., Pescor F.T. Classical conditioning of a morphine abstinence phenomenon, reinforcement of opioid-drinking behavior and "relapse" in morphine-addicted rats. *Psychopharmacologia*, 1967, 10, 255-84.

28.   Siegel S. Drug anticipation and drug addiction. The 1998 H. David Archibald Lecture. *Addiction*, 1999, 94(8), 1113-24.

29.   Ramsay D.S., Seeley R.J., Bolles R.C., Woods S.C. Ingestive homeostasis: The primacy of learning, in *Why We Eat What We Eat: The Psychology of Eating*. Ed. Capaldi E.D. Washington, D.C., American Psychological Association. 1996, 11-27.

30.   Michener W., Rozin P. Pharmacological versus sensory factors in the satiation of chocolate craving. *Physiology and Behavior*, 1994, 56, 419-22.

31.   Delamater A.R., LoLordo V.M., Berridge K.C. Control of fluid palatability by exteroceptive Pavlovian signals. *Journal of Experimental Psychology: Animal Behavior Processes*, 1986, 12(2), 143-52.

32.   McAuliffe W.E. A test of Wikler's theory of relapse: The frequency of relapse due to conditioned withdrawal sickness. *The International Journal of the Addictions*, 1982, 17(1), 19-33.

33.   Sherman J.E., Pickman C., Rice A., Liebeskind J.C., Holman E.W. Rewarding and aversive effects of morphine: Temporal and pharmacological properties. *Pharmacology, Biochemistry and Behavior*, 1980, 13, 501-5.

34.   Sherman J.E., Roberts T., Roskam S.E., Holman E.W. Temporal properties of the rewarding and aversive effects of amphetamine in rats. *Pharmacology, Biochemistry and Behavior*, 1980, 13, 597-9.

35.   Ternes J.W., Ehrman R.N., O'Brien C.P. Nondependent monkeys self-administer hydromorphine. *Behavioral Neuroscience*, 1985, 99(3), 583-8.

36.   Birch L.L., McPhee L., Steinberg L., Sullivan S. Conditioned flavor preferences in young children. *Physiology and Behavior*, 1990, 47, 501-5.

37.   Fedorchak P.M. The nature and strength of caloric conditioning, in *Learning, Motivation, and Cognition: The Functional Behaviorism of Robert C. Bolles*. Eds Bouton M.E., Fanselow M.S. Washington, D.C., American Psychological Association. 1997, 255-69.

38.   Mehiel R. Hedonic-shift conditioning with calories, in *The Hedonics of Taste*. Ed. Bolles R.C. Hillsdale, N.J., Lawrence Erlbaum Associates, Inc. 1991, 107-26.

39.   Mehiel R., Bolles R.C. Learned flavor preferences based on caloric outcome. *Animal Learning and Behavior*, 1984, 12(4), 421-7.

40.   Johnson S.L., McPhee L., Birch L.L. Conditioned preferences: Young children prefer flavors associated with high dietary fat. *Physiology and Behavior*, 1991, 50, 1245-51.

41.   Kern D.L., McPhee L., Fisher J., Johnson S., Birch L.L. The postingestive consequences of fat condition preferences for flavors associated with high dietary fat. *Physiology and Behavior*, 1993, 54, 71-6.

42.   Maller O., Desor J.A. Effect of taste on ingestion by human newborns, in *Fourth Symposium on Oral Sensation and Perception: Development in the Fetus and Infant*. Ed. Bosma J.F. Bethesda, Maryland, U.S. Department of Health, Education, and Welfare. 1973, 279-91.

43.   Steiner J.E. The gustofacial response: Observation on normal and anencephalic newborn infants, in *Fourth Symposium on Oral Sensation and Perception: Development in the Fetus and Infant*. Ed. Bosma J.F. Bethesda, Maryland, U.S. Department of Health, Education, and Welfare. 1973, 254-78.

44.   Zellner D.A., Rozin P., Aron M., Kulish C. Conditioned enhancement of human's liking for flavor by pairing with sweetness. *Learning and Motivation*, 1983, 14, 338-50.

45.   Jenkins H.M., Moore B.R. The form of the auto-shaped response with food or water reinforcers. *Journal of the Experimental Analysis of Behavior*, 1973, 20(2), 163-81.

46. Colwill R.M., Motzkin D.K. Encoding of the unconditioned stimulus in Pavlovian conditioning. *Animal Learning and Behavior*, 1994, 22(4), 384-94.

47. Stanhope K.J. Dissociation of the effect of reinforcer type and response strength on the force of a conditioned response. *Animal Learning and Behavior*, 1989, 17(3), 311-21.

48. Hill A.J., Heaton-Brown L. The experience of food craving: A prospective investigation in healthy women. *Journal of Psychosomatic Research*, 1994, 38(8), 801-14.

49. Cornell C.E., Rodin J., Weingarten H. Stimulus-induced eating when satiated. *Physiology and Behavior*, 1989, 45, 695-704.

50. Lambert K.G., Neal T., Noyes J., Parker C., Worrel P. Food-related stimuli increase desire to eat in hungry and satiated human subjects. *Current Psychology: Research and Reviews*, 1991-1992, 10(4), 297-303.

51. Fedoroff I.C., Polivy J., Herman C.P. The effect of pre-exposure to food cues on the eating behavior of restrained and unrestrained eaters. *Appetite*, 1997, 28, 33-47.

52. Rogers P.J., Hill A.J. Breakdown of dietary restraint following mere exposure to food stimuli: Interrelationships between restraint, hunger, salivation and food intake. *Addictive Behaviors*, 1989, 14, 387-97.

53. Schlundt D.G., Virts K.L., Sbrocco T., Pope-Cordle J., Hill J.O. A sequential behavioral analysis of craving sweets in obese women. *Addictive Behaviors*, 1993, 18, 67-80.

54. Pelchat M.L. Food cravings in young and elderly adults. *Appetite*, 1997, 28, 103-13.

55. Rozin P., Levine E., Stoess C. Chocolate craving and liking. *Appetite*, 1991, 17, 199-212.

56. Cooper P.J., Bowskill R. Dysphoric mood and overeating. *British Journal of Clinical Psychology*, 1986, 25(2), 155-6.

57. Herman C.P., Polivy J., Lank C.N., Heatherton T.F. Anxiety, hunger, and eating behavior. *Journal of Abnormal Psychology*, 1987, 96(3), 264-9.

58. Jansen A., Broekmate J., Heymans M. Cue-exposure vs self-control in the treatment of binge eating: A pilot study. *Behavioural Research and Therapy*, 1992, 30(3), 235-41.

59. Beauchamp G.K. The human preference for excess salt. *American Scientist*, 1987, 75, 27-33.

60. Mattes R.D. Fat preference and adherence to a reduced-fat diet. *American Journal of Clinical Nutrition*, 1993, 57, 373-81.

61. Harvey J., Wing R.R., Mullen M. Effects on food cravings of a very low calorie diet or a balanced, low calorie diet. *Appetite*, 1993, 21, 105-15.

62. Lappalainen R., Sjoden P., Hursti T., Vesa V. Hunger/craving responses and reactivity to food stimuli during fasting and dieting. *International Journal of Obesity*, 1990, 14, 679-88.

63. Tinklepaugh O.L. An experimental study of representative factors in monkeys. *Comparative Psychology*, 1928, 8(3), 197-236.

64. Colwill R.M. An associative analysis of instrumental learning. *Current Directions in Psychological Science*, 1993, 2(4), 111-6.

65. Colwill R.M., Rescorla R.A. Associations between the discriminative stimulus and the reinforcer in instrumental learning. *Journal of Experimental Psychology: Animal Behavior Processes*, 1988, 14(2), 155-64.

66. Mowrer O.H. *Learning Theory and Behavior*. New York, John Wiley and Sons, Inc. 1960.

67. Gibson E.L., Desmond E. Chocolate craving and hunger state: Implications for the acquisition and expression of appetite and food choice. *Appetite*, 1999, 32, 219-40.

68. Bindra D. A motivational view of learning, performance, and behavior modification. *Psychological Review*, 1974, 81(3), 199-213.

69. Weingarten H.P. Conditioned cues elicit feeding in sated rats: A role for learning in meal initiation. *Science*, 1983, 220, 431-3.

70. Weingarten H.P. Meal initiation controlled by learned cues: Basic behavioral properties. *Appetite*, 1984, 5, 147-58.

71. Weingarten H.P. Stimulus control of eating: Implications for a two-factor theory for hunger. *Appetite*, 1985, 6, 387-401.

3.2. LEARNING IN THE DEVELOPMENT OF FOOD CRAVING

Edward Leigh Gibson

3.2.1   Introduction

This chapter addresses what learning has to do with eating in general, and whether cravings might be expressions of learnt or unlearnt strong appetites for certain foods or nutrients within them. Is there any evidence that we instinctively know which foods to eat to replenish our bodies with a needed nutrient? If not instinctively, can such a trick be learnt? Do food cravings always arise in response to a need for a specific nutrient, such as salt, iron or protein? How do food cravings compare with drug cravings, for which there is considerable evidence of an important role for learning?

3.2.2   The Inescapable Logic of Learning

Men's natures are alike; it is their habits that carry them far apart.
Confucius, 'Analects'

It is easy to think of learning as synonymous with hours or even years of study; or the student of psychology might have in mind laboratory rats acquiring impressive if seemingly arbitrary skills with levers and maze-arms. But the process of learning is much more fundamental than these formal images suggest. In fact, it is the principal means by which an organism can adapt to a changing environment.

In some instances, the equation formed from the needs of the organism and the structure of the environment may be simple enough to be solved by innate, automatic reflexes. The straining of sun-seeking plants to grow out of the shade, or the newborn mammal rooting for its mother's nipple are examples of unlearnt quests for sustenance.

Whereas the plant can respond only by changes in growth (excepting a few talented carnivorous species), most animals benefit hugely in terms of adaptation by being able to move. However, this weapon in the animal's armoury of adaptation is a double-edged sword; for, by moving, the animal also changes its environment. At once, the relationship between animal and food becomes much more complex. Add to this equation variation in the nature of the food and in the nutritional status of the eater, and it becomes clear that solving the problem by reflexes alone would require a system so monstrous that the scalpel of evolution would swiftly cut it out. Instead, evolution has provided the answer in the form of an adaptable system for processing information known (in more advanced animals) as the nervous system. The ability of neural systems to learn and process complex information efficiently is precisely what excites information technologists about applying neural networks to computation.

The need for such an information processing system is well illustrated by a recent definition of the behaviour of eating and drinking as:

"...the control of the movements of gathering and ingesting materials by physical and social exteroceptive stimuli and interoceptive signals from the digestive tract, tissue metabolism and circulating substrates and hormones."

Thibault and Booth (1)

Of course, eating and drinking that are organised to meet an animal's needs will be the product of both learnt and unlearnt responses to stimuli both within and without the body. Yet, as Confucius implies, it is by understanding the learnt responses that we are likely to be able to explain most of the variation in eating and drinking.

3.2.3   The Language of Learning

Psychologists have developed various ways of describing learning, and a grasp of the basic concepts and jargon may help in understanding this chapter. Here, we are primarily concerned with associative learning, which is the way in which an animal acquires knowledge about the relationship between events (2). In its simplest form, it is the memory that a perceived 'cue' has a particular 'consequence'. A cue might be an event perceived in the external or internal environment (a stimulus), or even some action of the animal itself (an operant or instrumental response). If the association between the cue and the consequence, or outcome, is remembered, then the cue has been 'conditioned' (a conditioned stimulus, CS) or reinforced to the association. The reinforcing consequence is the unconditioned stimulus (US). In some cases, 'stimulus substitution' may occur, when the unconditioned response (UR) that would normally follow the US (e.g. saliva secretion in response to food) is now elicited by the CS (e.g. a bell previously paired with food presentation), so that salivation is now a conditioned response (CR). However, the CS-US contingency can elicit an anticipatory CR that is quite different from any UR induced by the US: the important evidence is that a CR is elicited by a CS as a result of a CS-US association (3).

In the case of operant conditioning, or action-outcome learning, the CS can act as a discriminative stimulus (S^D) predicting that the reinforcing outcome will follow the action. Reinforcement should not be confused with 'reward': it is the memory of the association between events that is reinforced, so that, if a CS is perceived, a CR is likely to follow. The reinforcing process may not be pleasurable, and could involve aversive motivational states.

Evidence that learning has occurred depends on measuring a change in behaviour in appropriate test conditions. In general, this involves demonstrating a CR to a CS, or an operant response to an S^D, in the absence of the reinforcing US. This is known as testing in *extinction*. The learnt response will usually be *extinguished* on repeated testing in this way, since the association of CS to US is no longer reinforced.

3.2.4   Learnt Control of Eating

One might easily get the impression that the burden of proof lies with those who consider that a particular outcome of eating behaviour is *not* under learnt control, or at least influenced by learning. Perhaps it should; but, in reality, over many decades, learning has lain fallow in the field of research into eating behaviour (in the sense of understanding normal control of meal size and food choice), with just occasional examples of promising growth along its history (4-9). This is particularly ironic, given that, by contrast, research into learning theory and motivation has frequently been dependent on studies employing changes in hunger state and food availability (2,10,11). Moreover, many classic studies of how animals learn to predict events have used reactions to taste as the behavioural outcome (12,13). Encouragingly, there are now signs of increasing interest in measuring the influence of learning on eating and drinking behaviour (14-16). Indeed, its inclusion in this book is one such sign. Not before time: in a classic paper published in 1933, Harris *et al.* (4) were confident that:

> "...this factor of experience plays an important part in determining dietary preferences in general, and it will certainly have to be taken into account in future work on that hitherto neglected subject, the psychology of appetite."

We have plenty of opportunity to learn about what we eat: if a person has, on average, five ingestive experiences each day of their lives (probably an underestimate), then by their eighteenth birthday they will have had almost 33,000 such experiences. To understand the relevance of learning to food cravings, it will be helpful to introduce here some of the evidence for learnt control of eating.

3.2.4.1 The appetite for energy

The physiological need for energy, and especially for sufficient availability of glucose to ensure a constant supply to the brain, probably provides the primary motivation to eat. This need is capable of overriding other nutritional needs; for example, when moved to a colder, more energy-demanding environment, the laboratory rat will eat more even when the only diet available is nutritionally inadequate and cannot sustain growth (17). However, energy can be derived from any of the three macronutrients - carbohydrate, protein and fat - and so no particular property of a food is likely to be a reliable indicator, or cue, as to its energy content. Moreover, the extent to which a given macronutrient in a food is metabolised to energy, rather than stored or used for growth or other physiological function, depends on the current nutritional status of the eater, as well as the nutrient content of the food.

Thus, to choose a food best suited to our momentary needs, we have to know about the consequences of eating that food in our current state, and how that state will change on eating. In essence, an animal must learn to associate a sensory stimulus or cue (CS), such as the taste or smell experienced while eating the food, with postingestive sensations or changes in state. Removal of an energy deficit as the food is absorbed will be a positive consequence (US) that will reinforce an appetite, or preference (CR), for flavours (CSs) in the eaten food. Thus, we do not strictly have an appetite for energy, but rather a learnt appetite for food providing that energy.

There is now abundant evidence that just this sort of cue-consequence learning of flavour preferences occurs, in rats and people (8,15,18) and in many other animals (19). In general, a hungry animal will prefer flavours associated with rich sources of energy. Indeed, rats even learnt to prefer a less sweet tasting diet over a sweeter one, when sweetness was artificially manipulated so that the less sweet diet had more energy (20). However, given enough exposure, even flavours associated with very dilute carbohydrate solutions (1% to 4%) will come to be preferred over flavours paired with water (21). Sclafani demonstrated convincingly that these flavour preferences resulted from postingestive reinforcement, rather than by association with the taste of the nutrient. In his experiments, whenever rats drank flavoured water, an equal volume of nutrient solution, or water, was infused directly into the stomach, so bypassing sensations in the mouth or nasal cavity (22). Rats learnt preferences for the flavour paired with nutrient (over that paired with infusions of water) just as easily by this method as when drinking flavoured nutrient solutions directly.

Postingestive conditioning of flavour preferences has been demonstrated also for protein (23-26) and fat (27). Fat appears to be the least effective of the macronutrients in reinforcing flavour preferences (27), despite having more than twice the energy density of either carbohydrate or protein. This may be partly due to additional aversive effects of intragastric loads of pure fat, in animals concurrently drinking flavoured water. Absorption of energy may be a primary component of the reinforcing stimulus, but more specific consequences, particularly for protein, may also be important (see below).

Similar nutrient-conditioned flavour preferences have been demonstrated in human beings, for flavours paired with carbohydrate (18,28), protein (29) and fat (30,31).

3.2.4.2 Learnt control of meal size

Thus, an appetite for a food can be learnt by the reinforcing effects of energy absorption. But how do we know when to stop eating a food? Clearly, some feedback from consequences of ingested food in the gut is critical. When food is drained from the stomach as an animal eats, the animal continues eating at a high rate, ingesting enormous volumes of food (32). It is tempting to think that all that is required is for some physiological detector to tell the brain that enough energy has been absorbed, so no more food need be eaten. However, nearly half a century ago, Le Magnen (5,33) recognised that the answer could not be that simple. The reason is that food is emptied far more gradually from the stomach into the upper small intestine, where absorption takes place, than the rate at which it is eaten. Therefore, by the time a person feels full and has had enough to eat – perhaps only after 20 minutes – very little energy will have been absorbed, say 40 kilocalories (34). Le Magnen realised that ending a meal was in essence a prediction of later energy absorption consequent on what had just been eaten.

At the time a meal ends, the brain is well aware of at least three changes in state other than arrival of nutrients into the circulation. One is the taste or other sensation from food in the mouth, or the recent memory of it. Another is distension of the stomach by the large volume of food eaten but not yet emptied. A third is the detection, by neural receptors in the gut wall, of a constant passage of nutrients from the stomach into the duodenum. Through a lifetime's experience, particular levels of these stimuli come to predict particular amounts and effects of subsequently absorbed nutrients.

Therefore, a large part of what ends a meal is a learnt rejection of food in the presence of particular internal states generated by eating food, such as gastric distension. Booth (7) provided the first unconfounded evidence to support such learnt control of meal size, or 'conditioned satiety'. Rats were trained on meals of dilute carbohydrate having one flavour, and of concentrated carbohydrate having another. The rats ate smaller volumes of the concentrated carbohydrate, with eating rate slowing specifically in the second half of the meal. When the rats were given meals of intermediate concentration of carbohydrate, but with the flavours previously paired with either dilute or concentrated carbohydrate, the meal size and second-half eating rate differed in the direction of that seen when the levels of carbohydrate still differed as well as the flavours. That is, the ending of the meal was to a large extent being controlled by what the rats had learnt was predicted by the different flavours.

More recently, Gibson and Booth (35) showed that rats would reject a flavour previously paired with concentrated carbohydrate in preference for a novel odour, but only in the late stages of a meal. This 'conditioned satiety' provides the only known mechanism by which the volume of food consumed can be adjusted to provide a needed amount of energy.

Clearly, this learning depends on being able to associate postingestive effects with particular internal states, such as gastric distension, together with sensory features of the diet. Gibson and Booth (36) demonstrated that rats learn such associations rapidly. Mildly food-deprived rats were given one meal of dilute carbohydrate (providing the US) containing a particular flavour (the CS). Half of the rats were given non-nutritive preloads immediately prior to this training meal, to generate gastric distension cues. On another day, the rats that previously had the preloads were given a non-nutritive meal with the same flavour (i.e. CS without US), without any distension. Conversely, those rats that had previously had the carbohydrate meal without any preload, were now given a flavoured non-nutritive meal after a preload. Thus, the combination of gastric distension and CS flavour predicted carbohydrate after-effects for half the rats, whereas lack of distension, or emptiness, and CS flavour, predicted carbohydrate after effects for the other half. When subsequently given a choice between two diets, one with the trained CS flavour, the other unflavoured but otherwise identical, rats preferred the flavoured diet, but only when choosing in the distended or empty state that had been associated with flavoured carbohydrate in training. In the other internal state, they were indifferent to the flavour (Fig. 3.2.1).

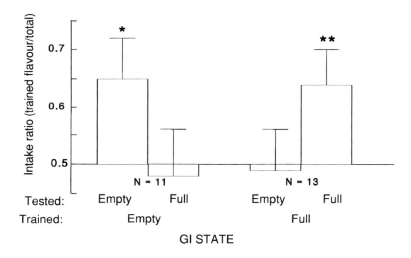

Fig. 3.2.1. Dependency of a conditioned preference for a carbohydrate-paired flavour on the level of gastrointestinal distension in which conditioning occurred (intake ratio from choice of flavoured and unflavoured diet: data from (36)).

This learnt association between a food's flavour, its after-effects and the internal state in which it is eaten, has also been demonstrated in people (18,37). A flavour previously paired with an energy-rich food is preferred only when hungry, whereas a flavour paired with a low-energy food is preferred when full. As with rats, appetite for a flavour was found to be altered only if assessed in the internal state in which that flavour's after-effects had been experienced previously (18).

Booth (8) interprets these state-dependent effects as evidence that the internal state cues and food sensory cues are configured into a Gestalt stimulus complex governing the conditioned response. That is, the learnt appetite CR is not fully expressed unless all components of the associated internal and external cues are present. Another interpretation is that the internal state, during which sensory cues come to predict postingestional effects, acts as an occasion setter (38), i.e. a stimulus that modulates associative strength between a CS and US. For example, in the experiment of Gibson and Booth (36), the distension cue (or emptiness in one half of the group) could strengthen the CS-US association because it allowed discrimination between the situation (internal state) in which the flavour CS was paired with after-effects of carbohydrate, and that in which the flavour CS was contained in a non-nutritive solution.

An important point that emerges from both these interpretations is that internal food-related states such as gut emptiness or fullness, or other feelings of hunger, do not simply elicit appetite, or remove it, in the sense of innate drives. Rather, they allow adaptive context-specific eating behaviour to be learnt, so that appetite and satiety largely reflect acquired 'metabolic expectancies' (39). However, the strength and valence of the reinforcing US may also depend on the internal state in which the food is eaten.

3.2.5   Specific Need-dependent Appetites

The ultimate aim of the evolutionary game is to survive long enough to reproduce, and to ensure that reproductive success carries over to each subsequent generation. A successful species will therefore have developed ways of obtaining sufficient nutrients from its environment to support growth and survival to maturity. The solution is likely to be a combination of innate reactions, social transmission of behaviours, and an inherent propensity of the nervous system to learn relationships between internal and external events.

To some extent, fluctuations in levels of nutrients can be buffered by physiological systems that react to changes in supply or use of those nutrients. This is the classic ability of an organism's internal milieu to maintain equilibrium, or homeostasis, described early in the 20th century (40). However, animals also need to consume a regular supply of *essential* nutrients, so called because the body has a limited or non-existent capacity to synthesise or store them. Thus, physiological regulation needs to be supplemented by *behavioural* regulation, as recognised by Curt Richter, who was among the first to demonstrate that rats can select appropriate diets to rectify particular nutrient deficiencies (41).

Adaptive innate reactions will have evolved where a specific stimulus or cue, such as the taste of a plant, consistently predicts a consequence of eating the plant that has an impact on the animal's survival or reproductive success. Thus, many animals instinctively reject bitter tastes, presumably because bitterness is associated with the presence of poisonous plant alkaloids. Conversely, animals commonly show an innate propensity to ingest sweet tasting food or fluids: sweetness might be a consistent cue for ripeness of non-toxic fruit and roots, although ripeness also means loss of acidity and inedible toughness. Instead, Booth (42,43) suggests that a more convincing evolutionary role in mammals may be as an anti-bitterness device in nitrogen-rich mother's milk. That is, 'sweet' receptors respond to chemical groups on both sugars and amino acids, so there would be strong selection pressure to develop an ingestive reflex when such receptors are stimulated, so that the protein-rich milk is not rejected. An exception to support that rule is the cat family: these arch-carnivores, which thrive on higher levels of protein than would be good for us, and have little interest in eating carbohydrates or plants, have lost the ability to taste sweetness (44). Cats (or kittens) are also poor at self-selecting adequate amounts of protein from a choice of diets (45), suggesting a lack of evolutionary pressure to do so.

The list of nutrients required for optimal health by omnivores such as rats and ourselves, and their potential sensory guises, is surely too extensive to depend on innate appetites (46). In other words, adaptive food choice cannot rely solely on a battery of innate reactions of acceptance or rejection to a world of varying sensory stimuli. Evolution's answer is to provide the machinery for learning about a changing and varied world - a nervous system designed to detect, record and respond to reliable relationships between two or more events.

One possibly unique exception to balancing nutrient intake through learning is sodium appetite. It is worth considering this phenomenon in more detail.

3.2.5.1   Sodium appetite

The crucial point about sodium is that the salty taste of a food is closely related to its sodium content; that is, for sodium, there is a sensory cue in the food eaten that predicts absorption of the nutrient. In that case, it is reasonable to expect that an unlearnt appetite for saltiness (the taste of sodium chloride) may have evolved where deficiency can occur, so that a sodium-deficient animal would select and consume saltier foods. Retention of sodium depends on hormones released from the adrenal glands. Therefore, one way to make a rat sodium-deficient is to remove these glands (an adrenalectomised rat). Using this procedure, Richter (41) demonstrated that sodium-deficient rats could survive by drinking concentrated solutions of sodium chloride, which intact rats found unacceptably salty.

Several lines of evidence have subsequently shown that rats express a rapid and unlearnt appetite for sodium when lacking that micronutrient (47). When rats are first made sodium-deficient, they avidly consume salt solutions, apparently without enough time to have learnt the benefit of replenishing their sodium levels (48). In another study, the increased appetite elicited by sodium depletion was expressed as enhanced lever pressing by rats that had been trained to press levers for sodium without experience of deficiency, i.e. the learning appeared to be 'latent' (49). This specific deficiency-induced rapid lever pressing occurred even when the response did not result in delivery of sodium, i.e. during extinction. This behaviour could be interpreted as the active expression of a craving: the animals are clearly highly motivated, and appear to be actively 'seeking sodium', despite the absence of reinforcement by the taste of sodium. The authors were concerned that the increased rate of lever pressing might merely reflect frustration-induced arousal: however, such a mechanism would not explain subsequent evidence that sodium-deficient rats preferred the arm of a 'T' maze previously paired with a source of sodium so concentrated as to be aversive during training (50). This 'latent' learning has been termed 'irrelevant incentive' learning, since the association appears to form in the absence of reinforcement (51). Moreover, it is the experience of consuming sodium chloride that is critical to the subsequent evidence of deficiency-induced appetite (increased lever pressing), not learning that lever pressing provides the sodium chloride (51). It is not just an operant action such as lever pressing that allows expression of sodium appetite: arbitrary flavour cues associated with sodium in the absence of deficiency acquire motivational or incentive value once the innate appetite for sodium is aroused by deficiency (52). Nevertheless, the strength of the innate appetite can be modified by experience: thus, flavour preferences predicting sodium are enhanced in relation to the degree of sodium depletion experienced during training (53).

Do human beings have an innate appetite for sodium? It might seem reasonable to expect such a mechanism to have evolved, since we need sodium for physiological function, and, like the rat, we can eat a very varied diet. Yet, such nature versus nurture questions are hard to answer definitively in people. Comparing fraternal and identical twins is one research tool for separating environment from inheritance. In a review of human salt appetite, Beauchamp (54) concluded that there was no evidence from twin studies to support genetic control of sodium appetite, but that the studies were methodologically weak (a particular difficulty is how to measure a stable salt preference sufficiently reliably and sensitively).

A classic case of sodium appetite in a child was reported by Wilkins and Richter (55). The child suffered from adrenocortical insufficiency (the pathological human analogue of Richter's adrenalectomised rats), and could not survive without considerable salt intake. He apparently craved salt and salty foods, and survived well enough, until misguided hospital staff restricted salt in his diet, to lethal effect. However, whilst the child clearly expressed a strong appetite (indeed, a craving) for salt, this poignant case does not tell us whether he did so innately or through rapid learning of the benefits to his health of eating salty food.

Infants aged 3 to 4 months do not show any preference for salt solutions over plain water, unlike their clear preference for sugar solutions at that age, or the preference for both sugar and salt over water seen in older children (56). Although this might reflect some maturational change, it is clear that experience modifies salt preference. Thus, adults typically enjoy salty foods but not salty water, and this preference is seen to develop in children by about 3 years of age (54), probably reflecting contextual experience of salty tastes. Also, 6-month-old infants previously fed high- or low-sodium cereal food preferred the salt level to which they had been exposed (57). In adults, if dietary sodium is either raised or lowered for several months, the preferred salt level shifts in the direction of the manipulation (54,58,59).

Clearly, our rather excessive preferred salt level is influenced by the levels to which we are exposed in our diet (54). Nevertheless, there is recent evidence that adult human salt appetite can be determined by neonatal or even foetal physiological experience. That is, if the developing baby is exposed to a loss of minerals, including sodium and chloride, whether through vomiting and diarrhoea (60), maternal vomiting during pregnancy (61), or deficient infant diet (62), salt appetite may be enhanced into adulthood. This implies that permanent changes in some neurohormonal system can occur as a result of the mineral insufficiency, to enhance intake of sodium. Yet the restructuring does not appear to adapt again once the insufficiency is removed: it may be an example of an innate, defensive adaptation to a nutritional need, not learning. This would seem to support the assertion that the basic appeal of salt to human beings may be innate (54).

However, it should be noted that appetite for salt, in rats at least, is also enhanced by other mineral deficiencies, especially calcium (63). It has been suggested that salty taste might be a marker for the presence of a number of essential minerals (64). Yet, salt appetite seems to be enhanced by protein deficiency, too (65). Perhaps any state of nutritional deficiency to some extent arouses the only innate appetite the brain can call upon; alternatively, such findings may be confounded by generalisation from past experience of tasting even slightly salty food.

3.2.5.2   Pica and iron appetite

Pica, the Latin for magpie, is the term given to consumption of and craving for non-foods, such as soil, clay or chalk, or unusual and near exclusive consumption of edible items, such as salt or a specific vegetable (66) (magpies being renowned horders of useless objects). It is associated with pregnancy and childhood, and it is tempting to believe that pica might represent an appetite for a needed nutrient. Several clinical reports suggest that pica is found in iron-deficient patients, and correction of the deficiency can coincide with a reduction in pica (67-69). However, in none of those cases was there any evidence that substances consumed were likely to correct the iron deficiency, and indeed, in these and other cases of pica, the consumption of non-foods is more likely to contribute to a number of deficiencies (70).

Therefore, pica is unlikely to involve a learned appetite or craving for foods redressing a nutritional need, although calcium appetite during pregnancy is a possible candidate for some pica (71). It seems more likely that, in many cases, it represents a broad aversion to foods - for example through nausea-induced aversions during pregnancy and at other times (72), or at least a dislike of a range of food textures, coupled with a non-specific urge to eat. (See also section 5.1.) Among non-foods that are easily available, and can be swallowed without too much discomfort or obvious lethality, most have probably been eaten by some people at some time. Even so, there are many examples where a learnt preference for the flavour of a nutrient-supplying food persists long after the preferred food ceases to provide benefit, thus obscuring the aetiology.

Despite a lack of evidence for iron appetite in people, one might expect that a food containing iron would come to be preferred, if it is eaten during deficiency in amounts sufficient to allow recovery. Such learning has been shown in rats recovering from vitamin deficiency. There is one quite convincing report of latent learning of an appetite for iron (73), akin to that found for sodium discussed above (49). Woods *et al.* (73) trained rats to lever press for ferrous ions in water, and subsequently made them iron-deficient. When tested in extinction (without iron in the water), the rats' rate of lever pressing correlated with the extent of their anaemia. One possible weakness in this study was that food intake might have been inhibited by prior water deprivation, so that the learning might not have been latent if the ferrous ions removed a need for iron in food-deprived animals. Nevertheless, at the very least, it is evidence that an appetite for a source of iron can be expressed when iron is needed.

3.2.6   Wisdom of the Body or Serendipity of the Individual?

Richter (74) championed what he saw as rats' instinctive ability to capitalise on Cannon's (40) concept of 'the wisdom of the body'. That is, the body should be equipped with systems to detect nutritional deficiency, and which Richter proposed then elicit 'special appetites' for any essential nutrient, so that the animals "make dietary selections which are conducive to normal growth and development" (75).

Central to this belief is the seductive concept that omnivores in particular must have evolved means of assuring an adequate nutrient intake from among a bewildering array of possible foods. Such a notion was already being defended vigorously in the early days of modern biology by nutritionists and biochemists flush with evolutionary zeal, when it was found that rodents self-selected good over poor sources of protein (76).

However, it soon became clear that not all rats were graced with this 'nutritional wisdom'. In one of the first studies to allow rats to 'self-select' between separate sources of protein, carbohydrate and essential micronutrients, Kon (77) reported that two rats died after failing to make wise choices over 2 months. The most likely explanation was extreme differences in palatability, or sensory acceptability, of the diets: the protein was a powdered casein, while the carbohydrate was sucrose. Rats prefer sweet, crunchy food, but in general avoid powdered casein (6,78). In a similar vein, Beck and Galef (79) housed 18 young rats individually in large cages with access to three sweet low-protein diets and one protein-rich (20% casein) diet. After a week, only four of the rats had developed a preference for the protein-rich diet, and the others lost weight.

Despite such problems, the 'self-selection' experimental design, or 'cafeteria diet', has become hugely popular. It has been suggested that this is by and large an unfortunate waste of research effort (3,80): simply measuring changes in intake of separate sources of nutrients as a treatment outcome tells one nothing of the behavioural processes that led to the outcome - the input to the output must be measured and controlled. In a critical review highlighting the failings and inconsistencies in this area, Galef (81) has pointed out that:

> "One should not ask whether rats (or humans) can self-select adequate diets but instead inquire as to the characteristics of choice situations affecting the probability that individuals with differing food preferences will come to eat an adequate diet."

Galef has shown that weanling rats can successfully choose the protein-rich diet in the above multiple-choice situation, if given the opportunity to smell odour cues on rats already trained to select that diet (79) – an important example of social transmission of food choice.

Galef also argued that the existence of a species in a particular environment does not imply that that species will successfully self-select a balanced diet in a different environment, let alone an artificial laboratory experiment (81). It tells us even less about a given *individual's* chances of success: if reproductive rates are great enough, a species as a whole may colonise an environment despite considerable numbers of individuals failing to thrive long enough to reproduce (81).

As for human beings, Davis's classic studies (82,83) of infants, apparently thriving when 'self-selecting' their own choice of food, have often been considered evidence of instinctive nutritional wisdom. In reality, this finding is more likely to be a result of serendipitous availability of reasonably nutritious foods without extremes of palatability (81,84). The infants were fed by a nurse responding to their reaching for a particular food among several on a tray (83); one can imagine that, if cola and candy had been available, the infants may well have fared no better than Kon's unfortunate sweet-toothed rats (77).

So, we need to be cautious about assuming that a species will have evolved an infallible mechanism for expressing the wisdom of the body, simply because it thrives in a given environment. Even two of the world's most successful and ubiquitous omnivores, *Homo sapiens* (you and I) and *Rattus norvegicus* (the brown or Norway rat), have limits to their natural range, and can be led astray into malnutrition by availability of the 'wrong' foods (even in the presence of the 'right' ones), and isolation from social support. Nevertheless, we shall see that there is good evidence that rats can learn to make adaptive food choices to avoid deficiencies in vitamins and protein (or essential amino acids from which proteins and other essential biochemicals are constructed).

3.2.7   Learnt Appetites for what is Needed

3.2.7.1   Vitamin-conditioned flavour preferences

In 1933, Harris *et al.* (4) published a seminal paper detailing a series of thoughtful experiments on diet choices of vitamin B-deficient rats. The essence of their design was to feed rats an unflavoured diet deficient in vitamin B, then give them a choice of unflavoured, Bovril-flavoured and Marmite-flavoured diets (Marmite is yeast extract rich in vitamin B). The latter two diets thus had a similar flavour, but only the Marmite-flavoured diet contained sufficient vitamin B. From the first day or two, the rats chose to eat mainly the Marmite-flavoured diet, their falling body weight was arrested, and they began to grow rapidly. Control (non-deficient) groups showed that this was not a chance liking for Marmite over the other diets. Could the rats taste even tiny amounts of vitamin B in the diet? No; when vitamin B was added to the unflavoured diet without other flavouring, the rats did not discriminate between unflavoured and supplemented diets (4). From these and other results, Harris *et al.* (4) concluded that "… the right choice of diet cannot be left to instinct but is an art that has to be taught."

The evidence was clear: given a distinctive sensory characteristic in the nutritious diet, such as its flavour, and sufficient exposure to its benefits, rats could learn to eat that diet so that their deficiency was removed. They had learnt a specific appetite, not for the vitamin *per se*, but for the flavour of the diet that removed their need. This was the first evidence for associative conditioning of a dietary flavour preference by removal of a nutritional need. The finding has since been confirmed by several other groups, primarily using recovery from vitamin B deficiency (85-88).

Two further points are worth noting about the findings of Harris *et al.* (4). First, once the preference for a particular flavour was established, it resisted extinction. That is, when the vitamin was removed from that diet, and added to another differently flavoured one, the rats largely maintained their established preference for the first diet, even though they lost weight owing to the vitamin deficiency[1]. This raises the question whether food cravings that no longer appear to have any basis in need might originate from some earlier potent learning experience, which resists extinction (cf. pica, above; drug craving and addiction, below).

Second, as the choice of diets offered increased, more and more of the rats failed to develop a clear preference for the vitamin-rich diet. If they were 'educated' by brief but exclusive exposure to the repleting diet, then the preference developed as before. Perhaps these failings reflect rather artificial situations unlikely to be encountered regularly by an evolving omnivore species. It would be a cruel world where a needed nutrient suddenly vanished from a diet without any detectable change: and being spoilt by a large choice of palatable foods all at once, only one of which could sustain growth, was probably not a test many species would face regularly.

3.2.7.2   *Amino acid and protein-conditioned flavour preferences*

One of the earliest findings in nutrition research was that optimal growth of young animals depends on an adequate supply of good-quality protein (76). It became clear that a particular pattern of essential amino acids from the protein source was the critical variable in determining the biological value

---

[1] The persistence of the initial preference, despite concurrent deficiency and illness, would suggest that the preference was not merely avoidance of the initially deficient diets. Later studies by other groups employing a variety of controls of exposure to flavours also support the conclusion that recovery from vitamin deficiency conditions a genuine preference for associated dietary flavours (146). Indeed, these recovery-paired flavours were shown to be more resistant to later experimental associations with illness than both novel and equally familiar 'safe' flavours (147).

of protein. In the 1960s and 1970s, a fascinating series of studies provided evidence that rats were particularly sensitive to imbalances or deficiencies in essential amino acids and protein in their diet. For instance, it was shown that rats ate less of a diet deficient in an essential amino acid compared with a balanced diet, within a day (89). Moreover, protein-deprived young rats acquired a preference for an odour paired with intake of a balanced mixture of amino acids, relative to an odour paired with water or saline (90,91). Conversely, a single pairing of an odour (92) or taste (93) with an imbalanced (histidine-free) amino acid load conditioned an aversion for that odour.

It is also clear that rats self-selecting from diets varying in protein content can adapt their intake to provide an appropriate level of protein (94,95). This ability depends on learning the relationship between some distinguishing sensory quality of a particular diet and its postingestional consequences (26,96); thus, rats rapidly learn to prefer flavours paired with adequate protein meals over flavours paired with protein-free meals (26). Similarly, rats learn preferences and aversions for, respectively, flavours of diets balanced or deficient in essential amino acids (97).

The conditioning US generated by imbalanced amino acid loads occurs within 2 hours - the aversion is not seen with greater delays between the imbalanced load and eating the odorised diet (92). Furthermore, it is well established that, by this time, the anterior pyriform cortex of the brain will have detected this imbalance in plasma amino acid pattern, through exposure to changes in competitive transport of amino acids across the blood-brain barrier (98-100). This area of the brain is critical for the rat's rejection of an amino-acid-deficient diet (101,102). In especially metabolically active animals, such as small mammals and birds, speed is of the essence in obtaining supplies of essential amino acids, before body proteins are broken down and negative nitrogen balance results (98). Recent examination of eating rates of rats given two novel diets, one imbalanced in amino acids, revealed a reduction in rate of eating the imbalanced diet within the second half of the first meal, i.e. after 12 minutes (98).

To be able to adapt its choice of diet in response to fluctuating protein availability and need, the rat must be able to learn a preference for a dietary flavour, which it will express only when concurrently lacking protein. This is exactly what has been found: rats trained to prefer a flavour paired with protein were then preloaded with either protein or equicaloric carbohydrate. After the protein preload, rats no longer preferred the protein-paired flavour, whereas the carbohydrate preload had no effect on the preference (23,103). Thus, rats can learn a protein-conditioned flavour preference that depends specifically on a protein need.

3.2.7.3   Human appetite for protein

Similar to the rat, human beings have a requirement for essential amino acids in the diet, even if exact quantification of protein requirements remains a matter for debate (104). Although the influences on human food preferences are many and varied, it seems a logical possibility that people may be capable of acquiring and expressing a need-dependent appetite for protein-rich foods. There are, in fact, several findings that support this notion. More than 40 years ago, it was observed that changes in appetite during the day correlated with levels of amino acids in the blood, but not with blood glucose levels (105). More recently, it was found that people chose to eat more protein in the 4 hours following a high-energy but protein-free drink than after a very low energy placebo (106). In another study, people with lower blood indices of protein status preferred the flavour of greater concentrations of casein hydrolysate added to an amino-acid deficient soup, while more protein-replete subjects preferred casein-free soup (107). Similarly, human infants recovering from protein-energy malnutrition, but not healthy controls, preferred a soup to which casein hydrolysate (which has a strong savoury flavour) had been added (108). Finally, Gibson *et al.* (29) extended their flavour preference conditioning designs from rats to people; thus, when people ate one meal of adequate protein, following a low-protein breakfast and overnight fast, they preferred the (arbitrary) flavours associated with that meal (particularly the desserts) compared with flavours associated with a low-protein meal. Furthermore, on a second test day, this protein-paired flavour preference was abolished specifically by a high-protein preload, just as it was in rats (23,103).

Therefore, in appropriate conditions, human beings can learn a protein-specific appetite for a food flavour, which depends on the presence of a mild protein need.

It is not known whether or how we consciously perceive the reinforcing consequences of eating protein when deprived of it. However, one possibility is suggested by a recent finding from a study of hormonal and mood responses to protein-rich lunches (109). When people who had been eating a low-protein diet for 5 days were given a protein-rich lunch, a substantial increase in positive arousal occurred 2-3 hours later. The change in mood was not immediate or even 1 hour after eating, and so is not likely to be merely satisfaction from the sensory properties of the meal. Rather, induction by some internal cue arising from amino acid absorption seems more likely. Indeed, the extent of increase in arousal correlated with the increased secretion of the glucocorticoid hormone, cortisol, which occurred immediately after the meal. This rise in cortisol is a recognised effect of meals, particularly at midday, when the normal circadian decline in cortisol is rapid (110). It is probably related to control of nitrogen metabolism, and is not seen after very low protein meals (111). However, cortisol has profound effects on neuronal function in limbic areas of the brain (112), and so could quite easily be involved in changes in mood state and memory.

3.2.7.4   Is there a 'protein taste'?

An interesting question, which has been a matter of some debate, is whether we, or rats, could have an innate ability to find protein sources when lacking it (42,113,114). The argument against such an innate skill is that it would require the existence of some reliable sensory quality of protein-rich foods, so that an ingestive reflex linked to it could evolve (1,42). The essential amino acids can be obtained from several different proteins, or their combinations, so it seems unlikely that they would impart a consistent sensory characteristic on foods as diverse as seeds, leaves, eggs, milk, flesh and fish. Nevertheless, it has been proposed that a savoury taste sensation, common to many protein-rich foods, could be a candidate for a 'protein taste' (115). This taste has been given the Japanese name umami, and the archetypal example is the flavour of monosodium glutamate (MSG), well-known for its ability to enhance acceptance of food. The naturally occurring components of foods imparting this flavour appear to be glutamates and 5'-ribonucleotides such as guanosine monophosphate (116). Furthermore, there is now molecular and physiological evidence for specialised taste receptors for glutamate on the tongue (116).

If umami taste is a sensory cue to the presence of protein, then one would expect its consumption to be increased during protein deficiency, in rats or people. In fact, the behavioural evidence suggests just the opposite. Rats on a protein- or amino-acid-deficient diet prefer the taste of sodium chloride over umami tastants, and express a preference for umami only during protein repletion (65). Human infants prefer soup with added MSG over plain soup, whether or not they are malnourished, unlike the preference for casein hydrolysate (108). Thus, there is no evidence that umami taste provides a sensory cue allowing innate expression of a protein appetite.

Some evidence suggests that rats may use odour cues from proteins (117); thus, protein-deficient rats ate more of a protein-free diet from bins smelling of proteins derived from plants and egg, but not soya or milk proteins, than from bins smelling of butter. No such preference was seen in protein-replete rats (117). Aside from needing to explain the selective nature of the odour preference (which suggests that there is not a specific and reliable odour cue for protein), the preferences expressed may be generalisations from flavours associated with the laboratory diet.

3.2.8 Learning and Craving

How do these examples of learnt control of eating relate to understanding food craving? Let us consider again what we mean by craving. It is a strong urge to find and eat a particular food – at that moment we feel a need for it, and nothing else will do. Such cravings often appear to be induced by particular situations, the sight, smell or taste of food, and internal (physical or emotional) states. We have already seen how the expression of learnt appetites for specific foods can depend on the presence of internal states.

Moreover, we have seen that, with the exception of sodium, it is unlikely that specific appetites or cravings could develop *without* learning. Therefore, Gibson and Desmond (118) hypothesised that cravings for energy-rich foods, such as chocolate, were essentially strong appetites created by repeated reinforcing experience of eating such food when hungry. Chocolate may be a dominant example of a craved food in part because of the salience (and even innate appeal) of its sweet, creamy, melt-in-the-mouth sensory properties. Thus, when a particular level of hunger is experienced, the trained chocolate eater would easily recall chocolate's sensory properties and the appetite acquired from the associated after-effects of eating it.

In support of this argument, Gibson and Desmond (118) showed that, after chocolate was eaten exclusively when hungry for 2 weeks, craving for it increased, even in people who did not report craving chocolate beforehand. Conversely, craving decreased substantially in people who had eaten the chocolate only when full (Fig. 3.2.2). The implication is that chocolate craving is indeed a learnt appetite, acquired through experience of the reinforcing after-effects of an energy-rich food eaten when hungry. If eaten when full, the reinforcing postingestive US is lost, and could even become aversive if negative sensations associated with too much richness are experienced, so craving is extinguished.

On this basis, one would expect that other energy-dense foods with salient sensory properties would be commonly craved. This does appear to be the case: foods such as pizza, crisps, cake and ice cream are also popularly craved (119,120). Furthermore, in a survey of food craving tendencies of 170 students, 54% reported eating other foods to assuage cravings for chocolate when none was available, and 44% of these substitute foods were savoury, such as crisps (E. Desmond and E.L. Gibson, unpublished data). This again supports the argument that craving for chocolate represents a learnt appetite for energy, which other energy-rich (even non-sweet) foods can to some extent alleviate. Similarly, Michener and Rozin (121) found that eating white chocolate partially removed the craving for milk chocolate, whereas merely ingesting cocoa powder ingredients in capsules had no effect. This is also evidence against chocolate craving being a need for a specific nutrient, such as magnesium, or an addiction to some psychoactive ingredient (122).

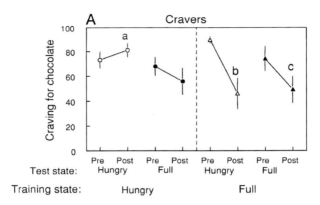

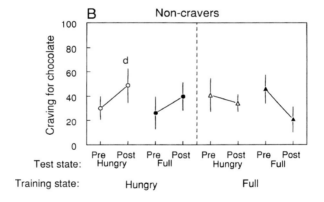

Fig. 3.2.2. Effect of eating chocolate when exclusively hungry or full (training state) and test state (hungry, open symbols; full, closed symbols) on the change in chocolate craving before (pre) and after (post) a 2-week training period.

Reproduced with permission from Gibson E.L., Desmond E. Chocolate craving and hunger state: implications for the acquisition and expression of appetite and food choice. Appetite, 1999, 32, 219-40. Copyright Academic Press.

It should be noted that the ubiquitous nature of reports of cravings for foods such as chocolate, cake and ice cream does not support claims that this represents so-called 'carbohydrate craving'. These foods are typically higher in fat than carbohydrate, and a craving for them is not evidence that carbohydrate, rather than some other property of the food, is being craved (42). It may just be the same strong learnt appetite for an energy-rich food, as discussed above, although, in the case of low-protein, high-carbohydrate foods eaten when hungry, other neurophysiological reinforcement might occur in some people (123) (see below).

3.2.9   Craving, Cue Reactivity and Sensory Stimulation

Most people are familiar with the experience of a dramatic stimulation of appetite upon seeing, smelling or tasting a familiar and liked food, particularly if hungry at the time. Similarly, appetite rises in the initial stages of a meal, even in already hungry subjects - the 'appetiser effect' (124), which the French describe as *"l'appétit vient en mangeant"*. Indeed, 'priming' with a taste of a liked (and often craved) food such as pizza or ice cream encourages eating of those foods in subjects already fed to satiety (125). Lambert *et al.* (126) found that both the sight and the taste of chocolate M&Ms (Mars) increased the desire to eat this confectionery more than mere thoughts or no stimulation, and to the same extent whether hungry or full. Also, dieters can be induced to overeat merely by smelling a food (127).

These are all examples of cue reactivity, or appetitive reactions to sensory stimulation by food, which presumably are influenced by experience. Indeed, Jansen (128) has argued that binge eaters will be particularly susceptible to food cues, because their large meals will generate strongly reinforcing USs, so conditioning powerful anticipatory appetites to associated stimuli. Unreinforced exposure to such cues was shown to extinguish food cravings in binge eaters (128) (see also section 7.2).

Therefore, experience with eating a food should influence the extent to which tasting that food would affect appetite or craving for it. Gibson and Desmond (unpublished data) looked at the change in craving rated before and after tasting chocolate, when hungry and full, in cravers and in non-cravers (who were frequent and infrequent chocolate eaters, respectively). To distinguish effects of sequence, half the subjects rated craving on day 1 when full, and on day 2 when hungry, whereas the other half did so while hungry on day 1 and full on day 2. As well as rating craving, the subjects actually ate the chocolate in the appropriate appetitive state for that day.

In chocolate cravers, tasting the chocolate had no effect, in any state, on rated craving (three-way repeated measures analysis of variance on tasting, hunger state and sequence factors: largest $F = 2.1$; on a 100-mm scale, largest mean change $= -3.4$; other data not shown). By contrast, in non-cravers, tasting increased craving moderately, except in subjects tested full on day 2, i.e. after previously being tested hungry. In those subjects, tasting the chocolate when full actually resulted in a reduction in craving, compared with their craving when hungry (Fig. 3.2.3: tasting x hunger state x sequence interaction, $F(1, 10) = 10.64$, $p < 0.01$).

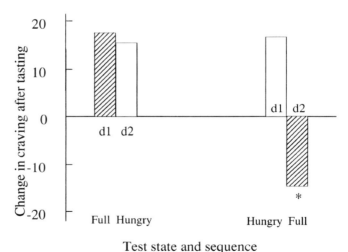

Fig. 3.2.3. Effect of hunger state and test sequence (day 1, day 2) on change in rated craving for chocolate after tasting one piece. Unpublished data (E.L. Gibson and E. Desmond). *d2 <d1 change, t(5)=3.11, p<0.05 2-tail

How can we explain these results? It seems likely that cravers are so experienced with eating chocolate that the sight and smell of chocolate were sufficient stimulation, so that tasting had no additional impact on craving. For non-cravers (for whom tasting chocolate was a relatively rare experience) who ate chocolate first when full then hungry, the orosensory experience of tasting chocolate on day 1 was presumably reinforcing despite their being full from eating other foods. This is rather like the release of appetite induced by tasting a food, or foods, not recently eaten (129). However, eating chocolate on this day when full would not allow positive postingestive reinforcement. Thus, on the next day, despite the subjects' now being hungry, one would not expect any more stimulation of craving than occurred on the previous day, since no hunger-dependent incentive had yet been learnt. The similar response also suggests that eating the chocolate when full the previous day was not aversive.

In the non-cravers tested first when hungry, one would expect a similar reaction to the taste as seen with the previous group, since on day 1 no hunger-dependent reinforcement had yet occurred. This is what was found. By day 2, these subjects should have experienced positive consequences of eating chocolate when hungry. If they had again been tested hungry, their craving might have been further increased by tasting. However, instead they were tested when full, and tasting the chocolate actually reduced their rated craving. Possibly, tasting the chocolate called attention to their current internal state, fullness, which was *not* configured with positive reinforcing after effects. Thus, the craving or appetite for chocolate is devalued in the absence of a previously associated hunger state. Even if this is not the correct explanation, the results clearly emphasise the differential impact that brief experience of eating a food in different states can have on craving in people without established habits with that food.

3.2.10   Food Craving vs. Drug Craving

It is worth comparing food craving with drug craving, not least because food cravings have often been discussed and explained with reference to an addiction model (122,128,130,131) (see sections 2.2, 4.2 & 6.2). Unlike food craving, drug craving has been extensively studied for more than a century, and there is now an enormous body of literature on this topic (132,133). This no doubt reflects the greater clinical and public health concerns in the area.

It is notable that learning is firmly established as having a critical influence on drug craving and the development of drug habits (132-134). Pavlovian conditioning has been invoked to explain aspects of drug-related phenomena such as withdrawal, tolerance and physiological changes, as well as relapse (135). One aspect of drug use that appears to share similarities with food craving is that relapse may often be precipitated by negative emotional states, which themselves may become learnt cues to reinforcing effects of the drugs (135,136). Self-proclaimed 'chocolate addicts' appear to crave chocolate as a means to alleviate negative moods, although their relief is short-lasting, and they typically report increased guilt or depressed mood after actually eating chocolate (130,131). Furthermore, as with drug addicts, chocolate-related cues elicit craving and physiological arousal in chocolate 'addicts' (131). In fact, there is recent evidence that sweet, fatty, high-carbohydrate/low-protein foods such as chocolate could protect susceptible individuals from some emotional and physiological consequences of stress (123). This suggests a reinforcing mechanism for a learnt appetite for such foods during emotional arousal (137).

Interestingly, there is also some evidence that enhanced appetite for sweet taste is associated with alcoholism (138). However, evidence for this association may be confounded by genetic insensitivity to bitter taste, which could allow greater acceptance of saccharin and concentrated sucrose solutions, as well as alcohol (139-141).

Another aspect of food craving reminiscent of drug use is the 'priming' of increased appetite or craving invoked by small tastes of the food. In both human beings and animals, exposure to a small dose of a drug can reinstate previously extinguished drug taking - a phenomenon known as drug priming, thought to be an important component of relapse. It is likely that this priming effect is mediated by learnt recognition of drug-induced subjective effects (142).

However, in terms of implications for the relationship between food craving and eating, it should be noted that the common assumption that drug craving provokes drug taking has recently been questioned (143). It was argued that, at least in experienced drug users, the stimulus-bound, stereotypic and uncontrollable nature of drug taking in fact suggests automatic, habitual behaviour. That is, the drug-taking habit is so well trained that it has become a largely subconscious motor behaviour, like the movements of a musician playing a familiar tune. This allows drug taking to occur independently of subjectively experienced motivational states such as craving, and to some extent in the absence of continued reinforcement (144). Such habitual addiction is also reminiscent of rats' persistence of preference for the diet previously, but no longer, providing needed vitamin B (4,87), as well as of the loss of control and cue reactivity experienced by habitual binge eaters (128). In people, eating a familiar food when surrounded by familiar stimuli might similarly become an automatic habit, requiring little cognitive input, but strongly stimulus-bound. So, perhaps we should be cautious about assuming that food craving would necessarily predict increased eating of that food. Craving and consuming may be learnt reactions to the same cues, but not necessarily causally linked.

3.2.11   Summary

Learning clearly has a fundamental role to play in the development of appetite and satiety. Learning mechanisms allow selection of appropriate foods (and drinks) to satisfy concurrent bodily needs. Meal size and satiation are also under learnt control, so that we can stop eating in anticipation of adequate nutrient delivery well in advance of actual replenishment of needy sites within the body (35).

Hunger is primarily an appetite for energy, and previous experience teaches us which foods will satisfy that hunger most effectively. A very hungry person may be thought of as craving energy, and if that person regularly eats a specific energy-rich food when hungry, he/she may well learn a habit whereby his/her thoughts will be focused on that food during hunger, as is likely with chocolate (118). However, if such foods evoke cognitive conflict and negative emotions, these feelings may also acquire stimulus control over appetite for those foods.

Aside from energy, there is good evidence that people and rats can learn to like foods supplying them with needed protein or amino acids, at least in laboratory conditions. They also express this specific appetite, once learnt, just when they lack the nutrient. However, it is not known to what extent food cravings, outside the laboratory, might reflect an appetite for protein, although it seems a possibility.

Cravings for salt have been observed clinically (55), although not always in response to sodium deficiency (69). Nevertheless, it seems clear that the rat at least can express a strong appetite for sodium when deficient, without the need for learning. The evidence for such an ability in people is weak, but it remains a possibility. What is apparent is that experience can modify liking for salty taste, and it may modify cravings too.

There is little evidence to support the argument that food craving necessarily represents a need for a particular nutrient, whether learnt or unlearnt. However, there is a paucity of good data. The position taken in this chapter is that food cravings are strong, and often specific, appetites, labelled as cravings for social, cultural and emotional reasons (118,145) (see also section 4.3). Given that appetites for specific foods by and large depend on learning about after-effects of those foods, it seems likely that some form of learning underlies most food cravings. However, caution, and evidence, are needed before it can be assumed that a food is craved because it is needed by the body, and not just the mind.

3.2.12   References

1.   Thibault L., Booth D.A. Macronutrient-specific dietary selection in rodents and its neural bases. *Neuroscience and Biobehavioral Reviews*, 1999, 23, 457-528.

2.   Dickinson A. *Contemporary Animal Learning Theory*. Cambridge, Cambridge University Press. 1980.

3.   Booth D.A. How to measure learned control of food and water intake, in *Feeding and Drinking*. Eds Toates F.M., Rowland N.E. Amsterdam, Elsevier. 1987, 111-49.

4.   Harris L.J., Clay J., Hargreaves F., Ward A. Appetite and choice of diet. The ability of vitamin B deficient rats to discriminate between diets containing and lacking the vitamin. *Proceedings of the Royal Society, London, Series B*, 1933, 113, 161-90.

5.   Le Magnen J. Le mécanisme d'établissement d'un appétit différentiel pour des régimes de diverses densités caloriques. *Journal de Physiologie, Paris*, 1957, 49, 1105-17.

6.   Lát J. Self-selection of dietary components, in *Handbook of Physiology, Section 6: Alimentary Canal*. Ed. Code C.F. Washington, DC, American Physiological Society. 1967, 367-86.

7.   Booth D.A. Conditioned satiety in the rat. *Journal of Comparative and Physiological Psychology*, 1972, 81, 457-71.

8.   Booth D.A. Food-conditioned eating preferences and aversions with interoceptive elements: conditioned appetites and satieties. *Annals of the New York Academy of Sciences*, 1985, 443, 22-41.

9.   Sclafani A. Nutritionally based learned flavour preferences in rats, in *Taste, Experience, and Feeding*. Eds Capaldi E.D., Powley T.L. Washington, DC, American Psychological Association. 1990, 139-56.

10. Bolles R.C. *Learning Theory*. New York, NY, Holt, Rinehart and Winston. 1975.

11. Toates F.M. *Motivational Systems*. Cambridge, Cambridge University Press. 1986.

12. Garcia J., Lasiter P.S., Bermudez Rattoni F., Deems D.A. A general theory of aversion learning. *Annals of the New York Academy of Sciences*, 1985, 443, 8-21.

13. Revusky S.H. Learning as a general process with an emphasis on data from feeding experiments, in *Food Aversion Learning*. Eds Milgram N.W., Krames L., Alloway T.M. New York, Plenum Press. 1977, 1-51.

14. Richardson N.J., Rogers P.J., Elliman N.A. Conditioned flavour preferences reinforced by caffeine consumed after lunch. *Physiology and Behavior*, 1996, 60, 257-63.

15.   Sclafani A. Learned controls of ingestive behaviour. *Appetite*, 1997, 29, 153-8.

16.   Yeomans M.R., Jackson A., Lee M.D., Nesic J., Durlach P.J. Expression of flavour preferences conditioned by caffeine is dependent on caffeine deprivation state. *Psychopharmacology*, 2000, 150, 208-15.

17.   Anderson H.L., Benevenga N.J., Harper A.E. Effect of cold exposure on the response of rats to a dietary amino acid imbalance. *Journal of Nutrition*, 1969, 99, 184-90.

18.   Booth D.A., Gibson E.L., Toase A.-M., Freeman R.P.J. Small objects of desire: the recognition of appropriate foods and drinks and its neural mechanisms, in *Appetite: Neural and Behavioural Bases*. Eds Legg C.R., Booth D.A. Oxford, Oxford University Press. 1994, 98-126.

19.   Provenza F.D. Postingestive feedback as an elementary determinant of food preference and intake in ruminants. *Journal of Range Management*, 1995, 48, 2-17.

20.   Booth D.A., Lovett D., McSherry G.M. Postingestive modulation of the sweetness preference gradient in the rat. *Journal of Comparative and Physiological Psychology*, 1972, 78, 485-512.

21.   Ackroff K., Sclafani A. Flavor preferences conditioned by intragastric infusions of dilute polycose solutions. *Physiology and Behavior*, 1994, 55, 957-62.

22.   Sclafani A., Nissenbaum J.W. Robust conditioned flavor preference produced by intragastric starch infusions in rats. *American Journal of Physiology*, 1988, 255, R672-R675.

23.   Baker B.J., Booth D.A., Duggan J.P., Gibson E.L. Protein appetite demonstrated: learned specificity of protein-cue preference to protein need in adult rats. *Nutrition Research*, 1987, 7, 481-7.

24.   Baker B.J., Booth D.A. Preference conditioning by concurrent diets with delayed proportional reinforcement. *Physiology and Behavior*, 1989, 46, 585-90.

25.   Pérez C., Ackroff K., Sclafani A. Carbohydrate- and protein-conditioned flavor preferences: effects of nutrient preloads. *Physiology and Behavior*, 1996, 59, 467-74.

26. Booth D.A. Acquired sensory preference for protein in diabetic and normal rats. *Physiological Psychology*, 1974, 2, 344-8.

27. Lucas F., Sclafani A. Flavor preferences conditioned by intragastric fat infusions in rats. *Physiology and Behavior*, 1989, 46, 403-12.

28. Birch L.L., McPhee L., Steinberg L., Sullivan S. Conditioned flavor preferences in young children. *Physiology and Behavior*, 1990, 47, 501-5.

29. Gibson E.L., Wainwright C.J., Booth D.A. Disguised protein in lunch after low-protein breakfast conditions food-flavor preferences dependent on recent lack of protein intake. *Physiology and Behavior*, 1995, 58, 363-71.

30. Johnson S.L., McPhee L., Birch L.L. Conditioned preferences: Young children prefer flavors associated with high dietary fat. *Physiology and Behavior*, 1991, 50, 1245-51.

31. Kern D.L., McPhee L., Fisher J., Johnson S., Birch L.L. The postingestive consequences of fat condition preferences for flavors associated with high dietary fat. *Physiology and Behavior*, 1993, 54, 71-6.

32. Young R.C., Gibbs J., Antin J., Holt J., Smith G.P. Absence of satiety during sham feeding in the rat. *Journal of Comparative and Physiological Psychology*, 1974, 87, 795-800.

33. Le Magnen J. La satiété induite par les stimuli sucrés chez le rat blanc. *Comptes Rendus des Séances de la Société de Biologie, Paris*, 1955, 149, 1339-42.

34. Carbonnel F., Lemann M., Rambaud J.C., Mundler O., Jian R. Effect of the energy density of a solid-liquid meal on gastric emptying and satiety. *American Journal of Clinical Nutrition*, 1994, 60, 307-11.

35. Gibson E.L., Booth D.A. Food-conditioned odour rejection in the late stages of the meal, mediating learnt control of meal volume by after-effects of food consumption. *Appetite*, 2000, 34, 295-303.

36. Gibson E.L., Booth D.A. Dependence of carbohydrate-conditioned flavor preference on internal state in rats. *Learning and Motivation*, 1989, 20, 36-47.

37. Booth D.A., Mather P., Fuller J. Starch content of ordinary foods associatively conditions human appetite and satiation, indexed by intake and eating pleasantness of starch-paired flavours. *Appetite*, 1982, 3, 163-84.

38.   Davidson T.L. The nature and function of interoceptive signals to feed: toward integration of physiological and learning perspectives. *Psychological Reviews*, 1993, 100, 640-57.

39.   Booth D.A. Appetite and satiety as metabolic expectancies, in *Food intake and chemical senses*. Eds Katsuki Y., Sato M., Takagi S.F., Oomura Y. Tokyo, University of Tokyo Press. 1977, 317-30.

40.   Cannon W.B. *The Wisdom of the Body*. New York, Norton. 1939.

41.   Richter C.P. Increased salt appetite in adrenalectomized rats. *American Journal of Physiology*, 1936, 115, 155-61.

42.   Booth D.A. Protein- and carbohydrate-specific cravings: neuroscience and sociology, in *Chemical Senses, Volume 4: Appetite and Nutrition*. Eds Friedman M.I., Tordoff M.G., Kare M.R. New York, Marcel Dekker. 1991, 261-76.

43.   Booth D.A., Thibault L. Macronutrient-specific hungers and satieties and their neural bases, learnt from pre- and postingestional effects of eating particular foodstuffs, in *Neural and metabolic control of macronutrient intake*. Eds Berthoud H.R., Seeley R.J. Boca Raton, CRC Press. 1999, 61-92.

44.   Pfaffmann C. Biological and behavioral substrates of the sweet tooth, in *Taste and Development*. Ed. Weiffenbach J.M. Bethesda, U.S. Department of Health, Education and Welfare. 1977.

45.   Cook N.E., Kane E., Rogers Q.R., Morris J.G. Self-selection of dietary casein and soy-protein by the cat. *Physiology and Behavior*, 1985, 34, 583-94.

46.   Rozin P., Schulkin J. Food selection, in *Neurobiology of Food and Fluid Intake: Handbook of Behavioral Neurobiology, Volume 10*. Ed. Stricker E.M. New York, Plenum Press. 1990, 297-328.

47.   Denton D.A. *The Hunger for Salt*. New York, Springer Verlag. 1982.

48.   Nachman M. Taste preferences for sodium salts by adrenalectomized rats. *Journal of Comparative and Physiological Psychology*, 1962, 1124-9.

49.   Krieckhaus E.E., Wolf G. Acquisition of sodium by rats: interaction of innate mechanisms and latent learning. *Journal of Comparative and Physiological Psychology*, 1968, 197-201.

50. Krieckhaus E.E. "Innate recognition" aids rats in sodium regulation. *Journal of Comparative and Physiological Psychology*, 1970, 117-22.

51. Dickinson A. Re-examination of the role of the instrumental contingency in the sodium-appetite irrelevant incentive effect. *Quarterly Journal of Experimental Psychology: Comparative and Physiological Psychology*, 1986, 38B, 161-72.

52. Berridge K.C., Schulkin J. Palatability shift of a salt-associated incentive during sodium depletion. *Quarterly Journal of Experimental Psychology: Comparative and Physiological Psychology*, 1989, 41B, 121-38.

53. Coldwell S.E., Tordoff M.G. Learned preferences for the flavor of salted food. *Physiology and Behavior*, 1993, 54, 999-1004.

54. Beauchamp G.K. The human preference for excess salt. *American Scientist*, 1987, 75, 27-33.

55. Wilkins L., Richter C.P. A great craving for salt by a child with corticoadrenal insufficiency. *Journal of the American Medical Association*, 1940, 114, 866-8.

56. Beauchamp G.K., Cowart B.J., Moran M. Developmental changes in salt acceptability in human infants. *Developmental Psychobiology*, 1986, 19, 17-25.

57. Harris G., Booth D.A. Infants' preference for salt in food: Its dependence upon recent dietary experience. *Journal of Reproductive and Infant Psychology*, 1987, 5, 97-104.

58. Bertino M., Beauchamp G.K., Engelman K. Long-term reduction in dietary sodium alters the taste of salt. *American Journal of Clinical Nutrition*, 1983, 36, 1134-44.

59. Blais C., Pangborn R.M., Borhani N.O., Ferrell M.F., Prineas R.J., Laing B. Effect of dietary sodium restriction on taste responses to sodium chloride: a longitudinal study. *American Journal of Clinical Nutrition*, 1986, 44, 323-43.

60. Leshem M. Salt preference in adolescence is predicted by common prenatal and infantile mineralofluid loss. *Physiology and Behavior*, 1998, 63, 699-704.

61. Crystal S.R., Bernstein I.L. Morning sickness: impact on offspring salt preference. *Appetite*, 1995, 25, 231-40.

62. Stein L.J., Cowart B.J., Epstein A.N., Pilot L.J., Laskin C.R., Beauchamp G.K. Increased liking for salty foods in adolescents exposed during infancy to a chloride-deficient feeding formula. *Appetite*, 1996, 27, 65-77.

63. Tordoff M.G. The importance of calcium in the control of salt intake. *Neuroscience and Biobehavioral Reviews*, 1996, 20, 89-99.

64. Schulkin J. The allure of salt. *Psychobiology*, 1991, 19, 116-21.

65. Torii K., Kondoh T., Mori K., Ono T. Hypothalamic control of amino acid appetite. *Annals of the New York Academy of Sciences*, 1998, 855, 417-25.

66. Feldman M.D. Pica: Current perspectives. *Psychosomatics*, 1986, 27, 519-23.

67. Arbiter E.A., Black D. Pica and iron-deficiency anaemia. *Child: Care, Health and Development*, 1991, 17, 231-4.

68. McLoughlin I.J., Hassanyeh F. Pica in a patient with anorexia nervosa. *British Journal of Psychiatry*, 1990, 156, 568-70.

69. Shapiro M.D., Linas S.L. Sodium chloride pica secondary to iron-deficiency anemia. *American Journal of Kidney Disease*, 1985, 5, 67-8.

70. Menge H., Lang A., Cuntze H. Pica in Germany — amylophagia as the etiology of iron deficiency anemia. *Zeitschrift für Gastroenterologie*, 1998, 36, 635-40.

71. Reilly J.J., Nardozzi J., Schulkin J. The ingestion of calcium in multiparous and virgin female rats. *Brain Research Bulletin*, 1995, 37, 301-3.

72. Crystal S.R., Bowen D.J., Bernstein I.L. Morning sickness and salt intake, food cravings, and food aversions. *Physiology and Behavior*, 1999, 67, 181-7.

73. Woods S.C., Vasselli J.R., Milam K.M. Iron appetite and latent learning in rats. *Physiology and Behavior*, 1977, 19, 623-6.

74. Richter C.P. Total self-regulatory functions in animals and human beings. *Harvey Lecture Series*, 1942, 38, 63-103.

75. Richter C.P., Holt L., Barelare B. Nutritional requirements for normal growth and reproduction in rats studied by the self-selection method. *American Journal of Physiology*, 1938, 122, 734-44.

76. Osborne T.B., Mendel L.B. The choice between adequate and inadequate diet, as made by rats. *Journal of Biological Chemistry*, 1918, 35, 19-27.

77. Kon S.C. The self-selection of food constituents by the rat. *Biochemical Journal*, 1931, 25, 473-81.

78. Sanders S., Ackroff K., Collier G.H., Squibb R. Purified diets: some cautions about casein. *Physiology and Behavior*, 1984, 33, 457-63.

79. Beck M., Galef B.G. Social influences on the selection of a protein-sufficient diet by Norway rats (Rattus norvegicus). *Journal of Comparative Psychology*, 1989, 103, 132-9.

80. Booth D.A., Conner M.T., Gibson E.L. Measurement of food perception, food preference, and nutrient selection. *Annals of the New York Academy of Sciences*, 1989, 561, 226-42.

81. Galef B.G., Jr. A contrarian view of the wisdom of the body as it relates to dietary self-selection. *Psychological Reviews*, 1991, 98, 218-23.

82. Davis C.M. Self-regulation of diet in childhood. *Health Education Journal*, 1947, 37-40.

83. Davis C.M. Self-selection of diet by newly weaned infants. *American Journal of Diseases of Children*, 1928, 36, 651-79.

84. Story M., Brown J.E. Do young children instinctively know what to eat? *New England Journal of Medicine*, 1987, 316, 103-6.

85. Garcia J., Ervin F.R., Yorke C.H., Koelling R.A. Conditioning with delayed vitamin injections. *Science*, 1967, 155, 716-8.

86. Rozin P. Specific hunger for thiamine: Recovery from deficiency and thiamine preference. *Journal of Comparative and Physiological Psychology*, 1965, 98-101.

87. Zahorik D.M., Maier S.F. Appetitive conditioning with recovery from thiamine deficiency as the unconditioned stimulus. *Psychonomic Science*, 1969, 309-10.

88. Scott E.M., Verney E.L. Self-selection of diet. VI. The nature of appetite for B vitamins. *Journal of Nutrition*, 1947, 34, 471-80.

89. Harper A.E., Benevenga N.J., Wohlhueter R.M. Effects of ingestion of disproportionate amounts of amino acids. *Physiological Reviews*, 1970, 50, 428-558.

90. Booth D.A., Simson P.C. Food preferences acquired by association with variations in amino acid nutrition. *Quarterly Journal of Experimental Psychology*, 1971, 23, 135-45.

91. Simson P.C., Booth D.A. Olfactory conditioning by association with histidine-free or balanced amino acid loads in rats. *Quarterly Journal of Experimental Psychology*, 1973, 25, 354-9.

92. Simson P.C., Booth D.A. Effect of CS-US interval on the conditioning of odour preferences by amino acid loads. *Physiology and Behavior*, 1973, 11, 801-8.

93. Simson P.C., Booth D.A. The rejection of a diet which has been associated with a single administration of a histidine-free amino acid mixture. *British Journal of Nutrition*, 1974, 31, 285-96.

94. DiBattista D., Holder M.D. Enhanced preference for a protein-containing diet in response to dietary protein restriction. *Appetite*, 1998, 30, 237-54.

95. Booth D.A. Food intake compensation for increase or decrease in the protein content of the diet. *Behavioral Biology*, 1974, 12, 31-40.

96. Miller M.G. Oral somatosensory factors in dietary self-selection in rats. *Behavioral Neuroscience*, 1984, 98, 416-23.

97. Naito Hoopes M., McArthur L.H., Gietzen D.W., Rogers Q.R. Learned preference and aversion for complete and isoleucine-devoid diets in rats. *Physiology and Behavior*, 1993, 53, 485-94.

98. Gietzen D.W. Amino acid recognition in the central nervous system, in *Neural and metabolic control of macronutrient intake*. Eds Berthoud H.R., Seeley R.J. Boca Raton, CRC Press. 1999, 339-57.

99. Gietzen D.W., Leung P.M.B., Rogers Q.R. Norepinephrine and amino acids in prepyriform cortex or rats fed imbalanced amino acid diets. *Physiology and Behavior*, 1986, 36, 1071-80.

100. Peng Y., Tews J.K., Harper A.E. Amino acid imbalance, protein intake and changes in rat brain and plasma amino acids. *American Journal of Physiology*, 1972, 222, 314-21.

101. Leung P.M.B., Rogers Q.R. Food intake: regulation by amino acid pattern. *Life Sciences*, 1969, 8, 1-9.

102. Leung P.M.B., Rogers Q.R. Importance of prepyriform cortex in food intake response of rats to amino acids. *American Journal of Physiology*, 1971, 221, 929-35.

103. Gibson E.L., Booth D.A. Acquired protein appetite in rats: dependence on a protein-specific need state. *Experientia*, 1986, 42, 1003-4.

104. McLarney M.J., Pellett P.L., Young V.R. Pattern of amino acid requirements in humans: an interspecies comparison using published amino acid requirement recommendations. *Journal of Nutrition*, 1996, 126, 1871-82.

105. Mellinkoff S.M., Frankland M., Boyle D., Greipel M. Relation between serum amino acid concentration and fluctuations in appetite. *American Journal of Physiology*, 1956, 8, 535-8.

106. Stockley L., Jones F.A., Broadhurst A.J. The effects of moderate protein or energy supplements on subsequent nutrient intake in man. *Appetite*, 1984, 5, 209-19.

107. Murphy C., Withee J. Age and biochemical status predict preference for casein hydrolysate. *Journal of Gerontology*, 1987, 42, 73-7.

108. Vazquez M., Pearson P.B., Beauchamp G.K. Flavor preferences in malnourished Mexican infants. *Physiology and Behavior*, 1982, 28, 513-9.

109. Gibson E.L., Sivapathasundaram V., Judd P.A. Learnt protein appetite in rats and human beings: role of the hypothalamic pituitary adrenal axis. *Appetite*, 2000, (Abstract), 35(3), 288.

110. Ishizuka B., Quigley M.E., Yen S.S.C. Pituitary hormone release in response to food ingestion: evidence for neuroendocrine signals from gut to brain. *Journal of Clinical Endocrinology and Metabolism*, 1983, 57, 1111-5.

111. Gibson E.L., Checkley S., Papadopoulos A., Poon L., Daley S., Wardle J. Increased salivary cortisol reliably induced by a protein-rich midday meal. *Psychosomatic Medicine*, 1999, 61, 214-24.

112. De Kloet E.R., Oitzl M.S., Joels M. Functional implications of brain corticosteroid receptor diversity. *Cellular and Molecular Neurobiology*, 1993, 13, 433-55.

113. Deutsch J., Moore B., Heinrichs S. Unlearned specific appetite for protein. *Physiology and Behavior*, 1989, 46, 619-24.

114. Galef B.G., Jr. Is there a specific appetite for protein?, in *Neural and metabolic control of macronutrient intake*. Eds Berthoud H.R., Seeley R.J. Boca Raton, CRC Press. 1999, 19-28.

115. Rolls E.T. Taste, olfactory, visual, and somatosensory representations of the sensory properties of foods in the brain, and their relation to the control of food intake, in *Neural and metabolic control of macronutrient intake*. Eds Berthoud H.R., Seeley R.J. Boca Raton, CRC Press. 1999, 247-62.

116. Chaudhari N., Roper S.D. Molecular and physiological evidence for glutamate (umami) taste transduction via a G protein-coupled receptor. *Annals of the New York Academy of Sciences*, 1998, 855, 398-406.

117. Heinrichs S.C., Deutsch J.A., Moore B.O. Olfactory self-selection of protein-containing foods. *Physiology and Behavior*, 1990, 47, 409-13.

118. Gibson E.L., Desmond E. Chocolate craving and hunger state: implications for the acquisition and expression of appetite and food choice. *Appetite*, 1999, 32, 219-40.

119. Rodin J., Mancuso J., Granger J., Nelbach E. Food cravings in relation to body mass index, restraint and estradiol levels: a repeated measures study in healthy women. *Appetite*, 1991, 17, 177-85.

120. Weingarten H.P., Elston D. Food cravings in a college population. *Appetite*, 1991, 17, 167-75.

121. Michener W., Rozin P. Pharmacological versus sensory factors in the satiation of chocolate craving. *Physiology and Behavior*, 1994, 56, 419-22.

122. Max B. This and that: chocolate addiction, the dual pharmacogenetics of asparagus eaters, and the arithmetic of freedom. *Trends in Pharmacological Sciences*, 1989, 10, 390-3.

123. Markus C.R., Panhuysen G., Tuiten A., Koppeschaar H., Fekkes D., Peters M.L. Does carbohydrate-rich, protein-poor food prevent a deterioration of mood and cognitive performance of stress-prone subjects when subjected to a stressful task? *Appetite*, 1998, 31, 49-65.

124. Yeomans M.R. Palatability and the micro-structure of feeding in humans: the appetizer effect. *Appetite*, 1996, 27, 119-33.

125. Cornell C.E., Rodin J., Weingarten H. Stimulus-induced eating when satiated. *Physiology and Behavior*, 1989, 45, 695-704.

126. Lambert K.G., Neal T., Noyes J., Parker C., Worrel P. Food-related stimuli increase desire to eat in hungry and satiated human subjects. *Current Psychology Research and Reviews*, 1991, 10, 297-303.

127. Jansen A., van den Hout M. On being led into temptation: "counterregulation" of dieters after smelling a "preload". *Addictive Behaviors*, 1991, 16, 247-53.

128. Jansen A. A learning model of binge eating: cue reactivity and cue exposure. *Behavior Research and Therapy*, 1998, 36, 257-72.

129. Rolls B.J., Rolls E.T., Rowe E.A., Sweeney K. Sensory specific satiety in man. *Physiology and Behavior*, 1981, 27, 137-42.

130. Macdiarmid J.I., Hetherington M.M. Mood modulation by food: an exploration of affect and cravings in "chocolate addicts". *British Journal of Clinical Psychology*, 1995, 34, 129-38.

131. Tuomisto T., Hetherington M.M., Morris M.F., Tuomisto M.T., Turjanmaa V., Lappalainen R. Psychological and physiological characteristics of sweet food "addiction". *International Journal of Eating Disorders*, 1999, 25, 169-75.

132. Carter B.L., Tiffany S.T. Meta-analysis of cue-reactivity in addiction research. *Addiction*, 1999, 94, 327-40.

133. Siegel S. Drug anticipation and drug addiction. The 1998 H. David Archibald Lecture. *Addiction*, 1999, 94, 1113-24.

134. O'Brien C.P., Testa T., O'Brien T.J., Brady J.P., Wells B. Conditioned narcotic withdrawal in humans. *Science*, 1977, 195, 1000-2.

135. Glautier S. Classical conditioning, drug cues and drug addiction, in *Appetite: neural and behavioural bases*. Eds Legg C.R., Booth D.A. Oxford, Oxford University Press. 1994, 165-92.

136. Childress A.R., Ehrman R., McLellan A.T., MacRae J., Natale M., O'Brien C.P. Can induced moods trigger drug-related responses in opiate abuse patients? *Journal of Substance Abuse and Treatment*, 1994, 11, 17-23.

137. Oliver G., Wardle J., Gibson E.L. Stress and food choice: a laboratory study. *Psychosomatic Medicine*, 2000, 62, 6, 853-66.

138. Kampov-Polevoy A.B., Garbutt J.C., Janowsky D.S. Association between preference for sweets and excessive alcohol intake: a review of animal and human studies. *Alcohol and Alcoholism*, 1999, 34, 386-95.

139. Kranzler H.R., Skipsey K., Modesto-Lowe V. PROP taster status and parental history of alcohol dependence. *Drug and Alcohol Dependence*, 1998, 52, 109-13.

140. DiCarlo S.T., Powers A.S. Propylthiouracil tasting as a possible genetic association marker for two types of alcoholism. *Physiology and Behavior*, 1998, 64, 147-52.

141. Kiefer S.W., Lawrence G.J. The sweet-bitter taste of alcohol: Aversion generalization to various sweet/quinine mixtures in the rat. *Chemical Senses*, 1988, 13, 633-41.

142. Stewart J., de Wit H., Eikelboom R. Role of unconditioned and conditioned drug effects in the self-administration of opiates and stimulants. *Psychological Reviews*, 1984, 91, 251-68.

143. Tiffany S.T., Carter B.L. Is craving the source of compulsive drug use? *Journal of Psychopharmacology*, 1998, 12, 23-30.

144. Robbins T.W., Everitt B.J. Drug addiction: bad habits add up. *Nature*, 1999, 398, 567-70.

145. Rogers P.J. Mechanisms of moreishness and food craving, in *Pleasure: the politics and the reality*. Ed. Warburton D.M. Chichester, John Wiley. 1994, 38-49.

146. Zahorik D.M., Maier S.F., Pies R.W. Preferences for tastes paired with recovery from thiamine deficiency in rats: appetitive conditioning or learned safety? *Journal of Comparative and Physiological Psychology*, 1974, 87, 1083-91.

147. Zahorik D.M., Bean C.A. Resistance of "recovery" flavors to later associations with illness. *Bulletin of the Psychonomic Society*, 1975, 6, 309-12.

4. CRAVINGS FOR CHOCOLATE

4.1. THE SPECIAL PLACE OF CHOCOLATE IN THE ANGLO-AMERICAN DIET: TOWARDS A SOCIOLOGY OF FOOD CRAVINGS AND ADDICTIONS

Leslie Gofton and Anne Murcott

4.1.1   Introduction

Crave *v.*

1. To demand (a thing), to ask with authority or by right (*obs*)...

2. *transf.* of persons, their appetites etc.: To long or yearn for, to desire earnestly; to call for or demand in order to gratify a desire or appetite: to have a craving for...

1586 B. Googe: 'Who so ploweth his olive gardens, craveth fruite'...

1737 Pope: 'If when the more you drink the more you crave, You tell the Doctor'.

(The Oxford English Dictionary)

While we can never know whether Alexander Pope grasped where usage of the word 'crave' would eventually lead, we may be more certain that the sociology of food cravings and addiction is as yet undeveloped. So, to address our brief, we aim to display aspects of what a distinctively sociological approach to craving for chocolate might eventually look like. We shall have succeeded if this chapter prompts questions for further sociological investigation in an area overdue for development.

Our own sociological approach is based on the presumption that, within certain physical and physiological limits, taste is socially shaped (1,2). In other words, the meanings of food are to be understood as socially distributed and culturally produced, as are the associated prescriptions and proscriptions. Furthermore, taste changes over time, meanings shift and pre/proscriptions vary in the extent of their force. It follows that, in order to understand the position of chocolate in any particular food system – positions that are quite different even within culturally and geographically contiguous western societies – account needs to be taken of the historically distinct processes that created that position. In this fashion, whatever might be involved in the craving for chocolate and in the possibility of anyone's becoming addicted to it, unavoidably leads to considerations extending far beyond what some might consider a frivolous topic – considerations that reflect fundamental epistemological matters.

It is our contention, then, that the particularities of craving and addictions in individuals cannot easily be separated from the distinctly socio-cultural – i.e. supra-individual – forces shaping the meaning and usage of chocolate, whether in our own society now, or in other places at other times, and that, correspondingly, the relationship of those forces to the copious psychological research findings currently available, cries out for extended analysis and debate. We presume only to initiate such debate in attempting to create a space for examining the very idea of cravings, rather than assuming that the expression is understood and its referents agreed – and thereby also providing for identifying the circumstances under which it has achieved currency in a non-psychiatric context. In the process, the discussion will seek to establish the beginnings of a sociological grasp of the history of chocolate's introduction into the Anglo-American diet.

4.1.2 Predominant Theories of Food Cravings – Mainly Psychology, Most Commonly Women and Chocolate

Among the social sciences, the study and definition of craving have largely been the uncontested province of psychology (e.g. 3,4). As will be seen later, some economists have offered a view, and reference can be found in the applied literatures of marketing and consumer behaviour. Such professional scientific approaches are to be distinguished from the realm of non-technical neologisms such as 'chocoholism' and its stablemate, 'workaholism'. These inventions need to be regarded as the popular, often metaphoric, usage of lay theorising about, or beliefs in, the existence of cravings, just as they need to be regarded as journalistic shorthands that might also carry ironic or playful overtones. Where professional sociological work has occasionally been found is in the study of such popular theorising (e.g. 5) and or reports of experience (e.g. 6).

In her authoritative review of the literature on food cravings, Marcia Pelchat (7) defines the term as 'an intense desire or longing' to eat a particular food. The most common type of explanatory cause, she says, invokes a deficit theory, that '...cravings have a homeostatic function... aris(ing) in response to a nutrient or caloric deficit' (7-11). McFadden and France's definition as 'an unmet desire for a pleasurable substance' (12) corresponds quite closely, and is presented in clear contrast to their definition of addiction as 'the habitual use of a substance, which becomes less and less effective at satisfying the need and results in unpleasant withdrawal symptoms should any attempt be made to give up the substance in question' (12). Understanding cravings as a deficit extends to the argument sometimes adopted that cravings are influenced by neurochemical variables, such as levels of endogenous opiates, brain serotonin (7) or by hormonal state (13-15). Professional science and lay theorising coincide in linking cravings to pregnancy (5,6) and perhaps the menstrual cycle (15-23). Pelchat's review further indicates a strong relation between the menstrual cycle and craving for chocolate and other sweets, although no specific mechanism has been identified (24,25) (See also 26 for a related study and sections 4.2, 5.2, 5.3, and 7.3 in this book).

As could be anticipated, other theories reflect particular epistemological pre-dispositions. For example, it is hypothesised that cravings may become conditioned responses to the environmental factors under which a particular food was eaten. Sensory factors may also influence cravings, or act as 'triggers' (27-29). Cravings may be triggered by the sensory properties of foods as a result of deprivation of certain sensory characteristics or cognitive categories of food (30,31). Other researchers propose that the antecedents of food cravings are multi-causal. Craving for pizza, for example, may be a consequence of sodium deficiency or the attraction of a forbidden food 'in itself' (3). To anticipate our approach, it must be added that reference to forbidden food in this fashion, however, begs the question. For what is left unexamined is the meaning of pizza as either/both attractive or/and forbidden, when the investigative issues need to *include* the reasons whereby pizza becomes 'forbidden', and the logic or otherwise of this quality that makes it thereby 'attractive'.

There is some suggestion in the literature that chocolate is disproportionately represented among the foodstuffs for which respondents reported experiencing a craving. There is a long history of chocolate's being regarded as an 'addictive' substance (4,32-40) and in one study accounted for 49% of all cravings (41). Turning to consider physiological/biochemical processes, Willner *et al.* (42), for instance, found that, in rat and human subjects, depression induced by stress increased the craving for chocolate, and performance increased when the craving was satisfied by sweet rewards.

Discussing whether chocolate should be considered a food or a drug, Bruinsma and Taren (43) find that chocolate may evoke a similar pharmacological and behavioural reaction in susceptible persons (see also 44). They indicate that the hedonic appeal of chocolate – deriving from fat, sugar, texture and aroma – is likely to be the crucial factor in these cravings. And, invoking a deficit theory, they note that chocolate may also be used as 'self medication' for dietary (magnesium) deficiency, or balancing low levels of neurotransmitters for the regulation of mood (45), food intake and compulsive behaviours (serotonin and dopamine) (39), and that chocolate cravings seem to be linked to hormonal changes related to menstruation. They observe:

Chocolate contains several biologically active constituents (methylxanthines, biogenic amines, and cannabinoid like fatty acids) all of which potentially cause abnormal behaviours and psychological sensations that parallel those of other addictive substances.' (43)

A number of factors probably combine, they believe, to form the model of chocolate cravings. These include chocolate's sensory characteristics, nutrient composition, and psychoactive ingredients alongside the monthly hormonal fluctuations and mood swings. They conclude that chocolate cravings are 'real' and need to be seriously treated by dietetics professionals.

Studies include attention to demographic variation. For instance, marked age differences are reported. In one of Pelchat's studies of 50 young and 48 old adults (7), a clear age effect was found, with the young significantly more likely to report cravings than the old. Unexpectedly perhaps, the study showed no obvious differences between 'weight loss dieters' and 'medically restricted dieters', and no significant link between body mass index (BMI) and cravings. Moreover, there were no differences across age or sex/gender in the frequency of cravings (see also 41). Their findings notwithstanding, research in both the USA and the UK reports that craving for chocolate is strongly gendered. A survey by Waterhouse (46), however, found 97% of women claimed to experience cravings. Of these, 68% reported that the foodstuff craved was chocolate. Indeed 50% said that they would choose chocolate in preference to sex while 22% were more likely than men to choose chocolate as a mood elevator. Waterhouse takes the view that the foods people crave are defined by a multitude of factors that may include cultural influences, emotional attachments, taste and habit, as well as biological, chemical and physiological factors. In the case of chocolate, which she describes as 'the Prozac of plants' Waterhouse lists serotonin – known for its 'calming properties' – among its mood-changing components.

Elements of Waterhouse's findings have swiftly been taken up more as a topic of general public discussion than specialist academic debate. Connections and comparisons between chocolate and sex have caught the public imagination (10,26,43,46). An idea that deserves investigation is that which suggests that chocolate's attractions involve 'mysterious' chemistry and 'invisible' genetic or biological factors that enable it to sit well alongside a general currency of popular theories linking health with 'lifestyle' and behaviour (47).

Michener and colleagues (16) report that almost half of the 50% of women in the USA who crave chocolate do so in the perimenstruum. When the team examined the role of low progesterone and tension as triggers of perimenstrual chocolate and sweets craving, neither progesterone nor alprazolam (a tranquiliser) supplements decreased experimental subjects' craving for sweets and chocolate. So the hypothesis that decreased progesterone levels and increased dysphoria (tension) in the pre-menstrual period trigger the craving was not confirmed. The authors speculate on a possible fault in the mechanism that regulates body levels of phenylethylamine (an endorphin with an effect similar to that of amphetamine), resulting in a tendency to binge after emotional upset (see also 23).

In a study of 'overlapping addictions', Greenberg *et al.* (37) found that gender differences in addictions were very pronounced; men scored higher than women on addiction to alcohol, cigarettes, gambling, television and Internet use, while women scored higher on caffeine and chocolate. Studying 'sweet food addiction' Tuomisto *et al.* (36) sought to identify, amongst chocolate 'addicts', correlates of the affective, physiological and craving responses manifested by drug addicts. They found that:

> Chocolate addicts may be considered to be a parallel with addicts generally, because they differ from controls in craving for chocolate, eating behavior, and psychopathology (in respect of eating and affect) (36).

Similarly, Gendall *et al.* found that:

> women who experience food cravings are more likely to have met criteria for alcohol abuse/dependency, and tend to have temperaments characterised by higher levels of novelty seeking. Higher rates of eating disorder symptomatology implies that they are over-concerned with body weight and shape (17).

Still concentrating on the question of chocolate use among women, Macdiarmid and Hetherington (48) examined the effect of chocolate intake on mood. They found significant differences between chocolate addicts and controls in terms of the number of eating episodes and amounts consumed. Differences between them were also reported before eating, with addicts rating guilt, depression and craving higher, and feeling content and relaxed as lower than controls. 'However', they observe, 'eating chocolate resulted in increased feelings of guilt in the addicts and no significant changes in feeling depressed or relaxed. On indices of disordered eating and depression, "addicts" scored significantly higher than controls; however, eating chocolate did not improve mood...Although chocolate is a food which provides pleasure, for those who consider intake of this food to be excessive, any pleasure experienced is short lived and accompanied by guilt' (48,49).

Our purpose in presenting this brief overview of key literature, which lies, of course, outside our own disciplinary expertise, is to underscore the importance of sociologists' taking such work seriously but also to argue for looking beyond it. Much of the research sketched so far involves a search for biochemical/physiological elements to explain cravings or addiction associated with chocolate. Yet finding the evidence does not demonstrate that chocolate cravings can exhaustively be explained in these terms. Many of the studies record that the meaning or definition of the craved foods – many of them 'junk' foods, e.g. certain types of snacks, soft drinks or other socially disapproved substances, alcohol, other drugs, chemicals, etc. – provide important motivations and attractions 'in themselves' for the subjects. Attempts to reduce explanations of craving and addiction simply to 'deficits' of particular kinds within the biochemistry/physiology of the brain have as yet to identify a clear causal relationship. Concluding that the effects of chemical components in these behaviours are crucial may well be necessary as an explanation, but it is not sufficient. The researchers do, however, report three important factors – age, gender and culture – immediately suggesting the relevance of sociological analysis. But, in proposing the makings of such an analysis, the contrast becomes evident between the scientific approaches of psychology on one hand and sociology on the other. In psychology, all three factors are treated as if they were attributes of the individual, whereas sociology has to regard them, especially culture, as supra- or inter-individual phenomena – simultaneously the historical product of human activity, but also a source of either opportunity or constraint on it. The beginnings of a sociological account of how chocolate came to occupy its present position in Anglo-American food systems will necessarily need to concern itself with the relationship of these factors to the history of chocolate, its production, marketing and adoption as a mass market item in Britain and the United States.

4.1.3   Cravings, Irrational or Rational – Diversion into Economics

Psychological and physiological studies of craving and addiction are, of course, reductionist in intent if not completely in deed. There is, however, a quite different story waiting to be told about contemporary use, addiction and chocolate with biochemical and psycho-physiological processes temporarily playing a more minor role. Although working towards a sociological approach, we would be unwise to consider consumption without paying attention along the way to economics, the social science that is devoted to analysing the allocation of scarce resources. Economics approaches consumption by theorising that goods are chosen by more or less rational consumers for the utility or benefits they provide. What is chosen, by whom and in what amounts are hypothesised as outcomes of complex relations between the resources available to putative consumers, the ends they desire, the amounts of goods available, the conditions under which they are available, and the consequent prices/resource expenditures they can command.

For most economists, however, addictions pose a problem. Surely the behaviour of those consuming hard drugs, or huge amounts of foods, cannot be said to be rational? 'Addictions would seem to be the antithesis of rational behaviour... does a heroin user or an alcoholic maximize or weigh the future? Surely his (sic) preferences shift rapidly over time, as his mood changes?' (50). At this point, a medical model of addiction is invoked to complement the neoclassical economic theory of rational consumption;

addictions are represented as compulsive and irrational, and those gripped by them are characterised as behaving in aberrant ways because of their 'illness'.

Not all economists subscribe to this complicity. Notably, the Nobel Laureate Gary Becker has extended the theory of rational choice to accommodate a whole range of behaviours, crime, single parenthood, as well as addictions. This is essential in his view, if only because they are so widespread. Addictions, he claims, extend beyond drugs and drink to a whole range of activities and substances, including 'eating, music, television, their standard of living, other people, religion, and many other activities' (51).

Given their ubiquity, Becker argues, excluding them from the rational choice model would involve an enormous loss of power and relevance for economics. In order to remove the apparent irrationality of addictive consumption, he maintains that those engaging in it are likely to apply past experiences to the decision process in a very different way. For example, those engaging in use likely to lead to long-term health damage may well 'discount' the future they are damaging, on the basis of the value they attribute to it given their past experience.

An economist of a different theoretical persuasion, Ben Fine (51) is not convinced:

> The way in which the model works is to allow an addictive good to affect current utility positively and future utility negatively. Rational consumers, maximizing utility over time, take this into account when deciding whether to consume in the present or in the future... You may well be rational in choosing addiction if the present pleasures outweigh the fully anticipated and discounted drawbacks of the relatively distant future.

He goes on to point out that this approach does not concern itself in any way with the nature of the goods to which the idea of addiction is applied; if we focus on goods simply as a means of providing utility, it is possible to reduce them to abstract mathematical terms and relations, or represent them in terms of demand curves. As a result, he reasons, 'addiction is seen as a common phenomenon, without distinction across [a wide] range of activities… the nature of addictions as differentiated social constructs is effectively obliterated. They are simply understood and explained on the basis of rational optimizing individuals' (51). Fine's point is that this kind of reductionism eliminates the very obvious differences between the objects of addictive or compulsive behaviour, and diminishes the importance of factors such as gender in the explanation of aberrant forms of consumption.

The central point here is that, even if there is a physiological or psychological basis to an item's repeated use, the effects of individual human agency on the decision to consume are not disposed of by confirmation of the existence of that basis. The relationship between the physiological and associated individual elements on the one hand and the workings of the social and cultural on the other remains something of an open empirical question. In order to work towards understanding that relationship, not only does the latter require analytical attention, but the way needs to be paved for the juxtaposition and analytical integration of the two. Only in that way will we be able to disentangle the soluble aspects of that open question from the insoluble – of which one may turn out to be never being able to disentangle cause from consequence in the increase in use of chocolate in the UK, the USA and elsewhere over the past three to four centuries.

4.1.4 The Prominent Position of Chocolate – Other Places, Other Times

An influential exemplar of the beginnings of an integrated analytical approach is provided by the anthropologist Sidney Mintz's account of the emergence of sugar consumption on so large a scale that, for some countries at some times, it is possible to talk of a 'national sweet tooth' (52). (See also refs 53-55). He pays careful attention to the evidence for a biological basis for the human preference for sweetness. But he is obliged to note that, even if some in-built predisposition is undeniable, it cannot possibly explain the extent of the contemporary predilection for sugar. Economics, human agency, culturally attributed meanings all have to be canvassed, if only because no one is literally being force-fed sugar.

In the case of cravings for chocolate, it is particularly its gendered aspect that suggests the value of such an approach. Gendering is not invariant and thereby cannot serve as the key factor in universally explaining craving for chocolate. A recent two-country study of chocolate cravings (56) found that the difference in chocolate craving found between men and women in Britain was absent in Spain, with the number of women craving chocolate at the same level as that for men (around the same figure as that in the UK). The authors conclude that the differences must be 'cultural', but make no attempt to articulate what might be involved, stopping at just the point where investigation needs to be initiated, examining cross-national variations in the way in which chocolate has come to be used and produced (see also section 4.3).

In this particular comparison, it turns out that Spanish and Anglo-American chocolate use has a dramatically divergent history. In Spain 'chocolateros' were still purveying the raw natural beans, ground in front of the customer, in villages until the 1930s (12,57,58). In Britain and the USA, chocolate was one of the very first mass marketed food products, a result of pioneering industrialised processing and marketing 60 years earlier. Noting that modes of production create the circumstances in which meanings arise, we might speculate about how the meaning of chocolate was shaped in the context of a Catholic country to which the item was brought via imperial conquest, implying a strong connection with the supposed lasciviousness of the Aztecs from whom it was first taken (57,59-61)[1]. In the Anglo-American context, however, chocolate production was dominated by non-conformist protestants and Quakers. The very least implication of this is a different attitude towards what marketers today would refer to as 'product concept', 'brand image' or 'brand personality' (62-67).

---

[1] Earliest accounts appear to have represented chocolate as an aphrodisiac taken by Montezuma before retiring to his harem.

Marshall Sahlins (another anthropologist) is among those who point to what he calls 'product indigenization'– citing the incorporation of western products into China, Hawaii and the Kwakiutl of British Columbia (68). He argues that items are not simply accepted passively, but are caught up in an active process whereby novelties acquire meanings in terms of the pre-existing belief system. Extrapolating, we would expect to find that this is also what happened when chocolate among other New World commodities arrived in Europe in the 'Columbian exchange' (see 69 for contemporary examples). Further, we might also expect that the manner of incorporation is likely to have a powerful influence on the subsequent 'success' of such items in the 'host' cultures. Given the profound differences in the contexts into which these novelties were received, it would be foolhardy to discount the likelihood of corresponding difference in their subsequent incorporations into the food systems and institutionalised usages of these differing societies (see also refs 70,71).

A closer examination of the history of Anglo-American chocolate production is needed – one that is a history not just of an industry, but of the emergence of mass production and mass consumption in short, of industrialization itself. A key development of the late nineteenth and early twentieth centuries was the technological innovation in transforming a raw ingredient to a powdered drink, and finally to a solid bar or flavoured 'tablet'. What was peculiar to Anglo-American industries, however, was not simply the new technology - many of the crucial technologies were developed in different parts of Europe (56), but the manner in which it was deployed by its entrepreneurs – Rowntree, Fry and Cadbury in the UK and Hershey in the US[2] – such that chocolate manufacture became more concentrated and capital intensive faster than other industrialising food processing. Mass production principles were adopted much sooner, not only in advance of the rest of the food sector, but also in advance of almost all the rest of the manufacturing sector (66,72,73).

---

[2] Technologically, food manufacturing probably contains more assembly lines than any other sector, although it is the car industry that has emerged as the major stereotype of routinised, alienated and fragmented labour in the 20th century.

A number of features of primary and secondary industry were key. Chocolate benefited from agricultural specialism in the colonies of the capitalist states and in being mainly capitalist commodities, with little or no existence in feudal or handicraft economies, becoming a mass product only through capitalist industrialisation. This included the separation of production and retailing, such that the former could be expanded via the creation of non-specialist outlets employing semi-skilled labour – an advantage over other food producers/retailers, who had to rely on craft labour. Thus mass markets for branded products could be created quickly, with chocolate confectionery 'positioned' as a so-called convenience food, retailed in a multiplicity of outlets. American mass marketing concentrated on small product ranges focused on mass markets – paying little attention to 'niche' sectors. British manufacturers, by contrast, carried a greater product range, aiming at the luxury and mass ends simultaneously (66,72,74).

Threaded through analysis of these developments is Gail Cooper's note of the coincident implications in the gendering of both production and consumption (72). Not only was the use of female labour in American chocolate production perpetuated from its late nineteenth century mechanisation, but, she argues, as manufacturers adopted the new methods of production, they also 'recast their relations to their consumers' (72). The timely adoption of mass advertising broke the link between price and production costs in the public mind but, more significantly, began to overcome the problem of pre-existing seasonality of demand, which, in the US, was concentrated around Christmas. In marketing terms, the twin strategies of 'intensification' and 'extensification' were involved. The former entailed spreading the idea of festive chocolate use throughout the year, inventing new occasions for chocolate and sweet-giving – Valentine's Day, Mother's Day and, later, Father's Day. This was matched by technologies that created artificial climates inside the factories to overcome the heat, and improved packaging, allowing products to be presented as more attractive and prestigious.

In addition to becoming ever more ubiquitous as festive gifts, chocolates were, Cooper argues, eventually counted less as a treat and more as an 'everyday indulgence' (72) as a result – following the British example[3] – of the inclusion of chocolate in US military rations for the first time during World War I. So doing provided for extensions to pre-existing meanings attached to chocolate use. Not only was familiarity with chocolate bars thus quickly and effectively spread; their provision as emergency rations, rather than as respite from the rigours of active service, carried officially sanctioned connotations of gravity and necessity (which, apparently, servicemen completely ignored, eating the ration at once). Thereby, further re-definitions of chocolate as a treat and indulgence were created – re-definitions picked up in marketing campaigns, which linked chocolate to courtship and family affection. Advertising in both countries showed young men – often in uniform – offering gifts of chocolate to their sweethearts: love and one form of gendering are invoked. Other advertising of the period showing nursemaids or mothers giving chocolate to children reflects the gendering of nurturing.

There is a strong, but as yet underdeveloped, case for arguing that the very nature of chocolate production is a critical factor in the way chocolate has fitted in Anglo-American patterns of food use generally. At the least, we note for now that the features of secondary processing in chocolate manufacture are an essential part of the overall pattern of chocolate use. Unlike many other more and less highly manufactured food products, which may be transformed after purchase for preparation in a wide variety of ways, the form created by the secondary processing is most commonly the final form of the product as it is eaten. It is infrequently modified before it is consumed, with its use in Anglo-American cuisines confined to certain dishes that occupy a minor place. The technologies necessary to create those final forms are thus critical. The point forms part of our preliminary proposals that developments in the mass production/consumption created the circumstances for the formation of a powerful and consistent image of and use for chocolate Anglo-American food systems, such that the social significance of chocolate becomes buttressed by its incorporation at the

---

[3] Cadburys' analysis of sugar and confectionery distribution in the post-war period (1949) found that most products were sold through general shops and grocers and provision dealers, followed by tobacconists, newsagents, bakers, cafés and outlets such as cinemas, railway kiosks and caterers. Of the 225,000 outlets, specialist confectioners accounted for only 10,000 (67).

heart of courtship behaviour and child/parent interactions – gift-giving rituals involved in marking relationships in the formation and maintenance of families.

4.1.5 Craved by Women – Towards a Sociology of the Prominent Position of Chocolate

An attempt to develop a sociological vantage point on both the idea of chocolate cravings and the finding that they are disproportionately reported by women necessarily concerns itself with other historical trends and contemporaneous associations. These include Anglo-American notions of femininity – in particular their portrayal in advertising – and a trend to which at times they are allied, toward the adoption of psychiatric discourse in the mass media and in marketing. While the neologism 'chocoholic' may well have eluded adequate analysis of differences in the forms and objects of addiction by glossing their complexity with a glib invention, the very presence of such invention and its consequences nonetheless require investigation by way of beginning to unpick their part in the phenomenon they purport to describe. An everyday conversational line of 'I'm addicted to dark chocolate' indicates that consumption involves far more than the act of ingestion. In any case, as the previous section suggests, chocolate cannot be considered as a 'consumer good' without inspecting the wrapping, the messages purveyed in the advertising campaigns.

4.1.5.1 *Chocolate advertising and gender*

As advertisers know, a product cannot be confined to a single dimension. The 'satisfactions' provided by a food product extend far beyond the nutritional 'value' it provides, beyond the sensory qualities involved as it is ingested, to encompass at the least (a) the way that it looks, (b) what is symbolised in the packaging, (c) its in-store location, (d) how it is displayed, and (e) the kinds of promotional messages to be communicated about how it should be used, its key attributes, its perception as part of a particular pattern of living – so-called 'image' or 'lifestyle' and so on (67,75-78).

So, from a marketing point of view, chocolate consumption is multi-sensorial and polysemic, involving a process from 'need' to 'deed', by way of a search, selection decision, purchase process, and usage. It can be supposed, then, that the kinds of chocolates purchased are likely to relate strongly to the marketing product-concept involved. Small daughters and female sweethearts may both be given chocolate, but they are offered quite different brands and types – and they may well buy quite other kinds for themselves. Key elements in the commercial presentation and presumed success of chocolate products are marketers' and advertisers' views of current 'fads', fashion and style, and their own interpretations of prevailing norms, conventions and experience.

On the basis of such general 'principles', we would, then, expect to find different kinds of chocolate products targeted at different market segments in distinctive ways. This is borne out in a fine grained sociological examination of the way in which women were represented in chocolate advertising (80). Several facets of gender difference are identified. Men were mainly portrayed eating chocolate at the conclusion of an activity – football, car chase, etc. – representing it as a reward or a restorative for the exertion or depletion of energies involved. Men are shown 'anchored' to reality. When they use chocolate they are engaged with the world, driving trucks, playing sport. Women, but not men, are portrayed as engaging in a private act of consumption as if eating chocolate were an end in itself, an escape into a private world of self-indulgence.

Indeed, 'escape' is often marked in other ways in these advertisements. Women are often presented as 'drifting off', 'being transported into another realm' in the act of eating chocolate. While humorous fantasies of male incompetence were also found to feature regularly, the implication seems to be that, unlike women, who are routinely represented as 'detached', men who become so risk becoming objects of ridicule – thus underscoring the image of women as 'not properly aligned with their surroundings' (79). Women's detachment to eat chocolate is set in a context where they go off to be alone in beautiful but empty landscapes, or dream in quiet solitude on soft chairs in luxurious apartments. The indulgence of the use is mirrored in their location, and their experience of it as enjoyment rather than work.

4.1.6   The Social Shaping of Taste – Inherent Contradictions

The previous four sections have sketched the clear and powerful set of social and economic forces shaping modern Anglo-American chocolate use and its associated discriminations and food taste systems. In this last section, we seek to draw the threads of our discussion together to suggest one way in which chocolate cravings may begin to be understood sociologically. To do so, we propose that closer attention needs to be paid to contradictions in the social shaping of taste – especially those contradictions in conventional cultural assumptions about women's place in the domestic sphere on the one hand, and the images of womanhood captured in chocolate advertising as an example of persisting broader notions of femininity[4]. A recent study of London shoppers by Daniel Miller (80) brings out the important issues – we might summarise them as 'love, thrift and treats'.

Miller notes a disjunction. On one hand is an abstract notion of 'shopping', a discourse implying hedonism and materialism, abandoned acquisition, extravagant consumption. On the other are the practicalities of budgeting, planning, and provisioning; real shopping, in which people have in mind who will use or eat what and how items are to be bought, against a backcloth of the social relationships – marital, parental, etc. – within the household for which this shopping is actually being done. A notion of shopping as greedy self-indulgence is one his research respondents would subscribe to, even though it is often at odds with the realities they can equally well describe.

Miller goes on to build a compelling, if provocative, portrait of shopping as analogous to ritual sacrifice – he too is an anthropologist. Capitalism, he points out (and certain styles of economics) propagates an essentially utilitarian world-view, in which consumers (sic) are reduced to a logic of commodities and less than glorious activity, denuded of sanctity. Yet, able to demonstrate (81) that the motives of shoppers are likely to vary greatly, even within developed western economies, he argues to the contrary. In effect, he claims, shopping practices are devotional activities, of

---

[4] We do not at all imply that these exhaust broader notions of femininity.

which destructive wastefulness is an essential part. Shopping shares defining dimensions with sacrifice: a vision of excess – where the act is a key moment in the transformation of accumulated production (money) into goods to be consumed, and the abstract idea of shopping invokes a fantasy of heedless, mindless dissipation of energy and effort in unfettered greed; a division of the accumulated wealth between the transcendent – the smoke of sacrifice, which ascends to the Gods – and the mundane – the human shopper. Turning away from the vision of excess involves a transformation of shopping from waste into saving – from the freedom of spending to the triumph of thrift. The practical outcomes of shopping are to provide for real people in real households, framed by the atavism of unfettered freedom to spend represented by the institutions of shopping in abstraction, and the ideal values embodied in the intended consumers postulated in the response to the 'vision of excess'.

Miller's account of shopping will, for some, have neo-Freudian resonances, and in any case will not be to everyone's analytical taste. Nonetheless, he captures a tension in shopping as simultaneously transcendent and mundane in combining an act of love – treats indulging beyond mere need – with practical reason – eking out a budget properly to satisfy no more than necessity. Contemporary trends notwithstanding, shopping remains firmly gendered, whether in the abstractions of journalistic commentary, the practicalities of commercial marketing or reports of actual behaviour. As Miller indicates, in those societies where production and consumption are treated as symbolically separate, where the former continues to be treated as the preserve of men, and the latter that of women,

> a female whose labour is unvalorized except where it expresses her agency as expenditure. In such a context women become the agents who expend what men are understood to have produced. Women then take on the symbolic burden of expenditure. Much of the aggressive misogyny that characterised the period of the 1950s and 1960s prior to feminism was directed against the woman shopper, who turned the seriousness of labour into the trivia of consumption (80).

Here is the source of 'fear and ambivalence' as production – symbolised by money – is released, dissipated even, in consumption. Thus, engrained in Miller's characterisation of modern shopping is a morality, threatening dangers of several kinds. Will the woman doing the shopping remain dutifully thrifty and provide appropriately for the needs of the household, at the same time as honouring the nurturing expectations of her that she provide treats for her family? Or will she slip across into extravagance, or, as bad, be tempted to err by providing courtship treats for herself? It is striking that the version of the shopper/consumer depicted here is consistent with the implicit views of motivation underlying the 'addiction' model. Depicting women as chocoholic slaves surrendering to their appetites departs from a notion of normality from which it simultaneously prescribes the way in which women ought to purchase, use and eat chocolate, i.e. only in accord with her giving and receiving it under the proper circumstances of gift exchange.

4.1.7   Concluding Summary and Comments

We propose that chocolate cravings are to be analysed as standing at the intersection of all we have discussed in this chapter. We have suggested that contemporary Anglo-American manifestations of such cravings cannot be understood without, at a minimum, setting them in the context of nation-specific, centuries-long historical development in the supply and processing of the raw commodity, the creation of associated marketing systems, the adoption of allied technological and other innovations that lie behind the modern mass production and consumption of commercially manufactured chocolate products. So saying is the weak version. The strong version is to argue that chocolate cravings are the outcome of such developments. The gendering of both production and consumption may be relevant, where, in any case, historical changes have created the current circumstances in which chocolate is used such that meanings are defined and re-defined.

The idea of craving itself might be said to rest on a peculiar kind of psychological defeasibility. If the abstract notion of consumers is as hedonistic and materialist, greedy to the bone, what is the place of those who are to buy the food not for themselves but primarily on behalf of others to stand amidst this greed? On the one hand, women are entrusted with the responsibility of allocating resources and resolving conflicts between the different dimensions of shopping itself; on the other, they are themselves members of the household, and bound up in relationships of devotion, service and care for other members of the household. One of the continuing meanings conveyed by chocolate is an expression of that very devotion – gifts of chocolate to women carry connotations absent in gifts offered to children or men.

Chocolate for men is related to re-fuelling and re-energising, as a just reward for effort. For women, chocolate is represented as a material expression of escape, detachment from the constraints and limits of daily responsibilities – a private indulgence and a vehicle for sensual pleasure and emotional satisfaction. Yet these qualities are in conflict with the normative role to be played by women as virtuous consumers, responsible for providing for the needs of others, partners and children, underpinned by an associated norm of female self-denial that requires the taste and preferences of husbands and children come first (82-84). This is all of a piece with the tight social constraints and proscriptions surrounding women's use of many kinds of foods – alcohol, red meat (2) – and other substances as well as their engagement in various activities (smoking, illegal drug use, car driving (85-87). Accordingly, we suggest, to talk of 'craving' and 'addiction' here is an expression less, perhaps, of a physiological state than an acceptable plea in the face of a questionable outcome to those conflicts and frailties in the face of contradictions.

For the future, a fully developed sociology of cravings for chocolate will require not just a sustained analysis of the history, economics and anthropology of the mass production and consumption of chocolate. It would also require thoroughgoing comparison with the sociology of other addictions to legal and illegal substances (alcohol, prescription drugs, illegal drugs of different classes, etc.) and with the sociology of 'unorthodox' eating (solitary eating, atypical meal patterns, geophagy or pica). Such comparison would permit a test of the suggestions presented here, as well as systematically identifying promising lines of enquiry that could be borrowed further to illuminate the case of chocolate. There is no doubt that fully developed sociology of chocolate cravings would require more besides. Here, though, we have aimed to do no more than initiate a discussion about what such a sociology might look like.

Notes

We are grateful to Irene Dunne, Short Loans Librarian at the University of Newcastle upon Tyne, for her advice in the early stages of work on this chapter.

4.1.8   References

1.   Mennell S. *All Manners of Food*. Oxford, Basil Blackwell. 1985.

2.   Mennell S., Murcott A., Van Otterloo A. *The Sociology of Food: Eating Diet and Culture*. London, Sage. 1992.

3.   Michener W., Rozin P. Pharmacological versus sensory factors in the satiation of chocolate craving. *Physiology & Behavior*, 1994, 56 (3), 419-22.

4.   Rozin P., Stoess C. Is there a general tendency to become addicted. *Addictive Behaviors*, 1993, 18 (1), 81-7.

5.   Murcott A. On the altered appetites of pregnancy; conceptions of food, body and person. *The Sociological Review*, 1988, 36 (4), 733-64.

6.   Macintyre S. The management of food in pregnancy, in *The Sociology of Food and Eating*. Ed. Murcott A. Aldershot, Gower. 1983, 57-72.

7.   Pelchat M.L. Food cravings in young and elderly adults. *Appetite*, 1997, 28 (2), 103-13.

8.   Florio R. Crazy about chocolate - is it an addiction. *Revue De Medecine Veterinaire*, 1988, 139 (8-9), 861-70.

9.   DiChiara G. A motivational learning hypothesis of the role of mesolimbic dopamine in compulsive drug use. *Journal of Psychopharmacology*, 1998, 12 (1), 54-67.

10. DiChiara G., Acquas E., Tanda G. Ethanol as a neurochemical surrogate of conventional reinforcers: The dopamine-opioid link. *Alcohol*, 1996, 13 (1), 13-7.

11. diTomaso E., Beltramo M., Piomelli D. Brain cannabinoids in chocolate. *Nature*, 1996, 382 (6593), 677-8.

12. McFadden C., France C. *Chocolate*. London, Anness Publishing. 1999.

13. Bancroft J., Williamson L., Warner P., Rennie D., Smith S.K. Perimenstrual complaints in women complaining of PMS, menorrhagia, and dysmenorrhea – toward a dismantling of the premenstrual syndrome. *Psychosomatic Medicine*, 1993, 55 (2), 133-45.

14. Cawood E.H.H., Bancroft J., Steel J.M. Perimenstrual symptoms in women with diabetes-mellitus and the relationship to diabetic control. *Diabetic Medicine*, 1993, 10 (5), 444-8.

15. Dye L., Blundell J.E. Menstrual cycle and appetite control: Implications for weight regulation. *Human Reproduction*, 1997, 12 (6), 1142-51.

16. Michener W., Rozin P., Freeman E., Gale L. The role of low progesterone and tension as triggers of perimenstrual chocolate and sweets craving: Some negative experimental evidence. *Physiology & Behavior*, 1999, 67 (3), 417-20.

17. Gendall K.A., Sullivan P.F., Joyce P.R., Fear J.L., Bulik C.M. Psychopathology and personality of young women who experience food cravings. *Addictive Behaviors*, 1997, 22 (4), 545-55.

18. Gendall K.A., Joyce P.R., Sullivan P.F. Impact of definition on prevalence of food cravings in a random sample of young women. *Appetite*, 1997, 28 (1), 63-72.

19. Gendall K.A., Joyce P.R., Sullivan P.F., Bulik C.M. Food cravers: characteristics of those who binge. *International Journal of Eating Disorders*, 1998, 23 (4), 353-60.

20. Cooksey N.R. Pica and olfactory craving of pregnancy – how deep are the secrets. *Birth-Issues in Perinatal Care*, 1995, 22 (3), 129-37.

21. Crystal S.R., Bowen D.J., Bernstein I.L. Morning sickness and salt intake, food cravings, and food aversions. *Physiology & Behavior*, 1999, 67 (2), 181-7.

22. Dufour D.L., Reina J.C., Spurr G.B. Food and macronutrient intake of economically disadvantaged pregnant women in Colombia. *American Journal of Human Biology*, 1999, 11 (6), 753-62.

23.   Dye L., Warner P., Bancroft J. Food craving during the menstrual-cycle and its relationship to stress, happiness of relationship and depression – a preliminary inquiry. *Journal of Affective Disorders*, 1995, 34 (3), 157-64.

24.   Green T.L. The chocolate time of the month. *Psychology Today*, 1988, 22 (5), 6.

25.   Nappi R.E., Veneroni F., Fignon A., Chiapparini I., Farina C., Verri A., Sances G., Polatti F. Menstrual cycle and eating behavior: an estrogen-dependent adaptive link. *Confinia Cephalalgica*, 1999, 8 (3), 119-26.

26.   Hamilton J.B., Hegsted M. Energy regulation: hormonal effects on body weight and energy, macronutrient, and chocolate intakes in female rats. *American Journal of Clinical Nutrition*, 1997, 65 (4) SS, S1349.

27.   Booth D.A. Protein and carbohydrate specific cravings; neuroscience and sociology, in *Chemical Senses, Volume 4 Appetite and Nutrition*. Eds Freidman M.I., Tordoff M., Kare M. New York, Dekker. 1991.

28.   Weingarten H.P., Elston D. The phenomenology of food cravings. *Appetite*, 1990, 15, 231-46.

29.   Weingarten H., Elston D. Food cravings in the college population. *Appetite*, 1991, 17, 167-75.

30.   Gibson E., Desmond E. Chocolate craving and hunger state; implications for the acquisition and expression of appetite and food choice. *Appetite*, 1999, 32, 219-40.

31.   Lambert K.G., Neal T., Noyes J., Parker C., Worrel P. Food-related stimuli increase desire to eat in hungry and satiated human-subjects. *Current Psychology-Research & Reviews*, 1992, 10 (4) 297-303.

32.   Max B. Chocolate addiction, the dual pharmacogenetics of asparagus eaters, and the arithmetic of freedom. *Trends in Pharmacological Sciences*, 1989, 10 (10), 390-2.

33.   Hetherington M.M., Macdiarmid J.I. Chocolate addiction – a preliminary-study of its description and its relationship to problem eating. *Appetite*, 1993, 21 (3), 233-46.

34.   Hetherington M.M., Macdiarmid J.I. The pleasure of eating - chocolate addiction explored. *Appetite*, 1995a, 24 (1), 83.

35. Smith S.S. Caffeine is not what makes chocolate popular. *Food Technology*, 1999, 53 (9), 180.

36. Tuomisto T., Hetherington M.M., Morris M.F., Tuomisto M.T., Turjanmaa V., Lappalainen R. Psychological and physiological characteristics of sweet food addiction. *International Journal of Eating Disorders*, 1999, 25 (2), 169-75.

37. Greenberg J.L., Lewis S.E., Dodd D.K. Overlapping addictions and self-esteem among college men and women. *Addictive Behaviors*, 1999, 24 (4), 565-71.

38. CriquillionDoublet S. Chocomania: A new eating disorder? *Evolution Psychiatrique*, 1995, 60 (4) 849-56.

39. Zarcone T.J., Hienz R.D., Brady J.V. Behavioral indices of food craving: A potential model for drug craving. *Integrative Physiological and Behavioral Science*, 1997, 32 (2), 194.

40. Zurer P. Chocolate may mimic marijuana in brain. *Chemical & Engineering News*, 1996, 74 (36) 31-2.

41. Hill A.J., Heaton-Brown L. The experience of food craving - a prospective investigation in healthy women. *Journal of Psychosomatic Research*, 1994, 38 (8), 801-14.

42. Willner P., Benton D., Brown E., Cheeta S., Davies G., Morgan J., Morgan M. "Depression" increases "craving" for sweet rewards in animal and human models of depression and craving. *Psychopharmacology*, 1998, 136 (3), 272-83.

43. Bruinsma K., Taren D.L. Chocolate: Food or drug? *Journal of the American Dietetic Association*, 1999, 99 (10), 1249-56.

44. Rossner S. Chocolate - Divine food, fattening junk or nutritious supplementation? *European Journal of Clinical Nutrition*, 1997, 51 (6), 341-5.

45. Rogers P.J., Anderson A.O., Finch G.M., Jas P., Gatenby S.J. Relationships between food craving and anticipatory salivation, bating patterns, mood and body-weight in women and men. *Appetite*, 1994, 23 (3), 319.

46. Waterhouse D. *Why Women Need Chocolate*. London, Vermillion. 1995.

47. Davison C., Davey Smith G., Frankel S. Lay epidemiology and the prevention paradox: the implications of coronary candidacy for health education. *Sociology of Health & Illness*, 1991, 13 (1) 1-19.

48. Hetherington M.M., Macdiarmid J.I. Pleasure and excess – liking for and overconsumption of chocolate. *Physiology & Behavior*, 1995b, 57 (1), 27-35.

49. Drewnowski A., Krahn D.D., Demitrack M.A., Nairn K., Gosnell B.A. Taste responses and preferences for sweet high-fat foods – evidence for opioid involvement. *Physiology & Behavior*, 1992, 51 (2), 371-9.

50. Becker G., Murphy K. A theory of rational addiction. *Journal of Political Economy*, 1988, 96 (4), 675-700.

51. Fine B. Playing the consumption game. *Consumption, Markets and Culture*, 1997, 1 (1), 7-30.

52. Mintz S. *Sweetness and Power; The Place of Sugar in Modern History*. New York, Viking. 1985.

53. Mintz S. Time, sugar and sweetness. *Marxist Perspectives*, 1980, 56-73.

54. Mintz S.W. Sweet, salt and the language of love. *MLN- French Issue, Cultural Representations of Food*, 1991, 106 (4), 852-60.

55. Mintz S.W. The Book of Chocolate - Bailleux, N. *Times Literary Supplement*, 1996, 4871, 10.

56. Zellner D.A., GarrigaTrillo A., Rohm E., Centeno S., Parker S. Food liking and craving: a cross-cultural approach. *Appetite*, 1999, 33 (1), 61-70.

57. Coe S., Coe M. *The True History of Chocolate*. London, Thames and Hudson. 1996.

58. Rubinstein H. *The Chocolate Book*. Harmondsworth, Penguin. 1982.

59. Mendez M.A. A story full of conflict: The inquisition of new Spain and chocolate. *Caravelle-Cahiers Du Monde Hispanique Et Luso-Bresilien*, 1998, 71, 9-21.

60. Pilcher J.M., Laudan R. Chiles, chocolate, and race in new Spain: glancing backward to Spain or looking forward to Mexico? *Eighteenth-Century Life*, 1999, 23 (2) 59-70.

61. Diaz del Castillo B. *The True History of the Conquest of New Spain*. London, Hakluyt Society. 1916.

62. Brenner J. The emperors of chocolate: Inside the secret world of Hershey and Mars. *Virginia Quarterly Review*, 1999, 75 (3), 81-2.

63. Erdman T.M. Hershey and history of the candy and chocolate manufacturer – sweet smell of success. *American History Illustrated*, 1994, 29 (1), 64-71.

64. Peters H.M. Milton S. Hershey: One of a kind - founder of the Hershey Chocolate Company. *Abstracts of Papers of the American Chemical Society*, 1996, 211, Pt1, 23-CHAL.

65. Peters H.M., Peters S.B. Death by chocolate: A brief history of chocolate. *Abstracts of Papers of the American Chemical Society*, 1999, 217, Pt1, 30-CHAL.

66. Smith C., Child J., Rowlinson M. *Reshaping Work: The Cadbury Experience*. Cambridge, Cambridge University Press. 1990.

67. Fitzgerald R., Wischermann C. Rowntree and the marketing revolution. *Zeitschrift fur Unternehmensgeschichte*, 1997, 42 (2), 243-4.

68. Sahlins M. Cosmologies of capitalism; the trans-pacific sector of 'the world system'. *Proceedings of the British Academy*, 1988, 74, 1-51.

69. Cook I., Crang P. The world on a plate: culinary culture, displacement and geographical knowledge. *Journal of Material Culture*, 1996, 1, 131-54.

70. Douglas M. *Thought Styles*. London, Sage. 1996.

71. Bauer G.H. Just Desserts. *Yale French Studies*, 1985, 68, 3-14.

72. Cooper G. Love, war and chocolate; gender and the American candy industry, in *His and Hers; Gender Consumption and Technology*. Eds Horowitz R., Mohun A. Virginia, University Press of Virginia. 1998.

73. Weiner M. We are what we eat; or democracy community and the politics of corporate food displays. *American Quarterly*, 1994, 46 (2), 227-50.

74. Cox C. *Chocolate Unwrapped; The Politics of Pleasure*. London, Women's Environmental Network. 1993.

75. Gofton L. *Marketing Messages; An Introduction to Marketing Communications*. Dublin, Blackhall. 1999.

76. Noel N.M., Hanna N. Benchmarking consumer perceptions of product quality with price: An exploration. *Psychology & Marketing*, 1996, 13 (6), 591-604.

77. Padberg D.J. *Food and Agricultural Marketing Issues for the 21st Century*. The Food and Agricultural Marketing Consortium, College Station. 1993.

78. Ackerman D. *A Natural History of the Senses.* New York, Random House. 1990.

79. Elliott J., Wooton A.J. Some ritual idioms of gender in British television advertising. *The Sociological Review,* 1997, 45 (3), 437-52.

80. Miller D. *A Theory of Shopping.* London, Polity. 1998.

81. Miller D. Consumption as the vanguard of history, in *Acknowledging Consumption.* Ed. Miller D. London, Routledge. 1995.

82. Murcott A. "It's a pleasure to cook for him": food, mealtimes and gender in some South Wales households, in *The Public and the Private.* Eds Garmarnikow E., Morgan D., Purvis J., Taylorson D. London, Heinemann. 1983.

83. Charles N., Kerr M. *Women, Food and Families.* Manchester, Manchester University Press. 1988.

84. DeVault M.L. *Feeding the Family; the social organization of caring as gendered work.* Chicago, Il: Chicago University Press. 1992.

85. Graham H. *Women, Health and the Family.* Brighton, Wheatsheaf. 1984.

86. Graham H. Women's smoking and family health. *Social Science and Medicine,* 1987, 25 (1), 47-56.

87. Graham H. *When Life's a Drag.* London, HMSO. 1993.

4.2. PSYCHOLOGICAL AND PHARMACOLOGICAL EXPLANATIONS OF CHOCOLATE CRAVING

David Benton

4.2.1　Introduction

For large sections of the population, chocolate is the food item with the greatest appeal. Many will admit readily to craving chocolate (1) or even being addicted (2). There has been speculation that chocolate's attraction can be explained in terms of the influence that it has on the brain's chemistry. The sugar in chocolate has been said to increase the synthesis of serotonin, the neurotransmitter believed to modulate mood. It has been suggested that the fat in chocolate releases endorphins, thus inducing a sense of well being. In addition, phenylethylamine, anandamide, methylxanthines and magnesium, supplied by chocolate, have been suggested to have mood-altering properties (3,4).

In reality, the basis of chocolate's popularity has been subject to speculation and rash statements rather than sober scientific attention. The present chapter considers the plausibility of various possible mechanisms. The key question is the extent to which psychological rather than physiological mechanisms are important in chocolate craving.

4.2.2　Measurement of Chocolate Craving

Food cravings are extremely common; for example, they were reported by 97% of young women and 68% of young men in a Canadian survey (5). Food cravings are powerful; 85% of the Canadian sample reported that, more often than not, they gave in to their cravings - they are clearly difficult to ignore. These cravings were, however, highly selective; chocolate was by far the most commonly and intensely craved food item.

To date, the term food craving has been used in a similar way to the lay definition; it is a strong desire or urge for a particular food. Most research has been limited by the way in which cravings have been measured; in the majority of studies, subjects have been asked simply to rate their desire to eat a particular food. A single-item scale is unreliable and it has the implicit assumption that craving can be explained using a single dimension. To counter these problems, Benton (5) asked 330 people to respond to eighty statements concerning chocolate. Statistical analysis produced three factors that were used to develop the Attitudes to Chocolate Questionnaire (5), which are described below.

4.2.3 'Attitudes to Chocolate' Questionnaire

4.2.3.1 Factor one - chocolate craving

The first dimension that was found was labelled craving and was associated with a considerable preoccupation with chocolate and the compulsion to eat it (5). Two groups of questions defined this first dimension. Firstly, chocolate was a source of some distraction; it is "overpowering;" it "preys on my mind;" you cannot "take it or leave it" and "can't get it out of my head." Those scoring heavily on this factor liked the taste and mouthfeel of chocolate. The second type of question on this first dimension reflected the eating of chocolate when under emotional stress; it was eaten "when I am bored", "to cheer me up", "when I am upset" and "when I am down." The coupling of these two groups of questions demonstrated a link between negative mood and an intense desire to consume chocolate. A colloquial way of describing those who eat chocolate for these reasons is that they are indulging in 'comfort eating.'

This association between negative mood and chocolate craving was found by Benton (5) in a sample chosen to be representative of the population, rather than having a history of psychiatric complaints. In contrast, others have described a group who reported "self-medicating" with chocolate, who were more likely to have personality traits associated with hysteroid dysphoria (6), a syndrome characterised by episodes of depression in response to feeling rejected. The experience of strong food cravings has been associated with being bored, anxious and having a dysphoric mood (7). Similarly, a desire for chocolate has been reported to be associated with depression, although not related to suicidal thoughts (8). Thus, there is considerable evidence that chocolate craving is associated with depression and other disturbances of mood.

The nature of the three factors associated with the Attitudes to Chocolate Questionnaire (5) has been explored by examining the association between the three dimensions and various other measures. A sample of 107 young women, aged 20 years, with a Body Mass Index of 21.6, responded to a series of questionnaires. Table 4.2.I reports the resulting factor analysis (Benton, unpublished observations).

TABLE 4.2.I
Relationship between attitudes to chocolate and other aspects of eating behaviour

	craving Factor 1	*guilt* Factor 2	*functional app* Factor 3
Attitudes to chocolate			
Craving	0.13	**0.71**	0.23
Guilt	**0.80**	0.15	0.28
Functional approach	0.06	0.38	**0.74**
Dutch eating behaviour questionnaire			
Emotional eating	0.37	**0.72**	-0.18
External eating	0.00	**0.81**	0.01
Restrained eating	**0.86**	-0.03	0.25
Eating disorder inventory			
Body dissatisfaction	**0.79**	0.20	0.14
Drive for thinness	**0.89**	0.16	0.12
Currently dieting	-0.19	0.15	**-0.72**
Self-esteem	**-0.65**	-0.08	0.18
Variance explained	40%	16%	11%

Note: 107 young adult females answered a series of questionnaires concerning their eating behaviour. The data were subjected to factor analysis with varimax rotation. The resulting three factors are reported. The dimensions that are weighted heavily on particular factors are in bold.

The 'craving for chocolate' measure from the Attitudes to Chocolate Questionnaire was associated with the 'emotional eating' dimension of the Dutch Eating Behaviour Questionnaire (9). Those displaying emotional eating indicated that they had the desire to eat when irritated, depressed, lonely, anxious, bored or frightened. Similarly, craving for chocolate was associated with the 'external eating' dimension of the Dutch Eating Behaviour Questionnaire. Those scoring highly on the external eating dimension are likely to eat more food when it tastes or smells good; are likely to eat something delicious straight away; if they see others eating, they have the desire to eat.

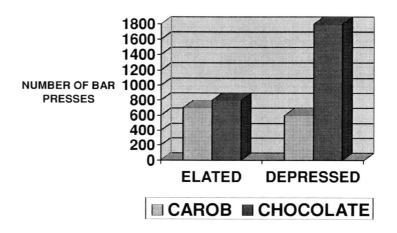

Fig. 4.2.1. Influence of mood on the number of times a bar was pressed to obtain chocolate

Note: Subjects pressed the space bar of a computer, under a progressive ratio schedule, to obtain chocolate buttons. That is they need to press 2, 4, 8, 16, 32, 64, etc., times to obtain subsequent rewards. The number of bar presses is a measure of motivation. Changes in mood was induced by the playing of either happy or sad music. It can be seen that sad music increased the motivation for chocolate but not the chocolate substitute, carob.

Although there was a consistent association between the craving for chocolate and poor mood, the relationship was simply a correlation. There was a need to manipulate mood and monitor the intake of chocolate. To date, this question has been considered by only a single study. Subjects pressed the space bar on a computer to earn chocolate buttons. The number of presses required to earn a chocolate button increased after each reinforcement according to a fixed ratio - 2, 4, 8, 16, 32, 64 presses, and so on. The measure was the number of presses made to obtain chocolate. Those with a higher craving score were prepared to press the space bar more frequently to receive more chocolate buttons. Figure 4.2.1 illustrates that, when mild depression was induced by playing miserable music, subjects pressed the space bar more often to receive chocolate (10).

4.2.3.2 Factor two - guilt

The second dimension of the Attitudes to Chocolate Questionnaire was labelled guilt, and again it included two types of question (5). Firstly, there were comments associating chocolate with negative experiences. I feel "unattractive," "sick," "guilty," "depressed" or "unhealthy" after eating chocolate. It is not surprising that, after eating chocolate, "I often wish I hadn't." The second type of question related to weight and body image: "I often diet," "I look at the calorific value of a chocolate snack," "If I ate less chocolate, I think I would have a better figure."

Those who scored highly on the guilt dimension of the Attitudes to Chocolate Questionnaire were dissatisfied with their bodies and had a high drive for thinness, as judged by their responses to the Eating Disorder Inventory (11); they were likely to score highly on the 'restrained eating' scale of the Dutch Eating Behaviour Questionnaire (9). Thus, there was a clear association between feeling guilty after eating chocolate and being concerned with weight and appearance (Table 4.2.I).

4.2.3.3 Factor three - a functional approach

A third factor reflected a pragmatic approach to chocolate (5). Those scoring highly on this dimension eat chocolate when it serves some useful purpose -

"to keep my energy levels up when doing physical exercise," "in the winter when it is colder," "only when I am hungry" and "as a reward when everything is going well." Unlike the guilt and craving factors, this third factor was not associated with mood, and those taking this functional approach were less likely to be dieting (Table 4.2.I). There is also an association between taking a functional approach to the eating of chocolate and glucose tolerance (12). The blood glucose of 47 young adult females, who had fasted overnight, was monitored for 3.5 hours after the consumption of 50 g of glucose. Typically, blood glucose values peaked after about half an hour and then fell. Having reached its lowest value, the extent to which individuals were able to raise their levels of blood glucose from this lowest point was associated with chocolate consumption. Those who scored highly on the functional approach to chocolate were less able to raise blood glucose, having reached the lowest point (12). Although it is a speculative comment, it is as if individuals who eat chocolate for functional reasons have difficulty in liberating endogenous stores to ensure that blood glucose levels do not stay at low levels for long periods. To deal with this problem, they were more likely to use exogenous sources of glucose.

4.2.4   Premenstrual Syndrome (PMS) and Chocolate Craving

Although the reporting of chocolate craving is common, it is particularly associated with women during the premenstrual stage. In the 1950s, surveys began to find that the premenstrual stage was associated with cravings for sweet items, particularly chocolate (13). For example, in one study, 58% of women reported that, in the premenstrual stage, appetite increased, and 61% reported an increased desire for sweet foods (13). Such is the consistency of this type of finding that food craving is seen as a symptom of PMS. (See also section 5.2.)

There is a large body of evidence that energy intake increases during the second half of the cycle (13). Various studies report differences in energy intake of between 87 and 674 kcal a day, that is a 4% to 35% rise, from the follicular to the luteal phase of the cycle. Similarly, there is substantial evidence that the basal metabolic rate increases over the menstrual cycle in both animals and humans (14). For example, rises of between 8% and 16% of basal metabolic rate between the follicular and luteal phase of the cycle have been reported (15).

Although there are parallel increases in premenstrual appetite, energy intake and increased metabolic rate, is there evidence of a specific increase in the intake of carbohydrate or sweet items? When Vlitos and Davies (13) reviewed the topic, they found that the majority of studies did not support such a view.

During menstruation, a preference for chocolate foods has been found (16). Fong and Kretsch (17) found that carbohydrate intake was higher during menstruation rather than ovulation - a reflection of an increased consumption of sweets, mainly chocolate. However, there is little evidence that it is carbohydrate that is craved; rather, it is pleasant-tasting high-fat/high-carbohydrate containing foods.

In summary, there is no consistent evidence that the intake of carbohydrate increases in the premenstrual stage. It is possible that carbohydrate craving is a reflection of a generally increased appetite, rather than a specific increase in carbohydrate intake. There is, however, some evidence that the pre-menstrual and menstrual periods are associated with a higher sugar intake and a corresponding decrease in the intake of fibre. In particular, the consumption of chocolate increases, although this is also true of other pleasant-tasting food items.

It has been found that in those suffering with PMS, the level of magnesium in plasma (18) and erythrocytes (19,20) is lower. A suggested possibility is that the attraction of chocolate is an attempt to increase the intake of magnesium. In a double-blind trial, women who suffered with premenstrual problems took either magnesium or a placebo (21). There was no benefit in the first cycle but, in the second, the taking of magnesium was associated with fewer symptoms. A 50-g bar of milk chocolate supplies 26 mg of magnesium, whereas plain chocolate offers 50 mg. In contrast, those on the trial (21) took 360 mg of magnesium, three times a day, for the second half of the menstrual cycle. Even then, the improvement did not occur until the procedure had been followed for two cycles. The much smaller amount of magnesium offered by chocolate, and the time scale involved make it improbable that the eating of chocolate reduces craving by supplying magnesium.

In summary, a consistent picture has emerged. Chocolate is by far the most common food item that is craved, particularly in females. There is considerable evidence that chocolate craving and poor mood are related. The question that arises is the origin of this relationship. To what extent do the mood-enhancing properties of chocolate reflect biological or psychological mechanisms. Chocolate is a chemically complex substance, rich in many pharmacologically active compounds, including histamine, tryptophan, serotonin, methylxanthines, phenylethylamine and octopamine (see also section 6.3). It is a source of certain minerals, including copper, magnesium and iron (2,3).

Initially, the possibility that various of the constituents of chocolate have a 'drug-like' action is considered. Subsequently, the role of psychological factors is examined.

4.2.5   Effects of Specific Constituents of Chocolate

4.2.5.1   Methylxanthines

As caffeine in various foods and drinks is known to influence alertness, it has been proposed that it may play a role in the attractiveness of chocolate. In fact, chocolate contains more of the naturally occurring alkaloid theobromine (3,7-dimethylxanthine) than caffeine (1,3,7-trimethylxanthine). Milk chocolate contains, on average, about 2 mg/g theobromine and 0.2 mg/g caffeine (about 88 mg theobromine and 9 mg caffeine per 44 g bar) (22). However, the level of methylxanthines differs even within a brand; a 40-g to 50-g Hershey chocolate bar supplies 86-240 mg theobromine, and 9-31 mg caffeine (23).

There is no doubt that cocoa contains methylxanthines; however, it is doubtful whether the resulting chocolate contains them in a dose sufficient to influence psychological functioning. Although the stimulant action of caffeine is well established, the impact of theobromine has been considered rarely. The question that arises with caffeine is whether the small dose present in a chocolate bar is high enough to influence neural functioning. In the case of theobromine, it must be considered whether it influences psychological functioning at all.

4.2.5.1.1 Theobromine

The response to theobromine, as assessed by behavioural measures, is less than that to caffeine. The study of the compound in animals has led some to conclude that it is behaviourally inert (24-26), although others have reported a modest impact on the behaviour of mice (27), rats (28) and cats (29). Studies of drug discrimination are amongst the most sensitive methods for establishing subtle drug effects. In rats trained to discriminate 32 mg/kg caffeine from saline, theobromine, at doses up to 75 mg/kg, did not cause a caffeine-like response (30). In a second study, rats were trained to discriminate either 10 or 30 mg/kg caffeine from saline (31). Doses of theobromine, up to 300 mg/kg, produced at best a 50% caffeine-like response. Reviews of the influence of theobromine in humans have concluded that it has no behavioural influence (32,33). There is little reason to suggest that the dose of theobromine present in chocolate influences craving.

4.2.5.1.2 Caffeine

Although there are consistent reports that caffeine, at any dose, does not influence learning and memory (34,35), there is evidence that other tasks benefit (36). Many of the studies of the influence of caffeine on psychological functioning have used doses of at least 200 mg, at which level there is clear evidence of a stimulant action. For example, there is consistent evidence that doses of 200 mg caffeine improve reaction times, although the findings with lower doses are less consistent (37). There is, however, a report that a dose of 32 mg caffeine improved reaction times (38), although this did not result with 20 mg (39), a level that could be ingested from the eating of a chocolate bar. Similarly, doses over 100 mg improve the ability to sustain attention in vigilance tasks, although there is a report that doses of caffeine as low as 32 and 64 mg affect such tasks (40).

Mood is the psychological parameter that has been most commonly found to be influenced by caffeine. Studies consistently report that 100 mg caffeine increase measures of alertness and vigour, and decrease boredom and fatigue (41-44). Unfortunately, there have been very few studies of low doses. Lieberman *et al.* (38) found that 64 mg increased feelings of alertness and vigour. The finding that low doses of caffeine improve mood is supported by reports that low doses of caffeine are reinforcing. If, under double-blind conditions, subjects were given the choice of two coffees, one without caffeine and the other with varying doses, there was evidence that some individuals chose a dose of 25 mg, but were unable to distinguish 12.5 mg (45).

Thus, the evidence is that a reliable psychological response to caffeine is most readily observed with doses in excess of 100 mg. Although there have been a few reports that lower doses are active, in no case has a response to a dose of 9 mg caffeine been reported. It is therefore unlikely that the eating of a typical chocolate bar, and certainly not one or two pieces of chocolate, would offer a dose of caffeine sufficient to influence mood. The possibility cannot be excluded that the consumption of an entire chocolate bar, with a high cocoa content, may offer a dose of caffeine that could influence some psychological measures, albeit weakly. Such possibilities would not, however, account for the widespread reporting of craving throughout the population, as it is often satisfied by a small intake of chocolate containing only small amounts of caffeine. The level of caffeine in chocolate should be compared with that in brewed coffee, which has 85 mg caffeine/150 ml and tea, with 50 mg/150 ml. These drinks offer much greater levels of caffeine than can be obtained from chocolate, yet they do not induce a similar level of craving.

4.2.5.2 *Phenylethylamine*

Two New York psychoanalysts associated passionate love and chocolate. They studied a group of 'love-addicted' women, who, they found, produced a large amount of phenylethylamine. When the women's infatuation stopped, so did the production of phenylethylamine (46). As chocolate contains phenylethylamine, the implication drawn was that chocolate can be a substitute for love.

Chocolate contains from 0.4 to 6.6 micrograms of phenylethylamine per gram (47), so a 50-g bar at the most contains about a third of a milligram. Phenylethylamine is naturally present in low concentrations in the brain (< 10 nanograms/g), where it has a rapid turnover (half-life 5-10 min). There are binding sites in the brain where it acts as a neuromodulator rather than as a neurotransmitter.

When injected into the brain of animals, phenylethylamine causes stereotyped behaviour, acting in a similar way to amphetamine. Although phenylethylamine does not bind directly to dopamine sites, its effects can be blocked by dopamine antagonists and it is assumed to release dopamine (48). At physiological doses, it potentiates the neurotransmitters dopamine and norepinephrine (49). Monoamine oxidase B preferentially oxidises phenylethylamine, although this enzyme also oxidises dopamine.

Given the biological role played by phenylethylamine, it was obvious to suggest that it might be responsible for the attraction of chocolate. All drugs to which humans become addicted influence the activity of brain dopamine. As phenylethylamine modulates the release of dopamine, it was reasonable to consider whether its intake could result in addiction. In animals, phenylethylamine increases the rate of lever pressing to receive stimulation of 'pleasure centres' in the brain (50) - something true of all drugs of abuse. The question is whether this is a likely scenario. Is the level of the compound in chocolate sufficient to cause addiction and thus craving during withdrawal?

In fact, the level of phenylethylamine is higher in some cheeses and sausage than in chocolate (51), yet these foods are craved rarely, if at all. It is instructive to consider the dose that influences behaviour. The behaviour of rats trained to press a lever to obtain electrical stimulation of the hypothalamus was influenced by a dose of 25 and 50 mg/kg phenylethylamine (52), and 20 to 60 mg/kg influenced food-rewarded response (53). Doses of phenylethylamine comparable to those that were effective in rats would require the administration of 2 or 3 g to humans. In fact, depressed patients respond to a dose of 2-6 g a day (54).

To achieve the required dose of phenylethylamine, one would need to eat 6,000 to 9,000 50-g chocolate bars. Obviously, the most extensive chocolate binge would not begin to approach this dose. Even if a large quantity of chocolate was consumed, the rapid rate at which phenylethylamine is broken down by monoamine oxidase means that it would be broken down more quickly than it could be consumed. Phenylethylamine is largely ineffective in animals unless they are treated with a drug that inhibits monoamine oxidase.

A series of case studies has been described where taking ecstasy (MDMA) was associated with bingeing on chocolate. It was speculated that phenylethylamine, with its amphetamine-like properties, could be useful in counteracting MDMA withdrawal (55). Clearly, as ecstasy is known to damage serotonergic mechanisms, we are dealing with a pathological population. Also, the low doses of phenylethylamine present in chocolate make it extremely unlikely that this is the correct explanation. A more recent study found that those who had taken ecstasy at least 20 times were no more likely to report chocolate craving than those who had not (M. Morgan 1997, personal communication).

In summary, although phenylethylamine can influence mood, the levels in chocolate are several magnitudes too low to influence central nervous system activity.

4.2.5.3   Anandamide

Cannabis acts in the brain at cannabinoid receptors, to which anandamide, a derivative of arachidonic acid, binds with high affinity (56). As anandamide is released from neurones, and is rapidly broken down by enzymic activity, it may be an endogenous cannabinoid neurotransmitter or neuromodulator. It is interesting that anandamide has been found as a constituent of brown but not white chocolate (57). It has been suggested that the presence of anandamide intensifies the sensory properties of chocolate.

The findings are very limited and must be treated as preliminary. To date, we have only the results of *in vitro* studies and it remains to be shown that the levels of cannabinoids in chocolate are high enough to produce similar actions *in vivo*. In the unlikely event that the level of anandamide in chocolate is high enough to influence physiological response, it would need to be shown that it can survive digestion and absorption. To be active, anandamide would need to cross the blood-brain barrier and arrive in sufficient concentrations at those areas of the brain with cannabinoid receptors. (See also sections 2.3 and 6.3).

4.2.6 Carbohydrate Intake and Serotonin Synthesis

Perhaps the most quoted suggestion is that carbohydrate, offered by chocolate, increases the level of brain serotonin and for this reason improves mood. It is believed that serotonergic mechanisms modulate aggressiveness, mood and pain sensitivity. More specifically, it has been hypothesised that a high-carbohydrate, as opposed to a high-protein meal, will decrease alertness, and is associated with a general decline in cognitive efficiency (58). There are, however, many problems with the idea that the high sugar content of chocolate leads to enhanced serotonin synthesis. The idea that carbohydrates can relieve depression is associated with Richard and Judith Wurtman (59), who developed the hypothesis.

The hypothesis of the Wurtmans associated protein and carbohydrate intake to the level of brain serotonin (59). A sequence of events was proposed based on the study of rats. The increase of blood glucose after a meal stimulates the release of insulin, which causes the uptake of most amino acids, but not tryptophan, by peripheral tissues such as muscle. In contrast, insulin increases the affinity of albumin for tryptophan and thus more is left in the blood stream. A high- rather than a low-carbohydrate meal thus increases the ratio of tryptophan to large neutral amino acids (tyrosine, phenylalanine, leucine, isoleucine and valine) in the blood.

When a high-carbohydrate meal increases the ratio of tryptophan to other large amino acids, relatively more tryptophan is transported into the brain, as all these amino acids compete with each other for a transporter molecule that allows their entry into the brain. In the brain, tryptophan is transformed by the enzyme tryptophan hydroxylase into the neurotransmitter serotonin (60).

Many studies have measured the relative levels of tryptophan and other amino acids in the blood after a variety of meals, Table 4.2.II summarises the results of 30 studies. There is clear support for the theory that the relative amount of carbohydrate and protein in a meal influences the ratio between tryptophan and long-chain neutral amino acids in the blood. When protein offers less than 2% of the calories, the make-up of amino acids in plasma markedly favours tryptophan. However, as little as 5% of the calories in the form of protein is enough to ensure that this does not happen. A high-protein meal markedly changes the ratio, so that it favours the long-chain neutral amino acids. It is easier to decrease the availability of tryptophan by consuming a large amount of protein than it is to increase it by consuming a large amount of carbohydrate.

TABLE 4.2.II
Different amounts of protein in a meal and the ratio between tryptophan and long-chain neutral amino acids in the blood

% Calories as protein	Tryptophan/LNAA % baseline	Studies with significant results
< 2%	123%	10/14
4%	109%	0/1
5–10%	101%	0/4
12-19%	94%	0/2
20–49%	75%	2/3
>50%	67%	4/6

Note: The data are summarised from 30 studies that have examined the influence of the percentage of calories in a meal as protein or carbohydrate, on the ratio of tryptophan to long-chain neutral amino acids (tryptophan/LNAA) in the blood. The data are reported as a percentage of baseline values.

The data in Table 4.2.II cause serious problems for the hypothesis associating carbohydrate intake and serotonin synthesis. An increased availability of tryptophan will occur only when protein offers less than 5% of the calories, yet it is difficult to find meals that contain so little protein. Chocolate offers approximately 13% of its calories as protein and bread 15%. With these foods, which have been traditionally described as being high in carbohydrate, the provision of tryptophan to the brain will be decreased rather than increased. It follows that the synthesis of serotonin would decline and mood might be expected to get worse. It is not possible to explain the choice of food rich in carbohydrate as an attempt to enhance mood that reflects enhanced serotonin synthesis.

A second problem is that the time-scale is wrong. The improved mood after eating chocolate takes place in a few minutes. Yet much of the digestion of protein takes place in the intestine; the release of amino acids into the blood stream will not be immediate. In summary, there is no reason to suggest that the attraction of chocolate results from an increased availability of tryptophan in the blood.

This speculative mechanism proposed by the Wurtmans depended on the study of three disorders — carbohydrate craving in obesity, the premenstrual syndrome, and seasonal affective disorders (SAD). It was suggested that an increase in carbohydrate intake reflected an attempt at self-medication, that carbohydrate intake enhanced serotonin synthesis. In normal individuals, an increase in brain serotonin influences food preferences; the subject no longer likes carbohydrate to the same extent and eats other macronutrients. According to the Wurtmans, some obese people have a disturbance of this feedback mechanism, such that after eating carbohydrate, the mechanism that stops further carbohydrate intake does not work. When snacks were offered to obese carbohydrate cravers in the late afternoon they chose almost entirely high-carbohydrate foods (59). They were more likely to report that these snacks made them calm or clearheaded; those who craved carbohydrate reported feeling less depressed and more alert. In contrast, those who did not crave carbohydrate felt more sleepy and fatigued.

Those suffering with SAD tend to eat more in the winter and put on weight; from this perspective, the increased food intake is an attempt to decrease depressive symptoms by eating carbohydrate-rich foods. In fact, it has been reported that the eating of carbohydrate-rich protein-poor meals was associated with improved mood in those suffering with SAD (61).

In these types of study, it was predicted that the consumption of a high-carbohydrate/low-protein meal should have a differential impact on those who were, and were not, depressed. However, there is evidence that carbohydrate does not selectively influence the depressed. There is also doubt whether the response selectively reflects carbohydrate intake, as a high intake of carbohydrate is taken as part of a high-fat or a high-protein meal.

De Castro (62) asked normal subjects to keep dietary diaries for 9 days. When the proportion of calories that were consumed as carbohydrates was calculated, he found that a higher intake of carbohydrate was also associated with feeling more energetic. Depression was positively correlated with the proportion of calories consumed as protein. Whereas Wurtman predicted that the eating of carbohydrate had an acute influence on mood, de Castro (62) failed to find an association between the carbohydrate in particular meals and mood shortly after eating. Rather, de Castro reported a longer-term influence, in that the amount of carbohydrate consumed over several days was associated with average mood over a period of time.

The feeding of experimental diets, differing in the amount of carbohydrate consumed, allows causal mechanisms to be established. When a diet containing low, medium or high levels of carbohydrate was eaten for a week, the consumption of the low-carbohydrate diet was associated with increased anger, depression and tension (63). These findings confirmed the previous report that the feeding of a low-carbohydrate/high-protein breakfast for 3 weeks resulted in increased levels of anger (64).

The consistency of the finding that the consumption of a diet high in carbohydrate is associated with better mood suggests that it is a robust phenomenon. For the reasons discussed above, the mechanism suggested by the Wurtmans (60) does not account for the phenomenon. The nature of the precise mechanism is unclear. Even if, over time, a higher carbohydrate intake is associated with better mood, the time-scale of the response is too slow to explain the attraction of chocolate.

4.2.7   Endorphins

The endorphins are brain peptides that act at the same site as morphine and may play a role in making chocolate attractive. In rats, the consumption of chocolate increases the release of β-endorphin (65). The amount of β-endorphin occupying receptors in the rat hypothalamus has been reported to increase when chocolate and candy are eaten (65). The response to sweet foods, high in fat, appears to be endorphin-mediated. In animals, the preference for a sweet taste, and the intake of sweet solutions are decreased by an opiate antagonist such as naloxone or naltrexone, and increased by opiate agonists (66). The taste of the food appears to be important. In the rat, naloxone decreased the consumption of chocolate-chip cookies more than the intake of standard rat food (67).

The rate at which rats will press a lever to stimulate electrodes placed in the lateral hypothalamus, one of the brains 'pleasure centres', is enhanced by food deprivation. As this food-deprivation-induced increase in self-stimulation was blocked by naloxone, it has been proposed that endogenous opiate activity, promoted by eating, enhances the reward value of the food (68). Thus there is increasing evidence that, in rodents, endogenous opiates regulate food intake by modulating the extent to which pleasure is induced by palatable foods. (See also sections 2.2 and 2.4.)

In humans, the data are more limited, but there are obvious parallels. Opioid antagonists have been reported to decrease both food intake (69) and feelings of hunger (70,71). Naltrexone has been reported to reduce the preference for sucrose (72). Spontaneous eating has been associated with an increased release of β-endorphin (73). The limited attempts to relate food intake to the level of plasma β-endorphins have reported an increase after eating meat soup (74) and glucose (75).

A role for opiate mechanisms in the pleasure associated with eating palatable food was supported by a human study that gave a long-lasting opioid antagonist (76). Nalmefene did not influence the intake of particular macronutrients, but rather it influenced the intake of palatable foods, for example high-fat cheese such as Brie. In this study, the choice was between various savoury food items; chocolate and sweet foods were not on offer.

(See also section 2.5). In a similar study, naloxone differentially decreased the intake of high-fat/high-sugar foods (77).

Mandenoff *et al.* (78) proposed that the endogenous opiate system was not necessary for the control of eating when a monotonous diet was consumed in a predictable environment. However, when under stress, or when a highly palatable food has been consumed, endogenous opiates are suggested to play a role. In the rat, a stressor, such as pinching the tail, will increase eating - an effect reversed by naloxone (79). There are parallels between the stress-induced increase in rodent eating and the stressed humans who 'comfort eat' palatable foods. There is a close association between negative mood and chocolate craving (see above).

Bingeing is typically associated with food cravings. Drewnowski *et al.* (80) compared patients with a diagnosis of bulimia nervosa with a group without this history. The infusion of naloxone, rather than saline, significantly reduced the total energy intake of binge eaters. The reduction in intake was most marked for the high-sugar/high-fat foods - for example, chocolate. The obvious explanation is that such foods are highly palatable and that the pleasure associated with eating such foods is mediated via opioid mechanisms. Thus drugs, such as naloxone, that block the action of endogenous opioids, reduce the pleasantness of high-sugar/high-fat foods such as chocolate.

The increase in β-endorphin may reflect either a pleasant sensory experience or alternatively a reaction to the metabolic consequences of eating. Psychological factors seem to play a role, as in rats the anticipation of eating palatable food was found to be associated with β-endorphin release (65). In humans, plasma endorphins were more elevated with chocolate drinks sweetened with aspartame rather than sucrose (81). The authors suggested that β-endorphin release was more associated with glucose homeostasis than a pleasant taste. The relative roles of taste and the metabolic consequences of eating are unclear.

In summary, a major theory is that the eating of palatable foods is associated with the release of endorphins. Blocking the action of endorphins, with drugs such as naloxone or naltrexone, decreases the intake of chocolate.

4.2.8   Psychological Reactions to Chocolate

It is difficult to distinguish the relative contribution of the putative pharmacological agents in chocolate and our psychological reaction to its obviously pleasant taste. In fact, only one study has attempted to distinguish the psychological and physiological mechanisms that underlie chocolate craving (82). The approach taken was to see which of the various constituents of chocolate satisfied craving. The known pharmacological ingredients are all in the cocoa powder, so, if a pharmacological action of chocolate is important, cocoa should satisfy chocolate craving. The removal of the cocoa powder leaves cocoa butter. Thus, in eating white chocolate, made from the cocoa butter, the consumer has the fat and sugar intake of chocolate, but not the pharmacological constituents.

Michener and Rozin (82) gave subjects boxes containing one of six treatments: i) a chocolate bar; ii) capsules containing the same amount of cocoa powder as in the chocolate bar; iii) placebo capsules containing flour that offered the same calories as the cocoa capsules; iv) a bar of white chocolate; v) white chocolate plus capsules containing cocoa powder; vi) nothing. When the subjects experienced chocolate craving they consumed one of the six items and rated the extent to which the craving for chocolate was satisfied.

If it is the sensory experience that is important, then chocolate itself, and to a lesser extent white chocolate, should be satisfying. If it is the increase in blood glucose that is important, then brown and white chocolate should have a similar impact. If the pharmacological ingredients or magnesium are important, then both cocoa powder and chocolate should equally satisfy cravings. Table 4.2.III lists various theories of the origin of chocolate craving tested by Michener and Rozin (82). In the event, only chocolate itself, and to a lesser extent white chocolate, had the ability to satisfy chocolate craving. Capsules containing the possible pharmacological ingredients had a similar effect to taking nothing. The addition of cocoa capsules to white chocolate did not increase the less than optimal effect of white chocolate. The obvious conclusion was that it was the sensory experience associated with eating chocolate, rather than a response to the pharmacological constituents, that was important.

TABLE 4.2.III
Ability of the different constituents of chocolate to satisfy craving

| | Theories of chocolate craving | | | |
	Sensory	Insulin release	Drug action	Result
Brown chocolate	++	++	++	++
White chocolate	+	++	0	+
Cocoa capsules	0	0	++	0
Placebo capsules	0	0	0	0
White chocolate plus cocoa	+	++	++	+
Nothing	0	0	0	0

Note: When subjects experienced chocolate craving, Michener and Rozin (82) offered one of the six possibilities listed in the far left column. Their ability to satisfy craving is indicated in the far right column; ++ full effect, + partial effect, 0 no effect. The middle three columns list the predictions of three major theories of the origin of chocolate craving.

4.2.9 Final Observations

Little, if any, evidence exists to support the view that chocolate craving reflects a biological need that is satisfied, in a drug-like manner. With all the putative 'drug-like' substances, the same problem arises. They are all present in levels too low to conceivably have a pharmacological action. The major hypothesis that the high carbohydrate levels found in chocolate induce changes in the rate of synthesis of brain serotonin similarly does not stand careful examination. Not only is the level of protein in chocolate high enough to ensure that there is no increase in the levels of blood tryptophan, but the level of protein is such that it is likely that the level of tryptophan in the blood will fall. There is no reason to expect that the synthesis of serotonin in the brain will increase after eating chocolate (Table 4.2.II).

The most probable explanation is that chocolate tastes good (Table 4.2.III). Both humans and other animals have a preference for foods that are both sweet and high in fats. Considerations of the palatability of combinations of fat and sugar have found an optimal combination of 7.6% sugar with cream containing 24.7% fat (83). The fat content of chocolate is close to this ideal, although the sugar content of chocolate is greater. As the profile was derived from a combination of cream and sugar, an obvious explanation is that more sugar is needed to counteract the bitterness of chocolate. Chocolate approaches this 'hedonic' ideal.

When we eat something that tastes pleasant, endorphin mechanisms in the brain are stimulated. Naloxone and other opioid antagonists influence the eating of pleasant-tasting food such as chocolate, in both animals (65-67) and humans (69,71,76,77,79). It is known that opioids play an important role in the initiation and maintenance of drug dependence (84); in the limbic forebrain, they are associated with drug craving and relapse following withdrawal. Heroin (85), alcohol (86) and nicotine (87) addictions are all associated with the perception of a sweet taste as more pleasant.

It should be remembered that there are relatively few data that deal directly with the topic of chocolate craving. Rather, the possibility that various constituents might, or might not, play a part in craving has been considered. A parsimonious explanation is that the attractiveness of chocolate reflects its taste and mouthfeel. For many, chocolate offers a pleasant taste that is likely to potently stimulate endorphin release.

4.2.10   Summary

Chocolate is by far the most commonly reported food item that is craved, and those who crave chocolate tend to do so when they are emotionally distressed. In some individuals, feelings of guilt are associated with the consumption of chocolate.

There are two major explanations of chocolate craving - its action may be predominantly biological or psychological.

A major hypothesis is that the high intake of carbohydrate increases the ratio of tryptophan to long-chain neutral amino acids in the blood. After tryptophan enters the brain, it has been suggested that mood improves when serotonin synthesis is enhanced. Although the phenomenon can be demonstrated in the laboratory, chocolate contains protein in levels too high for this mechanism to function.

Chocolate contains a variety of chemicals, including methylxanthines, phenylethylamine and anandamide, with possible 'drug-like' properties. (See also section 6.3). Although in appropriate quantities these substances act on the brain, in all cases the quantities supplied by eating chocolate are too low for a pharmacological reaction to occur.

The administration of the pharmacological constituents of chocolate does not satisfy chocolate craving. It has been concluded that the attraction of chocolate lies in its taste. Sweet fatty food items have a pleasant taste; chocolate approaches the ideal combination of sweetness and fat. Pleasant-tasting foods induce the release of endorphins in the brain, and drugs that block the action of endorphins selectively decrease the intake of palatable foods such as chocolate.

4.2.11   References

1.   Weingarten H.P., Elston D. Food cravings in a college population. *Appetite*, 1991, 17, 167-75.

2.   Hetherington M.M., Macdiarmid J.I. Chocolate addiction: a preliminary study of its description and its relationship to problem eating. *Appetite*, 1993, 21, 233-46.

3.   Bruinsma K., Taren D.L. Chocolate: food or drug? *Journal of the American Dietetics Association*, 1999, 99, 1249-56.

4.   Benton D. Chocolate craving: Biological or psychological phenomenon?, in *Chocolate and Cocoa*. Ed. Knight I. Oxford, Blackwell Science. 1999, 256-78.

5. Benton D., Greenfield K., Morgan M. The development of the attitudes to chocolate questionnaire. *Personality and Individual Differences*, 1998, 24, 513-20.

6. Schuman M., Gitlin M.J., Fairbanks L. Sweets, chocolate, and atypical depressive traits. *Journal of Nervous and Mental Disorders*, 1987, 175, 491-5.

7. Hill A.J., Weaver C.F.L., Blundell J.E. Food craving, dietary restraint and mood. *Appetite*, 1991, 17, 187-97.

8. Lester D., Bernard D. Liking for chocolate depression and suicidal preoccupation. *Psychological Reports*, 1991, 69, 570.

9. van Strien T., Frijters J.E.R., Bergers G.P.A., Defares P.B. The Dutch Eating Behaviour Questionnaire for assessment of restrained, emotional and external eating behavior. *International Journal of Eating Disorders*, 1986, 5, 295-315.

10. Willner P., Benton D., Brown E., Cheeta S., Davies G., Morgan J., Morgan M. Depression increases craving for sweet rewards in animal and human models of depression and craving. *Psychopharmacology*, 1998, 136, 272-83.

11. Garner D.M., Olmstead M., Polivy H. Development and validation of a multidimensional eating disorder inventory for anorexia and bulimia. *International Journal of Eating Disorders*, 1983, 2, 15-34.

12. Donohoe R. *The relationship between blood glucose and cognitive functioning in young adults.* University of Wales Swansea, Ph.D Thesis. 1997.

13. Vlitos A.L.P., Davies G.J. Bowel function, food intake and the menstrual cycle. *Nutrition Research Reviews*, 1996, 9, 111-34.

14. Buffenstein R., Poppitt S.D., McDevitt R.M., Prentice A.M. Food intake and the menstrual cycle: a retrospective analysis with implications for appetite research. *Physiology and Behavior*, 1995, 58, 1067-77.

15. Webb P. Twenty-four hour energy expenditure and the menstrual cycle. *American Journal of Clinical Nutrition*, 1986, 44, 614-9.

16. Tomelleri R., Grunewald K.K. Menstrual cycle and food cravings in young college women. *Journal of the American Dietetic Association*, 1987, 87, 311-5.

17. Fong A.K.H., Kretsch M.J. Changes in dietary intake urinary nitrogen and urinary volume across the menstrual cycle. *American Journal of Clinical Nutrition*, 1993, 234, E243-247.

18. Posaci C., Erten O., Uren A., Acar B. Plasma copper, zinc and magnesium levels in patients with premenstrual tension syndrome. *Acta Obsterica et Gynecoletrica Scandanavia*, 1994, 73, 452-5.

19. Sherwood R.A., Rocks B.F., Stewart A., Saxton R.S. Magnesium and the premenstrual syndrome. *Annals of Clinical Biochemistry*, 1986, 23, 667-70.

20. Rosenstein D.L., Elin R.J., Hosseini J.M., Grover G., Rubinow D.R. Magnesium measures across the menstrual cycle in the premenstrual syndrome. *Biological Psychiatry*, 1994, 15, 557-61.

21. Fachinetti F., Borella P., Sances G., Fioroni L., Nappi R.E., Genazani A.R. Oral magnesium successfully relieves premenstrual mood changes. *Obstetrics and Gynecology*, 1991, 78, 177-81.

22. Mumford G.K., Evans S.M., Kaminski B.J., Preston K.L., Sannerud C.A., Silverman K., Griffiths R.R. Discriminative stimulus and subjective effects of theobromine and caffeine in humans. *Psychopharmacology*, 1994, 115, 1-8.

23. Shively C.A., Tarka S.M. Methylxanthine composition and consumption patterns of cocoa and chocolate products, in *The methylxanthine beverages and foods: Chemistry consumption and health effects*. Ed. Spiller G. New York, Alan R Liss. 1984, 149-78.

24. Sprugel W., Mitznegg P., Heim F. The influence of caffeine and theobromine on locomotor activity and the brain of cGMP/cAMP ratio in white mice. *Biochemical Pharmacology*, 1977, 26, 1723-24.

25. Snyder S.H., Katims J.J., Annau Z., Bruns R.F., Daly J.W. Adenosine receptors and behavioural actions of methylxanthines. *Proceedings of the National Academy of Sciences*, USA, 1981, 78, 3260-4.

26. Carney J.M., Cao W., Logan L., Rennert O.M., Seale T.W. Differential antagonism of the behavioural depressant and hypothermic effects of 5'-(N-ethylcarboxamide) adenosine by theobromine. *Pharmacology Biochemistry and Behavior*, 1986, 25, 769-73.

27. Katims J.J., Annau Z., Snyder S.H. Interactions in the behavioural effects of methylxanthines and adenosine derivatives. *Journal of Pharmacology and Experimental Therapeutics*, 1983, 227, 167-73.

28. Beer B., Chasin M., Clody D.E., Vogel J.R., Horovitz Z.P. Cyclic adenosine monophosphate phosphodiesterase in brain: effect on anxiety. *Science*, 1972, 176, 428-30.

29. Herz A., Neteler B., Teschemacher H.J. Vergleichende untersuchungen uber zentrale wirkungen von xanthindeerivaen in hinblick auf deren stoffweechsel und verteilung im organismus (Comparative studies of the central effects of methylxanthines in relation to their catabolism and distribution in the body). *Naunyn-Schmiedebergs Archiv fur Pharmakologie und Expimentelle Pathologie*, 1968, 261, 1123-32.

30. Carney J.M., Holloway F.A., Modrow H.E. Discriminative stimulus properties of methylxanthines and their metabolites in rats. *Life Sciences*, 1985, 36, 913-20.

31. Holtzman S.G. Discriminative stimulus properties of caffeine in the rat: noradrenergic mediation. *Journal of Pharmacology and Experimental Therapeutics*, 1986, 239, 706-14.

32. Tarka S.M. The toxicology of cocoa and methylxanthines: a review of the literature. *Critical Review in Toxicology*, 1982, 9, 275-312.

33. Stavric B. Methylxanthines: toxicity to humans 3. Theobromines, paraxanthine and the combined effects of methylxanthines. *Food Chemistry and Toxicology*, 1988, 26, 725-33.

34. Battig J.J., Buzzi R., Martin J.R., Feierabend J.M. The effects of caffeine on physiological functions and mental performance. *Experientia*, 1984, 40, 1218-23.

35. Loke W.H. Effects of caffeine on mood and memory. *Physiology and Behavior*, 1988, 44, 367-72.

36. Fine B.J., Kobrick J.L., Lieberman H.R., Marlowe B., Riley R.H., Tharion W.J. Effects of caffeine or diphenhydramine on visual vigilance. *Psychopharmacology*, 1994, 114, 233-8.

37. Lieberman H.R. Caffeine, in *Handbook of Human Performance, Volume 2*. Eds Smith A.P., Jones D.M. London, Academic Press. 1992, 49-72.

38. Lieberman H.R., Wurtman R.J., Embe G.G., Coviella I.L.G. The effects of caffeine and aspirin on mood and performance. *Journal of Clinical Psychopharmacology*, 1987, 7, 315-20.

39. Kuznicki J.T., Turner L.S. The effects of caffeine on caffeine users and non-users. *Physiology and Behavior*, 1986, 37, 397-408.

40. Lieberman H.R., Wurtman R.J., Embe G.G., Roberts C., Coviella I.L. The effects of low doses of caffeine on human performance and mood. *Psychopharmacology*, 1987, 92, 308-12.

41. Goldstein A., Kaizer S., Warren R. Psychotropic effects of caffeine in man II. Alertness psychomotor coordination and mood. *Journal of Pharmacology and Experimental Therapeutics*, 1965, 150, 146-51.

42. Leathwood P., Pollit P. Diet induced mood changes in normal populations. *Journal of Psychiatric Research*, 1982, 17, 147-54.

43. Roache J.D., Griffiths R.R. Interactions of diazepam and caffeine: behavioral and subjective dose effects in humans. *Pharmacology Biochemistry and Behavior*, 1987, 26, 801-12.

44. Fagan D., Swift C.G., Tiplady B. Effects of caffeine on vigilance and other performance tests in normal subjects. *Journal of Psychopharmacology*, 1988, 2, 19-25.

45. Oliveto A.H., Hughes J.R., Pepper S.L., Bickel W.K., Higgins S.T. Low doses of caffeine can serve as reinforcers in humans, in *Problems of Drug Dependence. US Department of health and Human Services*. Ed. Harris L. Rockville, MD, National Institute on Drug. 1990.

46. Weil A. *Natural health natural medicine*. Boston, Houghton Mifflin. 1990.

47. Hurst W.J., Toomey P.B. High-performance liquid chromatographic determination of four biogenic amines in chocolate. *Analyst*, 1981, 106, 394-402.

48. Webster R.A., Jordan C.C. *Neurotransmitters drug and disease*. Oxford, Blackwell Scientific Publications, Oxford. 1989.

49. Paterson I.A., Juorio A.V., Boulton A.A. 2-phenylethylamine: a modulator of catecholamine transmission in the mammalian central nervous system? *Journal of Neurochemistry*, 1990, 55, 1827-183.

50. Greenshaw A.J. β-phenylethylamine and reinforcement. *Progress in Neuropsychopharmacology and Biological Psychiatry*, 1984, 8, 615-20.

51. Hirst W.J., Martin R.A., Zoumas B.L., Tarka S.M. Biogenic amines in chocolate – a review. *Nutrition Reports International*, 1982, 26, 1081-7.

52. Greenshaw A.J., Sanger D.J., Blackman D.E. Effects of d-amphetamine and beta-phenylethylamine on fixed interval responding maintained by self-regulated lateral hypothalamus stimulation in rats. *Pharmacology Biochemistry and Behavior*, 1985, 23, 519-23.

53. Goudie A.J., Buckland C. Serotonin receptor blockade potentiates the behavioural effects of beta-phenylethylamine. *Neuropharmacology*, 1982, 21, 1267-72.

54. Sabelli H.C., Javaid J.I. Phenylethylamine modulaton of affect: therapeutic and diagnostic implications. *Journal of Neuropsychiatry and Clinical Neuroscience*, 1995, 7, 6-14.

55. Schifano F., Magni G. MDMA (ecstasy) abuse: psychopathological features and craving for chocolate: a case series. *Biological Psychiatry*, 1994, 36, 763-7.

56. DiTomaso E., Beltramo M., Piomelli D. Brain cannabinoids in chocolate. *Nature*, 1996, 382, 677-8.

57. Waterhouse A.L., Shirley J.R., Donovan J.L. Antioxidants in chocolate. *Lancet*, 1996, 348, 834.

58. Spring B., Chiodo J., Bowen D.J. Carbohydrates, tryptophan, and behavior: a methodological review. *Psychological Bulletin*, 1987, 102, 234-56.

59. Wurtman R.J., Wurtman J.J. Carbohydrates and depression. *Scientific American*, 1989, 260, 50-7.

60. Wurtman R.J., Hefti F., Melamed E. Precursor control of neurotransmitter synthesis. *Pharmacological Reviews*, 1981, 32, 315-35.

61. Rosenthal N., Genhart M., Caballero B., Jacobsen F.M., Skwerer R.G., Coursey R.D., Rogers S., Spring B.J. Psychobiological effects of carbohydrate- and protein-rich meals in patients with seasonal affective disorder and normal controls. *Biological Psychiatry*, 1989, 25, 1029-40.

62. de Castro J.M. Macronutrient relationships with meal patterns and mood in spontaneous feeding behavior of humans. *Physiology and Behavior*, 1987, 39, 561-9.

63. Keith R.E., O'Keefe K.A., Blessing D.L., Wilson D.G. Alternations in dietary carbohydrate, protein and fat intake and mood state in trained females cyclists. *Medical Sciences in Sports and Exercise*, 1991, 23, 212-6.

64. Deijen J.B., Heemstra M.L., Orlebeke J.F. Dietary effects on mood and performance. *Journal of Psychiatric Research*, 1989, 23, 275-83.

65. Dum J., Gramsch C.H., Herz A. Activation of hypothalamic beta-endorphin pools by reward induced by highly palatable food. *Pharmacology Biochemistry and Behavior*, 1983, 18, 443-7.

66. Reid L.D. Endogenous opioid peptides and regulation of drinking and feeding. *American Journal of Clinical Nutrition*, 1985, 42, 1099-132.

67. Giraudo S.Q., Grace M.K., Welch C.C., Billington C.J., Levine A.S. Naloxone's anoretic effect is dependent upon the relative palatability of food. *Pharmacology Biochemistry Behavior*, 1993, 46, 917-21.

68. Carr K.D., Simon E.J. The role of opioids in feeding and reward elicited by lateral hypothalamic electrical stimulation. *Life Sciences*, 1983, 33, Suppl 1, 563-6.

69. Trenchard E., Silverstone T. Naloxone reduces the food intake of normal human volunteers. *Appetite*, 1982, 4, 249-57.

70. Spiegel T.A., Stunkard A.J., Shrager E.E., O'Brien C.P., Morrison M.F. Effect of naltrexone on food intake hunger and satiety in obese men. *Physiology and Behavior*, 1987, 40, 135-41.

71. Wolkowitz O.M., Doran M.R., Cohen R.M., Cohen T.N., Wise T.N., Pickar D. Single-dose naloxone acutely reduced eating in obese humans: Behavioral and biochemical effects. *Biological Psychiatry*, 1988, 24, 483-7.

72. Fantino M., Hosotte J., Apfelbaum M. An opioid antagonist naltrexone reduces preference for sucrose in humans. *American Journal of Physiology*, 1986, 251, R91-R96.

73. Davis J.M., Lowy M.T., Yim G.K.W., Lam D.R., Malven P.V. Relationships between plasma concentrations of immuno-reactive beta-endorphin and food intake in rats. *Peptides*, 1983, 4, 79-83.

74. Matsumura M., Fukuda N., Saito S., Mori H. Effect of a test meal, duodenal acidification and tetragastrin on the plasma beta-endorphin like immunoreactivity in man. *Regulatory Peptides*, 1982, 4, 173-81.

75.   Getto C.J., Fullerton D.T., Carlson I.H. Plasma immunoreactive beta-endorphin response to glucose ingestion. *Appetite*, 1984, 5, 329-35.

76.   Yeomans M.R., Wright P., Macleod H.A., Critchley J.A. Effects of nalmefene on feeding in humans. *Psychopharmacology*, 1990, 100, 426-32.

77.   Drenowski A., Gosnell B., Krahn D.D., Canum K. Sensory preferences for sugar and fat: evidence for opioid involvement. *Appetite*, 1989, 12, 206.

78.   Mandenoff A.F., Fumerton M., Apfelbaum M., Margules D.L. Endogenous opiates and energy balance. *Science*, 1982, 215, 1536-7.

79.   Koch J.E., Bodnar R.J. Involvement of mu1 and mu2 opioid receptor subtypes in tail-pinch feeding in rats. *Physiology and Behavior*, 1993, 53, 603-5.

80.   Drenowski A., Krahn D.D., Demitrack M.A., Nairn K., Gosnell B.A. Naloxone, an opiate blocker, reduces the consumption of sweet high-fat foods in obese and lean female binge eaters. *American Journal of Clinical Nutrition*, 1995, 61, 1206-12.

81.   Melchior J.C., Rigaud D., Colas-Linhart N., Petiet A., Giraard A., Apfelbaum M. Immunoreactive beta-endorphin increases after an aspartame chocolate drink in healthy human subjects. *Physiology and Behavior*, 1991, 50, 941-4.

82.   Michener W., Rozin P. Pharmacolgical versus sensory factors in the satiation of chocolate craving. *Physiology and Behavior*, 1994, 56, 419-22.

83.   Drenowski A., Greenwood M.R.C. Cream and Sugar: Human preferences for high-fat foods. *Physiology and Behavior*, 1983, 30, 629-33.

84.   Van Ree J.M. Endorphins and experimental addiction. *Alcohol*, 1996, 13, 25-30.

85.   Shufman P.E., Vas A., Luger S., Steiner J.E. Taste and odor reactivity in heroin addicts. *Israel Journal Psychiatry and Related Sciences*, 1997, 34, 290-9.

86.   Kampov-Polevoy A., Garbutt J.C., Janowsky D. Evidence of preference for a high-concentration sucrose solution in alcoholic men. *American Journal of Psychiatry*, 1997, 154, 269-70.

87.   Kos J., Hassenfratz M., Battig K. Effects of a 2-day abstinence from smoking on dietary, cognitive, subjective, and physiologic parameters among younger and older female smokers. *Physiology and Behavior*, 1997, 61, 671-8.

4.3. CHOCOLATE: FROM ADORATION TO ADDICTION

Marion M. Hetherington

4.3.1   Introduction

There is something very special about chocolate. Chocolate, like other forms of confectionery, occupies the unique position of both food and non-food (1,2). It is eaten on every continent and contributes to the diets of millions of consumers, but it is also regarded as an occasional treat or indulgence and is subject to particular scrutiny by healthy eating advocates. The history of chocolate from Mesoamerica to Europe is deeply intriguing (3,4) and some might say highly controversial (5). Contemporary notions of chocolate have been shaped by early associations between chocolate, the aristocracy and the elite, and by a long, but volatile history extolling its benefits. In this chapter, the historical, medicinal and cultural roots of chocolate will be explored in order to understand the context of its appeal. Contemporary references to chocolate craving and "addiction" will be examined against the social and cultural constructions of chocolate in Western societies.

4.3.2   A Brief History of Chocolate

Chocolate made its début in the cuisines of Europe as a frothy drink, initially consumed only by the wealthy. But for centuries before this, the seeds of *Theobroma cacao* served as currency and as a beverage to the élite in South American traditional culture. Cacao[1] beans could be exchanged for a range of commodities in early Mesoamerican cultures, and so drinking cocoa became the practice of only the upper echelons of society.

Theobroma cacao flourishes in humid, tropical rainforests under sheltering trees, and within 20 ° of the equator. The first time that a beverage from cacao seeds was prepared is not known, although most culinary books

---

[1] Cacao refers to the raw seed or pod; cocoa refers to the processed powder or drink.

are quick to associate the discovery of chocolate with the Aztecs of Mexico. It is more likely that ancient civilisations used the seeds of wild cacao trees for many years and that the first of those to cultivate these trees for their precious harvest were the ancient Olmec (1500–400 BC) living around the lowlands of the Mexican Gulf Coast (4). The earliest history of cacao is subject to much speculation, partly because the Olmec left very few hieroglyphs to decipher and partly because most of what has been gleaned about the origins of chocolate has been filtered through the eyes of Old World sources, particularly Jesuit Priests. Even the derivation of "chocolate" from the original Nahuatl language is disputed (4). It appears that the Aztecs used "cacahuatl" to mean cacao water, but the Spanish used a new word "chocolatl" which is a hybrid between a Maya word for hot, "chocol", and the Aztec word for water, "atl". This corruption is interesting since, like the Yucatan Maya, the Spanish preferred to drink their chocolate hot, unlike the Aztecs, who drank it cold. What seems clear is that the classic Maya and Aztecs of Mesoamerica roasted cacao nibs, added maize, water and spices, then created foaming drinks from this mix (6). In recognition of the divine links between the origins of cocoa and religious rituals involved in planting the trees, the Swedish botanist Linnaeus named the genus *Theobroma*, meaning "food of the gods". Originally, the Latin name applied was *Amygdalae pecuniaria*, or "money almond" (7), since cacao beans were used as currency.

The first known image of a chocolate drink being prepared dates back to AD 750, and there are depictions of cacao pods on drinking vessels from 200 years earlier taken from tombs of Early Classic Maya in Guatemala (4). The Aztec Emperor Motecuhzoma the Younger (Montezuma), who reigned from 1502-1520, kept a warehouse with 960 million beans and generously supplied 2,000 containers of powdered chocolate to his guards each day (4). The chocolate was prepared by drying the seeds, then roasting them on a hot, grinding stone ("metate") before pounding the roasted seeds into a fine powder, which could then be shaped into wafers or tablets. These wafers could then be eaten or made into the typical drink by adding water. The highly prized foam was created by pouring from a great height the contents of one vessel to another (as depicted in Mayan art). However, the

Spanish changed this process by frothing the drink using a *molinet* or swizzle stick (3). In addition, Old World tastes determined that the drink should be hot and sweet; thus, cane sugar was added to the ground beans in addition to more familiar spices such as cinnamon. The Aztec preference was for chilli "chilcacahuatl" among the many flavourings and spices added to chocolate, and it is known that the Classic Maya used chilli in their drinks. For example, the glyph "ikal kakaw" (chilli cacao) has been found on Mayan ruins (4).

When the Italian historian and adventurer Girolamo Benzoni wrote "History of the New World" in 1575 (8), he described the cold, bitter murky drink "more a drink for pigs than a drink for humanity." However, over time, Benzoni resorted to drinking chocolate and revised his opinion: "The taste is somewhat bitter, it satisfies and refreshes the body, but does not inebriate, and it is the best and most expensive merchandise, according to the Indians of that country." The restorative powers of chocolate, together with its high price noted by Benzoni, are themes that re-emerge throughout the writings of the 16th and 17th centuries. Indeed, when the earliest visitors to the New World recounted their experiences, the ground was laid for notions of the appeal of chocolate, its special powers and the lengths to which people were willing to go to obtain chocolate. Such themes still resonate in contemporary views of chocolate.

4.3.3   Chacun à son Goût

With the great changes brought about by industrialisation, the manufacture of chocolate developed away from the traditional and ancient practices of drying, shelling, roasting and then grinding cacao into a powder. In 1795, J.S. Fry and Sons in Bristol, who had been producing cocoa since 1728, used steam to grind their beans, and the mass production of chocolate was born (3). In 1828, a Dutch chemist named Coenraad van Houten made the first advances towards a solid edible chocolate, by using a hydraulic device, which pressed out most of the cocoa butter, leaving a cocoa liquor behind. The process of "Dutching", named in honour of van Houten, involved treating the fine cocoa powder with alkaline salts so that it could mix better with water (4). By 1847, Fry's had produced the first eating chocolate, by combining cocoa powder, sugar and melted cocoa butter. This chocolate would have been coarse and somewhat bitter. Milk chocolate, as it is known today, emerged from the collaboration between Henri Nestlé, a Swiss chemist, and Daniel Peter, a Swiss chocolate manufacturer, when they experimented with adding evaporated milk powder to the mix in 1875. The first milk chocolate bar was produced in 1879. In the same year, conching was introduced by Rudolphe Lindt, which produced a creamy, smooth texture in the chocolate. Tempering was another process added in the late 1800s, which prevented cocoa butter from crystallising on the surface of the chocolate. Whilst conching involved agitating liquid chocolate for 72 or more hours to produce the "fondant" texture, tempering involved raising the temperature of cocoa mass then slowly lowering the temperature to destroy the crystal properties of the fat.

Modern chocolate manufacturing follows a similar process to that established by the 19th century pioneers of the industry. Chocolate is consumed in vast quantities around the world and it is universally popular. However, it is not the same chocolate, as Chiva (9) asserts: "Chocolate is loved everywhere, but it is not exactly the same chocolate, from an organoleptic point of view, that people in different countries like". Manufacturers develop chocolate to suit the taste of the market, and so in some countries the preference is for a bitter, dark chocolate and in others the ideal is a sweet, milk chocolate. Across different countries, there are some interesting similarities in patterns of consumption. Douglass and Amann (10), in their review of national diet surveys in the USA, UK and the former West Germany, observe that the greatest chocolate intake is reported by males in each age category, and both the quantity and frequency of consuming chocolate decline with age. The highest mean daily intakes of chocolate are reported by teenage males and females. In Europe, the largest per capita consumers of chocolate products are the Swiss, who have been consuming around 10 kg per capita per annum since 1991 (see Fig. 4.3.1). In the UK, annual consumption per capita is around 8.5 kg, whereas in Portugal and Greece, consumption is estimated at between 2 and 3 kg per capita. Within Europe, there is a degree of variance in the amount of chocolate consumed, and the markets cater to particular tastes within each country. Chocolate has universal acceptance, but some consumers like chocolate more than others. What contributes to the legendary attraction of chocolate?

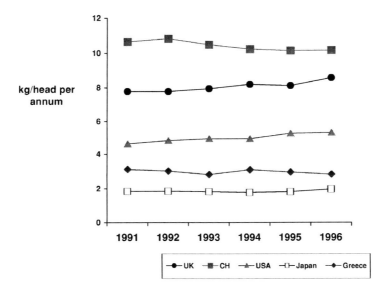

Fig. 4.3.1. Intake of chocolate (kg/per capita) for UK, Switzerland, USA, Japan and Greece (data adapted from (56)).

4.3.4   The Benefits of Chocolate

Part of the allure of chocolate when it was first introduced to Europe came from its putative medicinal benefits. The Aztecs considered chocolate to have divine powers, but the general population rarely consumed chocolate. Aztec warriors and travelling merchants were the exception. It seems that chocolate was taken to enhance courage and improve the spirit of soldiers and itinerant traders who faced great danger. Perhaps for the same reasons, in 1899 Queen Victoria dispatched a Christmas shipment of half a million pounds of chocolate to her troops in South Africa during the conflict with the Boers (3). Similarly, Milton Hershey was decorated for his contribution to the war effort in producing a ration D chocolate bar that packed 600 kcal into 4 oz for American soldiers (3). Reaching for chocolate during times of stress has a long and politically sanctioned history. That it was considered a comfort by those sent to war is testimony to the power of chocolate as both fuel and tonic.

Therapeutic benefits of chocolate were initially advocated with some conviction, particularly its stimulating and digestive properties. During the reign of Louis XIII, Cardinal de Richelieu attributed his great energy to chocolate, and the Cardinal's brother Alphonse gained emotional support from chocolate, taking it "to modify the vapours of his spleen and to fight against fits of anger and bad moods" (1642; cited by Coe and Coe (4)). In his treatise of the "Indian Nectar" (11), Henry Stubbe, a physician, wrote that one ounce of chocolate contained more fat and greater nourishment than a pound of meat. He also wrote with great eloquence on its aphrodisiac qualities: "[Chocolate] becomes provocative to lust upon no other account than that it begets good blood". Stubbe carefully outlined a variety of chocolate concoctions to take as medicine. James Wordsworth translated the following from Spanish in his "Curious History of the Nature and Quality of Chocolate" (12): "By the wise and moderate use whereof, health is preserved, sicknesse diverted, and cured". The English diarist Samual Pepys regularly drank a morning draft of "chocolatte", and his first encounter with the drink in 1662 was taken to settle his stomach. Taking chocolate with or just after breakfast became a popular practice amongst 17th century Europeans. In 1675, Madame de Sévigné praised the unique properties of chocolate in her letters. She remarked that chocolate was excellent to aid digestion and to assist a fast. Indeed, she felt that chocolate was so "agreeable, because it acts according to one's wishes (cited in Morton and Morton (3)). The French food writer Louis Lémery, in "A Treatise of Foods" (13), reinforced the idea of chocolate assisting digestion, but also favoured its ability to "repair decayed strength" and remarked that, as an aphrodisiac, it "promotes venery". Thus, the allure of chocolate in Europe was partly attributable to its energising and medicinal qualities. Clearly this was no ordinary foodstuff.

When Louis XVI ascended to the throne in 1774, Marie Antoniette appointed a personal chocolatier who created a variety of novel chocolate combinations to suit the taste of the courtiers - for example, chocolate with powdered orchid bulbs or scented with orange blossom (3). Marie Antoniette was famously disciplined in her diet of white meat, bouillon, water and biscuits, but, according to Madame Campan's mémoirs (14), began each day with coffee or chocolate. The Marquis de Sade (1740-1814), among his many predilections, was a lover of chocolate. According to de Sade's biographer Maurice Lever (15): "Chocolate inspired an irresistible passion. He loved it in it all its forms: in cream, in cakes, in ice cream, in bars". No discussion of chocolate's capacity to arouse passion would be complete without mentioning Casanova. Morton and Morton (3) note that Casanova liked chocolate for breakfast and found the drink "as useful a lubricant to seduction as Champagne." The temptation of chocolate was further enhanced by its exclusivity and putative aphrodisiac qualities. Today, access to chocolate is ubiquitous and affordable to the great majority of people. Links to sexual desire are reflected in contemporary advertising for some chocolate products, and many chocolate manufacturers continue to develop expensive, exclusive brands to attract the connoisseur. Notions of the sensual nature of chocolate and connections to élitist tastes still pervade modern constructions of chocolate, particularly through marketing and advertising.

In contrast to the regal introduction of chocolate to Spain and later to France, chocolate, although taxed in Britain, was available in shops at a price that was affordable to many. A Frenchman opened London's first chocolate shop in Bishopsgate Street in 1657. The famous chocolate houses of London began to compete with coffee houses in the late 1600s, charging just a penny for entrance. In 1711, Mrs White took over the running of White's chocolate house, raising the entrance fee and limiting her clientele by their available funds. By the mid-1700s, the chocolate houses became private clubs (3), and, in some of these, chocolate drinking was associated with a rather "laddish" element, combining chocolate with gambling, politics and other vices.

Chocolate was, and still is, associated with providing a good source of energy. The German explorer Alexander von Humboldt travelling in equatorial America at the end of the 18th century seemed more impressed by the amazing nutritional economy of cacao than its alleged capacity to excite sexual desire: "Alike easy to convey, and employ as an aliment, it contains a large quantity of nutritive and stimulating particles in a small volume" (cited by McGee (16)). The theme of stimulation and nutritional value can be related to the pharmacological properties of chocolate, particularly caffeine and theobromine. A more detailed consideration of these "particles" is given elsewhere in this book (see section 4.4). Butler's Medicine Chest Directory in 1826 also promoted the use of Fry's Chocolate Lozenges for the traveller - "pleasant and nutritious substitute for food in travelling, or when unusual fasting is caused by irregular periods of meal times" (cited in (2)).

Jean-Anthelme Brillat-Savarin's much quoted "Physiology of Taste" (17) devotes a section in his chapter on "specialities" to chocolate. He was most impressed by the digestibility of chocolate, and its capacity to soothe the sick, and, with careful preparation, considered chocolate to be a "wholesome and agreeable form of food". He advised its use for anyone in occupations involving "great mental exertion". In all of Paris, Brillat-Savarin could recommend only one chocolate dealer, Monsieur Debauve, a pharmacist based at 26 rue des Saint-Pères, and supplier to the King. According to Brillat-Savarin, Debauve prepared "palatable antidotes against certain minor ailments", including irritability, weak nerves and poor strength. Brillat-Savarin was convinced of the restorative powers of chocolate. By 1862, when Arthur Mangin wrote "Le Cacao et le Chocolat" (18), few still believed that chocolate conferred any particular therapeutic benefit to its devotees. Nonetheless, following industrialisation and the wide availability of chocolate bars, chocolate manufacturers continued to extol the virtues of their wares to the general public - in particular, its energy giving effects. An early poster advertising cocoa demonstrates this: "Cadbury's Cocoa Makes Strong Men Stronger. The most refreshing, nutritious, and sustaining of all cocoas", and in a poster advertising

Hershey's milk chocolate, a mother is seen buying bars for her children as "a meal in itself".

In Anglo-American societies, there are powerful links between chocolate as fuel, sensual treat, tonic, and opulent indulgence (see also section 4.1 "The special place of chocolate in the Anglo-American diet"). But general attitudes about chocolate may be less positive than they were when chocolate was first introduced to Europe. There are many scientists who have demonstrated the health benefits of chocolate - for example, the high concentration of antioxidants in chocolate (19), or the neutral cholesterolaemic effects of stearic acid in chocolate (20). However, dietitians identify chocolate as a food to limit based more on moral than scientific grounds (21) and the temptation of chocolate clashes with contemporary health messages to reduce fat and sugar. Although chocolate was once associated with positive constructions of health and wealth, contemporary conceptualisations are much more ambivalent.

4.3.5   For the Love of Chocolate

Historically, chocolate has had its critics, and there have been numerous attempts by the church to restrict its use. Chocolate has played a role in several ecclesiastical intrigues. The death of Pope Clement XIV was attributed to poisoned chocolate, since his confectioner died just days after the pontiff. Most liturgical debate about chocolate centred on whether it was a drink or a food (4). This was an important question for Catholic countries, since, if chocolate was determined to be a food, it could not be consumed during fasting or in the hours before Holy Communion. However, if chocolate did not nourish the body but simply quenched thirst, then chocolate, like other drinks, did not break a fast: *Liquidium non frangit jejunum.* (Liquid does not break a fast). The more puritanical clerics tried to ban chocolate from fast days; however, Pope Gregory XIII declared chocolate acceptable and, in the centuries since, other Popes have followed his example (4).

In 1648, the English writer and traveller Thomas Gage (himself a great drinker of chocolate - at least five cups a day) related a classic example of conflict experienced by the church regarding the drinking of chocolate, and provided, perhaps, the first insight into chocolate addiction. In Chiapa Real, Mexico, Gage (22) noted that upper class Spanish women had cups of chocolate brought to them by their maids during mass. When the bishop tried to ban anyone who drank chocolate inside the cathedral, the ladies worshipped elsewhere, still taking their cups of chocolate. Shortly after his threats to excommunicate the women, the bishop fell ill and it was rumoured that he was poisoned with a cup of chocolate. Gage's account reinforces the notion that the church has often experienced conflict about chocolate drinking, and, for the first time, Gage implies that chocolate had a powerful hold on these Old World women. Drinking chocolate to excess was frowned upon, and the French physician Daniel Duncan noted in 1703 that too much chocolate was bad for the blood (4). Similarly, Dr. Giovanni Batista Felici (23) wrote "An Opinion about the Use of Chocolate", advising against giving chocolate to children since he believed it caused them great agitation. Thus, the seeds of ambivalence about chocolate were sown from the earliest records of the drink's introduction to European consumers.

Given that chocolate was associated with inflaming passion, it was subject to considerable suspicion by the church. However, dissension about the benefits of chocolate went beyond religious sources. Even during the time of the Aztecs, associations between chocolate and weight gain were made. Fray Diego Durán compiled a detailed account of the lives of the Aztecs from historical and ethnographic reports, translated in 1964 by Fernando Horcasitas and Doris Heyden (24). He describes a fabled visit to the ancestors of Motecuhzoma Ilhuicamina, one of the noble emperors of the mid-15th century. When Coatlicue, a goddess who lived at the top of a great hill, received visitors from Motecuhzoma offering chocolate, the guardian of the hill noticed that the esteemed visitors reached the summit with great difficulty. The guardian asked the Aztecs what had made them so heavy, and the visitors included chocolate in their list of typical foods. Both the custodian and the goddess identified chocolate as a burden to the people. The tale upset Motecuhzoma, but he continued to drink chocolate. The story incorporates a morality tale advising against rejecting the simple, traditional lifestyle of the Aztec ancestors and adopting such extravagances as chocolate. Early accounts of chocolate make the link between pleasure and potentially negative consequences, from excessive intake causing "bad blood" to its role in the development of obesity.

The connection between drinking chocolate and "heaviness" was also made by Martin Lister in his "Journey to Paris in 1698" (25). Lister blamed chocolate (with the addition of lots of sugar) for the increased weight of Parisian women. In particular, Lister believed that in those who "plead for chocolate", it creates "a false hunger". This early description of chocolate cravings reinforces an earlier account of addiction to chocolate recorded by the Spanish Jesuit José de Acosta in 1590 (26). He noted that his countrymen, particularly the women, were very taken with chocolate. "It is a valued drink which the Indians offer to the lords who come or pass through their land. And the Spanish men, and even more the Spanish women, are addicted to the black chocolate" (translated by Coe and Coe (4)). The theme of women's particular fondness for chocolate was also noted by Brillat-Savarin (17), who stated that chocolate, unlike coffee "holds no terrors for the fair sex" and that "Spanish ladies of the New World love chocolate to the point of madness". These suggestions that women, particularly, are drawn to chocolate are interesting since most studies of chocolate addiction indicate that the majority of self-identified addicts are women, and most popular images of the chocoholic feature women.

Addiction to chocolate is the exclusive province of women, suggests Barthel (27), who also identifies the link between feminine identity, sweetness and indulgence; in contrast, alcohol and tobacco "conferred and confirmed masculine privilege". She further states: "Chocolate is legal, yet sinful, the extent to which it skirts similarity with drugs is picked up in advertisements promising 'chocolate overload' and celebrating the breaking down of willpower and resistance." The desirability of chocolate may be so great that some consumers claim that they become "addicted" to chocolate, implying that the draw of chocolate is equivalent to that of substances such as drugs of abuse. References to chocolate addiction are rooted in historical accounts of its powerful allure, but scientific examination of addiction to chocolate has happened only relatively recently.

Chocolate has been linked to positive medicinal benefits, but ambivalence about chocolate has a long history, from its association with obesity to its potentially addictive qualities. A recent review (28) concludes that chocolate consumption does not specifically cause obesity. This is self-evident given the complex multifactorial nature of obesity. But the question of whether or not chocolate can be addictive requires some consideration.

4.3.6   Ideational, Hedonic and Sensory Attributes of Chocolate

It is clear that chocolate is generally rated as highly palatable. The palatability of chocolate in scientific terms can be equated with a number of organoleptic attributes derived from the seeds. The pure taste of cacao combines acidic, bitter and astringent qualities. Sourness is attributed to organic acids in the bean (29), bitterness to alkaloids, principally theobromine, and polyphenols contribute to cocoa's astringency. These basic attributes are common to other foods. Approximately 462 volatile compounds contribute to the exceptional aroma of cocoa following fermentation, drying and roasting the seeds. Cocoa butter accounts for almost half of the dry weight of cocoa beans and, at room temperature, it is a tasteless, odourless, off-white solid. But at temperatures at or above 37 °C (body temperature), cocoa butter melts rapidly. The combination of unique melting properties, over 400 volatiles, and the subtle bitter, sour, and astringent tastes, coupled with the far stronger sweet taste from the addition of sugar, creates the compelling flavour experience of chocolate. One chocolate manufacturer describes good chocolate as having an "unblemished, silky sheen"; when it is broken it "should break firmly and crisply, the edges are clean and the surfaces do not crumble. The aroma is full and rounded. Quality chocolate melts like butter, and its flavour is delicate and unique" (3).

Consumers tend to rate the taste of sweet, high-fat mixtures as extremely pleasant (30). This can be explained partly as a function of familiarity with foods containing fat and sugar, but also from an evolutionary standpoint fat/sugar mixtures are highly prized. Fats improve the texture of food, providing a soft, creamy quality (31) and the high energy density of fat

(9 kcal per gram) increases energy economy. Sweet tastes are liked from birth (32), since they signal a safe source of energy; thus biological and cultural determinants increase the pleasure of chocolate. The success of a food such as chocolate is not merely the sum of its sensory and hedonic qualities. Its attractiveness is also defined by social and cultural codes. Chocolate has had a particularly good press (with a few exceptions) over 500 years. Its introduction to Europe links it with royalty, exclusivity and medicinal benefits. Hedonic judgements of chocolate are universally high. But it is in ideational terms that chocolate is particularly compelling. Foods are avoided or accepted on the basis of how they taste and smell, and what nutritional benefits they confer. They are also sought out or rejected as a function of attitudes and beliefs, symbolism and meaning (33). Culture not only determines what is edible and inedible, but also dictates the status of foods as good or bad, healthy or unhealthy, staple or occasional (34). This suggestion, that eating is more than re-fuelling, is encapsulated in the following statement by Charles and Kerr (35): "Food is not only eaten to satisfy physiological needs and to keep body and soul together, ...the food we eat and the form we eat it in are themselves socially constructed, and meet many needs that are socially rather than biologically determined." Chocolate can be regarded as a model food in this regard. It is eaten for energy, it is given as a treat or present, it may be considered a luxury or extravagance, and, as suggested by James (2), it is both food and non-food. This odd combination was hinted at by the managing director of one of the top chocolate manufacturers in the UK, when he stated that "confectionery (including chocolate) is not a mainstream food, it is halfway between food and fashion" (1).

Over the years, chocolate has been appreciated for its luxurious and sensual sensory properties, its capacity to operate as both fuel and tonic, its particular status as a gift or reward, and its long association with elitism and indulgence. These associations are still evident in contemporary society, partly reinforced by folklore (e.g. that chocolate may have aphrodisiac qualities), partly by the media (e.g. that chocolate is addictive), and to some extent by the food companies themselves, who deliver particular messages about chocolate through advertising and marketing. Advertising attaches specific characteristics to chocolate spanning a variety of attributes, and this contributes to its identity. Indeed, advertising for chocolate products enjoys a vast array of seemingly opposite attributes depending on the particular product. As noted by Madame de Sévigné in 1675, chocolate is so agreeable because it acts in accordance with one's wishes - clearly a message promoted by advertisers. Given the powerful ideational, hedonic and sensory properties, together with ideas about the ubiquity of chocolate as snack, meal component, or treat, does this amount to a substance with addictive properties?

4.3.7   The Science of Cravings and Addiction

The World Health Organization describes addiction as "a state, psychic and sometimes physical, resulting from the interaction between the living organism and the drug, characterised by behavioural and other responses that always include a compulsion to take the drug on a continuous or periodic basis in order to experience its psychic effects and sometimes to avoid the discomfort of its absence." (cited in Ghodse (36)). To date, there have been no scientific studies demonstrating dependency on, withdrawal from or tolerance to chocolate. There are, however, several reports in the clinical literature of treating self-identified chocolate addicts using pharmacological therapies such as bupropion (37). There are cultural and historical references to chocolate addiction (22,25,27), although it is not clear if these references are for chocophilia (love of chocolate) rather than chocolate addiction. In any case, the term chocoholic has been part of social discourse for many years, and yet few scientists have attempted to describe the behaviour and to determine if such behaviour represents a true addiction.

We conducted four studies to examine a) the phenomenology of chocolate addiction (38); b) the effects of consuming chocolate on mood in self-identified addicts using diary records (39); c) changes in pleasantness following intake of chocolate under laboratory conditions (40); and d) the physiological and psychological responses to chocolate in addicts and controls (41).

The overall aim of these studies was to describe the behaviour in some detail, and then to place the behaviour in the context of other addictive behaviours or eating disorders. In the first study, 50 self-identified "chocoholics" were interviewed using a semi-structured format on a number of questions connected to chocolate eating. They also completed questionnaires on cravings and a variety of psychological tests from dietary restraint and eating pathology to body satisfaction and depression. The age range of the sample was wide (14 - 83 years) and body mass index ranged from 16.4 to 41.0, with the majority of respondents above normal weight. Of the 50 interviewees, only two were men[2]. Intake of chocolate was on average 12 bars (60 g) of chocolate per week, and the range of weekly intake was from 1 to 70 bars each week. Average consumption was four times higher than the national average for Scotland, based on figures from the British Market Research Bureau (42). The majority of participants (83%) consumed at least one bar of chocolate each day and 15% consumed at least three bars of chocolate each day. Cravings for chocolate, defined as a "strong urge to consume chocolate", were reported half as frequently as intake of chocolate. Therefore, episodes of eating chocolate were preceded by reported cravings only half of the time. Cravings were associated with negative affect, such as feeling depressed, stressed or lonely, in 52% of the participants. The majority reported positive affect during consumption of chocolate but for half of the participants this was followed by negative affect. Most participants considered their chocolate intake excessive (72%) and 54% of the sample believed that this excessive intake interfered with their lives. About one-third of the sample was moderately depressed, and 40% of the sample preferred to eat chocolate alone and in secret. Interestingly, secret eaters differed from the remainder of the sample, with higher levels of body shape dissatisfaction, dietary restraint, and eating pathology (including emotional and external eating measured by the Dutch Eating Behaviour Questionnaire (43)), but had a similar BMI and level of depression to the others. These participants also reported significantly greater problems with eating, including a greater degree of interference with

[2] Fewer men may experience chocolate addiction, or men may be less likely to volunteer for research.

daily life due to their "addiction". When asked what features of chocolate were addictive, most (72%) identified the orosensory features (taste, smell and texture) rather than the stimulant properties (12%) of chocolate. Most respondents reported negative affect when they attempted to reduce intake of chocolate. This was particularly true for secret eaters (80%) compared with the others (57%). When asked why they called themselves chocolate addicts, most participants responded by attributing their addiction to the inability to resist chocolate, either by moderating chocolate intake or being unable to stop once eating had begun. Given this description, there are clear parallels with binge eating disorder, which is defined by eating large amounts in a discrete period of time accompanied by feelings of loss of control (44). For at least some of this sample, there may be an underlying eating disorder rather than a *bona fide* addiction.

A number of similarities emerged from the descriptions of the respondents' use of chocolate and the definition of substance abuse, such as excessive consumption, interference with daily life, cravings, preoccupation with obtaining chocolate, and difficulty resisting and abstaining from chocolate. Despite this overlap, most of the participants in this sample would not meet strict criteria for substance dependence. One of the key aspects of dependency is the degree of debilitation experienced by the individual (45); therefore, although consumption of chocolate by most of these chocolate addicts is higher than is socially and medically acceptable, the degree of debilitation is manifestly not as severe as that observed in addiction to heroin or alcohol. Indeed, most foodstuffs cannot compete as targets for abuse with such "hyperincentives" (46). In part, this is due to the relatively subtle effects on neurochemistry elicited by the intake of foods such as chocolate (see sections 4.2 and 4.3). Although chocolate does contain stimulants, such as theobromine and caffeine, their effects are relatively minor since theobromine is only a weak stimulant and caffeine is present in only small doses. Chocolate is highly pleasurable and, like most foods, elicits release of β-endorphin (47). Again, in terms of magnitude, eating even a very large amount of chocolate cannot compare with the direct effects of dopamine and opioid agonists as targets for abuse (43).

Interestingly, Michener and Rozin (48), investigated pharmacological and sensory factors in the satisfaction of chocolate cravings and found no evidence for a pharmacological component in satisfying these cravings. Consuming chocolate (white or milk chocolate) reduced self-rated cravings, but cocoa capsules produced little effect on cravings.

Another explanation for the behaviour of chocolate "addicts" is that the pleasure obtained from consuming chocolate is negatively reinforcing. Thus, consuming chocolate diminishes or eliminates the discomfort of hunger, or satisfies a craving or reduces depression. Interviews revealed that a positive affect occurred during eating, but, for around half of the sample, these positive feelings dissipated after eating. Since the measurement tool was an interview, participants were relying on memory. Therefore, in the second study, we examined mood ratings prospectively before and after all episodes of eating chocolate during a 7-day period. Twenty self-identified chocolate addicts and 20 controls (who liked chocolate but were not "addicted") were asked to complete a diary recording each time they consumed chocolate over 7 days. The amount, type and context (alone by choice, alone through circumstance, with others) of eating chocolate were recorded. Before and after each occasion, participants recorded their mood on fixed point scales (depressed, content, relaxed, guilty) and hunger and cravings were also reported on the same five-point scales. As expected, addicts recorded significantly more episodes of eating chocolate (N = 174) than controls (N = 76) and reported consuming more bars of chocolate (9.4) than controls (2.2). Intensity of craving was higher in addicts before eating compared with controls, and addicts were more depressed, less relaxed and less content before eating. Eating reduced cravings for both groups and reduced hunger, but addicts reported feeling more guilty following intake compared with controls. Addicts also differed on a number of psychological dimensions, and these are summarised in Table 4.3.I. In brief, addicts were more depressed and displayed more emotional and external eating than controls. Again, a subset of participants met criteria for binge eating disorder, supporting the overlap between self-identified chocolate addiction and an eating disorder (39).

TABLE 4.3.I
Comparison between self-identified chocolate "addicts" and age-matched controls (adapted (37)).

Attribute	"Addicts"	Controls	Significance
Age	=	=	None
BMI	=	=	None
Depression	Moderate	Mild	Significant
Cognitive restraint	Moderate	Moderate	None
Emotional eating	High	Moderate	Significant
External eating	High	Moderate	Significant
Perceived hunger	Moderate	Low	Significant
Disinhibited eating	Moderate	Low	Significant
Eating attitudes	Moderate	Low	Significant
Body satisfaction	High	Average	Significant
EDI: bulimia	Moderate	Low	Significant

In a more recent study of chocolate addicts (41), we exposed addicts to chocolate and asked them to look, smell and imagine eating the food. In the presence of these external chocolate cues we measured salivation, heart rate, cravings, and finally intake. In response to this food, addicts reported greater cravings, experienced more negative affect, and ate more chocolate than control subjects. Reactivity to the sight, smell and taste of chocolate was greater in addicts than in controls as determined by levels of salivation to the sensory properties of the food. A potential explanation for heightened responsiveness to chocolate might be in terms of incentive salience.

Robinson and Berridge (49) define incentive salience as 'a psychological process that transforms the perception of stimuli, imbuing them with salience, making them attractive, "wanted, incentive stimuli"'. They have proposed that incentive salience can increase independently of pleasure derived from a stimulus, i.e. "liking". An increase in the incentive salience of a stimulus such as chocolate may follow a similar pattern to that seen in the development of drug abuse (49), but at a much lower magnitude.

Berridge and Robinson (50) have further demonstrated separate neural systems underlying incentive salience and hedonic responses. Using animal models, taste reactivity methodology is used to examine hedonic reaction independent of incentive salience. However, in applying these concepts to our understanding of chocolate addiction, the problem arises of dissociating "liking" from "wanting".

In the drug abuse literature, the incentive salience of a drug-related stimulus can be measured using the degree to which attentional resources are allocated to that stimulus relative to other more neutral stimuli. Lubman *et al.* (51) measured reaction time to drug-relevant and drug-irrelevant stimuli in methadone-maintained opiate addicts compared with age-matched controls. They found that addicts demonstrated a significant attentional bias towards drug cues. This methodology has not yet been applied to food-related stimuli in chocolate addicts, but studies of cue reactivity have been conducted in bulimia nervosa (52).

Another method of measuring incentive salience is to examine the hedonic response to a food stimulus and to examine amount consumed as an index of "wanting". We compared pleasantness ratings of chocolate before and after a fixed amount, *ad libitum* access to that food, and a fixed amount of most preferred chocolate in addicts relative to controls. Pleasantness ratings were equally high across conditions and between groups, with the collapsed average rating of 90 mm on a 100-mm visual analogue scale. Intake of chocolate as an index of wanting was significantly higher in addicts compared with controls across the *ad libitum* and favourite conditions. In the fixed condition, all subjects consumed a standard portion of chocolate (60 g: 312 kcal) whereas, in the *ad libitum* condition, addicts consumed more than double this amount (128.3 g: 655.8 kcal) and controls consumed 40% more (86.7 g: 447.5 kcal). Of greatest interest in this study was that, although pleasantness ratings of chocolate were equivalent for the two groups when they started eating, pleasantness ratings declined significantly for controls but not for addicts in the fixed and *ad libitum* conditions. Therefore, despite eating the same amount in the fixed condition and significantly more in the *ad libitum* condition, addicts reported a smaller magnitude of change in pleasantness following consumption. As an index of "liking", at 20 minutes after eating a large amount of chocolate, this food is still rated as significantly more pleasant by addicts than by controls. In this study, differences in the change in pleasantness of the taste of chocolate combined with greater intake of chocolate by addicts indicates effects on both hedonic impact (liking) and incentive salience (wanting). In a more recent series of studies, we have observed a tendency for liking and wanting to demonstrate independent effects.

Using subjects who are not "addicts", we conducted three experiments in which repeated exposure to chocolate produced decreased pleasantness ratings but no change, or an increase in amount of chocolate consumed. In our hands, daily intake of chocolate over 15 days (53) and 21 days (54) produced lower ratings of pleasantness but no decline in intake. Although subjects consumed the same amount of chocolate every day or progressively larger amounts of chocolate every day, pleasantness ratings declined and craving remained unaltered. Intriguingly, when participants consumed the same amount of chocolate or an increasingly larger amount of chocolate over 15 days, intake increased. It is not yet clear what underlies this seemingly paradoxical effect; however, an equivalent phenomenon is observed in drug addicts who report less pleasure in taking a drug but increase its dose to obtain the same effect.

Repeated exposure in itself does not produce incentive salience; rather, there must be a combination of affective, ideational and hedonic factors to produce so-called chocolate addiction. Of considerable interest in this regard is the work of Gibson and Desmond (55), who paired eating chocolate with feeling full or feeling hungry (see section 3.2). Using this manipulation, these investigators found that ratings of the pleasantness of chocolate increased only when paired with hunger. Therefore, in the associative conditioning paradigm generated by this experiment, liking for chocolate increased when it was associated with negative reinforcement (i.e. removal of aversive hunger sensations) and not only positive reinforcement (i.e. pleasantness of the taste of chocolate).

In summary, although there is some evidence of overlap between the behaviour of chocolate addicts and features of substance dependency, the core features of addiction have not been demonstrated. It is interesting to note that incentive salience seems to be high for chocolate in self-identified chocolate addicts; what is not clear is whether this represents "liking" rather than "wanting" in the same way that repeated drug use transforms the perception of the drug target to a highly salient, incentive stimulus (49).

4.3.8   Attempts to Reduce Cravings

Excessive food intake may develop over repeated exposures, in which there is an association between positive sensory cues (look, smell, texture and taste) and negative reinforcement. This begs the question of what will happen if food cues are presented but eating the food is prevented. Such an experiment has yet to be conducted using chocolate as the target stimulus; however, a pilot study using pizza as the target was conducted as a first attempt to assess this question.

Adapting the classic exposure-response prevention paradigm, we invited three groups of obese women to the laboratory on two occasions (Tuomisto, Murrie and Hetherington, unpublished manuscript). The first session was used to interview potential participants, to take height and weight measures, to complete a battery of questionnaires on eating pathology, body satisfaction and restraint, and to taste test the target food (pizza). Participants who rated the target food as pleasant, were then allocated to one of three conditions (control, exposure, or exposure/distraction). Allocation to the groups was done to match the groups in age (42 ± 6; 44.5 ± 4; 49.3 ± 2 years, respectively) and BMI (33.5 ± 2; 32.6 ± 2.1; 31.2 ± 1.3, respectively). For each laboratory session, participants were seated in a private cubicle and all timed instructions were delivered using an audiotape recorder. Heart rate was monitored using a pulse monitor; saliva was collected using dental rolls; and visual analogue scale ratings (hunger, fullness and how strong desire was to eat the target food) were made repeatedly over a 45-minute period for controls and a 90-minute period for the other groups. Baseline measurements were made in the absence of any food cues, and all subsequent measures in the presence of pizza, which was presented on a food warmer and replaced at 15-minute intervals (to preserve aroma and freshness). Subjects were asked to look at, smell and imagine eating the pizza and ratings were conducted every 10 minutes. The exposure group did this with no other competing task, but the exposure/distraction group also sipped chilled water from a container of 750 ml, which had to be consumed over a 45-minute period. We found that, for all subjects, an increase in hunger and desire to eat pizza increased and fullness decreased upon the first exposure to the target food. This continued in the control condition from the first to last exposure, and in the exposure condition. When participants drank water during the exposure period, hunger decreased and fullness increased. However, in all three conditions, desire to eat pizza remained high and was not diminished by sipping water.

This pilot study suggests that a single exposure period increases desire to eat the food, but that multiple exposures to the target food with response prevention (i.e. looking and smelling the food but not eating it) or even using a distracting task (such as drinking water) could reduce desire to eat or cravings (see section 7.2). Clearly, this kind of experimental manipulation is in its infancy. However, exposure-response prevention techniques have been used with some success in the treatment of alcoholism and phobias; it remains to be seen if chocolate cravings and over-consumption of chocolate can be reduced using these strategies.

a) Hunger

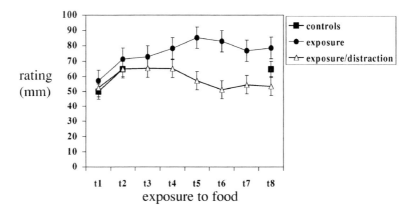

b) Fullness

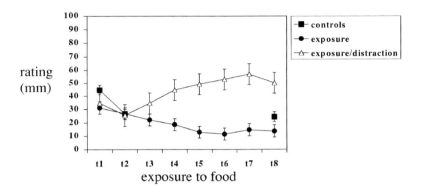

c) Desire to eat/craving

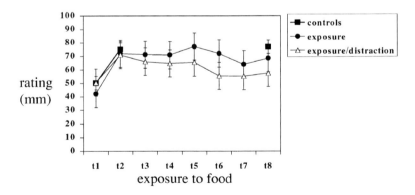

Fig. 4.3.2. Ratings of hunger (panel a); fullness (panel b) and desire to eat (panel c) during exposure to pizza under different experimental conditions (control, exposure, exposure/distraction).

4.3.9   Conclusions

In summary, chocolate has a very particular set of associations. Historically, chocolate was consumed for its health benefits, not just because it tasted good. Modern constructions of chocolate reflect the ambivalent nature of chocolate since, although it has a pleasing sensory profile, some argue that it should be consumed with restraint. Thus, the decision to consume chocolate is influenced by its history, its social and cultural context, and contemporary notions of what is acceptable to eat for health.

Individuals who report overeating chocolate have been named "chocoholics", suggesting an addiction to this food. Since chocolate contains stimulants such as caffeine and theobromine, it has been proposed that self-identified "chocoholics" seek the pharmacological effects of chocolate. However, most foods engage the endogenous opioid system and many foods have effects on neurotransmitter release, in a similar, though more subtle way to other substances, such as alcohol or nicotine. What is unique to chocolate is its symbolism and its status as "forbidden fruit". In our research on self-identified chocolate addicts, chocolate is craved for its orosensory properties, not its pharmacological effects, and, once consumed, increased feelings of guilt (39). The pleasure sought by those who overeat chocolate is derived from the taste and mouthfeel of chocolate, and not from its effects as a stimulant or mood modulator. Sensory-specific satiety should limit intake of a single food; however, addicts show a weaker decline in the pleasantness of the taste of chocolate relative to other consumers (40). Since liking for chocolate is developed as a result of associative conditioning, processes involved in learning have been exploited in the laboratory to reduce the desire for highly liked foods. Exploring learning theory further could produce therapeutic strategies for overeating. Extinction paradigms are aimed at reducing intake rather than complete abstinence as suggested by some addiction models.

The phenomenon of chocolate addiction exists both in our cultural vocabulary and as a reality to those whose intake is excessive and for whom chocolate is irresistible. However, despite some similarities with substance dependence, on many different levels chocolate addiction does not compare to addiction to drugs such as nicotine, alcohol or opiates. It seems prudent to re-conceptualise the behaviour of some self-identified chocolate addicts as chocophilia and that of others as a sub-type of binge eating disorder.

4.3.10   References

1.   Keynote R. *Confectionery*. Middlesex, Keynote Publications Ltd. 1990.

2.   James A. The good, the bad, and the delicious: the role of confectionery in British Society. *Sociological Review*, 1990, 38, 666-88.

3.   Morton M., Morton F. *Chocolate, An Illustrated History*. New York, Crown Publishers. 1986.

4.   Coe S.D., Coe M.D. *The True History of Chocolate*. London, Thames and Hudson. 1996.

5.   Cox C. *Chocolate Unwrapped: The Politics of Pleasure*. London, WEN. 1993.

6.   Lupien J.R. Overview of the nutritional benefits of cocoa and chocolate, in *Chocolate and Cocoa: Health and Nutrition*. Ed. Knight I. Oxford, Blackwell Science Ltd. 1999, 3-8.

7.   Nielsen N. *Chocolate*. Stockholm, Trevi. 1995.

8.   Benzoni G. *Storia del Mondo Nuevo*. Graz, Akademische Druck-u. Verlaganstalt. 1575.

9.   Chiva M. Cultural and psychological approaches to the consumption of chocolate, in *Chocolate and Cocoa: Health and Nutrition*. Ed. Knight I. Oxford, Blackwell Science Ltd. 1999, 321-38.

10. Douglass A., Amann M.M. Chocolate consumption patterns, in *Chocolate and Cocoa: Health and Nutrition*. Ed. Knight I. Oxford, Blackwell Science Ltd. 1999, 293-309.

11. Stubbe H. *The Indian Nectar, or, a Discourse concerning Chocolata*. London. 1662.

12. Wordsworth J. *Curious History of the Nature and Quality of Chocolate*. London. 1655.

13. Lémery L. *Traité des Aliments*. London, John Taylor. 1704.

14. Campan M. *Memoire sur la vie privée de Marie Antoniette.* London, Henri Colburn and Co. 1823.

15. Lever M. *Sade: A Biography.* New York, Farrar, Strauss and Giroux. 1993.

16. McGee H. *On Food and Cooking. The Science and Lore of the Kitchen.* London, HarperCollins Publishers. 1991.

17. Brillat-Savarin J.-A. *La Physiologie du Goût.* Paris. 1825. Translated by M.F.K. Fisher New York, Harcourt Brace Jovanovich 1978.

18. Mangin A. *Le Cacao et le Chocolat.* Paris, Guillamin et Cie. 1862.

19. Waterhouse A.L., Shirley J.R., Donovan J.L. Antioxidants in chocolate. *Lancet,* 1996, 87, 311-5.

20. Kris-Etherton P., Etherton T.D. Cardiovascular health: role of stearic acid on atherogenic and thrombogenic factors, in *Chocolate and Cocoa: Health and Nutrition.* Ed. Knight I. Oxford, Blackwell Science Ltd. 1999, 89-104.

21. Rössner S. Chocolate: divine food, fattening junk or nutritious supplement? *European Journal of Clinical Nutrition,* 1997, 51, 341-5.

22. Gage T. *The English-American, His Travail by Land and Sea, or a New Survey of the West Indies.* London. 1648.

23. Felici G.B. *Parere Intorno all'uso della Cioccolata.* Florence, Guiseppe Manni. 1728.

24. Durán F.D. *The Aztecs.* New York, Orion Press. 1964.

25. Lister M. *Journey to Paris in 1698.* Urbana, University of Illinios Press. 1967.

26. de Acosta J. *Historia natural y moral de las Indias.* Seville. 1590.

27. Barthel D. Modernism and marketing: the chocolate box revisited. *Theory, Culture and Society,* 1989, 6, 429-38.

28. Bolton-Smith C., Hetherington M.M. Chocolate and Obesity, in *Chocolate and Cocoa: Health and Nutrition.* Ed. Knight I. Oxford, Blackwell Science Ltd. 1999, 177-94.

29. Macdonald H. Flavour development from cocoa bean to chocolate bar. *The Biochemist,* 1993 (April/May), 3-5.

30. Drewnowski A., Schwartz M. Invisible fats: sensory assessment of sugar/fat mixtures. *Appetite 14,* 1990, 203-17.

31. Mela D.J. Understanding fat preference and consumption: applications of behavioural sciences to a nutritional problem. *Proceedings of the Nutrition Society*, 1995, 54, 453-64.

32. Steiner J. Facial expressions of the neonate infant indicating the hedonics of food-related chemical stimuli, in *Taste and development: the genesis of sweet preference*. Ed. Weiffenbach J.M. Washington, DC, US Government Printing Office. 1977, 176-89.

33. Rozin P. Development in the food domain. *Developmental Psychology*, 1990, 26 (4), 555-62.

34. Rozin P. Food and cuisine: education, risk and pleasure. *Journal of Gastronomy*, 1993, 7, 111-20.

35. Charles N., Kerr M. *Women, Food and Families*. Manchester, Manchester University Press. 1988.

36. Ghodse A.H. *Drugs and Addictive Behaviour: A Guide to Treatment*. Oxford, Blackwell Science Ltd. 1989.

37. Michell G.F., Mebane A.H., Billings C.K. Effect of bupropion on chocolate craving. *American Journal of Psychiatry*, 1989, 146, 119-20.

38. Hetherington M.M., Macdiarmid J.I. Chocolate addiction: a preliminary description and report of its relationship to problem eating. *Appetite*, 1993, 21, 233-46.

39. Macdairmid J.I., Hetherington M.M. Mood modulation by food: an exploration of affect and cravings in chocolate addicts. *British Journal of Clinical Psychology*, 1995, 34, 129-38.

40. Hetherington M.M., Macdairmid J.I. Pleasure and excess: liking for and overconsumption of chocolate. *Physiology & Behavior*, 1995, 57, 27-35.

41. Tuomisto T., Hetherington M.M., Morris M.F., Tuomisto M.T., Turjanmaa V., Lappalainen R. Psychological and physiological characteristics of sweet food "addiction". *International Journal of Eating Disorders*, 1999, 25, 169-75.

42. British Market Research Bureau. *Chocolate Confectionery*. London. 1990.

43. Van Strien T., *et al.* Dutch eating behaviour questionnaire for assessment of restrained, emotional and external eating. *International Journal of Eating Disorders*, 1986, 5, 295-315.

44. American Psychiatric Association. *Diagnostic and Statistical Manual: 4th edition*. Washington, DC. 1994.

45. Koob G., Le Moal M. Drug abuse: hedonic homeostatic dysregulation. *Science*, 1997, 278 (5335), 52-8.

46. Nesse R.M., Berridge K.C. Psychoactive drug use in evolutionary perspective. *Science*, 1997, 278, 63-6.

47. Melchior J.C., Rigaud D., Colas-Linhart N., Petiet A., Girard A., Apfelbaum M. Immunoreactive beta-endorphin increases after an aspartame chocolate drink in healthy human subjects. *Physiology and Behavior*, 1991, 50 (5), 941-4.

48. Michener W., Rozin P. Pharmacological versus sensory factors in the satiation of chocolate craving. *Physiology & Behaviour*, 1994, 56, 419-22.

49. Robinson T.E., Berridge K.C. The neural basis of drug craving: an incentive-sensitization theory of addiction. *Brain Research Reviews*, 1993, 18 (3), 247-91.

50. Berridge K.C., Robinson T.E. What is the role of dopamine in reward: hedonic impact, reward learning, or incentive salience? *Brain Research Reviews*, 1998, 28, 309-69.

51. Lubman D.I., Peters L.A., Mogg K., Bradley B.P., Deakin J.F. Attentional bias for drug cues in opiate dependence. *Psychological Medicine*, 2000, 30 (1), 169-75.

52. Staiger P., Dawe S., McCarthy R. Responsivity to food cues in bulimic women and controls. *Appetite*, 2000, 35, 27-33.

53. Hetherington M.M., Bell A., Rolls B.J. Effects of repeat exposure on pleasantness, preference and intake. *British Food Journal*, 2000, 102, 507-21.

54. Hetherington M.M., Pirie L.M., Nabb S. Pleasure and monotony: effects of repeat exposure on pleasantness, desire to eat and intake. *Appetite*, 1998, 31, (abstract), 251.

55. Gibson E.L., Desmond. Chocolate craving and hunger state: implications for the acquisition and expression of appetite and food choice. *Appetite*, 1999, 32(2), 219-40.

56.   IOCCC. *International Statistical Review of the Cocoa, Chocolate and Sugar Confectionery Industries 1996.* Brussels, International Office of Cocoa, Chocolate and Sugar Confectionery. 1997.

4.4. POTENTIALLY PSYCHOACTIVE CONSTITUENTS OF COCOA-CONTAINING PRODUCTS

Hendrik J. Smit and Peter J. Rogers

4.4.1   Food Craving: Attitudes and Physiology

In a recent review we argued for a primarily attitudinal rather than physiological explanation of (self-reported) food craving and food 'addiction' (1). We proposed that attitudes towards frequently craved foods such as chocolate could be highly ambivalent. Chocolate is 'nice but naughty': it is highly liked, but nutritionally suspect.[1] In other words, chocolate is perceived as an indulgence, a treat not a staple food, and therefore a food that should be eaten with restraint. Paradoxically, though, attempts to resist the desire to eat chocolate can increase the salience of and thoughts about chocolate (cf 2), intensifying this desire sufficiently for it to be labelled a craving. This, perhaps together with the need to provide a reason for why resisting eating chocolate is difficult and sometimes fails, can in turn lead the individual to an explanation in terms of addiction (e.g. 'chocoholism'). According to this view, chocolate is the most frequently craved food because it is the food that people most often try to resist eating. In contrast to craving, moreishness ('the effect of causing a desire for more') occurs during rather than preceding an eating episode. Nevertheless, restraint is again an essential feature, because moreishness is experienced when the eater attempts to limit consumption before appetite for the food has been satiated (1,3).

One of the competing explanations for chocolate craving and 'addiction' is that cocoa-containing products contain psychoactive or mood-altering compounds (1,4). This idea was recently given renewed impetus by a widely reported article published in Nature (5), claiming to find 'brain cannabinoids in chocolate'. The purpose of the present chapter is to

---

[1] 'Naughty but nice' was a slogan devised by the author Salman Rushdie as part of a 1970s UK advertising campaign for cream cakes.

examine in detail these speculations about potentially psychoactive constituents of chocolate in the light of what is known about the concentrations of these substances in the products that are most widely eaten, and their likely effects on the brain when administered orally.

4.4.2   Caffeine

Caffeine (1,3,7-trimethylxanthine) occurs naturally in a variety of agriculturally significant plants, including the coffee bean, cola nut, tea, and the cocoa bean (6). Table 4.4.I provides an overview of the occurrence of caffeine in some beverages, foods, food ingredients and medicines.

The physiological effects of caffeine have been extensively researched. Caffeine acts primarily to competitively block adenosine receptors, causing, for example, increases in blood pressure, rennin and catecholamine release, and increased urine output, lipolysis, respiration, and intestinal peristalsis (7,8). After oral administration, absorption of caffeine is rapid and complete. In the presence of sugar, uptake is slower but still complete (9), and typically the maximum blood plasma concentration (peak plasma time) is reached within an hour (7). Mumford *et al.* (10) found a peak plasma time of 30 minutes after oral administration of 72 mg caffeine, and participants in this study reported onset of subjective effects between 10 and 45 minutes (mean 21 minutes) after dosing.

Consumption of excessive amounts (> 1 g /day) of caffeine can result in caffeinism, the symptoms of which are: tachycardia, dyspepsia (disturbed digestion, decreased appetite, oppressive feeling in the stomach and unpleasant taste), irritability and insomnia (8). Other authors have described the symptoms following intake of high doses of caffeine as 'a variety of unpleasant subjective states including anxiety, dysphoria and depression' (11), 'signs and symptoms indistinguishable from those of anxiety neurosis', and nervousness, irritability, tremulousness, occasional muscle twitching, insomnia and sensory disturbances (6).

TABLE 4.4.I
Caffeine content of various products

Product	Portion size[1]	Number of samples	Concentration (mg per portion)
Coffee (filter, percol.)	7.6 g/200 ml	8	105 (61-126)[2]
Coffee (instant)	1.6 g/200 ml	16	58 (42-68)[2]
Tea (regular, bag)	230 ml	NA	46[2]
Cola drinks	can (330 ml)	32	23 (11-70)[2,3]
Energy drinks	can or bottle, 250 or 330 ml	26	63 (0.2-115)[2]
Medicines	tablet or capsule	NA	15-200[4]
Chocolate, milk	50 g	4	8.4 (5.5-11)[2]
Chocolate, dark	50 g	2	27 (17-36)[2]
Cocoa powder	10 g[5]	8	21 (8-35)[6]

NA = not available

[1] (ref. 68)

[2] (ref. 69), figures re-calculated using comments in Annex C of this reference where appropriate

[3] Dried kola nut contains 2.0% caffeine (ref. 70)

[4] (ref. 71)

[5] equivalent to two heaped teaspoonfuls to make, for example, one cup of hot chocolate (ref. 68)

[6] (refs 72,73)

Caffeine is widely known as a psychostimulant, and many studies have found that caffeine in amounts consumed in coffee and tea can increase feelings of energy (more alert, less tired, etc.) and improve some other aspects of mood, and can enhance psychomotor and cognitive performance (reviewed in 7 and 12). Unfortunately, it is not clear from this research whether there is a real benefit of caffeine consumption, or whether such effects are mainly due to the reversal of negative effects of caffeine withdrawal, which occur even after overnight caffeine abstinence (13).

Fatigue and headache, for example, are well-recognised consequences of caffeine withdrawal. Related to this, though, is evidence that 70-100 mg caffeine can (negatively) reinforce flavour preferences (14,15), which helps to explain the very widespread popularity of caffeine-containing drinks. Although we are not aware of any studies showing reinforcing effects of doses of caffeine in the range of 8-30 mg (i.e. 0.1-0.4 mg/kg), these amounts of caffeine do have significant, albeit mild, psychostimulant effects (16). Therefore, caffeine reinforcement could conceivably contribute to the development of preferences for chocolate.

It remains the case, nonetheless, that coffee, tea and cola are much more important dietary sources of caffeine than is chocolate. The amount of caffeine present in a cup of instant coffee is similar to that contained in seven 50-g bars of milk chocolate or two 50-g bars of dark chocolate (calculated from Table 4.4.I). In other words, chocolate is far from being a unique or substantial source of caffeine.

4.4.3   Theobromine

In contrast to caffeine, its metabolite theobromine (3,7-dimethylxanthine) is found in unusually high amounts in chocolate and cocoa products (Table 4.4.II).

Compared with caffeine or theophylline, the action of theobromine on the central nervous system is considered weak or even virtually absent (17). Tarka (6) describes theobromine as having, on the other hand, the strongest effect of all three of these methylxanthines on the coronary vessels (with caffeine having the weakest effect). Theobromine is generally considered a diuretic, a heart muscle stimulant, a vasodilator and a smooth muscle relaxant (18). The Merck Index (19) places theobromine in the therapeutic categories 'diuretic', 'bronchodilator', and 'cardiotonic'. Although it has been used to treat arteriosclerosis and some peripheral vascular diseases (8), there is no current therapeutic use of theobromine (6).

In a study comparing the subjective effects of theobromine and caffeine, Mumford et al. (20) found that four of their seven volunteers could discriminate theobromine from placebo at a dose of 560 mg. For one participant, the discriminable dose was as low as 100 mg. The basis for the discrimination involved changes in mood and behaviour, including feeling more energetic, and having increased motivation to work. Caffeine had similar effects, but stronger and at lower doses. There was no significant group effect of theobromine for any of the mood measures included in the study. The onset of the subjective effects of theobromine was reported to be 35 (15-60) minutes after oral ingestion, and subjective ratings of 'magnitude of drug effect' peaked between 1 and 2 hours after administration (20), whereas its peak plasma time was on average 2.6 hours (10). Therefore, although chocolate can contain relatively high concentrations of theobromine, this methylxanthine is a weak central nervous system stimulant and has only minor subjective effects.

TABLE 4.4.II
Theobromine content of various products

Product	Portion size[1]	Number of samples	Concentration (mg per portion)
Coffee (filter, percol.)	7.6 g/200 ml	8	0.3 (0.3-0.3)[2]
Coffee (instant)	1.6 g/200 ml	16	0.2 (0.1-0.5)[2]
Tea (regular, bag)	230 ml	14	3.1 (1.4-4.4)[2]
Cola drinks	can (330 ml)	32	ND[3]
Energy drinks	can or bottle, 250 or 330 ml	26	0.1 (ND-1.6)[2]
Chocolate, milk	50 g	4	95 (65-160)[2]
Chocolate, dark	50 g	2	378 (237-519)[2]
Cocoa powder	10 g	8	189 (146-266)[2]

ND = not detected
[1] (ref. 68)
[2] (ref. 69), figures re-calculated using comments in Annex C of this reference where appropriate
[3] Dried kola nut contains 0.05 % theobromine (ref. 70)
[4] (refs 72,73)

4.4.4   Biogenic Amines

Biogenic amines are formed by decarboxylation of amino acids. Cocoa and cocoa products contain fairly high concentrations of biogenic amines (e.g. β-phenylethylamine, tyramine, tryptamine and serotonin), and their precursors (phenylalanine, tyrosine and tryptophan). Biogenic amine concentrations in cocoa increase during fermentation of the cocoa beans, and decrease with roasting and alkalisation (21).

For healthy people, the amount of biogenic amines in foods is irrelevant, since the amines are inactivated by the monoamine oxidase (MAO) in the mucosa of the small intestine, and in the liver and kidneys (22). Because of the endogenous abundance of MAO, "even the intraduodenal injection of amines in the absence of enzyme inhibition would be unlikely to lead to their absorption and appearance in systemic blood unless the amount was sufficiently large to swamp the deaminating mechanisms" (23). The amount of amines in foods becomes meaningful only in people treated with drugs containing MAO inhibitors (22) and in people with an MAO deficiency, as has been suggested for migraine sufferers (23). If the amine oxidation is inhibited, symptoms such as headaches, increased blood pressure or even a life-threatening 'amino shock' can occur (22). If anything, these adverse effects would presumably lead to the avoidance of chocolate.

4.4.4.1   Phenylethylamine

β-Phenylethylamine (PEA) is the basic molecule of the phenylethylamine family, which includes the stimulant and hallucinogenic substances amphetamine, mescaline, dopamine, adrenaline and noradrenaline (24). The Merck Index describes endogenous PEA as "related structurally and pharmacologically to amphetamine" (19). Although the name 'phenylethylamine' has also been used to refer to its entire family (e.g. 25), it is the basic structure (2- or β-phenylethylamine) that is referred to here. Some cheeses, red wines, but especially chocolate 'contain large amounts of phenylethylamine' according to the Leatherhead Food Research Association (26). According to this organisation, chocolate contains at least

3 mg PEA per 2-ounce (56.7-g) bar. More recent research has not revealed such high figures, and even suggests that PEA is present in chocolate in very small amounts (Table 4.4.III).

TABLE 4.4.III
Phenylethylamine content of various products

Product	Portion size[1]	Number of samples	Concentration (mg per portion)
Danish Blue cheese	100 g	1	2.5[2]
Cheddar cheese	100 g	22	2.1 (ND-30.3)[3]
Dutch cheese	100 g	8	0.9 (0-4.6)[4]
Fermented sausage	100 g	14/13	1.4 (0.5-4.5)[4]
			7.1 (ND-69.6)[3]
Marmite	4 g	1	ND[2]
Chocolate, milk	50 g	4/6/10	0.08 (ND-0.33)[5]
			ND[3,6]
Chocolate, dark	50 g	8/1/1/10	0.03 (0.01-0.11)[6]
			0.10[5] ND[2,3]
Cocoa powder	10 g	12/1	0.01 (0.003-0.03)[6]
			0.2[7]

ND = not detected
[1] (ref. 68)
[2] (ref. 74)
[3] (ref. 75)
[4] (ref. 76)
[5] (ref. 77)
[6] (ref. 21)
[7] (ref. 78)

Endogenously, PEA has been found in the nervous tissue of most, if not all, animal species researched. In the mammalian brain, it has been detected in minute quantities (single nanograms per gram of nervous tissue). PEA is synthesised by decarboxylation of phenylalanine by the enzyme aromatic L-amino acid decarboxylase, almost certainly in dopaminergic neurones, and is rapidly metabolised by monoamine oxidase type B (MAO-B). It appears to co-exist in the brain with dopamine, and is proposed to be a modulator of catecholamine neurotransmission (27).

Although, in the past, researchers have linked a depletion of endogenous PEA with depression, and an excess with mania, the evidence is mixed and inconclusive (28). Liebowitz and Klein (29) identified an affective disorder involving atypical depression and attention-seeking behaviour, which they named 'hysteroid dysphoria' and linked to an abnormal regulation of PEA. Without referring to any published evidence, the authors mention that the production of PEA is "stimulated by positive life events", and that "depressed, hysteroid dysphorics often binge on chocolate, which is loaded with phenylethylamine".

In popular writing, PEA has been associated with romance, love, and sex. For example, PEA has been claimed to be an essential element in the euphoric feelings we experience when we are in love. "When scientists injected some mice with PEA, they jumped about and squealed with a kind of mouse exuberance and exhilaration animal behaviourists call 'popcorn behaviour'. When rhesus monkeys are injected with PEA they smack their lips and make pleasure calls, much as they do when they are courting another monkey. Baboons injected with PEA will press a lever in their cage more than 160 times in three hours when pressing that lever will give them PEA-laced food that maintains their high PEA level of euphoria" (30, but see also 31 and 32). Shulgin and Shulgin (33), however, could not replicate any of these effects in tests on human beings. Assisted by close friends and colleagues, these authors acted as guinea pigs in their own experiments, in which they assessed the effects of numerous synthesised amphetamines, administered (usually orally) in various doses. PEA was the only substance they found not to show any subjective effects. It was administered in oral doses of 200 to 1,600 mg, and intravenously, in doses of 25 and 50 mg. These latter findings contradict what we suggest is the 'PEA myth' of chocolate. That is, the idea that people eat chocolate to feel more 'sexy' or 'sensual' because eating chocolate raises endogenous PEA is simply a myth, which is attractive to the popular media, but which has not been seriously proposed or supported in the recent peer-reviewed scientific literature.

4.4.4.2   Tyramine

Tyramine can be detected in many foods, but is found in chocolate in relatively small amounts (Table 4.4.IV).

TABLE 4.4.IV
Tyramine content of various products

Product	Portion size[1]	Number of samples	Concentration (mg per portion)
Danish Blue cheese	100 g	1	62.5[2]
Cheddar cheese	100 g	22/1	19.2 (ND-112)[3] 6.2[4]
Dutch cheese	100 g	8	13.8 (0-62.5)[5]
Fermented sausage	100 g	14/13	11 (4-31)[5] 11.2 (ND-37.4)[3]
Marmite	4 g	1	0.4[2]
Chocolate, milk	50 g	4/6/10	0.33 (0.19-0.60)[6] 0.02 (0.01-0.03)[7] ND[3]
Chocolate, dark	50 g	8/1/1/10	0.03 (0.01-0.11)[6] 0.19[5] ND[2,3]
Cocoa powder	10 g	12	0.01 (0.003-0.03)[7]

ND = not detected
[1] (ref. 68)
[2] (ref. 74)
[3] (ref. 75)
[4] (ref. 78)
[5] (ref. 76)
[6] (ref. 77)
[7] (ref. 21)

Intravenously injected tyramine releases noradrenaline from the sympathetic nervous system, and can lead to various physiological reactions, including increased blood pressure, dilation of the pupils, lachrymation, salivation and increased respiration (34). However, we found no published evidence suggesting positive effects of tyramine on mood or behaviour.

On the other hand, tyramine has been implicated in triggering migraine headaches in migraine sufferers, and it also appears to be responsible for the so-called 'cheese reaction'. In the late fifties and sixties, monoamine-oxidase inhibitors prescribed for depression and hypertension were found to make patients receiving these drugs very sensitive to the toxic action of tyramine, known to be present in cheese. Symptoms are hypertensive crisis and severe headache, sometimes leading to intracranial bleeding and even cardiac failure (34). The amounts of tyramine in cheese are much greater than the amounts present in chocolate (Table 4.4.IV).

4.4.4.3   Serotonin

Serotonin (5-HT; 5-hydroxytryptamine) is formed by decarboxylation of 5–hydroxytryptophan. It has been identified in a variety of foods, some of which are shown in Table 4.4.V. There have been claims that bananas, pineapples and tomatoes contain especially high concentrations of serotonin (e.g. 24); however, this could not be confirmed from the literature we obtained, which indicated that walnuts have relatively the highest concentration of serotonin identified in food. Compared with walnuts, chocolate contains only a small amount of serotonin.

Serotonin is a neurotransmitter in both the central and peripheral nervous systems, and plays an important role in the regulation of mood and behaviour (35-39). However, because orally ingested serotonin is deaminated by monoamine oxidase (see above), consumption of foods containing serotonin will not directly affect brain levels of serotonin.

TABLE 4.4.V
Serotonin content of various products

Product	Portion size[1]	Number of samples	Concentration (mg per portion)
Pineapple	125 g	not reported	2.4-8.1[2]
Avocado	130 g	not reported	1.2[2]
Walnuts	25 g	not reported	13.8[2]
Chocolate, milk	50 g	4	0.52 (0.05-1.36)[3]
Chocolate, dark	50 g	1	0.43[3]
Cocoa powder	10 g	1	0.6[4]

[1] (ref. 68)
[2] (ref. 79)
[3] (ref. 77)
[4] (ref. 78)

4.4.5   Tryptophan

Tryptophan is an essential amino acid, meaning that foods are normally its only natural source (8). Although other foods, especially peanuts, cheese and certain meat products, contain far more tryptophan than chocolate, it is present in chocolate in significant amounts (Table 4.4.VI).

Tryptophan is a precursor of the neurotransmitter serotonin (40), and oral administration of amounts of tryptophan in the order of 1.5 to 5 g has been shown to induce feelings of drowsiness and fatigue, decrease sleep latency, and reduce appetite, including rated hunger and actual food intake (reviewed in 41-44). Daily intakes of tryptophan from dietary sources are typically in the range of 1 to 1.5 g (41).

Tryptophan in larger pharmacological doses can also be an effective antidepressant, both when given alone and when given in combination with other treatments. Mild or moderately depressed people appear to benefit most from treatment with tryptophan, although it is less potent than standard antidepressant drugs (41). This would be consistent with the view that a deficit in serotonergic activity is important as a vulnerability factor, but is not the proximate cause of depression (38). Tryptophan has also been found to improve depressive symptoms in Seasonal Affective Disorder and Premenstrual Syndrome (44,45). Another research strategy has been to measure the effects of administering amino acid mixtures devoid of tryptophan. The results have shown that a lowering of mood following tryptophan depletion is most likely to occur in individuals with high baseline depression scores or who have a family history of depression (46; and reviewed in 36,37,47). Taken together, these studies of tryptophan and tryptophan depletion add significantly to the evidence indicating a role for serotonin in the aetiology of depression.

TABLE 4.4.VI
Tryptophan content of various products

Product	Portion size[1]	Concentration[2] (mg per portion)
Cheese (ripened: Stilton, Cheddar, Edam, etc.)	100 g	300-500
Peanuts	50 g	320
Peanut butter	10 g	38
Crisps	100 g	90
Meat and fish	100 g	100-400
Chocolate, milk	50 g	80
Chocolate, dark	50 g	34
Cocoa powder	10 g	30

Numbers of samples used for analysis not reported
[1] (ref. 68)
[2] All data from ref. 80

The pharmacological manipulation of tryptophan intakes, however, is not evidence for an influence on mood of the tryptophan content of typical diets. Crucially, significant alterations in brain levels of serotonin, and consequently any serotonergically mediated effects on mood and behaviour, would not be expected to occur when tryptophan is consumed along with the other amino acid constituents of protein-containing foods (36,37,39,40). In other words, it is very unlikely that tryptophan is responsible for any mood changes that might follow the consumption of chocolate.

4.4.6   Magnesium

The main sources of dietary magnesium are whole grains, green vegetables, meat, nuts (48), soya beans and chocolate (49). Although, according to Seelig (50) and Rozin *et al.* (51), cocoa has one of the highest magnesium levels of all foods listed, this argument cannot be sustained when the calculations are adjusted for serving size (see Table 4.4.VII).

Magnesium is a co-factor in more than 300 enzymic reactions, including those involving ATP formation (52) and the synthesis of fatty acids (53). It is an important factor in bone structure (49), and affects protein and carbohydrate metabolism, muscle functioning and the cardiovascular system (48). Some authors have suggested that the recommended daily amount (RDA) for magnesium of 4.5 mg/kg is too low, and should be 6-8 mg/kg (50).

Gibson (49) states that dietary factors are unimportant in the development of magnesium deficiency and that dietary magnesium depletions are rare. This, however, seems to contradict large-scale dietary surveys in the USA, which indicate that the average American diet is deficient in magnesium-rich foods (low in green vegetables, fish, whole grains and nuts, but providing relatively high amounts of magnesium-inhibiting elements such as fat, sugar, alcohol, salt, vitamin D, inorganic phosphate, proteins, and supplementary calcium and fibre) (50). Indeed, magnesium depletion is rarely seen in areas where green leafy vegetables form a significant portion of the diet (54).

TABLE 4.4.VII
Magnesium content of various products

Product	Portion size[1]	Concentration (mg per portion)
Grain and grain products	100 g	60-420[2]
Rolled oats	50 g	69.5 (56.5-75)[3]
Soya beans (whole corn)	100 g	247 (210-284)[3]
Haricot beans	100 g	132 (130-134)[3]
Shellfish	100 g	34-414[2]
Sole (fish)	100 g	73 (51-94)[3]
Shrimps	80 g	54 (34-74)[3]
Cashew nuts	40 g	107[3]
Roasted peanuts	25 g	45.5 (36-59.3)[3]
Fruit gums	50 g	55[4]
Chocolate, milk	50 g	27.5[4,5] 43 (31-52)[6] 52[5]
Chocolate, dark	50 g	50[1,2,3,5]
Cocoa powder	10 g	52.0[2] 41.4 (37.0-45.7)[5]

Number of samples unknown for most references
[1] (ref. 68)
[2] (ref. 50)
[3] (ref. 70)
[4] (ref. 81)
[5] (ref. 82)
[6] (ref. 83)

Premenstrual tension has been strongly associated with magnesium deficiency, and magnesium therapy has been claimed to have a beneficial effect for premenstrual tension, especially when it is combined with vitamin B6 (55). Moreover, it has been reported that women aged 50 years and over who were on a hormone replacement developed sudden cravings for chocolate when they entered their monthly 10-day period of progesterone administration. These cravings became less intense when they were given a daily amount of 100 mg magnesium (56, and A. Weil personal communication). Subclinical magnesium deficiency can occur in pregnancy and lactation, whereas severe depletion is associated with clinical disorders, for example, gastrointestinal disorders, severe burns, alcoholism (49), starvation, digitalis toxicity, and excessive sweating (52), and can result in arterial and cardiac lesions, blood coagulation and thrombosis (50). Alcoholism is most often the cause of symptomatic hypomagnesium (48).

Chocolate has the potential to contribute significantly to the dietary intake of magnesium, and even to counteract magnesium deficiency. Other foods, however, contain similar or larger amounts of magnesium. Furthermore, despite speculations concerning changes in mood and food preference associated with the menstrual cycle (e.g. 35,57), there appears to be no reliable evidence showing that magnesium-deficient people display an increased craving or liking for chocolate.

4.4.7   Anandamide

Separating a presumed lipid-soluble endogenous animal brain cannabinoid, Devane *et al.* (58) isolated and purified one substance, an N-acylethanol-amine, which they named anandamide. It bound to the cannabinoid receptor, and its sensitivity, assessed by its ability to inhibit twitch responses in mouse vasa deferentia, suggested a potency 'relatively close to that of Δ^9-THC', the main psychoactive compound in cannabis (reviewed in 59). The latter authors also pointed out that anandamide is relatively unstable: it was found to hydrolyse rapidly. Di Tomaso *et al.* (5), however, found that this reaction is inhibited by at least two other N-acyl-ethanolamines, which were found to co-exist with anandamide in chocolate. Furthermore, they detected these substances in both cocoa powder and chocolate, but not in white chocolate or coffee. This suggests that, in chocolate, they are confined to the cocoa solids, and not to any added soya lecithin, milk powder or sugar (60).

Although not substantiated with any research or literature, di Tomaso *et al.* (5) suggest that anandamides present in food might 'heighten sensitivity and produce euphoria' and, in doing so, intensify the oro-sensory effects of chocolate. However, Δ^9-THC, one of the most psychoactively potent natural cannabinoids, was found to produce a perceived 'high' at doses of 18.77 micrograms/kg body weight (= 1.3 mg for a 70 kg person) in human volunteers (61). Using an anandamide concentration of 0.05 micrograms/g chocolate (5), and making the generous assumption of an anandamide uptake of 100%, a plasma concentration of 18.77 micrograms/kg body weight could be achieved in an adult after ingestion of some 25 kg of chocolate. Clearly, consumption in a single sitting of such an amount of chocolate is impossible. Furthermore, other results show that amounts of anandamide several orders of magnitude higher than those present in cocoa products are required to produce significant cannabimimetic behavioural effects in mice (60). These calculations and subsequent results therefore contradict the suggestion of di Tomaso *et al.* (5) that their findings "point to an unexpected link between non-drug craving and the endogenous cannabinoid system".

4.4.8   Further Considerations and Conclusions

Of course, this review of the psychoactive effects of various minor constituents of chocolate is not exhaustive; nor, realistically, could it ever be, since even very extensive chemical analysis might fail to identify a crucial compound. Also, we have not discussed the possibility that interactions between two or more constituents will produce effects not predicted from their individual actions (62). In any case, identifying a compound in a food is only a first step towards demonstrating that this can have psychoactive effects as consumed in everyday life, and that in turn these effects play a role in influencing consumption of the food. As described earlier, recent research on caffeine has demonstrated significant preference-reinforcing effects, at least at the levels of caffeine found in coffee and tea (14,15), but this method has not yet been applied widely in the investigation of other psychopharmacologically active constituents of foods and drinks. Furthermore, it is perhaps significant that, while regular caffeine consumers do become mildly dependent on caffeine (withdrawal results in fatigue and headache), people tend not to describe cravings for caffeine-containing drinks. We suggest that this is because the urge to consume, for example, tea or coffee is rarely resisted (1). Indeed, even when caffeine intake is reduced as a result of changes in daily routines, such as occurs at weekends, it appears that the 'need' for caffeine is often not recognised (12).

A different way to attack the problem is simply to test the mood and psychostimulant effects of, for example, cocoa powder in double-blind, placebo-controlled studies. Cocoa powder is assumed to contain most if not all of the potentially psychoactive compounds present in chocolate (4). Results from a series of such double-blind, placebo-controlled studies showed small but significant alerting effects of cocoa powder at a dose level equivalent to a typical serving of dark chocolate (63). A full report on these studies is currently in preparation. A similar but less direct approach was taken by Michener and Rozin (4). They provided chocolate 'cravers' (individuals who reported having a craving for chocolate at least once per week) with sealed boxes containing a bar of milk chocolate, or a bar of white chocolate, or capsules containing cocoa (and therefore many of the presumed psychoactive ingredients of chocolate), or placebo capsules, or white chocolate plus cocoa capsules, or nothing. These participants consumed, in random order, the contents of one of these boxes when they experienced a craving for chocolate, and, just before, just after and 90 minutes after doing this, they rated the intensity of that craving. The results showed that only consumption of chocolate itself, either white or milk chocolate, substantially reduced the craving, suggesting that there is "no role for pharmacological effects in the satisfaction of chocolate craving" (4). Finally, another observation is that the most widely consumed chocolate is milk chocolate and chocolate-covered confectionery (64). This is also true for self-reported chocolate 'addicts' (65). Compared with dark chocolate, these contain a lower amount of cocoa solids, and therefore a lower concentration of many of the potentially psychoactive compounds unique to chocolate.

Based on the evidence discussed above, we agree with other investigators (4,6,50,66,67) that there is little support for the suggestion that experiences arising from eating chocolate, including its effects on mood, are related to the activity of psychoactive minor constituents. Instead, it is far more plausible to suggest that liking and appetite for chocolate are due mainly to the oro-sensory and post-ingestive effects of its principal constituents, sugar and fat (3,4,66), and that chocolate craving and 'addiction' are ultimately manifestations of a culturally determined ambivalence towards chocolate (1,3).

4.4.9   References

1.   Rogers P.J., Smit H.J. Food craving and food "addiction": A critical review of the evidence from a biopsychosocial perspective. *Pharmacology Biochemistry and Behavior*, 2000, 66, 3-14.

2.   Wegner D.M. Ironic processes of mental control. *Psychological Review*, 1994, 101, 34-52.

3.   Rogers P.J. Mechanisms of moreishness and food craving, in *Pleasure: The Politics and the Reality*. Ed. Warburton D.M. Chichester, Wiley. 1994, 38-49.

4.   Michener W., Rozin P. Pharmacological versus sensory factors in the satiation of chocolate craving. *Physiology and Behavior*, 1994, 56, 419-22.

5.   di Tomaso E., Beltramo M., Piomelli D. Brain cannabinoids in chocolate. *Nature*, 1996, 382, 677-8.

6.   Tarka S.M. The toxicology of cocoa and methylxanthines: a review of the literature. *CRC Critical Reviews of Toxicology*, 1982, 9, 275-312.

7.   James J.E. *Caffeine and Health*. London, Academic Press. 1991.

8.   Landau S.I. *International Dictionary of Medicine and Biology*. New York, Wiley. 1986.

9.   Yesair D.W., Branfman A.R., Callahan M.M. Human disposition and some biochemical aspects of methylxanthines, in *The Methylxanthine Beverages and Foods: Chemistry, Consumption and Health Effects*. Ed. Spiller G.A. New York, Alan R. Liss. 1984, 215-33.

10.   Mumford G.K., Benowitz N.L., Evans S.M., Kaminski B.J., Preston K.L., Sannerud C.A., Silverman K., Griffiths R.R. Absorption rate of methylxanthines

following capsules, cola and chocolate. *European Journal of Clinical Pharmacology*, 1996, 51, 319-25.

11. Mumford G.K., Holtzman G. Qualitative differences in the discriminative stimulus effects of low and high doses of caffeine in the rat. *Journal of Pharmacology and Experimental Therapeutics*, 1991, 258, 857-65.

12. Rogers P.J., Dernoncourt C. Regular caffeine consumption: A balance of adverse and beneficial effects for mood and psychomotor performance. *Pharmacology Biochemistry and Behavior*, 1998, 59, 1039-45.

13. Rogers P.J. Why we drink caffeine-containing beverages, and the equivocal benefits of regular caffeine intake for mood and cognitive performance, in *Caffeinated Beverages: Health Benefits, Physiological Effects, and Chemistry.* Eds Parliament T.H., Ho C.-T., Schieberle P. ACS Symposium Series No. 754. Washington DC, American Chemical Society. 2000, 37-45.

14. Rogers P.J., Richardson N.J., Elliman, N.A. Overnight caffeine abstinence and negative reinforcement of preference for caffeine-containing drinks. *Psychopharmacology*, 1995, 120, 457-62.

15. Yeomans M.R., Spetch H., Rogers P.J. Conditioned flavour preference negatively reinforced by caffeine in human volunteers. *Psychopharmacology*, 1998, 137, 401-9.

16. Smit H.J., Rogers P.J. Effects of low doses of caffeine on cognitive performance, mood and thirst in low and higher caffeine consumers. *Psychopharmacology*, 2000, 152, 167-73.

17. Czok G. Zur Frage der biologischen Wirksamkeit von Methylxanthinen in Kakaoprodukten (Addressing the question of the biological activity of methylxanthines in cocoa products). *Zeitschr. Ern. wiss.* 1974, 13, 165-71.

18. Stavric B. Methylxantines: Toxicity to humans. 3: Theobromine, paraxanthine and the combined effects of methylxanthines. *Food Chemistry and Toxicology*, 1988, 26, 725-33.

19. Merck & Co. *The Merck Index: An encyclopedia of Chemicals, Drugs, and Biologicals: 12th Edition.* Whitehouse Station, NJ, Merck & Co. Inc. 1996.

20. Mumford G.K., Evans S.M., Kaminski B.J., Preston K., Sannerud C.A., Silverman K., Griffiths R.R. Discriminative stimulus and subjective effects of theobromine and caffeine in humans. *Psychopharmacology*, 1994, 115, 1-8.

21. Ziegleder G., Stojacic E., Stumpf B. Vorkommen von beta-Phenylethylamin und seinen Derivaten in Kakao und Kakaoerzeugnissen (The occurrence of beta-phenylethylamine and its derivatives in cocoa and cocoa products). *Z. Lebensm. Unters. Forsch.*, 1992, 195, 235-8.

22. Askar A., Morad M.M. Lebensmittelvergiftung. I: Toxine in Natürlichen Lebensmitteln (Food poisoning I: Toxins in natural foods). *Alimenta*, 1980, 19, 59-66.

23. Marley E., Blackwell B. Interactions of monoamine oxidase inhibitors, amines, and foodstuffs. *Advances in Pharmacology and Chemotherapy*, 1970, 8, 185-239.

24. Passmore R., Robson J.S. *A Companion to Medical Studies in Three Volumes. Volume 2: Pharmacology, Microbiology, General Pathology and Related Subjects, 2nd edition.* Oxford, Blackwell. 1970.

25. Morgan J.P. *Phenylpropanolamine: Risks, Benefits and Controversies (Clinical Pharmacology and Therapeutics Series, Volume 5).* New York, Praeger. 1985.

26. Sandler M., Youdim M.B.H., Hanington E. A phenylethylamine oxidising defect in migraine. *Nature*, 1974, 250, 335-7.

27. Paterson I.A., Juorio A.V., Boulton A.A. 2-Phenylethylamine: a modulator of catecholamine transmission in the mammalian central nervous system? *Journal of Neurochemistry*, 1990, 55, 1827-37.

28. Davis B.A., Boulton A.A. The trace amines and their acidic metabolites in depression - an overview. *Progress in Neuropsychopharmacology and Biological Psychiatry*, 1994, 18, 17-45.

29. Liebowitz M.R., Klein D.F. Hysteroid Dysphoria. *Psychiatric Clinics of North America*, 1979, 2, 555-75.

30. Kohl J.V., Francoeur R.T. *The Scent of Eros.* New York, Continuum. 1995.

31. Liebowitz M.R. *The Chemistry of Love.* Boston, Little Brown. 1983.

32. Crenshaw T.L. *Why we love and lust: how our sex hormones influence our relationships.* London, Harper Collins. 1996.

33. Shulgin A., Shulgin A. *PIHKAL: A Chemical Love Story.* Berkeley, CA, Transform Press. 1991.

34. Joosten H.N.L.J. The biogenic amine contents of Dutch cheese and their toxicological significance. *Netherlands Milk and Dairy Journal*, 1988, 42, 25-42.

35. Wurtman R.J., Wurtman J.J. Carbohydrates and depression. *Scientific American*, 1989, 260, 50-7.

36. Young S.N. Some effects of dietary components (amino acids, carbohydrate, folic acid) on brain serotonin synthesis, mood and behaviour. *Canadian Journal of Physiology and Pharmacology*, 1991, 69, 893-903.

37. Young S.N. The use of diet and dietary components in the study of factors controlling affect in humans: A review. *Journal of Psychiatry and Neuroscience*, 1993, 18, 235-44.

38. Maes M., Meltzer H.Y. The serotonin hypothesis of major depression, in *Psychopharmacology: The Fourth Generation of Progress*. Eds Bloom F.E, Kupfer D.J. New York, Raven Press. 1995, 933-44.

39. Rogers P.J. Food, mood and appetite. *Nutrition Research Reviews*, 1995, 8, 243-69.

40. Wurtman R.J., Hefti F., Melamed E. Precursor control of neurotransmitter synthesis. *Pharmacological Reviews*, 1981, 32, 315-35.

41. Young S.N. The clinical psychopharmacology of tryptophan, in *Nutrition and the Brain: Volume 7*. Eds Wurtman R.J., Wurtman J.J. New York, Raven Press. 1986, 49-88.

42. Spring B., Chiodo J., Bowen D.J. Carbohydrates, tryptophan, and behavior: A methodological Review. *Psychological Bulletin*, 1987, 102, 234-56.

43. Hill A.J., Blundell J.E. Role of amino acids in appetite control in man, in *Amino Acids in Health and Disease*. Ed. Heuther G. Berlin, Springer-Verlag. 1988, 239-48.

44. Steinberg S., Annable L., Young S.N., Bélanger M.-C. Tryptophan in the treatment of late luteal phase dyphoric disorder: A pilot study. *Journal of Psychiatry and Neuroscience*, 1986, 19, 114-19.

45. McGrath R.E., Buckwald B., Resnick E.V. The effect of L-tryptophan on seasonal affective disorder. *Journal of Clinical Psychiatry*, 1990, 51, 162-3.

46.   Young S.N., Smith S.E., Pihl R.O., Finn P. Tryptophan depletion causes a rapid lowering of mood in normal males. *Psychopharmacology*, 1985, 87, 173-7.

47.   Benkelfat C., Ellenbogen M.A., Dean P., Palmour R.M., Young S.N. Mood-lowering effect of tryptophan depletion. *Archives of General Psychiatry*, 1994, 51, 687-97.

48.   Terry J. The other electrolytes: magnesium, calcium, and phosphorus. *Journal of Intravenous Nursing*, 1991, 14, 167-76.

49.   Gibson R.S. Assessment of calcium, phosphorus, and magnesium status, in *Principles of Nutritional Assessment*. Oxford, Oxford University Press. 1990, 487-510.

50.   Seelig M. Cardiovascular consequences of magnesium deficiency and loss: pathogenesis, prevalence and manifestations - magnesium and chloride loss in refractory potassium repletion. *American Journal of Cardiology*, 1989, 63, 4G-21G.

51.   Rozin P., Levine E., Stoess C. Chocolate craving and liking. *Appetite*, 1991, 17, 199-212.

52.   Reinhart R.A. Magnesium metabolism. *Wis. Medical Journal*, 1990, 89, 579-83.

53.   Shils M.E. Magnesium, in *Modern Nutrition in Health and Disease, 8th edition*. Eds Shils M.E., Olson J.A., Shike M. Philadelphia, Lea & Febinger. 1994, 164-84.

54.   Beal A., Walker A.F. Dietary mineral supplementation and bioavailability, in *Nutrition and the Consumer: Issues in Nutrition and Toxicology, Volume 1*. Eds Walker A.F., Rolls B.A. London, Elsevier Applied Science. 1992, 127-60.

55.   Abraham G.E. Premenstrual tension. *Current Problems in Obstetrics and Gynecology*, 1980, 3, 1-39.

56.   Roach M. More reasons to love chocolate. *New Woman*, February 1989, 135-6.

57.   Bancroft J., Cook A., Williamson L. Food craving, mood and the menstrual cycle. *Psychological Medicine*, 1988, 18, 855-60.

58.   Devane W.A., Hanus L., Breuer A., Pertwee R.G., Stevenson L.A., Griffin G., Gibson D., Mandelbaum A., Etinger A., Mechoulam R. Isolation and structure

of a brain constituent that binds to the cannabinoid receptor. *Science*, 1992, 258, 1946-9.

59.   Mechoulam R., Fride E. The unpaved road to the endogenous brain cannabinoid ligands, the anandamides, in *Cannabinoid Receptors*. Ed. Pertwee R.G. London, Academic Press. 1995, 233-58.

60.   Di Marzo V., Sepe N., De Petrocellis L., Berger A., Crozier G., Fride E., Mechoulam R. Trick or treat from food endocannabinoids? *Nature*, 1998, 396, 636.

61.   Perez-Reyes M., Timmons M.C., Davis K.H., Wall E.M. A comparison of the pharmacological activity in man of intravenously administered Δ^9-tetrahydrocannabinol, cannabinol, and cannabidiol. *Experientia*, 1973, 29, 1368-9.

62.   Beltramo M., Piomelli D. Reply to Di Marzo *et al. Nature*, 1998, 396, 636-7.

63.   Smit H. *The liking for chocolate: attitudes, mood and psychopharmacological effects*. PhD thesis, University of Reading, UK. 1998.

64.   BCCCA. *BCCCA Statistical Yearbook 1997*. London, Biscuit Cake Chocolate and Confectionery Alliance. 1997.

65.   Hetherington M.M., Macdairmid J.I. "Chocolate addiction": A preliminary study of its description and its relationship to problem eating. *Appetite*, 1993, 21, 233-46.

66.   Max B. This and that: chocolate addiction, the dual pharmacogenetics of asparagus eaters and the arithmetic of freedom. *Trends in Pharmacological Science*, 1989, 10, 390-3.

67.   Gibson E.L., Desmond E. Chocolate craving and hunger state: Implications for the acquisition and expression of appetite and food choice. *Appetite*, 1999, 32, 219-40.

68.   MAFF. *Food Portion Sizes, 2nd edition*. London, Ministry of Agriculture Fisheries and Food, HMSO. 1988.

69.   MAFF. *Survey of Caffeine and Other Methylxanthines in Energy Drinks and Other Caffeine-containing Products: Food Surveillance Information Sheet 103*. London, Ministry of Agriculture Fisheries and Food. 1997.

70. Souci S.W., Fachmann W., Kraut H. *Food Composition and Nutrition Tables 1981/1982, 2nd edition.* Stuttgart, Wissenschaftliche Verlagsgesellschaft mbH. 1981.

71. Barone J.J., Roberts H.R. Caffeine consumption. *Food Chemistry and Toxicology*, 1996, 34, 119-29.

72. Shively C.A., Tarka S.M. Methylxanthine composition and consumption patterns of cocoa and chocolate products, in *The Methylxanthine Beverages and Foods: Chemistry, Consumption and Health Effects.* Ed. Spiller G.A. New York, Alan R. Liss. 1984, 149-78.

73. Zoumas B.L., Kreiser W.R., Martin R.A. Theobromine and caffeine content of chocolate products. *Journal of Food Science*, 1980, 45, 314-6.

74. Ingles D.L., Back J.F., Gallimore D., Tindale R., Shaw K.J. Estimation of biogenic amines in foods. *Journal of the Science of Food and Agriculture*, 1985, 36, 402-6.

75. Koehler P.E., Eitenmiller R.R. High pressure liquid chromatographic analysis of tyramine, phenylethylamine and tryptamine in sausage, cheese and chocolate. *Journal of Food Science*, 1978, 43, 1245-7.

76. ten Brink B., Damink C., Joosten J.M.L.J., Huis in 't Veld J.H.J. Occurrence and formation of biologically active amines in foods. *International Journal of Food Microbiology*, 1990, 11, 73-84.

77. Hurst W.J., Toomey P.B. High-performance liquid chromatographic determination of four biogenic amines in chocolate. *Analyst*, 1981, 106, 394-402.

78. Baker G.B., Wong J.T.F., Coutts R.T., Pasutto F.M. Simultaneous extraction and quantitation of several bioactive amines in cheese and chocolate. *Journal of Chromatography*, 1987, 392, 317-31.

79. Smith T.A. Amines in food. *Food Chemistry*, 1981, 6, 169-200.

80. Paul A.A., Southgate D.A.T., Russell J. *First Supplement to McCance and Widdowson's The Composition of Foods.* Amsterdam, Elsevier/North-Holland Biomedical Press. 1980.

81. Paul A.A., Southgate D.A.T. *McCance and Widdowson's The Composition of Foods, 4th edition.* Amsterdam, Elsevier/North-Holland Biomedical Press. 1978.

82.   NEVO. *NEVO Tabel: Nederlands Voedingsstoffenbestand 1989/90*. Zeist, The Netherlands, Stichting NEVO. 1989.

83.   Souci S.W., Fachmann W., Kraut H. *Food Composition and Nutrition Tables 1986/1987, 3rd edition*. Stuttgart, Wissenschaftliche Verlagsgesellschaft mbH. 1986.

5. HORMONAL STATUS AND CRAVINGS

5.1. CRAVINGS AND TASTE CHANGES DURING PREGNANCY

Deborah J. Bowen and Susan Crystal

5.1.1 Importance of Taste Changes in Pregnancy

Eating behaviour and nutrient needs during pregnancy have received much research attention (1). Much of this research has focused on a lack of needed nutrients and subsequent deleterious effects on mother and child. Based on this research, the Institute of Medicine, in Washington DC, has published a set of specific weight goals for pregnant women (2). Little is known, however, about how pregnant women choose the foods that create their dietary intake when food is plentiful and even in excess. This caloric overload is currently the state in many industrialised countries and therefore food choices under such conditions need research attention.

Taste plays a major role in food choice and consumption in non-pregnant individuals (3,4). Therefore, taste could play a role in guiding the consumption of pregnant women, along with other key factors, such as genetics (5), availability (6), and medical guidance. These other factors provide many opportunities for taste changes during pregnancy, whether psychological in nature (e.g., trying to "eat for two") or biological in nature. This chapter will discuss the literature on taste changes and identify new avenues for research.

5.1.2 Sweet Taste Changes

5.1.2.1 Rationale for studying sweet taste

The need for calories in the diet is accepted and it is generally recognised that over-consumption of calories contributes to the development and maintenance of obesity (3,7). However, the density of energy, rather than the specific content of sweetness or fat, has been proposed to be the main food characteristic that contributes to obesity (8). In general consumption, sweet taste is one of the taste-related markers of caloric density, and so preference

353

for sweet taste has been studied as one possible mechanism for the development of obesity.

Post-partum weight retention is common and can contribute to obesity. Excess weight gain during pregnancy poses a health hazard for both mother and child (9), and potential changes in sweet taste preference could be responsible. For most women, general food consumption increases during pregnancy because caloric need increases by 300 kcal/day. By the third trimester, women have stored a small layer of fat to meet the caloric drain imposed by breast feeding (10). The recommended weight gain during pregnancy for normal weight women is 25-35 pounds (10). However, some women gain 40-60 pounds or more during their pregnancy. These women tend to have higher post-partum weight retention and therefore are at increased risk to be overweight or obese after delivery. It may be that mothers experience an increase in preferences for sweet taste, due to the biological changes that occur during pregnancy. Increased sweet preference may lead to excessive consumption of calories, resulting in an average of 8-10 pounds of excess body fat. Therefore, studying changes in preference for sweet foods could reveal pathways to explain excess weight gain.

5.1.2.2   Determinants of sweet preference

What drives sweet taste preferences? First, hunger increases preferences for sweet-tasting foods, and satiety reduces them (11). Changes in physiological state, such as those across the menstrual cycle (12) are associated with changes in sweet food preference (see section 5.3). Women who give up smoking report increases in preference for sweet tasting, calorie-dense foods, and also gain excess weight during the cessation process (13). These transient changes in sweet preferences provide support for the possibility of pregnancy as another time when physiological changes could drive increases in sweet preferences and over-consumption.

5.1.3   Taste Changes During Pregnancy

There is some empirical support for the theory that changes in preference for sweet tastes during pregnancy can contribute to overeating and excess weight gain. For example, animal studies indicate that rats provided with glucose solutions in addition to their laboratory chow gained more weight and more adipose tissue during pregnancy compared with rats eating only chow (14). Early human research indicated that there were no changes in sweet taste preference during pregnancy (15). However, all participants in this and other studies were in the third trimester of pregnancy. Hormonal changes increase most dramatically during the second trimester, and therefore taste might be expected to change early in pregnancy. In a laboratory study, women preferred sweet foods most strongly during the second trimester (16), corresponding to the pregnancy period with the most dramatic hormonal increase. Other studies have documented increases in sweet and fat preference during pregnancy (17) and in women with gestational diabetes mellitus, compared with women without diabetes (18). These preference changes for sweet foods are not found when solutions of sucrose are used in taste tests, compared with using real foods (19). This suggests that any sweet and fat taste changes during pregnancy are not necessarily due to simple taste, but to taste combined with other properties of real foods, such as calorie content, mouthfeel, and other more sociocultural expectations about foods.

5.1.4   Salt Taste Changes

5.1.4.1   Rationale for studying salt taste

The ingestion of sodium or NaCl in excess of physiological need is of particular interest because human salt preference and intake have an impact upon health. Diets high in sodium (or NaCl) have been implicated in the aetiology of essential hypertension (20-23). In pregnancy, excessive sodium may be associated with pre-eclampsia. Participants randomly assigned to diet education intervention groups show reduced dietary sodium intake and blood pressure as compared with controls (24).

Often, efforts to reduce an individual's dietary salt level are unsuccessful (25) and an acceptable salt substitute has yet to be found (26). Under controlled experimental conditions, salt preference appears modifiable. Individuals maintained on decreased sodium diets, such that there is limited exposure to salty tastes, for at least 2 months, show a hedonic shift toward lower sodium (27-29). However, it has not been determined whether this shift leads to persistent decreases in dietary sodium intake. Further, the shift in preference is reversed by re-exposure to foods higher in salt (29). Together, these studies support the suggestion that habitual dietary sodium preferences override health concerns. If future interventions are to be successful, a better understanding is needed of the mechanisms responsible for the broad variations in salt preference across the population.

People vary widely in their preference for and consumption of salty foods, and our understanding of the factors that contribute to this variation is limited. Twin studies that have looked at preference for NaCl solutions and salty foods failed to provide evidence of significant genetic contributions to variations in human salt preference (25,30). The strongest known predictor of salt preference and intake in humans appears to be taste exposure or habit (25). However, the sources of this habit have not been identified. In an attempt to identify the sources of habit, researchers have turned to animal models to identify experiential influences that may affect life-long salt preference.

5.1.4.2 *Determinants of salt preference*

Animal studies demonstrate that manipulation of diet and/or physiological state in pregnancy can alter salt preference in offspring. (31-34). This research suggests that life-long salt preferences can be affected by activation of hormone systems responsible for osmotic and fluid volume regulation. Nicolaïdis, Galverna and colleagues (35,36) offered one hypothesis based on this model in humans. Extending their findings from animal studies they speculated that, in humans, extracellular volume depletion and electrolyte imbalance, which may occur as a consequence of vomiting during pregnancy, could significantly affect salt preference of the offspring. This intriguing hypothesis provides a possible explanation for some of the variation that exists in human salt preference. Assessment of this hypothesis could lead to a better understanding of human salt intake.

5.1.4.3 Salt taste changes during pregnancy

Crystal and Bernstein (37,38) investigated this hypothesis. These studies showed that adult offspring of mothers who reported vomiting moderate or severe amounts during pregnancy had higher self-reported salt use, and displayed higher salt intake and higher preference for salty snack foods than offspring of women who reported no or mild vomiting. A third study measured this phenomenon in infants. Infants of mothers who reported moderate or severe symptoms of vomiting during pregnancy had a significantly higher preference for 0.2M NaCl than infants of mothers with less severe symptoms of vomiting. Research has failed to demonstrate an association between maternal sodium intake and vomiting during early pregnancy. Taken together, these studies demonstrate a consistent relationship between maternal vomiting, but not nausea, during pregnancy and offspring salt preference both in infancy and adulthood. The effects of maternal pregnancy-related vomiting and female offspring's pregnancy-related salt preferences have not been studied.

It appears, then, that vomiting during pregnancy could lead to alterations in the levels of hormones responsible for maintaining osmotic and fluid volume. In animal studies, changes in these homeostatic states and increases in these hormones have led to permanent increases in salt preference. Therefore, in humans, vomiting during pregnancy could create physiological conditions that perhaps temporarily alter salt preference in mothers and permanently alter salt preference in offspring.

5.1.5 Cravings During Pregnancy

The classic public image of unusual eating during pregnancy is that of cravings for specific foods. The "pickles and ice cream" need, expressed as an anecdote by many, has received only sketchy research support. Part of the difficulty with doing research in this area may be the confusion over definition of craving (39). For this discussion we can use Kozlowski's definition: "a distinct state of especially urgent desire for a substance" (40). The literature has several reports of cravings for specific foods during pregnancy (41-43). Often, the data for these cravings are collected and reported for specific foods, such as pizza and coffee, rather than for classes or groups of foods. This individual food approach to the measurement of cravings makes linking any one craving to health outcomes almost impossible, because reported cravings for specific foods are so diverse and they are not generally consumed at levels that are harmful. Also, it is unclear whether cravings are associated with food intake.

5.1.6   Conclusions

What have we learned from this relatively sparse amount of research? It seems that there is evidence for the occurrence of taste or preference changes during pregnancy. These preference or taste changes might be specific to sweet or salty food tastes and some might be described as hedonic shifts; in addition to taste sensitivity, taste judgement changes. For bitter foods, the actual taste intensity increases from pre-pregnancy levels to first trimester levels. Increases in salt preferences, and also in sour and bitter preferences, may provide a means for women to consume enough taste-related nutrients to maintain proper nutritional status. If a taste is less unpleasant, then individuals may be able to consume more foods that carry the particular taste. Hedonic preference judgements for sweet foods also seem to increase, although the evidence is not consistent. The studies using real foods found increases in preference, while the studies testing solutions of sucrose identified fewer changes during pregnancy. This might mean that sweet taste is a marker for other contents, such as calories or fat, and, when varied independently, does not show any pregnancy-related changes.

There is also some evidence for individual differences in taste changes and their accompanying effects on health and behaviour. For example, based on animal research, differences in women's salt preferences and consumption have been hypothesised to lead to alterations in offspring's salt preferences. In retrospective studies, this hypothesis was supported. Similar studies need to be conducted with other tastes and other health-related behaviours combined. The outcomes could be measured in mother or in offspring, or both. In a situation such as that of gestational diabetes, maternal energy management and nutritional status can have dramatic effects on the mother's health, and can alter infant size and survival, in addition to taste preference. Given the potential for taste and related consumption to affect both mother and child, these outcomes need critical research attention.

These data, by themselves, are not conclusive. We are missing key studies in several areas. First, we need studies that measure taste sensitivity, hedonic judgements, choice, preference and actual changes in consumption before, during, and after pregnancy. Many of the studies cited here use laboratory methodology to assess preference and choice. It will be very important to relate the finely controlled laboratory hypotheses and findings to measurements of consumption of specific nutrients, both levels and types of nutrients, in real-world free-living settings. The measurement of dietary intake is difficult and labour-intensive, but necessary to gain a full understanding of the phenomenon at hand.

Also important to measure will be the psychological issues that surround food choice and eating behaviour in contemporary Western cultures. The effects of knowledge about foods and recommendations for consumption, the issues of body image before and during pregnancy, and the idea of cognitive restraint from eating foods that might lead to health problems were not carefully considered in the studies cited here. We know that eating behaviour is under strong psychological control and influence (44), and, during pregnancy, similar factors could control eating behaviour, but very few have been studied in the context of pregnancy-related changes in taste and eating.

Finally, the ultimate goal is to relate the mother's taste preference and sensitivity, and consumption, to health outcomes of both mother and offspring.

As Drewnowski points out (44), we believe that taste changes have a protective biological significance. Therefore, we hope that, during pregnancy, these signify some protective function for mother and/or her offspring. But this process relies on evolutionary forces selecting for these taste changes, and in modern times the role of evaluation in human behaviour is much less clear. Therefore, any taste changes could have unanticipated "side effects". Increases in sweet preferences could have cued mothers to ingest more calories during pregnancy, protecting her against calorie deficits and inadequate nutrition. However, now these taste changes could cue overnutrition, weight and adipose tissue gain, and subsequent obesity. Similarly, maternal increases in calorie consumption could lead to increases in infant obesity, possibly leading to longer-term fat deposition and obesity. Salt preference changes during pregnancy could lead to long-term changes in offspring salt consumption. The links to health outcomes of salt preference changes is less clear, but there may be deleterious effects of increased salt consumption on cardiovascular health.

Addressing these types of research questions and hypotheses requires demanding designs and complicated analyses. Relating maternal taste preferences and consumption to health outcomes requires a longitudinal design with analyses repeated over time and a relatively large sample size to account for the individual variability in dietary patterns. Adding infant taste and consumption measures to this design more than doubles the complexity. However, these studies need to be done if we are to establish better the links between taste changes in pregnancy and health outcomes.

Finally, taste changes during pregnancy could serve as a model system for understanding the relationship between biological, psychological, and social control of eating behaviour. As with other situations, taste changes during pregnancy are probably created and altered by multiple events and influences. To the extent that we can identify and understand them, we might learn something about the larger field of human eating behaviour.

5.1.7   References

1.   Hytten F.E. Weight gain and pregnancy-30 years of research. *South African Medical Journal*, 1981, 60, 15-9.

2.   Institute of Medicine. Committee on Nutritional Status during Pregnancy and Lactation. *Nutrition during pregnancy*. Washington DC, USA, National Academy Press. 1990.

3.   Drewnowski A. Sweetness, appetite, and energy intake: Physiological aspects. *World Review of Nutrition and Dietetics*, 1999, 85, 64-76.

4.   Clark J. Taste and flavour: their importance in food choice and acceptance. *Proceedings of the Nutrition Society*, 1998, 57, 639-43.

5.   Tepper B.J. 6-n-Propylthiouracil: A genetic marker for taste, with implications for food preference and dietary habits. *American Journal of Human Genetics,* 1998, 63, 1271-6.

6.   Birch L.L. Development of food preferences. *Annual Review of Nutrition,* 1999, 19, 41-62.

7.   Drewnowski A. Sweetness, appetite, and energy intake: physiological aspects, in *Low-calorie sweeteners; present and future.* Ed. Corti A. Basel, Karger, World Rev Nutr Diet. 1999, 85, 64-76.

8.   Rolls B.J., Bell E.A. Intake of fat and carbohydrate: role of energy density. *European Journal of Clinical Nutrition,* 1999, 53(Suppl 1), 166-73.

9.   Johnson J.W., Yancey M.K. A critique of the new recommendation for weight gain in pregnancy. *American Journal of Obstetrics and Gynecology,* 1996, 174, 254-8.

10.   Newcombe R.G. Development of obesity in parous women. *Journal of Epidemiology and Community Health,* 1982, 36, 306-9.

11.   Prentice A.M., Poppitt S.D. Importance of energy density and macronutrients in the regulation of energy intake. *International Journal of Obesity,* 1996, 20(Suppl), 18-23.

12.   Bowen D.J., Grunberg N.E. Variations in food preference and consumption across the menstrual cycle. *Physiology and Behaviour,* 1990, 47, 287-91.

13.   Grunberg N.E., Bowen D.J. Coping with the sequelae of smoking cessation, in *Behavioral Assessment and Management of Cardiovascular Disorders.* Eds Krantz D.W., Blumenthal J.A. Sarasota, FL: Professional Resource Exchange, Inc. 1987.

14.   Bowen D.J. Possible explanations for excess weight gains in pregnancy: An animal model. *Physiology & Behaviour,* 1989, 46, 935-9.

15.   Brown J.E., Toma R.B. Taste changes during pregnancy. *American Journal of Clinical Nutrition,* 1986, 43, 414-8.

16.   Bowen D.J. Taste and food preference changes across the course of pregnancy. *Appetite,* 1992, 19, 233-42.

17.   Skinner J.D. Alterations in adolescents' sensory taste preferences during and after pregnancy. *Journal of Adolescent Health,* 1998, 22, 43-9.

18. Tepper B.J., Seldner A.C. Sweet taste and intake of sweet foods in normal pregnancy and pregnancy complicated by gestational diabetes mellitus. *American Journal of Clinical Nutrition*, 1999, 70, 277-84.

19. Duffy V.B., Bartoshuk L.M., Striegel-Moore R., Rodin J. Taste changes across pregnancy. *Annals of the New York Academy of Sciences*, 1998, 805-9.

20. Dahl L.K., Heine M., Tassinari L. Effects of chronic salt ingestion: evidence that genetic factors play an important role in susceptibility to experimental hypertension. *Journal of Experimental Medicine*, 1962, 115, 1173-90.

21. Hunt J.C. Sodium intake and hypertension: a cause for concern. *Annals of Internal Medicine*, 1983, 98, 724-8.

22. Luft F.C., Weinberger M.H. Sodium intake and essential hypertension. *Hypertension*, 1982, 4 (5 part 2), III14-19.

23. Williams G.H., Hollenberg M.D. Sodium-sensitive essential hypertension: emerging insights into an old entity. *Journal of the American College of Nutrition*, 1989, 8, 490-4.

24. Iso H., Shimamoto T., Yokota K., Sankai T., Jacobs D.R. Jr., Komachi Y. Community based education classes for hypertension control. A 1.5-year randomized controlled trial. *Hypertension*, 1996, 27(4), 968-74.

25. Beauchamp G.K. The human preference for excess salt. *American Scientist*, 1987, 75, 27-33.

26. Beauchamp G.K., Engelman K. High salt intake. Sensory and behavioral factors. *Hypertension*, 1991, 17(1 Suppl.), I176-I181.

27. Beauchamp G.K., Bertino M., Engelman K. Modification of salt taste. *Annals of Internal Medicine*, 1983, 98 (5 part 2), 763-9.

28. DiNicolantonio R.B., Teow B.H., Morgen T.O. Sodium detection thresholds and preference for sodium salt in humans on high and low salt diets. *Clinical Experimental Pharmacology and Physiology*, 1984, 11, 335-8.

29. Mattes R.D. The taste for salt in humans. *American Journal of Clinical Nutrition*, 1997, 65(Suppl), 692S-7S.

30. Greene L.S., Desor J.A., Maller O. Hereditary and experience: their relative importance in the development of taste preference in man. *Journal of Comparative, Physiological Psychology*, 1975, 89, 279-84.

31. Hill D.L., Mistretta C.M., Bradley R.M. Effects of dietary NaCl during early development on behavioral and neurophysiological taste response. *Behavioral Neuroscience*, 1986, 100(3), 390-8.

32. Mouw D.R., Vander A.J., Wagner J. Effects of prenatal and early postnatal sodium deprivation on subsequent adult thirst and salt preference in rats. *American Journal of Physiology*, 1978, 234(1), F59-F63.

33. Contreras R.J., Kosten R. Prenatal and early post natal sodium chloride intake modifies the solution preference of adult rats. *Journal of Nutrition*, 1983, 113, 1051-62.

34. Vijande M., Brime J.I., López-Sela P., Costales M., Argüelles J. Increased salt preference in adult offspring raised by mother rats consuming excessive amounts of salt and water. *Regulatory Peptides*, 1996, 66, 105-8.

35. Nicolaïdis S., Galaverna O., Metzler C.H. Extracellular dehydration during pregnancy increases salt appetite of offspring. *American Journal of Physiology*, 1990, 258, R281-R283.

36. Galaverna O., Nicolaïdis S., Yao S.-Z., Sakai R.R., Epstein A.N. Endocrine consequences of prenatal sodium depletion prepare rates for high need-free NaCl intake in adulthood. *American Journal of Physiology*, 1995, 269, R578-R583.

37. Crystal S.R., Bernstein I.L. Infant salt preference and mother's morning sickness. *Appetite*, 1998, 30, 297-307.

38. Crystal S.R., Bernstein I.L. Morning sickness: impact on offspring salt preference. *Appetite*, 1995, 25, 231-40.

39. Gendall K.A., Joyce P.R., Sullivan P.F. *Impact of definition on prevalence of food cravings in a random sample of young women*. London, Academic Press Limited. 1997.

40. Kozlowski L.T., Mann R.E., Wilkinson D.A., Poulos C.X. "Cravings" are ambiguous: ask about urges or desires. *Addictive Behaviors*, 1989, 14, 443-5.

41. Pope J.E., Skinner J.D., Carruth B.R. Cravings and aversions of pregnant adolescents. *Journal of the American Dietetic Association*, 1992, 92, 1479-82.

42. Hook E.B. Dietary cravings and aversions during pregnancy. *American Journal of Clinical Nutrition*, 1978, 31, 1355-62.

43. Worthington-Roberts B., Little R.E., Lambert M.D., Wu R. Dietary cravings and aversions in the postpartum period. *Journal of the American Dietetic Association*, 1989, 89, 647-51.

44. Drewnowski A. Taste preferences and food intake. *Annual Review of Nutrition*, 1997, 17, 237-53.

5.2. CRAVINGS ACROSS THE MENSTRUAL CYCLE AND IN PREMENSTRUAL SYNDROME

Louise Dye

5.2.1   Introduction

The aim of this chapter is to examine the relationship between the menstrual cycle and food craving. The effect of the menstrual cycle on appetite control has been reviewed (1,2). Changes in food intake, preferences and cravings have been linked to mood (3-5). This chapter will focus on the timing, nature and a range of theories that have been suggested to account for food cravings during the menstrual cycle and in women with premenstrual syndrome (PMS).

5.2.2   Prevalence of Food Craving during the Menstrual Cycle

Food craving appears to be a very common phenomenon, although a widely accepted definition of food craving is not available despite being the subject of much debate (6,7). Between 40 and 97% of women and 16-68% of men report having experienced food cravings at some time (8-10). It has also been suggested that food cravings are more prevalent in young single women (11), although most studies have examined opportunistic student samples. Gendall *et al.* (7) report a prevalence rate of 58% in a random sample of women of reproductive age. Such high rates of reporting suggest that this is a very common experience, and not an abnormal event that occurs only in particular populations. Food cravings appear to be more common in women, and this has directed attention to the possible relationship between "strong urges to eat a specific food" or "uncontrollable desire(s) to eat a certain food or type of food" (7) and the regular fluctuations in hormonal state that underlie the menstrual cycle.

In studies examining food craving during the menstrual cycle, prevalence rates of some sort of cyclical craving have ranged from about 25% to 50%, although samples have ranged from university students

(10,12,13), magazine questionnaire respondents (14), women attending gynaecological clinics (15,16), prison inmates (17) and nursing staff (18). Craving, specifically in the premenstrual phase, occurred in between a third and three-quarters of women studied (3,5,15,17,19,20).

Prospective studies of food craving are rare. However, both retrospective and prospective studies have shown an increase in food craving frequency and severity in the premenstrual phase (3,5,8,12,13,15,17,18,20-25). This premenstrual increase in food craving has been demonstrated in women with PMS (15,26); in women with and without premenstrual depression (5,21) and in women without premenstrual symptoms (12). Two retrospective studies have observed perimenstrual patterns in food craving reports (13,27). Thus the temporal relationship of food cravings and the menstrual cycle is well-established. The predominant pattern that emerges from all of the studies to date is an increase in both the frequency and severity of food craving in the premenstruum (5,8).

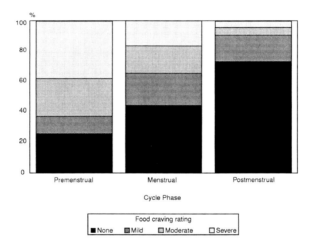

Fig. 5.2.1. Percentage of women (n = 5446) reporting no, mild, moderate or severe food cravings, during the premenstrual (week prior to menstruation), menstrual (all days of bleeding) and postmenstrual (remaining days) time of the menstrual cycle

This is clearly depicted in Fig. 5.2.1, based on data from 5,546 women who reported symptoms on a retrospective questionnaire (5). Even allowing for some elevation in reporting given the retrospective nature of the study, a clear increase in food craving in the premenstrual phase (compared with post-menstrual) is evident. This pattern is true for severe and moderate food cravings. Interestingly, for mild food cravings, the opposite pattern is observed. This suggests that food cravings are more frequent and more severe premenstrually, but they can also occur in a much weaker form at other points in the menstrual cycle in the same women.

Food cravings may be responsible for the premenstrual increase in energy intake that has been described in females. In humans, a distinct pattern of fluctuation in food intake during the menstrual cycle has been observed. Generally, energy intake is higher in the postovulatory or premenstrual/luteal phase of the cycle than in the preovulatory or follicular phase. This pattern of energy intake is also observed in other mammals. Of 30 human studies, reviewed by Dye and Blundell (2), 25 studies reported significantly higher luteal energy intake than follicular intake. The remainder show no significant effects of menstrual cycle phase. Ovulation represents the nadir of food intake during the menstrual cycle (9). It is not clear whether premenstrual increases in energy intake result from food cravings, but fewer food cravings are reported around the time of ovulation.

5.2.3 Nature of Cyclical Food Cravings

The clear pattern of cyclical food craving suggests a robust phenomenon. It gives rise to the question of whether particular foods or macronutrients are frequent targets for premenstrual cravings. It is clear from the previous chapters that chocolate is the most commonly reported food craving, particularly amongst women (10,13,28).

Some studies with a menstrual cycle focus report a large number of premenstrual cravings of all types (3,12,24) while others note increased craving for specific foods, most notably chocolate or sweet foods (13,18,22,27). One possible factor in explaining this discrepancy may be the specificity of the self-report measure. Frequently used menstrual cycle symptom questionnaires e.g. Moos' Menstrual Distress Questionnaire (MDQ) (29) include "food craving" as a single item and do not differentiate the types of food craved (3,25). Retrospective and prospective studies that have examined cravings for specific foods or food types confirm the high incidence of premenstrual cravings for chocolate and other sweet foods (8,19), although some studies appear to have asked only about sweet foods (16,18).

The nature of the foods craved does not appear to vary as a function of phase of menstrual cycle (8,30). Forty-five per cent of the young women in Pelchat's study (30) reported cravings related to the menstrual cycle, the vast majority in the luteal phase. However, 74% of these women also experienced cravings at other times, independent of their cycle. In this and Hill and Heaton-Brown's study (8), the type of foods craved in relation to the cycle did not differ from foods craved independently. Again, chocolate and sweet foods were predominant.

Very few studies have actually considered whether the cravings reported are indulged. One issue here is whether the subjects have free access to a choice of foods. In some studies, e.g. Tomelleri and Grunewald (27) and Manocha et al. (31), participants were college students living in accommodation where they were catered for and access may have been restricted. In Morton et al.'s (17) study of female prison and reformatory inmates, free access to such foods was even less likely. Jas (32) found that, although women reported craving chocolate premenstrually, they did not eat more chocolate at this time. Similarly, Gendall et al. (7) commented that "anything sweet" could be substituted for a specific food, suggesting that cravings are for a type of food rather than a specific item, and chocolate may typify that food.

Consumption of foods craved might be reflected by an increase in energy intake premenstrually. Furthermore, if specific foods are craved, there should be an increase in the percentage of energy provided from the macronutrient/s in the foods craved. A laboratory-based study using a between-subjects design to compare pre- and postmenstrual groups found that the increased energy intake of the premenstrual group was due to an increased consumption of high fat, high CHO and low-fat, low-CHO foods

(33). Patterns of macronutrient intake in the same women during the menstrual cycle are less consistent than for energy intake (1,2). Dye and Blundell (2) calculated the average macronutrient intake in the follicular and luteal phases of the menstrual cycle examined in 13 studies that provided sufficient details. Two studies showed significantly increased intake from carbohydrate in the luteal phase (4,34), with a concomitant significant decrease in fat intake. Three studies demonstrated that percentage energy from fat increased significantly in the luteal phase (23,35,36). Usually, the proportion of energy consumed from protein is relatively stable and it is the proportions of energy from fat and carbohydrate that vary. In this respect, Gallant's study (37) is unusual as it also documents a significant increase in the proportion of energy from protein. The macronutrient composition of the most craved food, chocolate, is approximately equal proportions of fat and carbohydrate with a much smaller protein content. Indulging a craving for chocolate should not increase the proportion of energy from a particular macronutrient. Therefore, although the nature of premenstrual food cravings is clear, it is difficult to attribute the increased energy intake premenstrually to the selective consumption of particular macronutrients. This has clear implications for some of the mechanisms suggested to be responsible for food cravings (see below).

5.2.4   Relationship of Food Craving to other Menstrual Cycle Symptoms

Food craving is one of a catalogue of symptoms that occur premenstrually. Therefore, one might expect it to be related in some way to other common menstrual cycle symptoms. If a relationship exists between food cravings and other menstrual cycle symptoms, this might have implications for the aetiology of premenstrual food cravings. For instance, Hill and Heaton-Brown (8) reported correlations between food craving and the number of other premenstrual symptoms, but no association between premenstrual symptom frequency and food craving. They did not examine the nature of the symptoms other than food craving reported premenstrually. Bancroft *et al.*

(3) found no association between physical symptoms, e.g. breast tenderness and food craving.

Furthermore, factor analytical studies have shown that food cravings do not load on any common factors and tend to remain as a single item on menstrual symptom checklists (25,29,38-41). Of 65 questionnaires designed to measure premenstrual symptoms, 28 include food craving as an item (42).

This supports the view that food cravings are independent of other symptoms, at least in the young and often asymptomatic samples that have been used to develop such scales. One problem in the assessment of food cravings and other menstrual cycle symptoms is that cravings are short-lived transient events and symptom checklists are often global, requiring reflection on occurrence of craving and other symptoms (not necessarily closely linked in time) during the course of the day, week or even month. Thus scales often do not have sufficient resolution to detect a relationship between food cravings and other symptoms.

The temporal link between the occurrence of food cravings and other symptoms premenstrually has been used to imply a common aetiology. Attention has been focused on those symptoms considered most likely to result in women complaining of premenstrual syndrome, namely affective symptoms, particularly depression (14).

5.2.5   Mood and Food Craving

Some associations of food craving and negative affect, mood change or depression in the premenstrual phase have been reported (5,11,15,18,21,23,43). However, a number of other studies, whilst noting the coexistence of food craving and depression, have indicated that they show a relative independence (12,15,25,44). Two studies have also shown that menstrual cycle related food craving can occur in the absence of depression (5,21). In both instances, however, food craving without depression was found in a much smaller proportion of women than showed food craving and depression, and severity ratings in the former group were much lower. Dye *et al.* (5) have demonstrated a relationship between depression rating and food craving rating during each phase of the menstrual cycle for a large sample of unselected women (n=5,546). They noted that food craving was more severe the more severe the rating of depression. Furthermore, the interrelationship between food craving and depression was maintained at all phases of the menstrual cycle. It is likely that some of the women in this sample were suffering from PMS and this may have exaggerated the strength of the relationship observed. However, taken together, there are indications that depression and food cravings may coexist premenstrually (3).

Given the effects of food on mood (45-48) and the well-documented premenstrual incidence of mood change and/or depression, a relationship between food craving and mood or depression seems logical. This relationship may result in the selection of foods that might ameliorate poor mood for reasons discussed below (49,50).

Using measures temporally linked to the occurrence of craving intake, Jas and Rogers (33) observed a positive relationship between intake of sweet foods and negative affect only in postmenstrual women and only following food consumption. In their premenstrual group, food intake and food choice were largely unrelated to mood. Similarly Hill and Heaton-Brown (8) did not find changes in mood across the experience of a food craving to be stronger premenstrually than during other phases of the menstrual cycle.

These data suggest only a weak relationship between cyclical food craving and mood, which may be produced by their co-incidence premenstrually. The studies considered above have tended to use samples of young, healthy women (often students) who do not tend to complain of more than mild cyclical symptoms. Thus the co-incidence of food cravings and depression may be more pronounced and therefore more easily detected in women who suffer higher levels of premenstrual symptomatology.

5.2.6   What is the Premenstrual Syndrome?

Premenstrual syndrome is a collection of behavioural, somatic and physical symptoms, which occur in the 7-10 days prior to the onset of menstruation and which is relieved at or shortly after commencement of menstrual flow, and is also known as late luteal phase dysphoric disorder - LLPDD (51). Although a large range of symptoms have been associated with PMS, the more common symptoms that can be said to characterise the syndrome include depression, irritability, mood swings, water-retention-based symptoms such as breast tenderness and bloating, changes in appetite and food cravings. These symptoms can be measured using subjective rating scales. To be clinically significant, it is generally accepted that the symptoms of PMS that a sufferer experiences must endure consistently, at a severe level, for at least six cycles (52). A number of assertions have been made about the relationship between the existence of this affective syndrome and food cravings.

5.2.7   Food Cravings and PMS

Increases in appetite and/or food cravings are considered characteristic of PMS (52). A frequent dilemma that arises in studies of PMS is whether PMS is an extreme of the normal experience of the menstrual cycle or is a qualitatively different phenomenon (see reference 53 for a general discussion of this issue). In relation to food cravings, the former view would imply that PMS sufferers experience similar temporal fluctuations in cravings to "normal" women but at a greater intensity. This tendency for increased food craving in the premenstrual phase has been observed in varied samples of women (e.g. with and without PMS and/or premenstrual depression), suggesting that the experience of PMS sufferers is more severe but not necessarily qualitatively different from that of normal women.

Retrospective and prospective studies find a premenstrual increase in food cravings and other symptoms in women with PMS (5,15,54). When comparison groups of women without PMS have been included, women with PMS show food cravings of greater severity. Moreover, in two prospective studies only in the PMS sufferers, food cravings were correlated with mood (21,55). Dye *et al.* (5) examined food cravings in 919 women, selected on the basis of their clear patterns of depression rating during three menstrual cycle phases. The pattern of craving shown by those women who reported severe or very severe depression only in the premenstrual phase (a feature that characterises PMS) confirms the relationship between food craving and depression. The food cravings of this PMS group were identical to those of the "chronic depressed" group when their depression ratings were the same, but the level of craving fell to that of the non-depressed group when depression also fell. This clearly suggests that these menstrual cycle related symptoms are not independent in women with PMS.

Diagnosis of PMS is clearly an important issue and premenstrual food craving is often a criterion for a positive diagnosis. Thus one might expect that cyclical food cravings would invariably be shown in all women with PMS. However, in Michener et al.'s (56) study, only 76% of the 71 women in the sample displayed cyclical food cravings.

It is worth considering closely whether the craved foods belong to any particular nutrient category. This is important because of the known effects of food on mood and the well-documented incidence of mood change (particularly depression) in the premenstrual phase, especially in PMS sufferers. Consequently, a relationship between food craving (possibly for carbohydrate-rich foods) and depression could be significant in women with PMS. The logic of this relationship is that women crave those particular foods whose consumption would ameliorate the depression through physiological or psychological mechanisms, as discussed in section 4.2 and 5.2.12.

In women with PMS, and "normal" women, the most common premenstrual food cravings are for chocolate and non-chocolate sweets (26,55-58). However, none of these studies has included questions on other non-sweet foods. Evans et al. (58) carefully screened participants for PMS and included food selection and consumption as well as a food desirability measure designed to tap food cravings to a large range of foods. Women with PMS showed greater desires for both savoury and sweet foods high in CHO and fat premenstrually. Fat in particular was the common feature of the foods craved in the luteal phase. The authors point out that premenstrual lunch consumption was not increased, indicating that craving does not necessarily equate with consumption. Another important point is the macronutrient composition of the most frequently craved food in all studies, chocolate. Chocolate is a high-fat, high-carbohydrate food, which has the majority of its metabolisable energy in the form of fat. In sum, there does not seem to be a difference in the foods that are craved (as opposed to frequency or severity) by PMS or non-PMS subjects.

5.2.8   Dietary Restraint, Dieting and PMS: Effects on Cyclical Food Craving

Much research reports that there is no relationship between food cravings and dietary restraint (9,59), or between dieting and craving (12,60). In contrast, Pelchat (30) found that dieters were more likely than non-dieters to report at least one craving. However, dieting and dietary restraint are not synonymous and studies differ in their assessment of restraint, dieting and cravings (for a general discussion see section 7.1).

Very few studies have examined dietary restraint or dieting in relation to the menstrual cycle. Given the well-documented physical and affective changes that accompany the menstrual cycle, in particular in women with PMS (15,53), there are good reasons to suggest that high levels of dietary restraint may exacerbate negative affect and food craving.

A retrospective questionnaire study found that high restraint, dieting and PMS interacted to exacerbate profiles of symptoms relating to weight gain, water retention and food craving (61,62). Food craving was most severe premenstrually in all groups, and levels of reporting were most extreme in dieters and highly restrained women with PMS. However, two other studies found no support for an interaction between the menstrual cycle and dietary restraint but failed to include women with PMS in their samples (12,32).

In a prospective study, Dye and Hill (62) found that the combination of high restraint and PMS was associated with heightened perception of weight gain and negative mood premenstrually. Negative mood is a factor that precipitates loss of motivation to limit food intake and avoid forbidden foods (49). Indeed, induction of negative mood can trigger overeating in dieters and highly restrained individuals (63-65). Cravings can also trigger binge eating (66) and these are also most prominent premenstrually, when mood is likely to be more negative.

Furthermore, measures of dietary restraint tend to identify successful restrained eaters or dieters (67). Less successful dieters show eating patterns more similar to those of bulimics (68). Consistent with this, Dye and Hill (62) have shown that food intake in highly restrained but not low restrained women decreases around menstruation. They suggest that this may be an attempt to re-establish dietary restraint after the premenstrual phase, where food cravings and bloating due to water retention function to exacerbate feelings of weight gain.

Thus the role of dietary restraint and dieting in the temporal nature of premenstrual cravings remains to be clarified. It is not clear whether it is more difficult to maintain dietary restraint premenstrually or whether highly restrained women are more or less susceptible to premenstrual food cravings and/or PMS. This is likely to be a fruitful avenue for future research, given the high prevalence of restrained eating as a lifestyle for many women and the potentially negative effects of PMS on the maintenance of dietary control.

5.2.9   Potential Mechanisms in Menstrual Cycle Mediated Food Craving

A range of hypotheses has been suggested to account for the cyclical fluctuations in food craving observed in women with and without PMS or depression. These include the role of hormones, serotonin, endogenous opioids and psychological factors. Each perspective as it relates to cyclical cravings is reviewed briefly below although a number are considered in more detail in chapters (2,3 and 4).

5.2.10   Ovarian Hormones and Food Craving

Weingarten and Elston (10) discuss theories of food craving on the basis of abstinence or expectation models used in addiction. Abstinence theories would suggest that food cravings occur as the result of a biological need. In relation to the menstrual cycle, examples of biological need that have been suggested to produce urges to eat a specific food or food type include hypoglycaemia and low red cell magnesium (69). More typically, the view that food cravings arise as a response to the premenstrual fall in the ovarian steroids oestrogen and progesterone has been propounded (1,2). This is based primarily on observations from animal studies, which have demonstrated that oestradiol inhibits food intake and abolishes cyclical feeding rhythms (70). In humans, the direct effects of ovarian steroids on food craving are less easy to substantiate, and much evidence points to the facilitating rather than causal effects of low hormone levels premenstrually. For instance, a prospective diary study demonstrated that low levels of progesterone, which normally occur premenstrually, are not causally related to chocolate craving (71).

Another recent suggestion is that food cravings arise as a function of the relationship between oestrogen and leptin (72). Levels of leptin are lower in the follicular phase when food cravings are less common. Low leptin levels would suggest that it is less likely that food cravings would occur and this may also relate to higher levels of serotonin and oestrogen in the follicular phase. This theory remains to be tested. Recent reports have suggested a lack of association between plasma leptin and food intake during the cycle (73), although cravings were not differentiated in this study.

During the luteal phase of the menstrual cycle, progesterone rises initially and then falls rapidly (luteolysis) towards the onset of menstruation (74). Studies often relate increased premenstrual food cravings to either high (75-78) or low (71) levels of progesterone in the second half of the cycle, without describing the exact days of cycle measured (the closer to menstruation, the lower levels of progesterone are likely to be) or, indeed, confirming the supposed hormone level by radioimmunoassay. If ovarian hormones were responsible for food cravings, one would expect women with premenstrual syndrome who report more severe food cravings to show a concomitant increase or decrease in those ovarian steroids responsible for food cravings. However, despite a wealth of studies, no differences have been found in levels of ovarian steriods in women with and without PMS (53).

The role of ovarian hormones in producing cyclical food cravings is therefore unclear. It is unlikely to be a direct effect and might function by mediating other neurochemicals involved in the control of eating, e.g. serotonin, or in reward mechanisms, e.g. endogenous opioid peptides. Alternatively, psychological mechanisms may be more influential in determining the timing and nature of food cravings during the menstrual cycle.

5.2.11 Endogenous Opioid Peptides (EOP) and Cyclical Food Craving

It has been proposed that changes in food preferences and cravings during the menstrual cycle are controlled by endogenous opioid peptides (EOP) (76) (see section 2.2). EOPs modulate the palatability and reward value of food and are inhibited by oestrogen. EOPs have been shown to produce a selective increase in fat intake, which has been argued to explain the increased intake of fat in the premenstrual phase observed in some studies (1,79). Mercer and Holder (75) propose that EOP activity is associated with increased premenstrual food cravings and lowered pain tolerance. Foods craved are those that have rewarding, analgesic or stress-relieving effects, such as chocolate and candy, but also milk and alcohol (80,81). Consumption of these foods produces short-term increases in brain opioid activity. Few studies have examined mood in close proximity to the ingestion of craved foods, i.e. within one hour. Two studies have demonstrated a post-consumption increase in hedonic tone (8,55). However, in Hill and Heaton-Brown's study (8) the effect was observable throughout the cycle, while in Wurtman *et al.*'s study (55), it was confined to the premenstrual phase. Wurtman's study also reported increased cravings for CHO, whereas the EOP theory would suggest the cravings should be for high-fat foods.

Therefore, while there is good evidence that EOPs mediate hedonic responses to food, it has not been convincingly demonstrated that EOP levels vary across the menstrual cycle or that fluctuations in EOP differ in women with PMS, who are more vulnerable to stress and cravings premenstrually (44,82). Furthermore, the foods ingested during cravings "... are not just palatable, sweet, high fat foods but foods that are perceived to have a "special" role in our diet." (42).

5.2.12 Serotonin and Cyclical Food Craving

Serotonin has been implicated as the mediating factor in the relationship between mood and appetite (50). This hypothesis is based on the evidence that low levels of serotonin induce dysphoric mood. It is argued that craving for particular food products (containing carbohydrates) occurs in order to raise the levels of serotonin in the brain, and it has been suggested that this may be an adaptive mechanism to compensate for a relative lack of 5-HT premenstrually. Therefore, eating CHOs serves as a form of self-medication to raise mood. The mechanisms through which the carbohydrate content of the diet influences the uptake of tryptophan into the brain and in turn increases the synthesis of serotonin has been well described (83).

It has been demonstrated (55) that the deliberate administration of carbohydrate can relieve premenstrual depression. The consumption of a CHO-rich, protein-poor evening rest meal improved mood in PMS sufferers in the late luteal phase but had no effect on mood in the follicular phase or in non-symptomatic control subjects. This is consistent with a carbohydrate-induced increase in serotonin occurring during the premenstruum. There is little evidence for a selective craving for carbohydrate foods premenstrually or for a preferential intake of carbohydrate. Indeed, high-CHO foods were often also high in fat and low in protein. In real-life situations, it is difficult to select foods that will have an effect, however modest, on brain serotoninergic activity. In addition, the timescale of physiological changes produced after manipulations designed to increase availability of tryptophan is too slow to account for the effects on mood observed shortly after eating (85). Consequently, the idea that individuals attempt to medicate themselves by eating carbohydrate is not yet substantiated. However, there are other reasons to consider a role for serotonin in premenstrual food craving.

Ovarian steroids may have a modulating role in the serotonergic system, affecting metabolism, activity and receptors (51,85). The concentration of serotonin (V_{max}) is lowest premenstrually (86,87). There is also evidence that serotonin levels in whole-blood, plasma and platelet uptake and content are lower premenstrually in women with PMS (88,89). Similar fluctuations have been observed in melatonin, which is synthesised from serotonin (90).

Neuroendocrine challenge tests have been used to measure changes in 5-HT function. Normally, infusion of the 5-HT precursor L-tryptophan (or fenfluramine) produces an increase in plasma prolactin. In women with

PMS, prolactin responses to a neuroendocrine challenge test are blunted premenstrually (91). The neuroendocrine response can be affected by dieting in women (92), a factor not controlled for in these studies.

Thus studies in women with PMS show a consistent trend toward decreased levels of serotonin premenstrually (51). Serotonin is also implicated in the aetiology of depression, and neuroendocrine findings in women are consistent with a higher incidence of depression in women than in men (93). However, we cannot infer that peripheral serotonin levels predict central levels in humans, although such a relationship has been demonstrated in non-human primates (94).

The effects of lowered serotonin are most likely to be observed in those behaviours most closely regulated by the neurotransmitter. It can be suggested that the fluctuation in cravings, appetite and energy intake observed in women during the menstrual cycle reflect cyclical rhythms in serotonin, which may be accompanied by affective symptoms in women with PMS but which are present to a lesser degree (or are better tolerated) in women without PMS. Serotonin has been shown to influence both satiation (meal size) and satiety (post-meal inhibition) (95). During the premenstrual phase, serotonin activity is relatively low, and therefore there is likely to be relatively weaker control over appetite. Indeed, it can be deduced that altered activity at particular serotonin receptors (5-HT_{1B} and 5-HT_{2C}) modulates the ability to resist risk factors for overeating and a positive energy balance (96). Consequently, Dye and Blundell (2) argue that, during the premenstrual phase, individuals will be more susceptible to many stimuli (internal and environmental) that facilitate eating and elicit food craving. Thus, the premenstrual phase of the menstrual cycle can be considered a time when women are especially vulnerable to craving, and also to depression (due to low serotonin activity). This, however, does not preclude the effect of psychological processes, which may mediate or even override biochemical fluctuations in cravings. For instance, significant cyclical variations in food intake have not been observed in highly restrained women, who exert strong cognitive control over their eating behaviour (62,97).

5.2.13   Psychological Processes in Cyclical Food Craving

It is clear that cyclical food cravings do not arise because of nutritional need. Indeed, all of the studies to date have examined well-nourished, healthy females. In addition, dietary restraint *per se* does not increase the incidence of food craving independent of menstrual cycle phase (9,10,59,98). Psychological processes may provide a partial explanation for premenstrual food cravings, particularly when we consider that more than 50% of cravings are for chocolate (10,13,56).

Rozin and colleagues (56,71,99) have proposed that a desire for the sensory properties of chocolate is the primary motivation in chocolate craving. Compatible with this is the view that eating "pleasant-tasting food" may elevate mood without a biological action of that food (49). The mood-elevating effects of chocolate, candy, milk and alcohol, by women premenstrually may be due to the perception of those foods as "special" and their psychologically rewarding taste and sensory qualities.

Another psychological process that has been demonstrated to operate, sometimes quite powerfully, in relation to the menstrual cycle is attribution. Phase of menstrual cycle has served as a source of biological attribution to explain subjective variations in cognitive performance, behaviour or affective state with effects most pronounced premenstrually (100-102). Recently, it has been suggested that such attributional processes may operate in a similar way to account for premenstrual food cravings (49). For example, Rogers and Jas (103) observed that women who tasted foods premenstrually were not distressed by their intake while postmenstrual women were. They suggest that the availability of a biological attribution "being premenstrual" was effective in both allowing increased consumption and negating any feelings of guilt in doing so.

The temporal relationship between food cravings and the menstrual cycle is not directly addressed by purely psychological theories, unless one considers that food cravings arise in relation to negative affect, which could have biological as well as psychological origins. Alternatively, fluctuations in hormones or neurochemicals such as 5HT or EOPs could lower the threshold for food cravings, which might then be triggered by exposure to the sensory features of foods (30).

5.2.14   Conclusions

During the premenstrual phase, food cravings are increased in frequency and intensity. Food craving appears to be more severe in women with PMS. Food craving is positively related to depression during the menstrual cycle. Food craving is more intense when depression is severe, and depression is greater during the premenstrual phase. Food craving is linked to depression in women with PMS. Possible neurochemical explanations of menstrual cycle related cravings have included ovarian hormones (76-78,104,105), endogenous opioids (75) and serotonin (2,50). Psychological and sensory factors have been used to account for cyclical cravings, particularly in relation to chocolate (30,49,71). These theories together suggest that it is likely that the temporal pattern of food cravings during the menstrual cycle results from an interaction of fluctuations in neurochemistry and psychological states and processes that make some women more susceptible to food cravings, e.g. PMS. It is unlikely, based on the evidence presented here, that these cravings serve to redress any kind of biological imbalance since the targets of premenstrual cravings are no different from those experienced at other points in the menstrual cycle. Indeed, the societal view of certain foods as "special treats" and the orosensory properties of these foods, particularly chocolate, may go a long way to explain the pole position of chocolate in the hit list of cravings.

5.2.15   References

1.   Buffenstein R., Poppitt S.D., McDevitt R.M., Prentice A.M. Food intake and the menstrual cycle: a retrospective analysis with implications for appetite research. *Physiology and Behaviour*, 1995, 58(6), 1067-77.

2.   Dye L., Blundell J.E. Menstrual cycle and appetite control: implications for weight regulation. *Human Reproduction*, 1997, 12(6), 1142-51.

3.   Bancroft J., Cook A., Williamson L. Food craving, mood and the menstrual cycle. *Psychological Medicine*, 1988, 18, 855-60.

4.   Brzezinski A.A., Wurtman J.J., Wurtman R.J., Gleason R., Greenfield J., Nader T. d-Fenfluramine suppresses the increased calorie and carbohydrate intakes and improves the mood of women with premenstrual depression. *Obstetrics and Gynecology*, 1990, 76, 296-301.

5.   Dye L., Warner P., Bancroft J. Food craving during the menstrual cycle and its relationship to stress, happiness of relationship and depression. *Journal of Affective Disorders*, 1995, 34, 157-64.

6.   Kozlowski L.T., Williamson D.A. Use and misuse of the concept of craving by alcohol, tobacco and drug researchers. *British Journal of Addiction*, 1987, 82, 31-6.

7.   Gendall K.A., Joyce P.R., Sullivan P.F. Impact of definition on prevalence of food cravings in a sample of young women. *Appetite*, 1997, 28, 63-72.

8.   Hill A.J., Heaton-Brown L. The experience of food craving: a prospective investigation in healthy women. *Journal of Psychosomatic Research*, 1994, 38, 801-14.

9.   Rodin J., Mancuso J., Granger J., Nelbach E. Food cravings in relation to Body Mass Index, restraint and estradiol levels: A repeated measures study in healthy women. *Appetite*, 1991, 17, 177-85.

10.   Weingarten H.P., Elston D. Food cravings in a college population. *Appetite*, 1991, 17, 167-75.

11.   Lee K.A., Rittenhouse C.A. Prevalence of perimenstrual symptoms in employed women. *Women and Health*, 1991, 17 No.3, 17-32.

12.   Cohen I.T., Sherwin B.B., Fleming A.S. Food cravings, mood and the menstrual cycle. *Hormones and Behavior*, 1987, 21, 457-70.

13.   Rozin P., Levine E., Stoess C. Chocolate craving and liking. *Appetite*, 1991, 17, 199-212.

14.   Warner P., Bancroft J. Factors related to self-reporting of the premenstrual syndrome. *British Journal of Psychiatry*, 1990, 157, 249-60.

15.   Bancroft J., Williamson L., Warner P., Rennie D., Smith S. Perimenstrual complaints in women complaining of PMS, menorrhagia and dysmenorrhea: towards a dismantling of the premenstrual syndrome. *Psychosomatic Medicine*, 1993, 55, 133-45.

16. Hargrove J.T., Abraham G.E. The incidence of premenstrual tension in a gynaecologic clinic. *Journal of Reproductive Medicine*, 1982, 27, 721-4.

17. Morton J.H., Additon H., Addison R.G., Hunt L., Sullivan J.J. A clinical study of premenstrual tension. *American Journal of Obstetrics and Gynecology*, 1953, 65, 1182-91.

18. Smith S.L., Sauder C. Food cravings, depression and premenstrual problems. *Psychosomatic Medicine*, 1969, 31, 281-7.

19. Warner P., Bancroft J. Mood, sexuality, oral contraceptives and the menstrual cycle. *Journal of Psychosomatic Research*, 1988, 32 No. 4/5, 417-27.

20. Warner P., Bancroft J., Dixson A., Hampson M. The relationship between perimenstrual depressive mood and depressive illness. *Journal of Affective Disorders*, 1991, 23, 9-23.

21. Both-Orthman B., Rubinow D.R., Hoban M.C., Malley J., Grover G.N. Menstrual cycle phase-related changes in appetite in patients with premenstrual syndrome and in control subjects. *American Journal of Psychiatry*, 1988, 145, 628-31.

22. Bowen D.J., Grunberg N.E. Variations in food preference and consumption across the menstrual cycle. *Physiology and Behaviour*, 1990, 47, 287-91.

23. Gallant S.J., Hamilton J.A., Popiel D.A., Morokoff P.J., Chakraborty P.K. Daily moods and symptoms – effects of awareness of study focus, gender menstrual cycle phase and day of week. *Health Psychology*, 1991, 10(3), 180-9.

24. Metcalf M.G., Livesey J.H., Hudson S.M., Wells E.J. The premenstrual syndrome: moods, headaches and physical symptoms in 133 menstrual cycles. *Journal of Psychosomatic Obstetrics and Gynaecology*, 1988, 8, 31-43.

25. Schechter D., Bachmann G.A., Vaitukaitis J., Phillips D., Saperstein D. Perimenstrual symptoms: time course of symptom intensity in relation to endocrinologically defined segments of the menstrual cycle. *Psychosomatic Medicine*, 1989, 51, 173-94.

26. Bancroft J., Rennie D. The impact of oral contraceptives on the experience of perimenstrual mood, clumsiness, food craving and other symptoms. *Journal of Psychosomatic Research*, 1993, 37, 195-202.

27.   Tomelleri R., Grunewald K.K. Menstrual cycle and food cravings in young college women. *Journal of the American Dietetic Association*, 1987, 87, No.3, 311-5.

28.   Macdiarmid J.I., Hetherington M.M. Mood modulation by food: An exploration of affect and cravings in 'chocolate addicts'. *British Journal of Clinical Psychology*, 1995, 34, 129-38.

29.   Moos R.H. *Menstrual Distress Questionnaire Manual*. Stanford, CA, Social Ecology Laboratory, Stanford University. 1977.

30.   Pelchat M.L. Food cravings in young and elderly adults. *Appetite*, 1997, 28, 103-13.

31.   Manocha S., Choudhuri G., Taylor B. A study of dietary intake in pre- and postmenstrual period. *Human Nutrition and Applied Nutrition*, 1986, 40A, 213-6.

32.   Jas P.E. *Changes in food intake and mood across the menstrual cycle.* Unpublished PhD Thesis, University of Reading, UK. 1996.

33.   Jas P.E., Rogers P.J. *Interrelationships between Mood and Eating Behaviour during the Menstrual Cycle.* Poster presented at the British Psychological Society Annual Conference, Blackpool, UK. 1993.

34.   Dalvit-McPhillips S.P. The effect of the human menstrual cycle on nutrient intake. *Physiology and Behavior*, 1983, 31(2), 209-12.

35.   Johnson W.G., Corrigan S.A., Lemmon C.R., Bergeron K.B., Crusco A.H. Energy regulation over the menstrual cycle. *Physiology and Behavior*, 1994, 56, 523-7.

36.   Tarasuk V., Beaton G.H. Menstrual cycle patterns in energy and macronutrient intake. *American Journal of Clinical Nutrition*, 1991, 53, 442-7.

37.   Gallant M.P., Bowering J., Short S.H., Turkki P.R., Badawy S. Pyridoxine and magnesium status of women with premenstrual syndrome. *Nutrition Research*, 1987, 7, 243-52.

38.   Richardson J.T.R. The menstrual cycle, cognition and paramenstrual symptomatology, in *Cognition and the Menstrual Cycle*. Ed. Richardson J.T.E. New York, Springer. 1992, 1-38.

39. York R., Freeman E., Lowery B., Strauss J.F. Characteristics of premenstrual syndrome. *Obstetrics and Gynecology*, 1989, 73, 601-5.

40. Endicott J., Nee J., Cohen J., Halbreich U. Premenstrual changes: patterns and correlates of daily ratings. *Journal of Affective Disorders*, 1986, 10, 127-35.

41. Freeman E.W., DeRubeis R.J., Rickels K. Reliability and validity of a daily diary for premenstrual syndrome. *Psychiatric Research*, 1996, 65, 97-106.

42. Budeiri D.J., Wan Po A.L., Dornan J.C. Clinical trials of treatments of premenstrual syndrome: entry criteria and scales for measuring treatment outcomes. *British Journal of Obstetrics and Gynaecology*, 1994, 101, 689-95.

43. Graham C.A., Sherwin B.B. The relationship between retrospective premenstrual symptom reporting and present oral contraceptive use. *Journal of Psychosomatic Research*, 1987, 31, 45-53.

44. Bancroft J. The premenstrual syndrome – a reappraisal of the concept and the evidence. *Psychological Medicine*, 1993, Monograph Supplement 24.

45. Rogers P.J., Edwards S., Green M.W., Jas P. Nutritional influences on mood and cognitive performance: the menstrual cycle, caffeine and dieting. *Proceedings of the Nutrition Society*, 1992, 51, 343-51.

46. Spring B. Dietary selection, snacks and overeating in individuals characterised by carbohydrate preference and dysphoric mood. *Current Therapeutics Supplement*, 1990, 22-5.

47. Wurtman J.J. Carbohydrate craving, mood changes and obesity. *Journal of Clinical Psychiatry*, 1988, 49(8) Suppl., 37-9.

48. Wurtman J.J. Carbohydrate craving: Relationship between carbohydrate intake and disorders of mood. *Drugs*, 1990, 39 (Supp 3), 49-52.

49. Rogers P.J., Smit H.J. Food craving and food "addiction": A critical review of the evidence from a biopsychosocial perspective. *Pharmacology, Biochemistry and Behavior*, 2000, 66(1), 3-14.

50. Wurtman J.J. Nutritional intervention in premenstrual syndrome, in *Modern Management of Premenstrual Syndrome*. Eds Smith S., Schiff I. New York, W.W. Norton & Co. 1993.

51. Severino S.K. A focus on 5-Hydroxytryptamine (serotonin) and psychopathology, in *Pre-menstrual Dysphorias; Myths and Realities*. Eds Gold J.H., Severino S.K. New York, American Psychiatric Association. 1994.

52. American Psychiatric Association (Editor). *Diagnostic and Statistical Manual of Mental Disorders, 4th edition*. Washington, DC, U.S. Department of Health and Human Services. 1994.

53. Walker A.E. *The Menstrual Cycle*. London, Routledge. 1997.

54. Metcalf M.G., Livesey J.H., Hudson S.M., Wells E.J. The premenstrual syndrome: moods, headaches and physical symptoms in 133 menstrual cycles. *Journal of Psychosomatic Obstetrics and Gynaecology*, 1988, 8, 31-43.

55. Wurtman J.J., Brzezinski A., Wurtman R.J., Laferrere B. Effect of nutrient intake on premenstrual depression. *American Journal of Obstetrics and Gynecology*, 1989, 161, 1228-34.

56. Michener W., Rozin P., Freeman E., Gale L. The role of low progesterone and tension as triggers of perimenstrual chocolate and sweets craving: some negative experimental evidence. *Physiology and Behavior*, 1999, 67, 417-20.

57. Brzezinski A.A., Wurtman J.J., Wurtman R.J., Gleason R., Greenfield J., Nader T. d-Fenfluramine suppresses the increased calorie and carbohydrate intakes and improves the mood of women with premenstrual depression. *Obstetrics and Gynecology*, 1990, 76, 296-301.

58. Evans S.M., Foltin R.W., Fischman M.W. Food "cravings" and the acute effects of alprazolam on food intake in women with premenstrual dysphoric disorder. *Appetite*, 1999, 32, 331-49.

59. Hill A.J., Weaver C.F.L., Blundell J.E. Food craving, dietary restraint and mood. *Appetite*, 1991, 17, 187-97.

60. Harvey J., Wing R.R., Mullen M. Effects on food craving of a very low calorie diet or a balanced, low calorie diet. *Appetite*, 1993, 21, 233-46.

61. Dye L. The Influence of the Menstrual Cycle on Eating Behaviour. *Proceedings of the British Psychological Society*, 2000, 8(2), 28.

62. Dye L., Hill A.J. Energy intake and menstrual cycle symptoms in high restraint women. *International Journal of Obesity*, 2000, 24 (Suppl.1), S403.

63.   Herman C.P. Restrained eating. *Psychiatric Clinics of North America*, 1978, 1, 593-607.

64.   Ruderman A.J. Dietary restraint: a theoretical and empirical review. *Psychological Bulletin*, 1985, 99, 247-62.

65.   Westenhoefer J., Broeckmann P., Munch A.K., Pudel V. Cognitive control of eating behaviour and the disinhibition effect. *Appetite*, 1994, 23, 27-41.

66.   Drewnowski A. Obesity and eating disorders: cognitive aspects of food preference and food aversion. *Bulletin of the Psychonomic Society*, 1991, 29, 261-4.

67.   Ogden J. The measurement of restraint – confounding success and failure? *International Journal of Eating Disorders*, 1993, 13, 69-76.

68.   Laessle R.G., Tuschl R.J., Kotthaus B.C., Pirke K.M. Behavioural and biological correlates of dietary restraint in normal life. *Appetite*, 1989, 12, 83-94.

69.   Abraham G.E. Nutritional factors in the etiology of premenstrual tension syndromes. *Journal of Reproductive Medicine*, 1984, 28, 446-64.

70.   Geary N. Estradiol and the control of eating. *Appetite*, 1997, 29, 386.

71.   Rozin P. Chocolate craving. *Appetite*, 1999, 33, 247.

72.   Mannucci E., Ognibene A., Becorpi A., Cremasco F., Pellegrini S., Ottanelli S., Rizzello S.M., Massi G., Messeri G., Rotella C.M. Relationship between leptin and oestrogens in healthy women. *European Journal of Endocrinology*, 1998, 139(2), 198-201.

73.   Paolisso G., Rizzo M.R., Mazziotti G., Rotondi M., Tagliamonte M.R., Varricchio G., Carella C., Varricchio M. Lack of association between changes in plasma leptin concentration and in food intake during the menstrual cycle. *European Journal of Clinical Investigation*, 1999, 29, 490-5.

74.   Johnson M.H., Everitt B.J. *Essential Reproduction*. 5th Edition. Oxford, Blackwell. 2000.

75.   Mercer M.E., Holder M.D. Food cravings, endogenous opioid peptides and food intake: a review. *Appetite*, 1997, 29, 325-52.

76.   Dalton K., Holton W.M. Diets of women with severe premenstrual syndrome and the effects of changing to a 3 hourly starch diet. *Stress Medicine*, 1992, 8, 61-5.

77. Geiselman P. Female sex hormones, specific macronutrients, taste and other oral responsivity in the control of appetite, food intake and body weight, in *Nutrition, Endocrinology and Disease*. Eds Bray G.A., Evans D.H. Baton Rouge, LSU Press. 1995, 204-14. 1998.

78. Geiselman P., Smith C.F., Wiiliamson D.A., Champagne C.M., Bray G.A., Ryan D.H. Perception of sweetness intensity determines women's hedonic and other perceptual responsiveness to chocolate food. *Appetite*, 1998, 31, 37-48.

79. Johnson W.G., Corrigan S.A., Lemmon C.R., Bergeron K.B., Crusco A.H. Energy regulation over the menstrual cycle. *Physiology and Behavior*, 1994, 56, 523-7.

80. Blass E.M. Opioids, sweets and a mechanism for positive affect: Broad motivational implications, in *Sweetness*. Ed. Dobbing J. Berlin, Springer-Verlag. 1987, 115-26.

81. Blass E.M., Hofmeyer L.B. Sucrose as an analgesic for newborn infants. *Pediatrics*, 1991, 87, 215-8.

82. Bancroft J. The menstrual cycle and the well-being of women. *Social Science and Medicine*, 1995, 41(6), 785-91.

83. Fernstrom J.D., Wurtman R.J. Brain serotonin content: Increase following ingestion of carbohydrate diet. *Science*, 1971, 174, 1023-5.

84. Young S.N., Smith S.E., Pihl R.O., Ervin F.R. Tryptophan depletion causes a rapid lowering of mood in normal males. *Psychopharmacology*, 1985, 87, 173-7.

85. Rapkin A. The role of serotonin in premenstrual syndrome. *Clinical Obstetrics Gynecology*, 1992, 35, 629-36.

86. Tam W.Y.K., Chan M.-Y., Lee P.H.K. The menstrual cycle and platelet 5-HT uptake. *Psychosomatic Medicine*, 1985, 47, 352-62.

87. Taylor D.L., Matthew R.J., Beng T.H., Weimann M.L. Serotonin levels and platelet uptake during premenstrual tension. *Neuropsychobiology*, 1984, 12, 16-8.

88. Ashby C.R. Jr., Carr L.A., Cook C.L., Steptoe M.H., Franks D.D. Alteration of platelet serotonergic mechanism and monoamine oxidase activity in premenstrual syndrome. *Biological Psychiatry*, 1988, 24, 225-33.

89. Ashby C.R. Jr., Carr L.A., Cook C.L., Steptoe M.M., Franks D.D. Inhibition of serotonin uptake in rat brain synaptosomes by plasma from patients with premenstrual syndrome. *Biological Psychiatry*, 1992, 31, 1169-71.

90. Rapkin A.J., Edelmuth E., Chang L.C., Reading A.E., McGuire M., Su T. Whole-blood serotonin in premenstrual syndrome. *Obstetrics Gynecology*, 1987, 70, 533-7.

91. Bancroft J., Cook A., Davidson D., Bennie J., Goodwin G. Blunting of neuroendocrine responses to infusion of L-tryptophan in women with perimenstrual mood change. *Psychological Medicine*, 1991, 21 (2), 305-12.

92. Parry B.L. Biological correlates of premenstrual complaints, in *Premenstrual Dysphorias; Myths and Realities*. Eds Gold J.H., Severino S.K. New York, American Psychiatric Association. 1994.

93. Halbreich U. Gonadol hormones and antihormones, serotonin and mood. *Psychopharmacology Bulletin*, 1990, 26, 291-5.

94. Goodwin G.M., Fairburn C.G., Cowen P.J. Dieting changes serotonergic function in women, not men: implications for the etiology of anorexia nervosa? *Psychological Medicine*, 1987, 17, 839-42.

95. Meltzer H.Y. Role of serotonin in depression. *Annals of the New York Academy of Science*, 1990, 600, 486-99.

96. Raleigh M.J., McGuire M.T. Biosocial pharmacology. *McLean Hospital Journal*, 1980, 2, 73-86.

97. Blundell J.E. Serotonin and the biology of feeding. *American Journal of Clinical Nutrition*, 1992, 55, 1555-95.

98. Blundell J.E. Food intake and body weight regulation, in *Regulation of Body Weight: Biological and Behavioural Mechanisms*. Eds Bouchard C., Bray G. Chichester, John Wiley & Sons. 1996, 111-33.

99. Schweiger U., Tuschl R.J., Platte P., Broocks A., Laessle R.G., Pirke K.M. Everyday eating behaviour and menstrual function in young women. *Fertility Sterility*, 1992, 57, 771-5.

100. Hetherington M.M., Macdiarmid J.I. "Chocolate addiction": a preliminary study of its description and its relationship to problem eating. *Appetite*, 1993, 21, 233-46.

101. Michener W., Rozin P. Pharmacological versus sensory factors in the satiation of chocolate craving. *Physiology and Behavior*, 1994, 56, 419-22.

102. Rodin J. Menstruation, reattribution and competence. *Journal of Personality and Social Psychology*, 1976, 33, 345-53.

103. Rogers P.J., Jas P. Menstrual cycle effects on mood, eating and food choice. *Appetite*, 1994, 23, 289.

104. Koeske R.K.D., Koeske G.F. An attributional approach to moods and the menstrual cycle. *Journal of Personality and Social Psychology*, 1976, 31, 473-8.

105. Campos F., Thurow C. Attribution of moods and symptoms to the menstrual cycle. *Personality and Social Psychology Bulletin*, 1978, 4, 272-6.

106. Dalton K. *Premenstrual Syndrome and Progesterone Therapy*. London, Heinemann. 1984.

107. Dalton K. *Once a Month, 3rd Edition*. London, Fontana. 1984.

5.3. THE PHARMACOLOGICAL TREATMENT OF PREMENSTRUAL DYSPHORIC DISORDER: EFFECTS ON APPETITE AND FOOD CRAVINGS

Suzette M. Evans

5.3.1   Introduction

Numerous studies report a relationship between food cravings and the menstrual cycle in women, with the majority of studies showing increased food cravings premenstrually (1-4). The most commonly reported food craving, particularly in women, is for chocolate (3,5,6), although the specific food items craved, when assessed, have varied across studies (7). Similarly, with respect to food intake, the most reliable finding across 19 studies is that food intake is lower during the follicular (postmenstrual) phase compared with the luteal (premenstrual) phase (8). Thus, the premenstrual phase appears to be a time within the menstrual cycle when women are more vulnerable to increased food cravings, and food intake, as well as fluctuations in mood (9,10) (see section 5.2).

One group of women who reportedly experience significant alterations in mood and changes in appetite control across the menstrual cycle are women with premenstrual dysphoric disorder (PMDD). The increases in appetite, food intake and food cravings during the premenstrual phase in women with PMDD appear to be correlated with the premenstrual mood changes, primarily depression (10-14). The purpose of this chapter is to summarise the findings on the various pharmacological treatments of PMDD, specifically regarding how these treatments alter the symptoms of increased appetite and food craving. Before addressing the pharmacological treatment of PMDD, a formal definition of this disorder is warranted. PMDD is a relatively new category in the "Depressive Disorders Not Otherwise Specified" section of the Diagnostic and Statistical Manual of Mental Disorders, Fourth Edition (DSM-IV) (15). Table 5.3.I presents the diagnostic criteria for severe PMS, or premenstrual dysphoric disorder (PMDD). PMDD is characterised by a cluster of symptoms, including mood changes (especially depression, tension, anxiety, irritability, fatigue), physical symptoms, and changes in appetite, food intake and specific food cravings. These symptoms regularly occur for a week or more during the late luteal (premenstrual) phase, diminish with the onset of menses, and cease during the follicular or postmenstrual phase. While as many as 30% of women have clinically significant premenstrual mood changes, only 2-10% of women actually suffer from premenstrual symptoms to such a degree that it interferes with normal functioning, i.e. PMDD (16-18).

TABLE 5.3.I
Research criteria for premenstrual dysphoric disorder

A. In most menstrual cycles during the past year, five (or more) of the following symptoms were present for most of the time during the last week of the luteal phase, began to remit within a few days after the onset of the follicular phase, and were absent in the week postmenses, with at least one of the symptoms being (1), (2), (3), or (4):

(1) markedly depressed mood, feelings of hopelessness, or self-deprecating thoughts
(2) marked anxiety, tension, feelings of being "keyed up," or "on edge"
(3) marked affective lability (e.g. feeling suddenly sad or tearful or increased sensitivity to rejection)
(4) persistent and marked anger or irritability or increased interpersonal conflicts
(5) decreased interest in usual activities (e.g. work, school, friends, hobbies)
(6) subjective sense of difficulty in concentrating
(7) lethargy, easy fatiguability, or marked lack of energy
(8) marked change in appetite, overeating, or specific food cravings
(9) hypersomnia or insomnia
(10) a subjective sense of being overwhelmed or out of control
(11) other physical symptoms, such as breast tenderness or swelling, headaches, joint or muscle pain, a sensation of "bloating," weight gain

Note: In menstruating females, the luteal phase corresponds to the period between ovulation and the onset of menses, and the follicular phase begins with menses. In non-menstruating females, (e.g. those who have had a hysterectomy), the timing of luteal and follicular phases may require measurement of circulating reproductive hormones.

TABLE 5.3.I cont'd

B. The disturbance markedly interferes with work or school or with usual social activities and relationships with others (e.g. avoidance of social activities, decreased productivity and efficiency at work or school).

C. The disturbance is not merely an exacerbation of the symptoms of another disorder, such as major depressive disorder, panic disorder, dysthymic disorder, or a personality disorder (although it may be superimposed on any of these disorders).

D. Criteria A, B, and C must be confirmed by prospective daily ratings during at least two consecutive symptomatic cycles. (The diagnosis may be made provisionally prior to this confirmation.)

Reprinted with permission from the Diagnostic and Statistical Manual of Mental Disorders, Fourth Edition. Copyright 1994 American Psychiatric Association.

As shown in Table 5.3.I, PMDD is a heterogeneous disorder comprising a constellation of symptoms, including primarily affective symptoms, but also some somatic symptoms. Given the range of symptoms, it is not surprising that it has been difficult to identify effective pharmacological treatments for females suffering from severe premenstrual symptoms. Moreover, studies conducted prior to the establishment of DSM-III-R, and subsequently DSM-IV criteria for PMDD included women based only on retrospective self-reports of premenstrual symptoms, rather than prospective ratings. Further, these studies included individuals with different levels of symptom severity, and did not distinguish between women who complained of affective versus somatic symptoms.

5.3.2   Issues of Measurement

There has been a great deal of inconsistency with respect to the diagnosis of PMDD and the associated symptoms. The terminology has also been confusing, with studies referring to this disorder as premenstrual tension, premenstrual dysphoria, premenstrual syndrome (PMS), late luteal phase dysphoric disorder (LLPDD; DSM-IIIR), or premenstrual dysphoric disorder

(PMDD; DSM-IV). Many studies, particularly those conducted before the DSM-IIIR and DSM-IV research criteria were established for PMDD, did not use the rigorous standards of prospective daily ratings of symptoms for at least two menstrual cycles, but used only retrospective self-reports or simply self-diagnosis. In addition, some studies have focused primarily on the physical symptoms, whereas others have focused on specific mood symptoms. For instance, Wikander *et al.* (19) conducted a double-blind trial with the specific serotonin reuptake inhibitor (SSRI) citalopram in women with premenstrual dysphoria, but irritability and/or depressed mood were the only symptoms required for entry into the trial.

There has also been little standardisation in the instruments used to measure premenstrual symptoms across studies. Out of 350 clinical trials in a review article by Budeiri *et al.* (20), 65 different scales or questionnaires were used to assess premenstrual syndrome. Of those 65 questionnaires, 28 included food craving as a symptom and 26 included increased appetite as a symptom. In contrast, the most commonly cited symptoms among the 65 scales were irritability (44), headache/migraine (40), and depression (37). Examples of the most commonly used questionnaires in studies evaluating the pharmacological treatment of premenstrual symptoms include: The Daily Symptom Rating Scale (21), The Daily Rating Form (22), the Calendar of Premenstrual Experiences (COPE) (23), the Moos Menstrual Distress Questionnaire (24), the Penn Daily Rating Symptom Report (25), the Premenstrual Tension Self-Rating Scale (26), and visual analogue scales (VAS) (27).

The Daily Symptom Rating Scale (21) consists of 17 items rated on a 6-point scale, but none of the items relates to changes in food intake or appetite. The Daily Rating Form (22) consists of 24 items describing problems with mood, behaviour, and physical symptoms, including two food-related items, rated on a 6-point scale, from 1 ("not at all") to 6 ("extreme"), which is filled out prospectively. Item 8a asks about increased appetite and overeating and item 8b asks about cravings for specific foods. However, the typical measure used to determine symptom severity is the mean score of all 24 items. The Calendar of Premenstrual Experiences (COPE) (23) consists of 22 items (10 physical and 12 behavioural symptoms) rated on a 4-point scale. This questionnaire does include a question on food cravings and one on increased appetite, but it is generally scored using a total daily score, or as two subscores of physical symptoms (10 items) and behavioural symptoms (12 items). Moos Menstrual Distress Questionnaire Form T (24) consists of 47 symptoms that have been factor-analysed, resulting in eight symptom subgroups (pain, water retention, impaired concentration, behaviour change, negative affect, arousal, autonomic reactions, and control). The limitation of treatment studies using the Mental Distress Questionnaire is that changes in appetite and/or food cravings are not reflected. The Penn Daily Rating Symptom Report (25) consists of 17 physical and emotional symptoms rated on a 5-point scale. One of the items is "craving foods," although a total daily score is typically used. The Premenstrual Tension Self-Rating Scale (26) is simply a yes/no 36-item self-report questionnaire, although there are specific questions related to weight gain, increased desire for foods and overeating. Lastly, the VAS questions that Sundblad *et al.* (28) and others have used include the following six items: irritability, depressed mood, tension, increased appetite and/or carbohydrate craving, breast tenderness, and bloating.

Despite the fact that increases in appetite and increases in food cravings constitute one of the 11 diagnostic criteria for PMDD, at this time, treatment studies have not focused their attention on these symptoms. Even though a reasonable proportion of treatment studies administer a daily questionnaire that either asks about changes in appetite and/or changes in food cravings as a specific item (as described above), the vast majority of studies average the ratings across the range of symptoms to derive a composite or total score that is averaged to compare mean scores between the late luteal phase and the follicular phase. Thus, based on the author's extensive, but not exhaustive, review of the literature, exceptionally few studies actually provide adequate information to determine if the pharmacological intervention specifically improved increased appetite or food cravings. This was made clear in an excellent review paper on the pharmacological treatment of PMDD (29). The authors reported that, out of 104 double-blind studies, 55 (53%) reported an overall improvement in premenstrual symptoms with drug compared with placebo. However, only

19 studies (18%) assessed and reported on the specific symptom of changes in appetite; of those, a total of 6 studies actually showed a greater improvement on this measure following drug compared with placebo. Unfortunately, the lack of attention to appetite and food cravings in pharmacological treatment studies for PMDD has not improved since 1995. It appears that no pharmacological studies have been conducted to specifically treat the symptoms of increased appetite and food cravings in women with PMDD.

The lack of research in this area could be related to several factors. First, from a clinical perspective, it is far more important to try to find pharmacological interventions to treat the most frequent and impairing symptoms of PMDD. The DSM-IV criteria require at least one of the following symptoms: depressed mood, anxiety, affective lability or marked irritability. In fact, the most common symptoms reported by women seeking treatment for premenstrual symptoms are anxiety, depression and irritability (30). Thus, although a marked change in appetite, overeating, or specific food cravings (Table 5.3.I, item 8) is one of the symptoms for PMDD, this particular symptom is not a requirement for the diagnosis of PMDD. While this particular symptom may be present, it does not presumably pose sufficient distress to the individual to seek treatment.

5.3.3   Prevalence of Changes in Appetite or Food Cravings in Women with PMDD

The results of several pharmacological treatment studies in women prospectively diagnosed with premenstrual syndrome would suggest that increases in food cravings and appetite are not prominent premenstrual symptoms and are present in only a small subset of these women. For example, among 23 women prospectively diagnosed with premenstrual syndrome, only two reported cravings for sweets and one reported an increase in appetite (31). Similarly, in a subsequent study (32), out of 32 women, 5 reported cravings for sweets and one reported an increase in appetite. However, these findings were based solely on spontaneous reports obtained before treatment, whereas, during treatment, appetite and food cravings were not measured. In addition, a recent study comparing the effectiveness of the SSRI citalopram with placebo in women with severe irritability and/or depressed mood, reported that several items measured daily on the VAS, including "increased appetite and/or carbohydrate craving," were present only in a subpopulation of the 69 completers, rendering non-significant decreases for those treated with citalopram compared with placebo (19). In a study assessing the efficacy of alprazolam for premenstrual syndrome (33), 11 of 14 (78%) women reported moderate to severe cravings for sweets, while only 7 of 14 (50%) women reported moderate to severe increases in appetite during the luteal phase under non-medicated conditions. However, in another treatment study that used the six-item VAS (34), 59 out of 65 women (91%) reported increases in appetite and/or carbohydrate craving in their prospective ratings before treatment.

The findings described above bring into question how common the "reported" increases in appetite and food cravings really are in females with PMDD during the luteal phase of the menstrual cycle and how this compares with the incidence in the population of females without PMDD. Based on these perplexing reports, I reviewed my own database, in which I have used a modified version of the Daily Rating Form (22) to prospectively monitor both women with PMDD and normal women. This questionnaire includes two food-related items: item 8a ("had increased appetite or overate") and item 8b ("had cravings for specific foods"). Figure 5.3.1 shows that mean ratings for "Increased Appetite or Overate" and "Specific Food Cravings" were significantly increased during the late luteal phase compared with the follicular phase in 36 women with prospectively confirmed PMDD. In contrast, women who did not meet criteria for PMDD failed to show any significant increases in either appetite or food cravings. Others have reported similar differences between normal controls and women with PMDD (35). Figure 5.3.2 shows the percentage of women (normal controls and those with PMDD) who reported mild, moderate or severe (mean rating of 4.5 or greater) increases in appetite and food cravings during the late luteal phase. Among the control women, increases in appetite and food cravings were minimal during the late luteal phase, with over 90% reporting only mild increases in appetite and food cravings. In contrast, a small percentage of women with PMDD reported mild increases in appetite (5%) and food cravings (14%). Rather, the majority of women with PMDD reported moderate to severe increases in appetite and food cravings. Severe increases in appetite or overeating were reported in 28% of women with PMDD, whereas severe increases in cravings for specific foods were reported in 39% of women with PMDD. Overall, in this sample of women with PMDD, the majority reported moderate to severe increases in appetite and food cravings (95% and 86%, respectively). The failure to show such levels of severity in previous studies assessing women with premenstrual syndrome may be related to poor application of DSM-IV criteria.

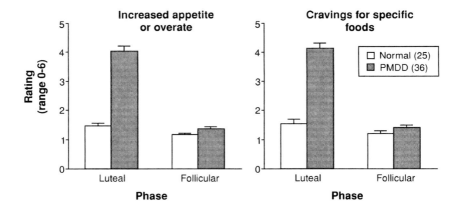

Fig. 5.3.1. Mean ratings from the Daily Rating Form for "Had increased appetite or overate" (left panel) and "Had craving for specific foods" (right panel) during the late luteal phase (premenstrual) compared with the follicular (postmenstrual) phase in normal women (n = 25) and in women with confirmed PMDD (n = 36). For these two items, late luteal phase scores were based on the mean rating during the 5 days preceding menses, and follicular phase scores were based on the mean rating from cycle days 6-10 (day 1 = the first day of menstruation).

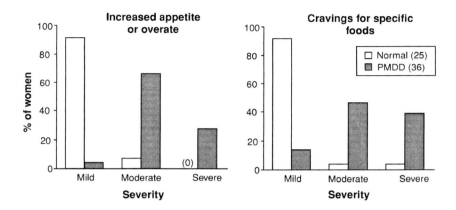

Fig. 5.3.2. Percentage of normal women (n = 25) and women with confirmed PMDD (n = 36) reporting mild, moderate or severe increases for "Had increased appetite or overate" (left panel) and "Had craving for specific foods" (right panel) during the late luteal phase.

5.3.4   Pharmacological Treatments

5.3.4.1   Hormonal Treatments

While the aetiology of PMDD remains unclear, several biological theories have been proposed and treatments targeting these presumed abnormalities have been evaluated (36,37). Previously, PMDD was presumed to be related to a hormonal dysregulation of the menstrual cycle. Consequently, early studies focused on hormonal treatments such as progesterone, oestradiol, oral contraceptives and other hormonal methods aimed at eliminating normal cyclical hormonal fluctuations.

The most frequently studied hormonal treatment for premenstrual symptoms has been progesterone. During the course of a normal menstrual cycle, progesterone levels increase after ovulation and then rapidly decrease during the late luteal phase. Green and Dalton (38) hypothesised that the abrupt withdrawal of progesterone in the latter half of the luteal phase was linked to the symptoms of PMDD. Although approximately 20 double-blind studies have been conducted to assess the efficacy of progesterone for premenstrual syndrome, the overwhelming majority have failed to show any improvement in premenstrual symptoms compared with placebo (32,39,40), and these studies did not provide any information on changes in appetite or craving. Freeman *et al.* (25) did include food cravings as one of the individual symptoms rated by 121 women with confirmed PMDD, and also found that progesterone did not differ from placebo. In another study (41), increased appetite was one of the symptoms rated daily among a group of 22 self-diagnosed women with premenstrual syndrome, and no differences between progesterone and placebo were observed.

Several studies evaluated the efficacy of danazol, a synthetic steroid that suppresses ovulation, for the treatment of premenstrual syndrome. Watts *et al.* (42) reported that, by the third month of treatment with 200 mg danazol, several symptoms, including increased appetite, showed an improvement compared with placebo. In another study, using the same dose of danazol, there was a significant improvement in overall symptoms when ovulation was suppressed, but reported side effects included weight gain and increased craving for sweets (43). Other hormonal strategies for premenstrual syndrome have included oestradiol, oral contraceptives and gonadotropic-releasing-hormone agonists, but the few double-blind studies conducted have been negative, and they did not measure or report changes in appetite or food cravings (29).

5.3.4.2 Anxiolytics

Another approach to treating the anxiety associated with PMDD has been the use of anxiolytics. The benzodiazepine alprazolam has been evaluated for the treatment of PMDD in six double-blind placebo-controlled studies, and four concluded that alprazolam was more effective than placebo in reducing premenstrual mood symptoms (33,44-46). In contrast, two other studies failed to support these findings (47,48). While three of these studies (33,46,48) provided information on food cravings and/or appetite, only one of them (33) reported that alprazolam decreased appetite and cravings for sweets premenstrually in women with PMDD. Unfortunately, none of the studies using alprazolam to treat PMDD has actually measured food intake. We conducted a study in which we administered acute doses of alprazolam to women with PMDD during the late luteal phase and the follicular phase (49) and were in a unique position to monitor food intake at lunchtime (50). Alprazolam produced significant dose-related increases in food intake, an effect that was observed only in the luteal phase, not the follicular phase. Moreover, alprazolam produced selective alterations in macronutrient intake; the number of calories consumed from fat and protein increased in the luteal phase following 0.75 mg alprazolam, with a corresponding decrease in the proportion of calories consumed from carbohydrates.

5.3.4.3   Antidepressants

The primary symptoms of PMDD, such as irritability, anxiety, affective lability and depression, are consistent with the serotonin hypothesis of depression, and there is accumulating evidence that PMDD is related to abnormalities (i.e. reductions) in serotonergic functioning (51). For instance, whole blood serotonin levels (35) and platelet serotonin uptake (52) were significantly lower in the late luteal phase in women with PMDD compared with normal controls. Several studies have conducted pharmacological challenge tests to assess serotonin functioning in women with PMDD. Bancroft et al. (53) investigated the neuroendocrine response to L-tryptophan in women with PMDD and normal controls during both the follicular and late luteal phases of the menstrual cycle. The growth hormone and cortisol responses were blunted in women with PMDD compared with normal controls during both phases of the menstrual cycle, whereas the prolactin response was blunted only in the luteal phase in women with PMDD. Oral fenfluramine has also been used to assess serotonergic functioning. Some studies have found that women with PMDD show a blunted prolactin response to fenfluramine compared with normal controls in the luteal phase (54), while others have reported no differences (55,56). Further support for the serotonin dysregulation theory is that, to date, the most promising treatments for the depression and anxiety associated with PMDD are the selective serotonin-reuptake inhibitors (SSRIs).

5.3.4.3.1 Fluoxetine

Among the numerous studies that have evaluated fluoxetine as a treatment for PMDD, only a few have reported on changes in appetite or food cravings. In a double-blind crossover trial comparing fluoxetine and placebo for premenstrual dysphoria, approximately 65% of women with PMDD had improved symptoms following fluoxetine treatment compared with placebo treatment, including improvement on the luteal increase in food cravings (57). Similarly, Stone *et al.* (58) showed that fluoxetine (20 mg/day) improved each of the ten diagnostic categories measured compared with placebo, including the late luteal increases in appetite in women with confirmed PMDD. In a subsequent study (59), there were no significant differences on ratings of increased appetite across three treatment groups: placebo, fluoxetine, and bupropion (a non-serotonergic antidepressant). However, close inspection of the data in that study suggests that both fluoxetine and bupropion reduced the luteal phase increases in appetite compared with placebo, but that a larger sample size would be needed to achieve statistical significance. In a small pilot study, although fluoxetine (20 mg/day) improved somatic symptoms compared with placebo in women with premenstrual syndrome, there was no change on the item "craving foods" (60). While several other studies have assessed fluoxetine for the treatment of PMDD and found it to be superior to placebo, changes in appetite and/or food cravings were either not reported or not measured (61-63).

5.3.4.3.2 Paroxetine

Several studies have assessed the SSRI paroxetine for the treatment of PMDD. In an open trial with 14 participants, specific food cravings were one of the five most severe symptoms reported before treatment with paroxetine (64). After 3 months of paroxetine treatment (mean dose of 22 mg/day), paroxetine improved the luteal increases in appetite compared with the placebo-treated cycle, but there were no changes in specific food cravings. Similarly, Sundblad et al. (28) reported that the luteal increases in appetite and/or carbohydrate craving were lower during ten cycles of treatment with paroxetine, but, again, this was an open trial. In a double-blind trial comparing paroxetine and maprotiline (a noradrenaline reuptake inhibitor) with placebo, paroxetine was superior to both placebo and maprotiline for five of the six symptoms measured, including irritability, depressed mood, anxiety/tension, sense of bloating and breast tenderness (34). In contrast, paroxetine did not significantly reduce the increases in appetite and/or carbohydrate craving overall compared with placebo; however, by the third month of paroxetine treatment, these ratings were significantly lower compared with both placebo and maprotiline treatment.

5.3.4.3.3 Sertraline

Sertraline is perhaps the most extensively studied antidepressant for PMDD, and most studies demonstrate that sertraline is an effective treatment for the majority of women with PMDD. Unfortunately, information on appetite and/or food cravings were either not obtained or not reported in several studies. Although Halbreich and Smoller (65) used the Daily Rating Form, which includes two items related to appetite and food craving, only ratings from the depression item and impairment item were presented. Two other studies used the Calendar of Premenstrual Experience (COPE), but only composite scores for behavioural and physical symptoms were analysed (66,67), even though the behavioural factor contains the items food cravings and increased appetite. Further, although Yonkers et al. (68) used a modified version of the Daily Rating Form (22), results from that questionnaire were not included. In an open trial comparing sertraline with desipramine, food cravings and several other mood symptoms were improved with both drugs (69). However, in a subsequent double-blind placebo-controlled trial comparing sertraline with desipramine, the food cravings/increased appetite item was not significantly different between the three groups (70). In a study comparing full- or half-cycle treatment with sertraline, there was no difference in food cravings between the two treatment regimens; no data were presented to determine if there was a reduction in food cravings following sertraline compared with pretreatment (71).

Several other serotonergic antidepressants have been reported to be effective for PMDD, including clomipramine (27), citalopram (19), and nefazodone (72). For two of these studies (19,27), although ratings of increased appetite and/or carbohydrate craving were assessed daily throughout the trial and decreased over time, no significant differences were noted between the treatment drug and placebo. One explanation provided for the failure to see drug-specific decreases on this symptom, is that it was reportedly present in only a subpopulation of participants. However, when only those women who normally experienced increases in appetite/carbohydrate craving were included in the analysis, ratings on this item were significantly lower in the clomipramine group compared with the placebo group (27). Lastly, in an open-label trial with nefazodone, significant improvements in food cravings were observed following treatment with nefazodone compared with baseline (72).

In addition to the fact that the vast majority of pharmacological treatment trials for PMDD described above did not routinely address the symptoms of increased appetite and food craving, none of these trials measured food intake or even changes in body weight during treatment. This may be particularly relevant when using the various SSRI antidepressants. Although the SSRIs, such as fluoxetine and sertraline, initially suppress appetite and food intake, after long-term treatment significant weight gain has been observed (73-75). Since women with PMDD already experience increased appetite and food craving during the late luteal phase, studies using SSRIs for the long-term treatment of PMDD need to explore whether eventual weight gain is a potential side effect for this population.

5.3.5   Improved Methods for Assessing Food Cravings and Food Intake

Despite reports from women with PMDD of significant alterations in mood and increases in both food cravings and food intake premenstrually, few studies, and no pharmacological treatment studies, have been conducted specifically on either food cravings or food intake in these women. Early studies showed a relationship between premenstrual tension and an increase in appetite and/or cravings for sweets (11,76). Similarly, Metcalf *et al.* (77) showed that daily ratings of food cravings were increased premenstrually, along with other mood and physical symptoms in women with confirmed premenstrual syndrome. More recently, it has been argued that women with PMDD specifically crave high-carbohydrate food items during the luteal (premenstrual) phase as a means of self-medicating the low serotonin levels and the corresponding depressed mood state (10,78,79). In one study, cravings for foods high in carbohydrate were increased during the luteal phase compared with the follicular phase in women with reported premenstrual syndrome, but not in control women (14). In that study, the question was specifically about carbohydrate craving; thus, it is unclear if women were craving high-carbohydrate foods or foods also high in fat or protein. Pretreatment with the serotonin agonist, d-fenfluramine, improved mood and also suppressed the premenstrual increases in carbohydrate and fat intake in women with premenstrual depression (80). Similarly, a carbohydrate-rich beverage consumed during the premenstrual phase has also been shown to improve mood and decrease carbohydrate craving in women with premenstrual syndrome (81).

Although previous studies and data extracted from our Daily Ratings Form (see Figs 5.3.1 and 5.3.2), indicate that women with PMDD show increased cravings for specific foods, these standard questions do not address what types of food, including the macronutrient profile (e.g. carbohydrates or fats) that women are actually craving. In a recent study (50), we attempted to address this question by administering a locally derived Food Desirability questionnaire to women with PMDD. The Food Desirability questionnaire consisted of 38 food and beverage items, and participants were instructed to rate how much they would like to eat each item that day on a 5-point scale, from 0 ("not at all") to 4 ("extremely"). Ratings for individual items were grouped according to food type to derive six different food categories: 1) savory carbohydrate/fat foods (e.g. potato chips); 2) sweet carbohydrate/fat foods (e.g. chocolate candy); 3) protein/fat foods (e.g. cheese); 4) carbohydrate alone foods (e.g. bread); 5) beverages (e.g. juice); and 6) alcohol. The left panel of Fig. 5.3.3 compares desires for each of the six food groups as a function of menstrual cycle phase in a group of 19 females with prospectively confirmed PMDD (50). There were significant increases in desire for savoury carbohydrate/fat foods, sweet carbohydrate/fat foods and protein/fat foods in the late luteal phase compared with the follicular phase. Desire for alcohol was also significantly higher in the late luteal phase. In contrast, while the overall magnitude of desires for carbohydrate alone or beverages (other than alcohol) was higher than for the other food groups, there were no differences in desires for these items as a function of menstrual cycle phase.

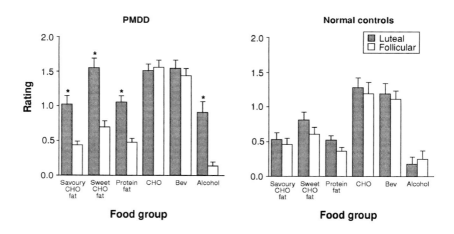

Fig. 5.3.3. Ratings of food desires for each of six food groups averaged over the 4 days during the late luteal phase (premenstrual) compared with the 4 days during the follicular phase (postmenstrual) for women with PMDD (left panel; n = 19) and normal control women (right panel; n = 25). Bev = beverages CHO = carbohydrate. An asterisk (*) indicates a significant difference between the luteal and follicular phases.

We have also administered the Food Desirability questionnaire to 25 normal women without PMDD (unpublished data). As shown in the right panel of

Fig. 5.3.3, these normal women did not show differences in their desire for any of the six food groups between the luteal and follicular phases of the menstrual cycle. Further, ratings for the various food groups during the follicular phase were similar in the women with PMDD compared with normal women. These findings suggest that, among women with PMDD, but not normal women, food "cravings," specifically for food items containing fat, are increased during the luteal phase of the menstrual cycle. While these results differ from those in other reports, it should be noted that, in this case, food "cravings" were measured prospectively using a questionnaire that allowed individuals to report their desire for a variety of food items, as opposed to simply asking if they had increased food cravings, or more pointed questions asking if they craved carbohydrates. As can be seen in Fig. 5.3.3, although desire for items consisting of carbohydrates alone, along with beverages (also primarily consisting of carbohydrates), was higher in magnitude than that for the other food groups, it did not change as a function of having PMDD or as a function of menstrual cycle phase. Unfortunately, a full discussion of the definition of "craving" and the issue of carbohydrate or fat craving is beyond the scope of this chapter, but other sections in this book (see sections 4.2 and 4.3) and other papers address these issues (3,5).

A few non-pharmacological studies have actually measured food intake in women with and without premenstrual syndrome (14,50,80). In two of these studies (14,80), women resided as inpatients and the food provided consisted of high-carbohydrate and high-protein foods, with fat content held relatively constant across the various foods. Under these conditions, only those women with PMDD showed a significant increase in food intake during the late luteal phase compared with the follicular phase, and this was attributed to an increase in carbohydrate intake. Another study showed that both women with and those without PMDD reported an increase in appetite premenstrually compared with postmenstrually, and that this increase was greater in the PMDD group (13), but food intake was not assessed. In a recent study (50), food intake was measured in women with confirmed PMDD who were given free access to a range of foods at lunch, to test the hypothesised relationship between PMDD and increased carbohydrate intake. Although overall food intake was not increased in the luteal phase compared with the follicular phase when placebo was administered, the proportion of calories derived from carbohydrates was significantly decreased in the luteal phase, with a corresponding significant increase in the proportion of calories derived from fat and no change in the proportion of calories derived from protein.

5.3.6   Conclusions

Future studies designed to treat females with PMDD should make better attempts to target the pharmacological agent to the subset of symptoms endorsed (37). Also, it is important to make an accurate diagnosis of PMDD by prospectively tracking women for at least two menstrual cycles and ruling out any other Axis I disorder, such as depression and anxiety. Naturally, it will be important to include that subset of women with PMDD who experience moderate to severe increases in food cravings and/or appetite during the luteal phase. If strict DSM-IV criteria are met, the majority of women should experience these symptoms. In order to address specifically the treatment of increased appetite and/or food cravings associated with PMDD, studies need to define these terms carefully and measure them in a more meaningful way, including monitoring actual changes in food intake and weight. Further, it is imperative that studies determine whether the foods craved or consumed during the luteal phase represent any particular nutrient category, rather than presume that it is strictly simple carbohydrates. This can be done only if women have a range of food items varying in macronutrient content to select from. Lastly, studies need to be conducted to determine the efficacy of long-term pharmacological treatment of PMDD on controlling food intake.

This research was supported by DA-09114 from the National Institute on Drug Abuse.

5.3.7   References

1.   Cohen I.R., Sherwin B.B., Fleming A.S. Food cravings, mood, and the menstrual cycle. *Hormones and Behavior*, 1987, 21, 457-70.

2.   Bancroft J., Cook A., Williamson L. Food craving, mood and the menstrual cycle. *Psychological Medicine*, 1988, 18, 855-60.

3.   Rozin P., Levine E., Stoess C. Chocolate craving and liking. *Appetite*, 1991, 17, 199-212.

4.   Hill A.J., Heaton-Brown L. The experience of food craving: a prospective investigation in healthy women. *Journal of Psychosomatic Research*, 1994, 3, 801-14.

5.   Weingarten H.P., Elston D. Food cravings in a college population. *Appetite*, 1991, 17, 167-75.

6.   Macdiarmid J.I., Hetherington M.M. Mood modulation by food: An exploration of affect and cravings in 'chocolate addicts'. *British Journal of Clinical Psychology*, 1995, 34, 129-38.

7.   Weingarten H.P., Elston D. The phenomenology of food cravings. *Appetite*, 1990, 15, 231-46.

8.   Buffenstein R., Poppitt S.D., McDevitt R.M., Prentice A.M. Food intake and the menstrual cycle: a retrospective analysis, with implications for appetite research. *Physiology and Behavior*, 1995, 58, 1067-77.

9.   Dye L., Warner P., Bancroft J. Food craving during the menstrual cycle and its relationship to stress, happiness of relationship and depression. *Journal of Affective Disorders*, 1995, 34, 157-64.

10.   Dye L., Blundell J.E. Menstrual cycle and appetite control: implications for weight regulation. *Human Reproduction*, 1997, 12, 1142-51.

11.   Smith S.L., Sauder C. Food cravings, depression, and premenstrual problems. *Psychosomatic Medicine*, 1969, 31, 281-7.

12.   Giannini A.J., Price W.A., Loiselle R.H., Giannini M.C. Hyperphagia in premenstrual tension syndrome. *Journal of Clinical Psychiatry*, 1985, 46, 436-8.

13.   Both-Orthman B., Rubinow D.R., Hoban M.C., Malley J., Grover G.N. Menstrual cycle phase-related changes in appetite in patients with premenstrual syndrome and in control subjects. *American Journal of Psychiatry*, 1988, 145, 628-31.

14. Wurtman J.J., Brzezinski A., Wurtman R.J., Laferrere B. Effect of nutrient intake on premenstrual depression. *American Journal of Obstetrics and Gynecology*, 1989, 161, 1228-34.

15. American Psychiatric Association. *Diagnostic and Statistical Manual of Mental Disorders, 4th edition.* Washington, DC, U.S. Department of Health and Human Services. 1994.

16. Logue C.M., Moos R.H. Perimenstrual symptoms: prevalence and risk factors. *Psychosomatic Medicine*, 1986, 48, 388-414.

17. American College of Obstetricians and Gynecologists. *Premenstrual syndrome. Committee Opinion, No. 66.* Washington, DC, American College of Obstetricians and Gynecologists. 1989.

18. Rivera-Tovar A.D., Frank E. Late luteal phase dysphoric disorder in young women. *American Journal of Psychiatry*, 1990, 147, 1634-6.

19. Wikander I., Sundblad C., Andersch B., Dagnell I., Zylberstein D., Bengtsson F., Eriksson E. Citalopram in premenstrual dysphoria: Is intermittent treatment during luteal phases more effective than continuous medication throughout the menstrual cycle? *Journal of Clinical Psychopharmacology*, 1998, 18, 390-8.

20. Budeiri D.J., Wan Po A.L., Dornan J.C. Clinical trials of treatments of premenstrual syndrome: entry criteria and scales for measuring treatment outcomes. *British Journal of Obstetrics and Gynaecology*, 1994, 101, 689-95.

21. Taylor J.W. The timing of menstruation-related symptoms assessed by a daily symptom rating scale. *Acta Psychiatrica Scandinavica*, 1979, 60, 87-105.

22. Endicott J., Nee J., Cohen J., Halbreich U. Premenstrual changes: patterns and correlates of daily ratings. *Journal of Affective Disorders*, 1986, 10, 127-35.

23. Mortola J.F., Girton L., Beck L., Yen S.S.C. Diagnosis of premenstrual syndrome by a simple, prospective, and reliable instrument: The calendar of premenstrual experiences. *Obstetrics and Gynecology*, 1990, 76, 3002-7.

24. Moos R.H. *Menstrual Distress Questionnaire Manual.* Stanford, CA, Social Ecology Laboratory, Stanford University. 1977.

25. Freeman E.W., Rickels K., Sondheimer S.J., Polansky M. Ineffectiveness of progesterone suppository treatment for premenstrual syndrome. *Journal of the American Medical Association*, 1990, 264, 349-53.

26. Steiner M., Haskett R.F., Carroll B.J. Premenstrual tension syndrome: The development of research diagnostic criteria and new rating scales. *Acta Psychiatry Scandinavia*, 1980, 62, 177-90.

27. Sundblad C., Hedberg M.A., Eriksson E. Clomipramine administered during the luteal phase reduces the symptoms of premenstrual syndrome: A placebo-controlled trial. *Neuropsychopharmacology*, 1993, 9, 133-45.

28. Sundblad C., Wikander I., Andersch B., Eriksson E. A naturalistic study of paroxetine in premenstrual syndrome: efficacy and side-effects during ten cycles of treatment. *European Neuropsychopharmacology*, 1997, 7, 201-6.

29. Altshuler L.L., Hendrick V., Parry B. Pharmacological management of premenstrual disorder. *Harvard Review of Psychiatry*, 1995, 2, 233-45.

30. Freeman E.W., Sondheimer S.J., Rickels K., Weinbaum P. PMS treatment approaches and progesterone therapy. *Psychosomatics*, 1985, 26, 811-6.

31. Dennerstein L., Spencer-Gardner C., Gotts G., Brown J.B., Smith M.A., Burrows G.D. Progesterone and the premenstrual syndrome: a double blind crossover trial. *British Medical Journal*, 1985, 290, 1617-21.

32. Dennerstein L., Morse C., Gotts G., Brown J., Smith M., Oats J, Burrows G. Treatment of premenstrual syndrome A double-blind trial of dydrogesterone. *Journal of Affective Disorders*, 1986, 11, 199-205.

33. Smith S., Rinehart J.S., Ruddock V.E., Schiff I. Treatment of premenstrual syndrome with alprazolam; results of a double-blind, placebo controlled, randomized cross over clinical trial. *Obstetrics and Gynecology*, 1987, 70, 37-42.

34. Eriksson E., Hedberg M.A., Andersch B., Sundblad C. The serotonin reuptake inhibitor paroxetin is superior to the noradrenaline reuptake inhibitor maprotiline in the treatment of premenstrual syndrome. *Neuropsychopharmacology*, 1995, 12, 167-76.

35. Rapkin A.J., Edelmuth E., Chang L.C., Reading A.E., McGuire M.T., Su T-P. Whole-blood serotonin in premenstrual syndrome. *Obstetrics and Gynecology*, 1987, 70, 533-7.

36. Rausch J.L., Janowsky D.S. Premenstrual tension: etiology, in *Behavior and the Menstrual Cycle*. Ed. Friedman R.D. New York, Marcel-Dekker. 1982, 397-427.

37. Steinberg S. The treatment of late luteal phase dysphoric disorder. *Life Sciences*, 1991, 49, 767-802.

38. Green R., Dalton K. The premenstrual syndrome. *British Medical Journal*, 1953, 1, 1007-14.

39. Sampson G.A. Premenstrual syndrome: A double-blind controlled trial of progesterone and placebo. *British Journal of Psychiatry*, 1979, 135, 209-15.

40. Maddocks S., Hahn P., Moller F., Reid R.L. A double-blind placebo-controlled trial of progesterone vaginal suppositories in the treatment of premenstrual syndrome. *American Journal of Obstetrics and Gynecology*, 1986, 154, 573-81.

41. Richter M.A., Haltvick R., Shapiro S.S. Progesterone treatment of premenstrual syndrome. *Current Therapeutic Research*, 1984, 36, 840-50.

42. Watts J. Ff., Butt W.R., Edwards R.L. A clinical trial using danazol for the treatment of premenstrual tension. *British Journal of Obstetrics and Gynaecology*, 1987, 94, 30-4.

43. Halbreich U., Rojansky N., Palter S. Elimination of ovulation and menstrual cyclicity (with danazol) improves dysphoric premenstrual syndromes. *Fertility and Sterility*, 1991, 56, 1066-9.

44. Harrison W.L., Endicott J., Nee J. Treatment of premenstrual dysphoria with alprazolam: a controlled study. *Archives of General Psychiatry*, 1990, 47, 270-5.

45. Berger C.P., Presser B. Alprazolam in the treatment of two subsamples of patients with late luteal phase dysphoric disorder: a double-blind, placebo-controlled crossover study. *Obstetrics and Gynecology*, 1994, 84, 379-85.

46. Freeman E.W., Rickels K., Sondheimer S.J., Polansky M. A double-blind trial of oral progesterone, alprazolam, and placebo in the treatment of severe premenstrual syndrome. *Journal of the American Medical Association*, 1995, 274, 51-7.

47. Dennerstein L., Morse C., Burrows G., Brown J., Smith M. Alprazolam in the treatment of premenstrual syndrome, in *Hormones and Behaviour*. Eds Dennerstein L., Fraser I. Amsterdam, Elsevier. 1986, 175-82.

48. Schmidt P.J., Grover G.N., Rubinow D.R. Alprazolam in the treatment of premenstrual syndrome. *Archives of General Psychiatry*, 1993, 50, 467-73.

49.   Evans S.M., Haney M., Levin F.R., Foltin R.W., Fischman M.W. Mood and performance changes in women with premenstrual dysphoric disorder: Acute effects of alprazolam. *Neuropsychopharamcology*, 1998, 19, 499-516.

50.   Evans S.M., Foltin R.W., Fischman M.W. Food "cravings" and the acute effects of alprazolam on food intake in women with premenstrual dysphoric disorder. *Appetite*, 1999, 32, 331-49.

51.   Halbreich U., Tworek H. Altered serotonergic activity in women with dysphoric premenstrual syndromes. *International Journal of Psychiatry Medicine*, 1993, 23, 1-27.

52.   Ashby C.R.J., Carr L.A., Cook C.L., Steptoe M.M., Franks D.D. Alteration of platelet serotonergic mechanisms and monoamine oxidase activity in premenstrual syndrome. *Biological Psychiatry*, 1988, 24, 225-44.

53.   Bancroft J., Cook A., Davidson D., Bennie J., Goodwin G. Blunting of neuroendocrine responses to infusion of L-tryptophan in women with perimenstrual mood change. *Psychological Medicine*, 1991, 21, 305-12.

54.   FitzGerald M., Malone K.M., Li S., Harrison W.M., McBride P.A., Endicott J., Cooper T., Mann J.J. Blunted serotonin response to fenfluramine challenge in premenstrual dysphoric disorder. *The American Journal of Psychiatry*, 1997, 154, 556-8.

55.   Bancroft J., Cook A. The neuroendocrine response to d-fenfluramine in women with premenstrual depression. *Journal of Affective Disorders*, 1995, 36, 57-64.

56.   Steiner M., Yatham L.N., Coote M., Wilkins A., Lepage P. Serotonergic dysfunction in women with pure premenstrual dysphoric disorder: is the fenfluramine challenge test still relevant? *Psychiatry Research*, 1999, 87, 107-15.

57.   Su T.P., Schmidt P.J., Danaceau M.A., Tobin M.B., Rosenstein D.L., Murphy D.L., Rubinow D.R. Fluoxetine in the treatment of premenstrual dysphoria. *Neuropsychopharmacology*, 1977, 16, 346-56.

58.   Stone A.B., Pearlstein T.B., Brown W.A. Fluoxetine in the treatment of late luteal phase dysphoric disorder. *Journal of Clinical Psychiatry*, 1991, 52, 290-3.

59.   Pearlstein T.B., Stone A.B., Lund S.A., Scheft H., Zlotnick C., Brown W.A. Comparison of fluoxetine, bupropion, and placebo in the treatment of premenstrual dysphoric disorder. *Journal of Clinical Psychopharmacology*, 1997, 17, 261-6.

60. Rickels K., Freeman E.W., Sondheimer S., Albert J. Fluoxetine in the treatment of premenstrual syndrome. *Current Therapeutic Research*, 1990, 48, 161-6.

61. Wood S.H., Mortola J.F., Chan Y.F., Moossazadeh F., Yen S.S.C. Treatment of premenstrual syndrome with fluoxetine: A double-blind, placebo-controlled, crossover study. *Obstetrics and Gynecology*, 1992, 80, 339-44.

62. Pearlstein T.B., Stone A.B. Long-term fluoxetine treatment of late luteal phase dysphoric disorder. *Journal of Clinical Psychiatry*, 1994, 55, 332-5.

63. Steiner M., Steinberg S., Stewart D., Carter D., Berger C., Reid R., Grover D., Streiner D. Fluoxetine in the treatment of premenstrual dysphoria. *The New England Journal of Medicine*, 1995, 332, 1529-34.

64. Yonkers K.A., Cullion C., Williams A., Novak K., Rush A.J. Paroxetine as a treatment for premenstrual dysphoric disorder. *Journal of Clinical Psychopharmacology*, 1996, 16, 3-8.

65. Halbreich U., Smoller J.W. Intermittent luteal phase sertraline treatment of dysphoric premenstrual syndrome. *Journal of Clinical Psychiatry*, 1997, 58, 399-402.

66. Young S.A., Hurt P.H., Benedek D.M., Howard R.S. Treatment of premenstrual dysphoric disorder with sertraline during the luteal phase: A randomized, double-blind, placebo-controlled crossover trial. *Journal of Clinical Psychiatry*, 1998, 59, 76-80.

67. Jermain D.M., Preece C.K., Sykes R.L., Kuehl T.J., Sulak P.J. Luteal phase sertraline treatment for premenstrual dysphoric disorder. *Archives of Family Medicine*, 1999, 8, 328-32.

68. Yonkers K.A., Halbreich U., Freeman E., Brown C., Pearlstein T. Sertraline in the treatment of premenstrual dysphoric disorder. *Psychopharmacology Bulletin*, 1996, 32, 41-6.

69. Freeman E.W., Rickels K., Sondheimer S.J., Wittmaack F.M. Sertraline versus desipramine in the treatment of premenstrual syndrome: An open-label trial. *Journal of Clinical Psychiatry*, 1996, 57, 7-11.

70. Freeman E.W., Rickels K., Sondheimer S.J., Polansky M. Differential response to antidepressants in women with premenstrual syndrome/premenstrual dysphoric disorder. *Archives of General Psychiatry*, 1999, 56, 932-9.

71. Freeman E.W., Rickels K., Arredondo F., Kao L.-C., Pollack S.E., Sondheimer S.J. Full- or half-cycle treatment of severe premenstrual syndrome with a serotonergic antidepressant. *Journal of Clinical Psychopharmacology*, 1999, 19, 3-8.

72. Freeman E.W., Rickels K., Sondheimer S.J., Denis A., Pfeifer S., Weil S. Nefazodone in the treatment of premenstrual syndrome: a preliminary study. *Journal of Clinical Psychopharmacology*, 1994, 14, 180-6.

73. Fogelson D.L. Weight gain during fluoxetine treatment. *Journal of Clinical Psychopharmacology*, 1991, 11, 220-1.

74. Fisher S., Kent T.A., Bryant S.G. Postmarketing surveillance by patient self-monitoring: preliminary data for sertraline versus fluoxetine. *Journal of Clinical Psychiatry*, 1995, 56, 288-96.

75. Sussman N., Ginsberg D. Effects of psychotropic drugs on weight. *Psychiatric Annals*, 1999, 29, 580-94.

76. Morton J.H., Additon H., Addison R.G., Hunt L., Sullivan J.J. A clinical study of premenstrual tension. *American Journal of Obstetrics and Gynecology*, 1953, 65, 1182-91.

77. Metcalf M.G., Livesey J.H., Hudson S.M., Wells E.J. The premenstrual syndrome: moods, headaches and physical symptoms in 133 menstrual cycles. *Journal of Psychosomatic Obstetrics and Gynaecology*, 1988, 8, 31-43.

78. Wurtman J.J. Carbohydrate craving: Relationship between carbohydrate intake and disorders of mood. *Drugs*, 1990, 39 (Supp 3), 49-52.

79. Moller S.E. Serotonin, carbohydrates, and atypical depression. *Pharmacology and Toxicology*, 1992, 71, 61-71.

80. Brzezinski A.A., Wurtman J.J., Wurtman R.J., Gleason R., Greenfield J., Nadir T. d-Fenfluramine suppresses the increased calorie and carbohydrate intakes and improves the mood of women with premenstrual depression. *Obstetrics and Gynecology*, 1990, 76, 296-301.

81. Sayegh R., Schiff I., Wurtman J., Spiers P., McDermott J., Wurtman R. The effect of a carbohydrate-rich beverage on mood, appetite, and cognitive function in women with premenstrual syndrome. *Obstetrics and Gynecology*, 1995, 86, 520-8.

6. MOOD, FOOD, ALCOHOL AND ADDICTION

6.1. ADDICTION TO THE CHILLI BURN?

Martin Yeomans

To a consumer who regularly eats spicy foods, the sensation experienced in the mouth when eating chilli-based foods (the chilli burn) is highly pleasurable. In contrast, consumers who do not eat chilli-based food find the same chilli burn highly objectionable, and they avoid foods containing chilli. The questions addressed in this chapter are how these disparate responses may have developed, how it is that a sensation that is based on stimulation of pain receptors can be experienced as pleasurable, and whether regular use can (as has been suggested by some authors (1)) reach the level of an addiction.

6.1.1 What is Special about the Chilli Burn?

There are five main recognised species of chilli, with another 90 species with chilli-like properties. However, it is the chemical capsaicin (8-methyl-N-vanillyl-6-nonenamide), which is common to all these plants, that produces the irritation that is experienced as the "chilli burn". Capsaicin is an extremely potent irritant, with even 4 ppm concentrations producing the characteristic physiological responses experienced by consumers (e.g. sweating, running eyes, salivation, etc.). It has been suggested that these responses may have evolved as a reflexive defence mechanism, and may be an attempt to expel the source of irritation (2). Capsaicin has no impact on taste or olfactory receptors, but instead produces its oral sensation through stimulation of nociceptors (pain receptors), with the strongest sensation experienced at the tip of the tongue (3). This information is transmitted to the brain through the trigeminal nerve, unlike information about taste and smell. The burning sensation adds pungency to food, which is an important element of the flavour of a wide range of savoury foods. Pungency is added by a variety of stimuli, including carbonation of water, ethanol and piperine, but chilli produces by far the strongest burning sensation. Consequently, the question why do many consumers like an oral sensation based on an irritating, painful sensation has intrigued psychologists and food scientists alike.

The most common way of exploring liking for foods is through some form of affective rating of their sensory properties. If, for example, a group of consumers was asked to rate how much they liked chocolate on a scale of "Not at all" to "Extremely", the modal response would be predicted to be at or near the "Extremely" end of the scale, with responses distributed around the peak rating. Indeed, for most flavourings, the response to this question shows a single distribution, even for foods that are not widely liked. However, for chilli, the response appears to be bi-modal (Fig. 6.1.1). The data in Fig. 6.1.1 are based on a large sample of undergraduate students, and contrast the rated liking for cooked chilli with that of two other common savoury flavours (onion and garlic (4)). Although the modal response for all three food components suggests these are all liked on average, only with chilli is there a small but significant group of confirmed dislikers. Although it might be expected to find some "dislikers" with virtually all food flavours, even sweet tastes (5), what appears to be unusual about chilli, and possibly other oral irritants, is the discontinuity between liker and disliker. Few consumers are neutral when rating the burning sensation produced by chilli, which is either liked or disliked. Since there is no evidence for any innate tendency to like chilli, even in societies where foods containing chilli form the staple diet (6), the important question is how do people come to like the sensation generated by chilli, and (in the present context) whether this liking ever reaches an addictive level.

6.1.2   Why do People like the Chilli Burn?

All the models that try to describe why consumers like the chilli burn assume that the sensation is initially either objectionable (7,8) or neutral (4). Either way, the key question remains how do consumers change from an initial state of aversion or neutrality to one of extreme like? The simplest model describing how liking for a stimulus can change from objectionable/neutral to positive is the mere exposure hypothesis (9). This model simply suggests that liking increases with familiarity, and has been suggested to be a component of how liking for chilli develops (10). The idea with chilli-based foods is that initial liking is based on the characteristics of the food rather than the burning sensation itself. However, repeated exposure to the burning sensation increases familiarity and consequently the sensation itself becomes liked independently of the food in which it is served. This model has since been tested experimentally (11), and liking was found to increase with repeated exposure to a simple food containing either 2.5 or 5 ppm capsaicin for consumers who were pre-selected as neither liking nor disliking the burning sensation at the start (Fig. 6.1.2). However, in both of the experiments reported in that paper, there was a suggestion that exposure to the burning sensation also lessened the intensity of the burn, particularly with the higher capsaicin dose. This questions whether the change in liking can truly be explained by mere exposure effects, since an alternative model in which liking is a consequence of reduced sensitivity to the burning sensation is also possible.

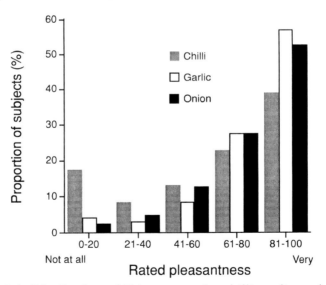

Fig. 6.1.1. Distribution of liking scores for chilli, garlic and onion

A) Experiment 1

B) Experiment 2

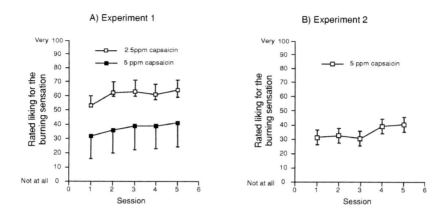

Fig. 6.1.2. Changes in rated liking for the chilli burn across five exposure sessions. (data from Stevenson and Yeomans (11)).

There is a large and consistent body of literature demonstrating that repeated exposure to chilli-based foods leads to oral desensitisation (12-15), mediated at least in part by desensitisation of the nociceptive fibres, which are stimulated by capsaicin (16,17). For example, small differences in detection thresholds for chilli have been found between likers and non-likers, with lower detection thresholds in non-likers (8,18). Although this difference was too small to account for the differences in liking by itself (19), desensitisation will make re-exposure to the same capsaicin concentration less aversive. Differences in the rated intensity of the chilli burn have also been reported above threshold level, with lower burn ratings at higher concentrations in likers than in non-likers (20-23). However, differences in rated liking for the burning sensation between likers and non-likers remained even when variations in burn-intensity were normalised (23). Thus, desensitisation reduces burn intensity in a quantitative manner, but cannot itself explain why some consumers like chilli and others dislike it. Desensitisation may, however, help explain why likers tend to increase their consumption of chilli over time, as they seek to maintain their preferred level of burn.

Along with desensitisation, researchers have also shown that repeated exposures to capsaicin in laboratory tests with capsaicin solutions, where the duration between stimuli was 60 s or less, leads to an increase in the perceived intensity of the burning sensation (12,13,15). However, when the interval between capsaicin-based stimuli was increased to 10 min, desensitisation was seen (15). Whether sensitisation is relevant to the normal experience of eating chilli-based foods is debatable, however, since sensitisation was not seen when capsaicin was experienced in food even when the capsaicin concentrations used were carefully matched to those that did produce sensitisation when exposed as solutions (15). In contrast, desensitisation was seen for both capsaicin solutions and foods (15), and prior sensitisation to capsaicin is not necessary to observe desensitisation (12).

Sensitisation can also be seen once desensitisation has been established (24), suggesting that the two effects are additive. In terms of understanding liking for chilli-based foods, it appears that desensitisation may play a role in terms of the experience of the burning sensation, but whether sensitisation plays a separate role is still unclear. Since capsaicin desensitises nociceptors, an intriguing question is whether this effect is specific to capsaicin. There is good evidence that capsaicin desensitisation reduces the subsequent response to other painful stimuli (25), and, indeed, topically applied capsaicin creams are now used in the treatment of pain (26-28).

How then might some consumers come to like the chilli burn? Rozin (10) has developed a model for the development of liking for the chilli burn based on the opponent-process theory first developed by Solomon and Corbit (29). This model is based on the premise that the body is designed to counteract the effects of any stimulus that causes an affective response, either positive or negative (30). Accordingly, when the body experiences a hedonic response, this leads to the development of an automatic counter-reaction, which Solomon and Corbit (29) called the opponent process. These opponent processes become stronger with repeated experience of the affective stimulus, and the expression of these processes can be conditioned to cues predicting the affective stimulus. Applied to chilli liking (10), the idea is that the chilli burn is initially disliked. If this dislike prevents further ingestion, there is no opportunity for the opponent process to develop, and so the consumer remains a disliker. However, the more often the chilli burn is experienced, perhaps driven by social pressure (10), the stronger the opponent process becomes. Since the chilli burn is painful and objectionable, the opponent process is hypothesised to be pleasant, and eventually the pleasant sensation produced by the opponent process exceeds the objectionable sensation generated by the chilli. At this time, the consumer becomes a chilli liker. The main attraction of this hypothesis is its elegance, and its ability to build on a well-known psychological model. However, there have been few empirical tests of this hypothesis, and these have not been successful (4).

There are also alternative models that try to explain the development of liking for the chilli burn. For example, since chilli is usually consumed as part of a meal, liking for the burning sensation could develop through conditioned associations between the burning sensation and the positive consequences of the food it is consumed with (10). Alternatively, learning that there are no harmful consequences of ingesting chilli could also lead to liking development (2). Whichever model is correct, the question that remains is whether the level of liking generated by these models can lead to an addiction to the chilli burn.

6.1.3 Can People become Addicted to the Chilli Burn?

The idea that chilli can be addictive has been discussed in the lay press, possibly spurred on by the use of terminology associated with addiction in some accounts of chilli use. The description of the effects of chilli leading to a "proper rush" (1), for example, draws a parallel between chilli use and opium addiction. The difficulty in finding a clear definition for addiction in general was made clear early in this book (see also section 6.2). The same problem is seen when trying to determine whether the level of use of chilli by individual consumers could be seen as a form of addiction. Two approaches to this question are described here. The first contrasts the self-reported chilli use of people who define themselves as chilli addicts, while the second looks for potential physiological mechanisms that could, conceivably, make chilli "addictive" (31).

Table 6.1.I contrasts the self-reported behaviour of individuals who consider themselves to be chilli addicts with the American Psychiatric Association's Diagnostic and Statistical Manual (IV) for substance dependence criteria (31). An individual is considered to be dependent on a substance if his/her use of that substance meets three of the seven defining criteria. Although there has been no systematic research into excessive chilli use, we have collected summaries of the usual chilli consumption of people who self-define as chilli addicts, and three such cases are described below. Each of these could meet 3/7 of the DSM IV substance dependence criteria.

6.1.3.1   Case histories

1.   Woman, aged 37. Her 7-day food diary indicated she consumed 5-10 raw chilli peppers daily, 2-3 before breakfast. This was reported as normal consumption by the individual. She had a self-reported elevated mood after consumption: "It wakes me up and cheers me up in the morning". She also reported depressed mood on days when she was unable to find a source of fresh chillies (and kept dried chillies for consumption on these days).

2.   Male, aged 28. He ate "hot spicy food" daily as his evening meal, with a variety of cuisine (Indian, Thai and Mexican food). When using take-away food or eating in a restaurant, he always chose the food advertised as the "hottest" item. At home, he usually used 10-20 raw chilli peppers in each serving of food. He avoided eating situations where hot spicy options were not available.

3.   Male, aged 35. He ate Indian food containing at least 2-3 "hot" chilli peppers daily. If he was in a social situation where spicy food was unavailable, he would eat sparingly and then consume chilli-based snacks or raw chilli peppers on his return home. He had increased his level of chilli use progressively over a 2-year period.

These three cases have some common features: they all report a need to consume increasingly large doses of chilli to experience the same level of pleasure during eating (see Table 6.1.I under Tolerance), and they all experience some level of psychological discomfort when spicy foods are unavailable.

TABLE 6.1.I
Comparison of the characteristics of extreme chilli consumption and criteria for definition as substance dependence

Criteria for substance dependence	Use of chilli
Tolerance, as defined by one of the following: a) a need to take markedly increased amounts of the substance to achieve intoxication or desired effect b) markedly diminished effect with the continued use of the same amount of substance.	Tolerance, in the form of oral desensitisation, is well known for capsaicin (12,13).
Withdrawal, as manifested by either of the following: a) the characteristic withdrawal syndrome for the substance b) the same (or a closely related) substance is taken to relieve withdrawal.	There is no withdrawal syndrome associated with ingestion of capsaicin-containing foods. However, some consumers report dysphoria associated with not consuming chilli (see Case Histories).
The substance is often taken in larger amounts or over a longer period than was intended	Evidence of overconsumption of chilli in some regular chilli consumers.
There is a persistent desire or unsuccessful efforts to cut down or control substance use.	None
A great deal of time is spent in activities necessary to obtain the substance, use the substance or recover from its effects.	Although there are some unpleasant consequences (chiefly gastro-intestinal effects) following chilli consumption, these do not meet any clinical criteria.
Important social, occupational or recreational activities are given up or reduced because of substance use.	No evidence for this.
The substance use is continued despite knowledge of having a persistent or recurrent physical or psychological problem that is likely to have been caused or exacerbated by the substance.	No evidence for this.

However, none of these cases (or any other self-reported chilli addicts we have seen) shows any significant disruption to normal social or psychological functioning as a consequence of high-level chilli use beyond some annoyance at not being able to find appropriate food at all social events. These self-defined chilli addicts all considered that their use of chilli was not a problem for them, and indeed many individuals appeared to be proud of their ability to tolerate the pain generated by high-level chilli use, as well as gaining considerable pleasure from the burning sensation. Thus it would seem that the level of chilli use described by these consumers is better described as a compulsive habit rather than a true "addiction".

6.1.4   A Mechanism for Chilli Addiction?

One important link between models of drug addiction and liking for chilli is the hypothesised involvement of the opponent process theory. The opponent process theory remains an important component of current theories of drug addiction, particularly in relation to opiate abuse (32). The essential idea is that repeated exposure to the large affective response produced by opiate drugs such as heroin leads to the development of opponent processes, which counteract opiate effects. Thus, the opponent process theory has been used to develop an important theory of how tolerance to opiate develops (33,34), particularly in relation to the role of opiates in pain control (35,36). Since opiate drugs act by stimulating opioid receptors (specific post-synaptic receptors, which are normally stimulated by endogenous opioid peptides - see also section 2.2), it has been suggested that the opponent process underlying tolerance to opiate drugs might involve some change in activity in the endogenous opioid system (37). Opioid peptides are also known to be involved in the normal regulation of pain (38), and have been widely implicated, particularly, in the natural ability to reduce the sensation of pain. Opioids are also implicated in appetite regulation (see also section 2.2 and 2.5). The combined role of opioids in the neurobiology of addiction and control of appetite suggests a potential role in food addiction. Rozin (10) has suggested that opioid peptides may play a specific role in the liking response to the chilli burn, perhaps through generation of the opponent process to the burning sensation. Thus, repeated exposure to the burning sensation may lead to increased opioid activity as the body tries to tolerate the irritation produced by the burn, possibly by social demands to consume the food. As the strength of the hypothesised opioid response increases, so the consumer comes to associate the burning sensation with the positive effects of opioid release, and so comes to like the burning sensation. Thus the opioid opponent model is a potential neurochemical basis for chilli addiction.

One way of testing the involvement of opioid peptides in liking for chilli is to see how this liking is altered by administration of drugs that block endogenous opioid receptors, such as naloxone. However, these studies only found a trend for reduced liking for the chilli burn following naloxone treatment (10). Although another study found a significant reduction in the rated liking for a spicy food (pakora) following administration of the opiate antagonist nalmefene (39), liking for pakora was reduced by the same magnitude as that for a number of non-pungent foods. If opioids were the key neurochemical underlying the development of liking for chilli, opioid receptor blockade should have had much more dramatic effects on liking. Instead, the data are consistent with a general role of opioids in the perception of pleasure when eating.

6.1.5   Conclusions

Despite frequent discussion of the chilli burn as an addictive sensation in the lay press, there is at present no good evidence that the use of chilli meets the criteria needed to define it as an addiction. However, the nature of the processes underlying the development of liking for chilli are still unclear, and, until we understand more clearly how consumers come to like the burning sensation generated by chilli, the idea that chilli might be addictive cannot be fully dismissed.

6.1.6   References

1.   Weil A. Hot! Hot! - 1: Eating chilies. *Journal of Psychedelic Drugs*, 1976, 8, 83-6.

2. Prescott J., Stevenson R.J. Pungency in food perception and preference. *Food Reviews International*, 1995, 11, 665-98.

3. Lawless H.T., Stevens D.A. Responses of humans to oral chemical irritants as a function of locus of stimulation. *Perception and Psychophysics*, 1988, 43, 72-8.

4. Stevenson R.J. The nature of and psychological mechanisms underlying the development of liking for the chilli burn. 1992, DPhil, University of Sussex, 192.

5. Looy H., Weingarten H.P. Effects of metabolic state on sweet taste reactivity in humans depend on underlying hedonic response profile. *Chemical Senses*, 1991, 16, 123-30.

6. Rozin P., Vollmecke T.A. Food likes and dislikes. *Annual Review of Nutrition*, 1986, 6, 433-56.

7. Rozin P., Gruss L., Berk G. Reversal of innate aversions: attempts to induce a preference for chili peppers in rats. *Journal of Comparative and Physiological Psychology*, 1979, 93, 1001-14.

8. Rozin P., Schiller D. The nature and acquisition of a preference for chili pepper in humans. *Motivation and Emotion*, 1980, 4, 77-101.

9. Zajonc R.B. Attitudinal effects of mere exposure. *Journal of Personality and Social Psychology*, 1968, 9, 1-27.

10. Rozin P. Getting to like the burn of the chili pepper: biological, psychological and cultural perspectives, in *Chemical Senses, Volume 2, irritation*. Eds Green B.G., Mason J.R., Kare M.R. New York, Marcel Decker. 1990, 231-69.

11. Stevenson R.J., Yeomans M.R. Does exposure enhance liking for the chilli burn? *Appetite*, 1995, 24, 107-20.

12. Green B.G. Capsaicin sensitisation and desensitisation on the tongue produced by brief exposures to a low concentration. *Neuroscience Letters*, 1989, 107, 173-8.

13. Green B.G. Temporal characteristics of capsaicin sensitisation and desensitisation on the tongue. *Physiology and Behavior*, 1991, 49, 501-5.

14. Karrer T., Bartoshuk L. Capsaicin desensitisation and recovery on the human tongue. *Physiology and Behavior*, 1991, 49, 757-64.

15. Prescott J. The generalizability of capsaicin sensitization and desensitization. *Physiology and Behavior*, 1999, 66, 741-9.

16. Dray A., Bettaney J., Forster P. Capsaicin desensitisation of peripheral nociceptive fibres does not impair sensitivity to other noxious stimuli. *Neuroscience Letters*, 1989, 99, 50-4.

17. Szolcsanyi J. Capsaicin, irritation, and desensitisation: neurophysiological basis and future perspectives, in *Chemical senses, volume 2: irritation*. Eds Green B.G., Mason J.R., Kare M.R. New York, Marcel Dekker. 1990, 148-69.

18. Rozin P., Mark M., Schiller D. The role of desensitisation to capsaicin in chili pepper ingestion and preference. *Chemical Senses*, 1981, 6, 23-31.

19. Rozin P., Ebert L., Schull J. Some like it hot: a temporal analysis of hedonic responses to chili pepper. *Appetite*, 1982, 3, 13-22.

20. Cowart B.J. Oral chemical irritation: does it reduce perceived taste intensity. *Chemical Senses*, 1987, 12, 467-79.

21. Lawless H., Rozin P., Shenker J. Effects of oral capsaicin on gustatory, olfactory and irritant sensations and flavor identification in humans who regularly or rarely consumed chili pepper. *Chemical Senses*, 1985, 10, 579-89.

22. Prescott J., Stevenson R.J. Effects of oral chemical irritation on tastes and flavors in frequent and infrequent users of chili. *Physiology and Behavior*, 1995, 58, 1117-27.

23. Stevenson R.J., Yeomans M.R. Differences in ratings of intensity and pleasantness for the capsaicin burn between chilli likers and non-likers; implications for liking development. *Chemical Senses*, 1993, 18, 471-82.

24. Green B.G., Rentmeister-Bryant H., Cruz A. Factors affecting "stimulus induced recovery:" Capsaicin concentration, frequency of exposure, and site of stimulation. *Chemical Senses*, 1997, 22, 690.

25. Green B.G., McAuliffe B.L. Menthol desensitisation of capsaicin irritation: evidence of a short-term anti-nociceptive effect. *Physiology and Behavior*, 2000, 68, 631-9.

26. Chizh B.A., Dickenson A.H., Wnendt S. The race to control pain: more participants, more targets. *Trends in Pharmacological Sciences*, 1999, 20, 354-7.

27. Sindrup S.H., Jensen T.S. Efficacy of pharmacological treatments of neuropathic pain: an update and effect related to mechanism of drug action. *Pain*, 1999, 83, 389-400.

28. Wachtel R.E. Capsaicin. *Regional Anesthesia and Pain Medicine*, 1999, 24, 361-3.

29. Solomon R.S., Corbit J.D. An opponent-process theory of motivation: 1. Temporal dynamics of affect. *Psychological Review*, 1974, 81, 119-45.

30. Solomon R.L. The opponent-process theory of acquired motivation: the cost of pleasure and the benefits of pain. *American Psychologist*, 1980, 35, 691-712.

31. American Psychiatric Association. *Diagnostic and statistical manual of mental disorders*, 4th ed, 1994, Washington DC, APA.

32. Baker T.B., Morse E., Sherman J.E. The motivation to use drugs: a psychobiological analysis of urges, in *The Nebraska symposium on motivation: alcohol use and abuse*. Ed. Rivers P.C. Lincoln, University of Nebraska Press. 1986, 257-323.

33. Goudie A.J. Conditioned opponent processes in the development of tolerance to psychoactive drugs. *Progress in Neuro-Psychopharmacology and Biological Psychiatry*, 1990, 14, 675-88.

34. Siegel S. Drug anticipation and drug addiction. The 1998 H. David Archibald Lecture. *Addiction*, 1999, 94, 1113-24.

35. Siegel S. Morphine analgesic tolerance: its situation specificity supports a Pavlovian conditioning model. *Science*, 1976, 193, 323-5.

36. Siegel S. Morphine-induced attenuation of morphine tolerance. *Science*, 1981, 211, 1533-4.

37. Schulteis G., Koob G.F. Reinforcement processes in opiate addiction: A homeostatic model. *Neurochemical Research*, 1996, 21, 1437-54.

38. Ramabadran K., Bansinath M. The role of endogenous opioid peptides in the regulation of pain. *Critical Reviews in Neurobiology*, 1990, 6, 13-32.

39. Yeomans M.R., Wright P. Lower pleasantness of palatable foods in nalmefene-treated human volunteers. *Appetite*, 1991, 16, 249-59.

40. Green B.G. Capsaicin cross-desensitization on the tongue: psychophysical evidence that oral chemical irritation is mediated by more than one sensory pathway. *Chemical Senses*, 1991, 16, 675-89.

6.2. ALCOHOL ADDICTION AND ALCOHOL CRAVINGS

Richard Hammersley and Marie Reid

6.2.1 Introduction

This section will examine concepts of addiction and craving that are used in understanding alcohol and drug dependence. During this examination, it will consider the extent to which these concepts are relevant to the understanding of food cravings and addictions. To begin with, it is worth pointing out that, for most of human history, alcohol was a food (1), which was considered as a valuable alternative to polluted water and a source of nutrients. Reading both estimated consumption figures and novels from the 19th century, one gets the impression that few were sober, ever, by modern standards (1). Even children drank 'small beer'. The boundary between what is considered a food and what is a drug or medicine has varied over time and this variation will probably continue. For example, the preliminary programme of the 17th International Congress on Nutrition in 2001 offers symposia on 'Functional Foods?' and 'Nutrients as Drugs?'[1]

6.2.2 Meaning of Addiction

That nutrients might be drugs does not mean that they must be addictive. Although 'addiction' has become part of the popular imagination, nowadays most researchers on addiction agree that 'addiction' refers to an interdisciplinary field of study, rather than a specific state with distinct neuropsychological and biological characteristics. As we shall see, people cannot be neatly divided into alcoholics and normal drinkers. The most melodramatic examples of alcoholics appear very different from normal drinkers, but most people with alcohol problems do not appear markedly different from other people who drink. Instead of 'alcoholism' it is now generally accepted in addiction research that there is at most a syndrome of

---

[1] http://www.univie.ac.at/iuns2001

alcohol (or other drug) dependence (2), where no simple set of features of the syndrome is essential.

It is also accepted that alcohol problems can take forms other than dependence. Chronic heavy use may be damaging – to health, social life, finances or work – even without meeting criteria for dependence. Acute intoxication may lead to acute problems, including traffic and other accidents, violence and regrettable sexual or other behaviour. People who experience repeated or extensive problems related to drinking are advised to moderate or cease drinking. The sensible form of change depends on the problem. For example, a man who binges after Saturday matches with his sports club and then repeatedly gets arrested for disorder offences might be advised to change his Saturday nights, rather than abstaining entirely or seeking sophisticated counselling. One reason for people believing in alcoholism is to reduce cognitive dissonance about their own drinking, which may be problematic but is not 'really' alcoholic.

6.2.2.1   Diagnostic and Statistical Manual of Mental Disorders

Might food dependence meet recognised criteria for substance dependence?

The DSM-IV (Diagnostic and Statistical Manual of Mental Disorders) (3) defines substance dependence as outlined below. The underlined concepts are subjective, to show that clinical or personal judgement is an inescapable part of the definition of dependence. The DSM-IV also has criteria for eating problems, but here we are going to consider if substance dependence applies also to food dependence.

6.2.2.1.1   DSM-IV Criteria for Substance Dependence and how foods may fit these criteria

In the following definitions, underlined concepts are subjective.

A <u>maladaptive</u> pattern of substance use leading to <u>clinically significant</u> impairment or distress, as manifested by three (or more) of the following, occurring at any time in the same 12-month period.

(1)   Tolerance, as defined by either of the following:

(a) a need for markedly increased amounts of the substance to achieve intoxication or desired effect
(b) markedly diminished effect with continued use of the same amount of the substance.

Relevance to food:

The difficulty with tolerance for food is that there is a lack of clarity about the nature of the psychological effects achieved by binge eating or over-consumption of a specific foodstuff. The psychoactive effects of foods tend to be subtle and it is not clear how tolerance can be demonstrated except by the following circular argument: If a person markedly increases consumption, then this itself may be evidence for tolerance. Yet it equally could be evidence for other processes, such as learning, as the measurement of food 'effects' is difficult. This issue becomes even more convoluted for anorexia nervosa, where, if there was 'tolerance', this would be to the effects of fasting.

(2) Withdrawal as manifested by either of the following:

(a) the characteristic withdrawal syndrome for the substance (varies from substance to substance)
(b) the same (or a closely related) substance is taken to relieve or <u>avoid</u> withdrawal symptoms

Relevance to food:

Food withdrawals are also problematic for similar reasons. There appears to be a mild caffeine withdrawal syndrome (4); but for most foods any withdrawal appears to be primarily 'psychological'. Which means that it should be contentious whether or not there really is a specific and theoretically important 'withdrawal', as opposed to a generic loss or regret over things that one no longer has, or have decided to refrain from. If someone gives up meat then they may miss bacon and may even show arousal and salivation at the smell of bacon, but that is not withdrawal. Again, in the absence of a specific withdrawal syndrome, there is a risk of defining withdrawal circularly so that repeatedly ingesting something is taken to be evidence that it is being taken to avoid withdrawal. Bill Saunders once argued that men are addicted to trousers because if their trousers are removed then they display 'withdrawal' – anxiety and 'trouser seeking behaviour'. He meant this to be irony, before anybody sets up a self-help group for trouser dependence. Self-help is an issue to which we will return in the next section.

(3)   The substance is often taken in larger amounts or over a longer period than was intended.

Relevance to food:
    This can clearly apply to food, whether eating too much of a specific food, eating too much in general, or even eating too little; e.g. dieting is often more severe or lasts longer than was intended.

(4)   There is a persistent desire or unsuccessful efforts to cut down or control substance use.

Relevance to food:
    This can clearly apply to food, perhaps even more so than with drugs or alcohol, because cyclical restraint and excess can be a central feature of eating disorders.

(5)   A great deal of time is spent in activities necessary to obtain the substance (e.g. visiting multiple doctors or driving long distances), use the substance (e.g. chain-smoking), or recover from its effects.

Relevance to food:
    This may apply to bulimia nervosa, but it has not been considered otherwise as an issue for food, which is generally straightforward to obtain.

(6)   Important social, occupational, or recreational activities are given up or reduced because of substance use.

436

Relevance to food:

This can apply in some cases of eating disorders, but further research is needed.

(7) The substance use is continued despite knowledge of having a persistent or recurrent physical or psychological problem that is likely to have been caused or exacerbated by the substance (e.g. current cocaine use despite recognition of cocaine-induced depression, or continued drinking despite recognition that an ulcer was made worse by alcohol consumption).

Relevance to food:

Again, this can clearly apply to food; examples include anorexics starving to death, and patients who have undergone surgical procedures to limit their food intake bursting the stitches or staples that reduced their stomach in size.

Specify whether:

'With physiological dependence': evidence of tolerance or withdrawal (i.e. either item 1 or 2 is present)

'Without physiological dependence': no evidence of tolerance or withdrawal (i.e. neither item 1 nor item 2 is present)

An important point here is that the clinician's and the patient's subjective assessments of the situation are central to this most objective diagnosis of dependence. However, a person can be diagnosed alcohol-dependent on the criteria of tolerance, withdrawal and major problems related to drinking, even if they feel that they have no problems. The most common place for such a diagnosis is a general medical ward, where a person has been admitted because of an acute health crisis, such as liver disease. Being in hospital produces an alcohol withdrawal syndrome and tolerance is established by the enormous amount the person admits to drinking (perhaps a bottle of spirits a day or more). Nonetheless, these people are rarer than alcohol-dependent people whose problems are obvious to them and their families.

Relevance to food:
   It would appear that the DSM-IV criteria for substance dependence might apply to food, but only 'substance dependence without physiological dependence' because neither tolerance nor withdrawal will be shown for foods. It is also worth emphasising that drug and alcohol dependence syndrome may also occur without physiological dependence and, despite what common sense may suggest, physiological dependence is not highly correlated with frequency and quantity of intake. Some people show signs of physiological dependence at relatively low levels. To summarise, compared with alcohol or other drugs, if foods are 'addictive', then they are only 'psychologically addictive', which is not to deny the potential for suffering.

6.2.3   Addiction Culture

In a book about food cravings and addiction, it is also worth drawing attention to the social factors that sustain a view of alcohol problems as being about a minority of addicts or misusers. Large industries manufacture and promote alcohol and provide many governments with substantial revenue. In the UK, the alcohol industry's expressed view is that 'The misuse of alcohol by the minority' is the problem (5) and that most people drink alcohol without causing harm. The industry has a motive for defining 'misusers' as a small out-group, in order to sustain sales to 'users'. This is in contrast to what Kreitman (6) called the preventative paradox, that, because there are masses of users but only a few alcoholics/misusers, more problems come from the masses than from the minority. There is also a substantial treatment industry, particularly in the USA, which makes money from treating addiction, is ideologically entrenched behind the concept of addiction as a disease state, and is reluctant to shift to broader health promotion work. Again, it is in the treatment industry's interests to construct 'alcoholism' as a specific condition that can be treated. Alongside this industry are large self-help group movements, originally Alcoholics Anonymous, which do much good, but which also encourage people to (re)construct their identities around their status as recovered alcoholics, or recovered overeaters, or recovered narcotics addicts, or recovered marijuana addicts. This is obviously preferable to a continued alcoholic identity, but these movements admit anyone who wants to come and feels that he/she has or has had the relevant problem. In consequence, they can include people who would never have met criteria for dependence, as well as people who have been sober for many more years than they were drunk. Finally, the mass of normal drinkers find comfort in normalising their drinking habits by pathologising alcoholism.

Another issue perhaps relevant to food is that addiction history suggests that intensely delivered substances are bad news. Gin was a problem, when beer was not (1). Heroin injecting became more of a problem than opium smoking had been. Cigarettes appear to have more dependence-forming potential than pipe and cigar tobacco, which are absorbed in the mouth rather than the lungs. Not only are intensely delivered substances bad news, but technology tends to develop them, often with good intentions.

Review of the harm caused by all types of drinking and possible responses in addition to treating alcoholism has recently been provided by the Society for the Study of Addiction (7), incidentally demonstrating that 'addiction' now is an area of study, not a specific syndrome. Popular ideas about food and eating addictions may be on the rise for similar reasons: an obese population eager to normalise their eating; a massive manufacturing industry keen to promote food that is cheap to make and highly palatable (maximising profits and sales) rather than nutritionally balanced products; a booming treatment and dieting industry. The last-named group does not necessarily promote 'addiction' but seems willing to locate the problem 'in the person', where it can be treated, rather than in society, where it may slip our grasp or require social engineering (8). It seems unnecessary for society to manufacture food 'addictions' after addiction research had moved on from that construction of alcohol and drug problems. Alcoholics

Anonymous appears to help people (9), but we don't know whether this means that 'Overeaters Anonymous', which is modelled on AA, right down to the emphasis on abstinence one day at a time (10), helps people. While there have been some academic papers on Overeaters Anonymous (11,12), it has not yet been evaluated objectively. Because of the voluntarism and anonymity of these organisations, they are difficult to research. OA is certainly popular, with over 8,000 meetings worldwide, and its objective is that "By the year 2010 Overeaters Anonymous will be the #1 recognized program for help with the problem of overeating" (10). Despite modelling itself on AA, OA is careful to avoid the term 'addiction' on its Web site.

Another note of caution from the alcohol literature is to avoid equating the popularity of a programme with its success. AA is capable of reaching a very large number of drinkers. However, true success rates are as modest as those for other forms of intervention (i.e. approximately 20% of people have improved after 12 months or more). The surface success of self-help organisations tends to be distorted by the fact that they rarely monitor early drop-outs (people who attend only once or twice) and that long-term members represent survivors, who are not dead and have not relapsed long-term to dependent or binge drinking (or overeating). In consequence, the sheer number of people who will testify to the importance of a 12-step programme for their recovery is not evidence that treatment resources should be funnelled solely in that direction.

Is there any mileage in the analogy of high-fat, high-carbohydrate, highly processed foods being 'intense' and hence perhaps more likely to lead to psychological problems with their use? This specific question is discussed in section 6.4. But, as this section discusses, 'addiction' is obsolete as a guide to understanding substance use problems.

6.2.4   Beyond Addiction

There is alcohol dependence that applies to a minority of drinkers and to a minority of drinkers with problems. There is alcohol misuse, which is drinking that is likely to or has already caused significant problems and is engaged in by a substantial minority of the population – probably 10-15%

overall and more among young men. There is moderate drinking of up to 3 units in a day for men, 2 for women, without binges and with breaks between some drinking days. Normal drinkers lie somewhere between this last temperate ideal and misuse. There is the potential for drift towards misuse and pulling back towards temperance. Society's dilemma is how to acknowledge problems without pathologising them. These difficulties resonate for food, where there are also some spectacular problems, widespread lesser problems and a healthy ideal that relatively few people achieve all the time.

6.2.5 Craving

The concept of craving is undergoing a renaissance in addiction research, with three major journals devoting entire issues to craving (Alcohol & Alcoholism, 1999, 34, 2; Alcohol Research & Health, 1999, 23, 3; Addiction, 2000, 95, 8, Supplement 2). There are three major approaches to craving: a neuropsychological approach that seeks to understand the brain pathways that are involved in craving (13), a cognitive approach that seeks to understand how craving may be caused by the ways in which drugs use is learned and thought about (14), and a cue-exposure that sees craving as the result of exposure to environmental or mental cues that have been associated with drugs use (15). There is also continued debate about whether craving is an essential causal factor in dependence or not (16).

One important point to notice is that theories of addiction do not attempt to explain substance use by invoking craving, but only substance dependence. It is accepted that people can and do use alcohol and other drugs on purpose, because they intend to and for mundane reasons, including that they expect to like the effects and that they regard use as socially positive in some sense at the time of use. No special craving is required to explain splitting a bottle of wine with your dining partner, or indeed consuming seven pints of beer with your team after the match. However, use that seems positive at the time may not seem so the next morning and may not be safe or healthy behaviour. Thus, before comparing food cravings with drug cravings, one must consider whether the resultant eating behaviour is comparable to drug dependence. If it is not, then 'craving' is being used to describe a rather different psychological state, with different neuropsychological and cognitive causes.

Understanding of craving is contaminated by the fact that people often retrospectively invoke cravings and other irresistible urges to apologise for misbehaviour. Orford (17) called his book 'Excessive Appetites' and argued that dependence requires a behaviour that the person does more than he or she thinks that he/she should. Tiffany (18) put forward an influential theory that craving was due to the attempt to block habitual behaviours (automatic action schemata). These may involve regular, repetitive habits, such as cigarette smoking, or infrequent, situation-specific habits, such as taking an ecstasy tablet before going to a club on a Friday night. In the latter case, craving may occur, but only in the relevant situation. The person might crave ecstasy in the club on Friday, but not during the week. However, intermittent craving in specific situations has not been researched. According to Tiffany (18), substance use can occur without craving, when an automatic action schema is invoked and not blocked. For example, somebody in a bar with friends may consume several drinks while paying minimal conscious attention. Eating can be similar.

Blocking is attempted only if the person has some conscious reason to avoid the habit, or the drug is not available. From this cognitive approach, as food is usually available, at least in the shops if not in the home, then, unless food is deviant in some sense, it is not clear how it can be craved. The most common forms of deviance are that the food is excessive in quantity, sinful, unhealthy or bizarre. People may afterwards say that they craved such food, even if they did not - whatever it means to crave - before or during eating. We would add that, as with all mental states, the study of craving is primarily the study of self-reports about mental states, usually retrospective self-reports (19). These comments about blocking and the role of self-reports apply to all theories of craving other than those that consider behaviour alone to be evidence for craving.

Alcohol-dependent people can crave alcohol in some or all of the following senses:

- They think about drinking when they are not drinking.
- When not drinking, they plan out their next binge and may even engineer excuses to go off on it.

These two cognitive activities are not normally considered to be craving, although they might be evidence of it. But one can plan one's next drinking session 'coldly' without any craving, or with intense desire, just as one can book a holiday while wishing it were happening tomorrow, or without even looking forward to it at that time. Binge eaters may think and behave similarly.

- They wish that they could have a drink right now, or feel an intense desire for a drink.

This intense desire has been studied with rating scales (20). People who are abstaining from alcohol or cigarettes, and are asked to rate their craving over time usually report episodes of intense desire or craving for the drug. These tend to be brief and extremely intense. They can be triggered by stressors, or by reminders of substance use, such as the sight of alcohol, or environmental cues to drinking. They can also seemingly appear from nowhere. Craving tends to be more common in the early days of abstinence, but has the potential to reappear unexpectedly months, even years after the last drink or smoke. Sometimes, craving leads to substance use, particularly if the substance is readily available. Sometimes it doesn't. Indeed, most abstainers will go through a number of episodes of craving before relapsing. Some go through hundreds and then relapse. Despite popular depictions of heroin withdrawal and alcohol withdrawal, craving does not stop when the withdrawal syndrome is over, and can occur with drugs that do not produce a strong withdrawal syndrome, such as cannabis (21). To further complicate matters, sometimes relapse occurs without craving, even if the person had prior episodes of craving. Indeed, relapse is only moderately correlated with craving (about 0.4 - (18)). It is not clear whether or not food cravings are of comparable intensity. For food there is also the complexity that, as restrained eating can be part of the disorder, abstinence from specific foods is not a recommended treatment outcome. Instead, the treatment objective would be that the client wanted or desired a food and ate some of it in a normal fashion rather than craving it and then bingeing on it.

It seems unlikely that people who are not being researched have clear memory for the nature and frequency of their cravings. People may also use the word 'craving' to describe planning and thinking about alcohol consumption - for instance, saying that they had been craving alcohol all day. This obscures the nature of cravings. Drummond *et al.* (22) point out that we do not know enough about the temporal dynamics of craving. For instance, can people experience mild, prolonged cravings that eventually lead to use, as well as intense, brief ones?

● Alcohol-dependent people also report that alcohol itself triggers a strong desire for more alcohol and, after a certain amount of alcohol, this desire is uncontrollable.

Once they start drinking, alcohol-dependent people may drink a great deal rapidly, may have difficulty sticking to only one or two drinks, and may have difficulty stopping until unable to obtain further alcohol or until unconscious. Furthermore, abstaining drinkers are remarkably able to rapidly resume their previous pattern of drinking. In some cases, this is at levels that would literally kill a less alcohol-tolerant person (23). Some physiological adaptation to alcohol, probably in the enlarged liver and perhaps elsewhere, clearly lasts a long time after abstinence. For obvious ethical and practical reasons, craving has not often been studied during relapse or bingeing.

Craving remains a part of modern theories of dependence. There is considerable further lack of clarity about the meaning and operational definition of craving (22). One problem is that animal models of craving often assume that the amount of a drug ingested per unit time is an index of craving, but this does not work for people. A further difficulty is that much neuropsychological research assumes that craving is an epiphenomenon of the neuropsychological effects of chronic drug use, while the cognitive approach regards these neuropsychological effects as necessary but not sufficient for craving to occur, because further cognitive processes, such as blocking, are also required. Another problem is that symbolic craving – verbal expressions, thoughts, or indeed ratings – may occur largely independently of non-symbolic craving – acquired via non-verbal conditioning mechanisms. We have indeed found that the psychomotor effects of alcohol can be more easily influenced by non-verbal cues to alcohol than by verbal expectations about alcohol (24). That people report craving does not guarantee that they are experiencing a psychological process that is likely to lead to drinking. To further complicate the study of craving, it is plausible that there are substantial individual differences in the various processes and phenomena that construct it.

Thus, the idea that craving for alcohol or a drug is like an appetite for it is too simple; indeed, the 'biological appetite' model of hunger is too simple anyway (25). How hungry somebody rates themselves to be tends to be correlated with how much they will eat. This does not work for craving. Returning to Orford's theory (17), this is because, with drug dependence, any basic appetite-like craving is mediated by one's cognitive appraisal of that feeling (18). This may apply even if craving originates in a neurological adaptation to a drug (26). Somebody who craves a whole bottle of gin may either drink it or not. If not, then this may be because he/she interprets the craving as evidence that it would be unwise to drink more. In other words, he/she may exercise restraint in the face of craving and may be more or less successful at restraint, for shorter or longer periods of time. Perhaps this is not so different from eating after all. Appetite is correlated with the amount consumed when all other things are equal, such as when the subjects are hungry students with no reason to restrain. When there are reasons to restrain, then the correlation may disappear.

Restrained eating has come to have slightly negative connotations, but, as with alcohol and drugs, there are positive reasons for restraint other than a desire for thinness. These reasons include social rules about sharing food, or saving food for later. By analogy with alcohol and drug craving, it seems unlikely that food cravings will be recognised without restraint of some kind, the exception being, perhaps, food cravings that are caused solely by a specific dietary deficiency. Linking back to our earlier point, with any ingestive behaviour it is possible to consume without restraint at the time, then afterwards feel that one should have been restrained and consequently invoke craving retrospectively to explain that lack of restraint. For drugs and alcohol, the relapse literature is beset by this problem that people's cognitions while relapsing can only be retrospectively reconstructed. In the case of alcohol and some other drugs, this problem is compounded by drug-induced amnesia. Only a faint shadow of relapse can ethically be induced for research purposes. Food studies have the potential to clarify the relationship between craving, ingestion and restraint because the ethical difficulties are less. But, how similar are food cravings to drug cravings?

As can be appreciated from the above, craving is a conceptual tangle. Many papers on craving begin with apologies for this, before going on to operationalise the definition in one way or another (see 27). So, measures of craving vary widely, are not used consistently, and may or may not measure the same things (16,22). Perhaps, strangely, when drug users who have not been treated talk spontaneously about drugs, they do not mention craving at all (16). In contrast, people do seem to talk spontaneously about food cravings.

Are there purely physiological cravings?

This idea was romanticised by William Burroughs (28) in his fictional but autobiographical account of his heroin use.

> "Why do you *need* narcotics, Mr. Lee?" is a question that stupid psychiatrists ask. The answer is "I need junk to get out of bed in the morning, to shave and eat breakfast. I need it to stay alive."

> Of course junkies don't as a rule die from the withdrawal of junk. But in a very literal sense, kicking the habit involves the death of junk-dependent cells and their replacement with cells that do not need junk." (p23)

Much recent research has examined the neuropsychological changes associated with dependence and craving (29), perpetuating a superficially more sophisticated version of Burrough's (28) account. Techniques such as neuroimaging have advanced understanding of the brain areas involved in craving. Hommer (29) suggests that craving for alcohol involves the basal ganglia, thalamus and orbital cortex, as well as other areas. Findings are not as yet conclusive, and there is a risk of their becoming complex and non-specific as further studies are conducted.

What is absent from the purely neuropsychological approach is a recognition that cravings are psychologically mediated. The most striking demonstration of this was that Robins *et al.* (30) studied Vietnam veterans who had been heroin-dependent in Vietnam. On return home, those who returned to environments lacking in heroin generally ceased use. On the basis of purely physiological need they ought to have moved to the nearest deprived inner city area where heroin was available (as it was in America's largest cities at the time). On the other hand, those who returned to environments where heroin was available, or had dabbled before going to Vietnam, were much more likely to use. But if the majority craved heroin, then they did nothing about it.

One theory is that craving is part of a classically conditioned response to certain environments and stimuli, which has led to cue exposure research and treatment where dependent people are exposed to drug or alcohol stimuli to recondition them. This has had some success, but of a limited kind (31). Another problem is that it is unclear whether this response is an anticipatory response (alcohol-like) or an adaptation response (alcohol-opposite), or a mixture of both. A final problem is that the links between subjective state and physiological changes are unclear and inconsistent.

Drug- and alcohol-dependent people often say that specific environments trigger craving - walking past the pub; coming back to the city where it all happened. But other ex-users are able to avoid relapse living in exactly the same environment where they used. It has been suggested (32) that the mental environment is likely to provide more important cues to trigger craving. There is also some evidence that dependent people process alcohol- or drug-related information differently, perhaps more sensitively, than control groups (14,33,34). Mechanisms for food craving would plausibly be similar. In theory at least (e.g. 18), people could come to crave anything given the right history of reinforcement.

Yet, at least for alcohol and drugs, there may also be a physiological component. To help explain craving, this component would have to involve neurological changes that persisted for months, at least, in the absence of the substance, and produced subjective feelings of craving intermittently. These changes would not necessarily have to be substance-specific, because the subjective craving for a specific drug would be conditioned, with the specific drug being the conditioned response to whatever the state was. In existing models it is unclear why craving should be intermittent. It could be that the changed systems malfunction only when certain demands are placed upon them, such as stress to the person (13). There would be scope here for the considerable individual differences that are observed in people's experiences of craving. We will leave it to others to consider whether such a physiological component is at all plausible for food cravings (see also 35).

Craving research is hindered by the confusion over the meaning of craving, as well as by the difficulties of studying craving during substance use. Drummond (22) also call for more phenomenological studies of craving: What do people actually say they are experiencing and what do they do, under what conditions and how often? People who are being treated for substance dependence rapidly learn the professional jargon, including 'craving.' Perhaps some of the confusion in the literature originates because substance-dependent people do not know what 'craving' means either.

6.2.6   Conclusions

Addiction as a state has been abandoned by addiction research, but the state remains a popular idea outside the academic community and indeed still motivates drug and alcohol policies, despite calls for reconsideration (7,36). We do not think that food problems should be squeezed into this obsolete mould. Psychological dependence on food, or eating, or not eating, is more plausible. Amongst the unwelcome addiction stereotypes that nutritional research should resist are to assume that food problems belong to a small minority with clear psychiatric problems; that they are necessarily located entirely within individual people, rather than having environmental or social causes; that all 'addicts' are more or less the same and can therefore be given the same treatment; that the 'addiction' is necessarily a lifelong disease or struggle, which people cannot put behind them; and that, without crisis, change will not occur, because 'addicts' 'deny' their problems. There should probably instead be early identification of and minimal interventions for food problems, before they have got out of hand, as well as steps to control high-risk food, if there is such a thing.

Craving remains important in addiction research, but is a complex and confusing concept, which has leaked out of addiction research into everyday language. Ordinary people now say that they crave a chocolate, or a beer, when in times past they would only have wanted one. Only dependent people seem to crave in a strict sense and when they do it is not strongly related to relapse. How and if craving occurs during a drinking bout is less clear; nor is it clear how it can be researched. Retrospective accounts of craving, indeed all of mental states, are somewhat unreliable (19). To crave it is probably necessary to be trying to restrain or control one's behaviour. It would be useful if food research could disentangle craving. It may have a good chance of doing so because it is not encumbered with the problems of studying mental states while people are intoxicated, or with the ethical difficulties of administering drugs of dependence to people. However, it is not clear that people can be dependent upon food as they can be with drugs. Thus, craving for foods may not be the same as craving when a person is dependent upon alcohol or another drug. At minimum, the neuropsychological mechanisms involved must be different. The relative importance for craving of neuropsychological mechanisms and cognitive mechanisms remains to be established.

6.2.7   References

1.   Barr A. *Drink. An informal social history*. London, Bantam Press. 1995.

2.   Edwards G., Gross M.M. Alcohol dependence: provisional description of a clinical syndrome. *British Medical Journal*, 1976, 295, 1058-61.

3.   American Psychiatric Association. *Diagnostic and statistical manual of mental disorders: DSM-IV, 4th edition.* Washington DC, American Psychiatric Association. 1994.

4.   Strain E.C., Griffiths R.R. Caffeine dependence – fact or fiction. *Journal of the Royal Society of Medicine,* 1995, 88, 437-40.

5.   Coussins J. *Taking Responsibility.* Home page of the Portman Group website http://www.portman-group.org.uk/

6.   Kreitman N. Alcohol consumption and the preventative paradox. *British Journal of Addiction,* 1986, 81, 353-63.

7.   Rasitrick D., Hodgson R., Ritson B. *Tackling Alcohol Together: The Basis for a UK Alcohol Policy.* London, Free Association Books. 1999.

8.   Battle E.K., Brownell K.D. Confronting a rising tide of eating disorders and obesity: treatment vs. prevention and policy. *Addictive Behaviors,* 1996, 21, 755-65.

9.   Vaillant G.E. *The Natural History of Alcoholism Revisited.* Cambridge, MA. Harvard University Press. 1995.

10.   Overeaters Anonymous. *About Overeaters Anonymous.* http://www.overeatersanonymous.org/about.htm

11.   Room R., Greenfield T. Alcoholics Anonymous, other 12-step movements and psychotherapy in the United States Population 1990. *Addiction,* 1993, 88, 555-62.

12.   Weiner S. The addiction of overeating: Self-help groups as treatment models. *Journal of Clinical Psychology,* 1998, 54, 163-7.

13.   Verheul R., Van den Brink W., Geerlings P. A three-pathway psychobiological model of craving for alcohol. *Alcohol and Alcoholism,* 1999, 34, 197-222.

14.   Franken I.H.A., Kroon L.Y., Hendricks V.M. Influence of individual differences in craving and obsessive cocaine thoughts on attentional processes in cocaine abuse patients. *Addictive Behaviors,* 2000, 25, 99-102.

15.   Drummond D.C. What does cue-reactivity have to offer clinical research? *Addiction,* 2000, Supplement 2, 95, 8, 129-44.

16. James D. *The measurement of craving and its importance in drug misuse behaviour.* Unpublished PhD thesis. Department of Psychology, University of Wales, Swansea. 2000.

17. Orford J. *Excessive appetites: a psychological view of addiction.* Chichester, Wiley. 1985.

18. Tiffany S.T. A cognitive model of drug urges and drug-use behavior: Role of automatic and nonautomatic processes. *Psychological Review*, 1990, 97, 147-68.

19. Hammersley R.H. A digest of memory phenomena for addiction research. *Addiction*, 1994, 89, 283-93.

20. Flannery B.A., Volpicelli J.R., Pettinati H.M. Psychometric properties of the Penn Alcohol Craving Scale. *Alcoholism – Clinical and Experimental Research*, 1999, 23, 1289-95.

21. Hall W., Solowij N., Lemon J. *The health and social consequences of cannabis use.* Monograph Series No. 25. Canberra, Australian Government Publishing Service. 1994.

22. Drummond D.C., Litten R.Z., Lowman C., Hunt W.A. Craving research: future directions. *Addiction*, 2000, Supplement 2, 95, S247-55.

23. Edwards G., Marshall E.J., Cook C.C.H. *The treatment of drinking problems* 2nd edition. Cambridge, Cambridge University Press. 1997.

24. Hammersley R.H., Finnigan F., Millar K. Verbal expectancies and performance after alcohol. *Addictive Behaviors*, 1998, 23, 489-96.

25. Kassel J.D., Shiffman S. What can hunger teach us about drug craving? A comparative analysis of the two constructs? *Advances in Behaviour Research and Therapy*, 1992, 14, 141-67.

26. Anton R.F. What is craving? Models and implications for treatment. *Alcohol Research & Health*, 1999, 23, 165-73.

27. Kozlowski L.T., Wilkinson D.A. Use and misuse of the concept of craving by alcohol, tobacco and drug researchers. *British Journal of Addiction*, 1987, 82, 31-6.

28. Burroughs W.S. *Junky.* Harmondsworth, Penguin. 1977.

29. Hommer D.W. Functional imaging of craving. *Alcohol Research and Health*, 1999, 23, 187-96.

30. Robins L.N., Helzer J.E., Hesselbrock M., Wish E. Vietnam veterans three years after Vietnam: How our study changed our view of heroin, in *The Yearbook of Substance Use and Abuse*, 2. Eds Brill L., Winick C. New York, Human Sciences Press. 1980, 213-30.

31. Carter B.L., Tiffany S.T. Meta-analysis of cue-reactivity in addiction research. *Addiction*, 1999, 94, 327-40.

32. Hammersley R.H. Cue exposure and learning theory. *Addictive Behaviors*, 1992, 17, 297-300.

33. Weinstein A., Feldtkeller B., Malizia A., Wilson S., Bailey J., Nutt D.J. Integrating the cognitive and physiological aspects of craving. *Journal of Psychopharmacology*, 1998, 12, 31-8.

34. Schulze D., Jones B.T. The effects of alcohol cues and an alcohol priming dose on a multi-factorial measure of subjective cue reactivity in social drinkers. *Psychopharmacology*, 1999, 145, 452-4.

35. Rogers P.J., Smit H.J. Food craving and food 'addiction': a critical review of the evidence from a biopsychosocial perspective. *Pharmacology, Biochemistry and Behaviour*, 2000, 66, 3-14.

36. Parker H., Aldridge J., Measham F. *Illegal leisure - The Normalization of Adolescent Recreational Drug Use*. London, Routledge. 1998.

6.3. DEPRESSION, APPETITE AND EATING

Keith Matthews, Alasdair Rooney and Richard Day

6.3.1   Introduction

Depression is a devastating and common mental disorder, recently identified as the fourth-ranked cause of disability and premature death worldwide, predicted to attain second ranking by the year 2020 (1). Serious depressive disorders afflict 5% of individuals at some point in their lives, with less severe manifestations afflicting around 20% (2). Depressive disorders are chronic, often life-long illnesses, with a high risk of recurrence (3). Despite recent advances in the definition of the neuropsychological and neurobiological changes that are associated with depression, our understanding of its aetiology and pathophysiology remains rudimentary. In the absence of such information, the classification and diagnosis of depression remain symptom-based. Both of the major psychiatric classification systems currently in use, the multi-axial DSM-IV (North America) (4) and the World Health Organization's ICD-10 (5), consider a blunting, or loss, of the capacity to experience pleasure as a core feature of depression. Amongst the commonest presentations of this altered experience of pleasure, known as anhedonia, are reported changes in appetite. Indeed, altered appetite is enshrined as one of the key diagnostic features of depression, as are associated changes in body weight regulation. In addition, many of the drug treatments most commonly used in the management of depressive disorders are widely considered to exert significant effects on taste, eating and the regulation of body weight. In this section, we shall review briefly the available data in an attempt to answer two clinically important questions:

1.   How does depression affect appetite, eating and weight regulation?
2.   What effects do antidepressant drugs exert on appetite, eating and weight regulation?

To conclude, we will speculate briefly on the potential neurobiological substrates for such changes.

6.3.2   What is Depression?

Depression is a common, complex and poorly understood condition. In its more severe manifestations, it is life-threatening, either as a result of suicide (lifetime risk of 4-15%) or through a dramatic failure to maintain food and fluid intake. Death by dehydration and emaciation was a frequent clinical observation in the era prior to the introduction of effective treatments. Such presentations are now rare, at least in the developed world, although there has been an apparent increase in the prevalence of milder forms of illness during the latter half of the last century (2). Epidemiological research has identified several potent risk factors that increase the probability of developing depression, notably female gender, a history of depressive disorder in the immediate family, early childhood adversity and stressful life events in adulthood (2). Indeed, the role of early stress as a mediator of vulnerability and of adult stress as a precipitant of depression is acknowledged as influential by current psychological (6) and neurobiological (7) explanatory models. This predisposition, or vulnerability, to depression is a poorly understood and complex product of genetic and environmental factors that somehow influences the psychological perception of, and response to, social and environmental events, translating them into neurophysiological changes. In the absence of a comprehensive understanding of the aetiology and pathophysiology of depression, diagnosis remains clinical syndrome based. Nevertheless, extensive clinical studies have informed our understanding of the course and outcome of putative sub-categories of depression. Differences in appetite change represent one of the key criteria for these speculative sub-groupings.

6.3.3   Depression and Appetite Change

Depression is considered a spectrum disorder, reflecting an apparent continuity between the normal emotional responses of transient sadness and dysphoria in response to adverse events, through a range of disabling mood disorders that vary in their persistence and severity, to the severe, episodic, behavioural and cognitive disturbance of Bipolar Disorder. Within the major classification systems, depressive episodes are distinguished from the *'normal'* experience of sadness and adjustment to adversity by their persistence (>2 weeks), their pervasiveness and the degree of functional disturbance that accompanies them. A typical depressive episode will be defined by the presence of core symptoms: low or sad mood, loss of interest or the capacity to experience pleasure, and an array of associated features that include reduced energy, enhanced fatigue, sleep impairment, loss of appetite, weight change, persistent thoughts of guilt, worthlessness and/or suicide (4,5). Although present in some other psychiatric conditions, the altered capacity to experience pleasure, or anhedonia, is currently considered the defining feature of depressive disorders. An individual who suffers from Bipolar Disorder will also experience episodes of what often appears quite the reverse of depression, so-called mania or, if less severe, hypomania. During a period of mania, sufferers can appear euphoric, grandiose, full of energy and ideas, to have a diminished requirement for sleep and to be socially disinhibited. Bipolar Disorder has a lifetime prevalence of less than 1%, whereas unipolar depression (no current or lifetime history of manic episodes) carries prevalence rates of around 10% for males and 20% for females (2). In this section, we will focus on the influence of the commoner forms of depression on eating and appetite, although some of the relevant studies have included Bipolar subjects within their sample. Also, this section will focus on the disordered eating found with primary depressive disorder and will distinguish this from the depression that is commonly found in association with eating disorders such as anorexia and bulimia nervosa. However, it is acknowledged that this distinction may be entirely artificial.

6.3.4   The Evidence Base: Some Caveats

Despite longstanding and widespread recognition of the diagnostic and therapeutic importance of changes in appetite and weight regulation in depressive disorders, much of our knowledge comes from isolated clinical reports, or from small case series. Such studies usually report unsophisticated recordings obtained from diagnostically heterogeneous samples following naturalistic treatment responses. In recent years, increasing refinement of diagnostic criteria has raised confidence that the subjects from one study may be comparable with those in another. Unfortunately, many of the major studies of appetite and weight regulation were conducted prior to the adoption of recently conceptualised and agreed diagnostic refinement and rigour. As a consequence, patient sample characteristics within early studies were highly variable, rendering comparison from one study to another problematic. Further, the assessment of appetite was generally crude, often based entirely on unconfirmed self-report, using non-validated, bespoke rating scales. Weight changes were typically extrapolated from the subjects' verbal reports of their *'normal'* (pre-depression) weight. Clearly, neither of these measures can be considered highly reliable. The authors are unaware of any studies in which appetite changes have been measured directly in a laboratory setting. Indeed, given the methodological shortcomings, there are few studies that offer potentially informative data.

6.3.5   Subtypes of Depression and Appetite Change

The impact of anhedonia is pervasive and potentially debilitating. Fundamental biological functions, for example sex and eating, can lose their appeal. Food is often described as having lost its taste, or as having assumed a bland taste. However, depression sufferers may report either a reduction, or an increase, in eating. Indeed, some reporting the most marked changes in taste perception may exhibit the greatest increases in body weight. For some, perhaps up to 15% (see ref. 8), appetite is actually reported to *increase*, although this may be restricted to specific categories of food – notably sweet, high carbohydrate and fat-containing food such as biscuits, cakes and chocolate. This pattern of increased appetite, which has come to be thought of (erroneously) as "carbohydrate craving", may be more common in depressed females. Such individuals may also report an increased duration of sleep, unlike the more frequent presentation of difficulty entering sleep and of persistent early morning wakening. When accompanied by other specific clinical features (so-called mood reactivity, 'leaden paralysis' and 'interpersonal rejection sensitivity'), this clinically identified subgroup is considered to report 'atypical' depression (9). In both DSM IV and ICD 10, 'atypical' depression is classified separately from other forms. The clinical significance of the typical/atypical distinction lies in putative differences in treatment responsiveness. Specifically, atypical forms of depression are considered to be less responsive to the tricyclic antidepressant drugs (so-called because of their distinctive three-ring chemical structure), possibly more so to the monoamine oxidase inhibitors (MAOIs) and selective serotonin reuptake inhibitors (SSRIs). However, the different symptom patterns may also reflect differences in aetiology (see ref. 10) and underlying neurobiology (see ref. 11) for these 'atypical' forms. Although the validity and reliability of the 'atypical' distinction remain open to challenge, recent longitudinal studies suggest that these symptom clusters remain fairly stable across time (12), and hence increased appetite and weight gain may reflect a specific depressive syndrome and pathophysiology.

6.3.6   Seasonal Affective Disorder

Following its description as a putative, discrete variant within the spectrum of depressive disorders (13), numerous epidemiological and clinical studies have supported the contention that some recurrent depressions observe a seasonal pattern. Typically, this would manifest with onset in autumn/winter and with remission in spring/summer, possibly as a consequence of varying levels and duration of daylight, hence so-called seasonal affective disorder (SAD). This pattern of recurrence features within the DSM IV classification system, not as a separate diagnostic entity, but as a 'course specifier' for other forms of depression (4). The characteristic features of the commonest form of SAD, known as 'winter depression', are listed as excessive sleeping, increased appetite with weight gain and 'carbohydrate craving'. It is also said to demonstrate a specific clinical response to regular exposure to high intensity (~ 10,000 lux) light therapy. The specificity and validity of both diagnosis and treatment-responsiveness remain questionable. For example, the SAD symptom clusters overlap substantially with those of atypical depression. Also, epidemiological studies conducted within different countries, at differing latitudes (a potent determinant of day length) have generated conflicting and inconsistent results. As a consequence, there is a paucity of detailed consideration of changes in appetite and weight regulation with SAD, but much speculation.

This speculation has revolved predominantly around the hypothesis that enhanced carbohydrate preference (or 'craving') in SAD might reflect an attempt to enhance the production of the neurotransmitter serotonin by increasing the ingestion of its essential dietary building block – the amino acid L-tryptophan. Since neurones cannot manufacture L-tryptophan, it must enter the brain through a generic amino acid transporter system. Under certain conditions (high dietary carbohydrate with low protein), the transport of tryptophan is favoured relative to other amino acid competitors, elevating levels of serotonin synthesis. Hence, increased carbohydrate/reduced protein intake might conceivably reflect a form of self-medication by encouraging the selective transport of L-tryptophan into the brain, with a consequent increase in serotonin production. However, although this hypothesis is intuitively attractive, there is no compelling, direct experimental support. For example, in an attempt to examine the potential pathophysiological significance of altered macronutrient intake in SAD, Rosenthal et al. (14) tested a small sample of SAD depressives (n=16) with two isocaloric meals with differing macronutrient constitution in a cross-over design. Compared with control subjects, SAD depressives reported an acute 'activation' effect with the high carbohydrate meal relative to the high protein one. However, no post-ingestion biochemical differences were detected and there were no objective measures of psychomotor performance. In a similar vein, Arbisi et al. (15) reported modality specific changes in the sensitivity of sweet taste thresholds in a further small sample of SAD sufferers during winter depression (n=25) – changes that normalised with transition into summer, but not with light therapy. They speculated that sweet taste insensitivity might be the immediate cause of carbohydrate cravings in such individuals. Regrettably, there are no studies examining appetite, taste sensitivity or food preference and selection in SAD that include direct comparisons with non-SAD depressed subjects, pre- and post-treatment. Indeed, Amsterdam *et al.* (16) have demonstrated similar taste insensitivity for sweetness in a mixed group (n=36) of non-SAD DSM III depressives; essentially a replication of an earlier report by Steiner *et al.* (17). Until direct comparative studies are conducted, the specificity and significance of these possible changes in taste sensitivity and macronutrient selection and mood response in SAD remain highly speculative.

6.3.7 Weight and Appetite Changes in Response to Antidepressant Drug Therapy

Eugene Paykel and colleagues (18) were the first to examine systematically the appetite changes associated with clinical depression and its treatment. A comparison was made between three groups of depressed female outpatients following successful response to a 3-month treatment phase with the tricyclic antidepressant drug amitriptyline. Following this clinical response to acute treatment, one group (n=19) was maintained on active drug treatment, one received inactive (placebo) drug treatment and the other group was simply withdrawn from drug treatment (combined n=32). Throughout the subsequent 9-month follow-up period, data on presence and severity of depressive symptoms, appetite perception and 'craving for carbohydrates' were collected. Almost all subjects showed a small gain in weight (around 1 kg) during the 3 months of active drug treatment. Thereafter, those maintained on active drug treatment demonstrated a substantial and sustained weight gain relative to those on no active treatment (mean of + 2.5 kg v + 0.5 kg). However, for some, weight gain was severe, with three subjects maintained on amitriptyline gaining over 11 kg. Withdrawal from active drug treatment appeared to be associated with a return to previous body weight. Paykel *et al.* (18) also reported that 'cravings' for carbohydrate-rich foods were significantly increased in the drug-maintained group, in a dose-dependent manner, although global appetite ratings were unaffected. In a subsidiary analysis, measurements of fasting glucose and insulin levels and an insulin tolerance test were conducted at 3 and 7 months. There was no relationship between drug treatment and any of these biochemical indices, irrespective of the presence of 'carbohydrate craving'. Since all subjects in this study remained well throughout follow-up (a sub-population from a larger study), the differences in weight gain between the groups might reasonably be attributed to their drug treatment – a conclusion offered by the authors. It is also of interest that the maintenance period, and not the acute treatment phase, appeared to represent the time of greatest risk for problematic weight gain. This point has rarely been acknowledged or addressed in subsequent research. Hence, the importance of this study lies in its evaluation of the potential effects of maintenance antidepressant drug treatment on appetite and weight, an issue of increasing importance as recommendations concerning the duration of continuation of treatment following clinical recovery are inexorably revised upwards. However, it should be noted that the group sizes in this study were small, depression severity was relatively mild, only female subjects were included and no data were presented on treatment non-responders.

Using a different experimental design, Kupfer *et al.* (19) studied 47 hospitalised, depressed patients randomised to treatment with amitriptyline or placebo over a 35-day period. In this study, data were collected over the acute treatment phase only. All subjects were either moderately severely or severely depressed. Each group contained both males and females and psychotic patients were not excluded. In essence, drug-treated patients gained weight during the treatment period; placebo-treated subjects did not (mean weight change + 4.6 v + 0.5 lb). However, no data were presented with respect to treatment response or change in symptom severity and it is not possible to exclude the possibility that weight gain was merely associated with a higher percentage of subjects demonstrating a clinical treatment response. Indeed, the authors mention that responder/non-responder sub-group analyses could not be reliably conducted because there was only a single 'responding' subject in the placebo group (N.B. 13 of 30 in the active treatment group responded). Also, no estimation of depression-related weight change prior to treatment was conducted. In addition to charting weight changes, ratings of appetite were made.

Unfortunately, the appetite perception data from this study are presented in a confusing manner, rendering conclusions difficult. Multiple correlational analyses failed to establish any clear relationships between drug treatment, symptom severity, treatment response and appetite perception. The authors concluded that weight gain could not be assumed to reflect eventual positive treatment outcome, contradicting the received wisdom of the day.

Pooling data from seven discrete acute (<6 weeks) antidepressant drug treatment studies in outpatients with mild to moderate depression (total n=168), Harris et al. (20,21) reported on weight changes and alterations in appetite perception assessed using simple visual analogue scales. An attempt was made retrospectively to assess weight and appetite change in response to the development of depression before treatment. As with other studies (see, for example, ref. 8), population characteristics were heterogeneous; only 31 reported a clear depression-related decrease in appetite, 20 a clear increase (20). For those treated with active drug, there was a modest increase in weight and in both appetite and 'carbohydrate craving' ratings. This effect was allegedly strongest in the group treated with the combination of the sedative tricyclic antidepressant trimipramine and the alerting monoamine oxidase inhibitor isocarboxazid (21). Unfortunately, as with the Kupfer et al. (19) study, the appetite data are very difficult to interpret. The authors elected to explore their data with multiple correlational analyses and much emphasis was placed on self-reported weight and appetite change *prior* to initiation of treatment as a grouping variable. A similar study design is that reported by Yeragani et al. (22), where 180 patients with mixed psychiatric diagnoses were evaluated following treatment with different antidepressant drugs. Most (n=158) were receiving treatment for panic disorder and not depression. Over an unspecified period of several weeks, 26 (14.4%) reported 'carbohydrate craving'. Of several clinical and demographic variables examined, only frequency of treatment change was significantly associated with the presence of 'carbohydrate craving', raising the possibility that these patients were relatively poor responders to drug treatment. However, with such a diagnostically heterogeneous group, using diverse pharmacological agents and non-standard outcome measures, it is difficult to place much confidence in these data. Nevertheless, the low rate of 'carbohydrate craving' in this population may reflect a degree of disorder specificity - an idea revisited later (see ref. 23 and below).

In a prospective evaluation of the medium-term effects of tricyclic antidepressant drug treatment (imipramine) in an outpatient population (n=52) with recurrent depressive disorder (24), a majority of subjects demonstrated minor weight change over 16 weeks (60% - mean change of < 5 lb), 19% had a weight gain of 6-10 lb and 9% gained 11-15 lb. Three subjects (6%) gained more than 15 lb, the same number that lost between 6 and 10 lb. Although these data raised the possibility of identifying weight-gain-vulnerable sub-groups, the authors were unable to demonstrate statistically reliable relationships between weight change, age, gender or treatment response. However, in subsequent work with a population of recurrent depressives, Stunkard *et al.* (25), reported that the direction of weight change in two discrete depressive episodes was remarkably consistent. Of 53 subjects studied, 45 reported the same direction of weight change in the second episode as in the first.

In an attempt to refine further the characterisation of these apparent changes in appetite and food preferences with antidepressant drug treatment, the same research group (26,27) developed a novel self-report instrument - the Pittsburgh Appetite Test (PAT). This questionnaire was constructed to obtain more detailed dietary and food preference information, with questions relating to experiences during the preceding week. The PAT included rating scales for the preference of sweet and salty foods, fruits and vegetables, meat and dairy products. Subjects were invited to indicate the frequency with which they had eaten specific foods during the preceding week and then to rate their 'appetite' for them.

One explicit aim of the PAT was to determine whether antidepressant treatment was associated with an enhanced preference for a macronutrient subgroup – carbohydrates, as originally suggested by Paykel and colleagues (18), or for the sensory properties of specific tastes. To achieve this, foods with high carbohydrate content but with differing tastes and other constituents, for example fat content, were compared within the instrument. Fifty depressed outpatients (74% female) were studied for 2 weeks prior to treatment and for 4 months during active treatment with imipramine and with a specific psychological intervention, interpersonal therapy (IPT). Prior to treatment, subjects rated their preference for sweet foods to have *increased* with the onset of depression. There were no changes in any of the other categories, including those of high carbohydrate content but non-sweet taste. For those treated with drug, 48% gained or lost less than 5 lb in weight over the 4 months, 28% gained 6-10 lb and 10% gained 11-15 lb. Around 12% lost between 6 and 10 lb, and only one subject lost >15 lb. These proportions were very similar to those reported during the previous study (24). Of the specific food preference ratings, only that for the 'dairy' category changed significantly from baseline, and, even then, only at the 4-month follow-up assessment. Importantly, there was *no change* in the high-carbohydrate food preference ratings, irrespective of taste. Unfortunately, much potentially illuminating information is absent. There is no reference to the efficacy of treatment; hence, we have no idea how many patients responded to treatment and how that response might relate to other variables of interest. Of course, having exposed subjects to two separate, clinically proven treatments simultaneously, opportunities to evaluate independently the consequences of drug and non-drug responses were lost.

Perhaps the most rigorous, methodologically sophisticated and potentially illuminating study is that of Kazes and colleagues (28). In a sample of severely depressed patients admitted to an in-patient treatment facility (25 men and 31 women), eating behaviour was assessed prospectively before, during and after the initiation of antidepressant drug treatment, and compared with that of a matched control group. For the 6 weeks of acute drug treatment, all subjects remained hospitalised. The sample contained a small number of patients (n=7) with Bipolar depression. Assessments of baseline mental status, anthropometric parameters, activity levels, dietary intake and food preferences were conducted, repeated after 6 weeks of drug therapy, and again after 4-6 months. Drug treatment consisted of a variety of different agents, with the majority from the tricyclic class. Unfortunately, virtually all patients received additional psychotropic drugs that are known to have the potential to influence physical activity and/or weight gain - for example, benzodiazepines (n=35), lithium carbonate (n=8) and neuroleptic (antipsychotic) drugs (n=18). However, comparison data were collected from an age, gender and educational level-matched control group with no history of mental disorder who had participated in previous eating studies. Unlike previous studies of depressed subjects, assessment of food intake was conducted using a 3-day diary method, in addition to the completion of hedonic ratings and food preference checklists.

6.3.7.1   Baseline data

Prior to treatment, depression was associated with a reduced total caloric intake and a small enhancement of energy intake from carbohydrate relative to protein and fat. Consistent with the reduced caloric intake, physical activity was reduced in the depressed group, and estimates of weight change during the depressive episode suggested a loss of around 1 kg per month for most subjects. However, whereas males tended to lose weight, a number of females reported significant weight gain (n=7). Although weight loss correlated highly with depression severity, there was no relationship between body mass index (BMI) and nature of weight change. Earlier work by the Pittsburgh group in the early 1990s led to the proposal that BMI determined the direction of weight change in depression (25,29) - a relationship most readily summarised as the 'heavy get heavier' whereas the 'light get lighter'. However, as with the Kazes *et al.* (28) study, this simple relationship was not replicated in a prospective evaluation of a larger sample of 89 New Zealand outpatients (30). Indeed, this group reported that direction of weight change was not predicted by *any* of the variables that had previously been suggested to exert influence, i.e. age, gender, depression severity and chronicity, history of previous episodes, or by the presence of 'melancholic' features (anhedonia, motor agitation or retardation, early wakening, guilt, consistent diurnal mood variation). Helpfully, Carter and colleagues draw our attention to the circularity of the argument presented by the Pittsburgh group. In each study, BMI was estimated at the commencement of drug treatment, by which time the subjects were already depressed. Hence, lower BMIs may be expected in weight losers, with higher BMIs in the weight gainers. Weight and BMI calculation prior to onset of depression would be required to address this hypothesis adequately.

Returning to the pre-treatment data from Kazes *et al.* (28), hedonic ratings (as described by visual analogue scales) confirmed a globally reduced desire to eat prior to mealtimes, reduced ratings of food palatability and reduced pleasure from eating in the depressed subjects. Depression was also associated with enhanced satiety ratings prior to, but not after meals. Depressed patients declared an increased preference for cookies, bread, milk and cheese relative to controls. However, these foods do not share common macronutrient properties and it is important to consider the possibility that these ratings may have been artificially distorted by differences in the palatability of the diet offered within the hospital relative to that available to the controls.

6.3.7.2   Response to drug treatment

Compared with pretreatment values, food intake, activity levels and weight each increased in the drug-treated depressives following 6 weeks of therapy. Ratings of food palatability increased, but there were no discernible changes in macronutrient selection. Equal numbers of subjects demonstrated good and poor responses to acute treatment (n=23 in each), permitting an interesting comparison of acute drug effects on appetite and weight regulation relative to acute drug effects on mental status. There were no differences in body weight change, BMI, measures of physical activity, food intake or food preferences. Hence, the mood response to drug treatment was dissociable and independent from these changes. Antidepressant drug treatment over 4 to 6 months was associated with a normalisation of mood ratings, increased physical activity and increased caloric intake. Again, roughly equal numbers of subjects could be categorised as good (n=19) and poor (n=16) responders. The only measure upon which the two subgroups could be distinguished was that of number of items chosen on a food preference checklist. Poor responders selected a greater number of preferred foods. These were predominantly foods of a sweet, high-carbohydrate/low-protein content. Again, mood response appears to have been dissociable and independent from this change.

The importance of this study (28) lies in the demonstration of an increased preference for, and increased relative consumption of carbohydrate-rich foods *prior to* the initiation of drug treatment. Hence, major depressive disorder, at least in its more severe manifestations, may be associated with discernible changes in food preference and macronutrient selection that extend beyond a simple, global blunting of hedonic responsivity. Whether this change ought to be conceptualised as a carbohydrate preference or as a fat/protein aversion remains unclear. However, the demonstration of an altered carbohydrate preference that is not drug-induced may have profound implications for the construct validity of both the atypical and seasonal depressive subtypes. Furthermore, and in direct contrast with some other studies, Kazes and colleagues (28) have demonstrated that antidepressant drug treatment was associated with a *normalisation* of activity levels, caloric intake and macronutrient selection. This normalising influence is consonant with an earlier report by Shioro *et al.* (31) of the effects of tricyclic drugs on the frequency distribution of body weights of hospitalised Japanese depressed patients (n=106). Further, Balon *et al.* (23) recorded weight changes and ratings from the PAT in a population of 44 non-depressed outpatients with Panic Disorder who were treated for 8 weeks with imipramine, diazepam or placebo. They observed no significant weight changes or alterations in appetite perception in any of the treatment groups, suggesting that altered macronutrient preference and selection may be disorder specific. However, Kazes and colleagues' data also suggest that poor antidepressant drug-treatment response, a common clinical problem, is associated with a persistent (or possibly even accentuated) sweet carbohydrate food preference. Unfortunately, the authors did not provide detailed macronutrient intake data for these two subgroups, although it is suggested that there was no difference. Presumably, therefore, there was a dissociation between macronutrient selection (which normalised with treatment) and the expressed preferences in the poor response subgroup. Hence, we must consider the possibility that, rather than antidepressant drugs inducing an altered food preference *per se*, they may act to normalise a pre-existing, pathological change, although subjective elements of preference may remain resistant to change in those exhibiting a poor clinical response.

6.3.8   Effects of Antidepressant Drugs on Metabolism

The preceding discussion has focused on the potential effects of antidepressant drugs on taste perception, macronutrient preference and selection. Of course, another possible mechanism by which drugs might influence weight regulation would be that of direct interference with tissue metabolism. This is a topic that has received relatively little attention, despite initial reports of detectable changes in resting basal metabolic rate (BMR) in response to antidepressant drug treatment in some depressed patients (32). Although bi-directional effects on BMR are reported, depending on the pharmacological characteristics of the antidepressant drug - tricyclics (imipramine) and monoamine oxidase inhibitors (tranylcypromine) may decrease BMR and SSRIs may increase BMR (32). The key implication of such observations is that individuals may gain (or lose) significant amounts of weight over a prolonged period without experiencing detectable changes in food intake or macronutrient selection. The mechanisms by which antidepressant drugs might influence resting BMR remain unknown.

6.3.9   Speculations on Pathophysiology

As mentioned at the beginning of this section, although there have been impressive recent advances in our understanding of the psychological and neurobiological features of depressive disorders, our knowledge remains rudimentary. From the preceding discussion, it will be clear that detailed and systematic study of many important clinical observations and problems is lacking. Accordingly, consideration of pathophysiological changes that might mediate changes in appetite and weight regulation is highly speculative and will, therefore be brief.

6.3.9.1 The monoamine hypothesis of depression: role for serotonin and noradrenaline

This theory of altered biogenic amine neurotransmitter function has dominated biological concepts of depression for over 40 years. In its simplest form, it posits that depression is caused by (or is at least associated with) neurochemical dysregulation in brain regions where the dominant transmitters include the monoamines noradrenaline (norepinephrine) and serotonin. The theory is essentially a work of conceptual 'reverse engineering', extrapolating backwards from robust clinical observations. Two of the major groups of chemical antidepressant drugs were discovered by serendipity in the 1950s - the monoamine oxidase inhibitors (iproniazid - originally used as anti-tuberculous drugs) and the tricyclic antidepressants (imipramine - originally manufactured as a putative antipsychotic drug). Following observations that these drugs enjoyed specific antidepressant activity, pharmacological characterisation revealed their capacity to potentiate the central nervous system actions of noradrenaline and serotonin. In addition, a drug that depleted stores of monoamine transmitter, reserpine - an antihypertensive agent, was reported to induce the symptoms of depression. The third major group of antidepressant drugs, the selective serotonin inhibitors (e.g. fluoxetine, also known as Prozac), which specifically enhance serotonin transmission, were created by design. Support for a continually revised monoamine hypothesis has accrued over the years from a variety of clinical studies – for example, autopsy studies demonstrating altered densities of serotonin and noradrenaline binding sites in post-mortem brain tissue samples from depressed patients and suicide victims. For a detailed account of the current status of the monoamine hypothesis, interested readers are directed to consult relevant chapters in Bloom & Kupfer (33).

If we are to accept that altered noradrenaline and serotonin neurotransmission represent key aspects of the neurobiology of depression, then dysregulation of either might be responsible for changes in appetite and weight regulation. For example, both noradrenaline and serotonin exert important influences over neuronal activity in hypothalamic centres that regulate eating. As a consequence, generalised dysregulation of noradrenaline and/or serotonin function that mediates the psychopathology of depression might also mediate the appetite and weight regulation changes, and offer at least a partial explanation for antidepressant drug effects.

6.3.9.2   Hypothalamic-pituitary-adrenocortical (HPA) system

Patients with depression frequently exhibit abnormalities in the activation and regulation of the HPA axis, a key component of the integrated bodily response to stress. A detailed review of this literature is beyond the scope of this section (but interested readers are directed to consult Arborelius *et al.* (33)). Generally, the abnormalities found with depressive disorder can be conceptualised as an excess of activity within the system, leading to the sustained release of elevated quantities of the steroid hormone cortisol, a potent inhibitor of eating and promoter of gluconeogenesis. Longitudinal studies of antidepressant treatment responses reveal that aspects of HPA system dysfunction are corrected prior to observing treatment effects upon classical symptoms and psychopathology (reviewed by Holsboer in Bloom and Kupfer (32)). Accordingly, antidepressant drug effects on appetite and weight gain could be mediated, at least to an extent, by effects on HPA system function.

6.3.9.3   Hypothalamic-pituitary-thyroid system

Antidepressant drugs have been shown to reduce plasma levels of T_4 and free T_3 hormone (34). Given the myriad actions of systemic thyroid hormones on human physiology, including the regulation of carbohydrate and fat metabolism, one possible consequence of antidepressant-treatment-induced changes in thyroid hormone function could be an alteration in basal metabolic rate. However, there are no directly supportive clinical research data.

6.3.9.4   Histamine

Blockade of central histamine H_1 receptors is thought to be another leading candidate mechanism for drug-induced weight gain. Several of the tricyclic antidepressant drugs are potent H_1 receptor antagonists, notably amitriptyline and doxepin. A definitive mechanism of action remains to be determined. However, histamine-containing neurones exert an inhibitory influence over both the ventromedial and paraventricular nuclei in the hypothalamus – both of which play critical roles in the regulation of appetite and satiety.

6.3.9.5   Leptin

Leptin is the protein product coded by the Ob (obesity) gene that is expressed in adipose tissue and released into the blood, profoundly affecting food intake (36). The role of leptin in humans and that of stress hormones in stimulating expression of the Ob gene remains unclear, although it is considered likely to be a critical signalling mechanism for the long-term regulation of energy stores. In addition to its peripheral tissue effects, leptin receptors have been identified in the lateral hypothalamus, the paraventricular nucleus and the ventromedial hypothalamus. Hence, leptin release can inhibit eating, stimulate thermogenesis and cause profound loss of weight. Given the frequent association between depression and loss of appetite, reduced food intake and weight loss, it has been proposed by several groups that altered leptin secretion might also be expected in depressed patients. Indeed, leptin receptors have been identified in the midbrain dorsal raphe nuclei (the cell bodies where serotonin neurones that project to the forebrain originate) in rats (37).

However, the clinical data are contradictory. Elevated nocturnal serum levels of leptin were found in one study of depressed patients (37, n=15) and these levels did not correlate with BMI - a relationship that is observed in healthy controls. This was interpreted as evidence for dysregulation of leptin release in depression. In the same subjects, the authors also demonstrated a trend towards nocturnal hypercortisolism. They subsequently proposed that elevated serum leptin in depression might promote corticotrophin releasing hormone (CRH) release, contributing to HPA system hyperactivity. However, this presupposes that elevations in corticosteroid release lead to an increase in leptin release. Although animal data suggest that this may occur, Oppert and colleagues (39) found no relationship between acute stimulation of the HPA axis and leptin secretion in humans. Furthermore, Deuschle and colleagues (40) studied a larger population of depressed subjects (n=23), who specifically reported loss of appetite, and found *no relationship* between diagnostic status and leptin release profile. Having also collected data on the release of several other hormones (cortisol, insulin, growth hormone), they concluded that plasma leptin concentrations were unchanged in depression, that they were unrelated to the release of stress hormones, and that there was no evidence for leptin playing a major role in loss of appetite and body weight in depressed patients.

Of course, there are many other possible hormonal and neurochemical influences that remain to be explored - for example, growth hormone and the neuropeptides somatostatin, neuropeptide Y, cytokines (e.g. Tumour Necrosis Factor) and the two recently isolated hypothalamic peptides, orexin-A and orexin-B.

6.3.10   Conclusions

Despite the clinical importance of changes in appetite and weight regulation in depression, both from the perspective of diagnosis and as a consequence of drug treatment, there has been relatively little study of these phenomena and their mediating neurobiology. Contrary to general belief, depression *per se* may be associated with altered macronutrient selection (increased carbohydrate preference) and this change may *normalise* with drug treatment. In turn, the increased carbohydrate preference and selection may reflect altered taste function, or more proximal neural pathophysiology. If these observations prove correct, the diagnostic validity of the atypical and seasonal subtypes of depression may become highly questionable. Before a comprehensive neurobiology of appetite and weight changes in depression can be compiled, further direct, longitudinal study of depressed subjects is required. This ought to include direct measures of appetite in a controlled environment, before and after initiation of treatment, with manipulation of those physiological processes that are known to modify eating behaviour.

6.3.11   References

1.   Murray C.J.L., Lopez A.D. *The Global Burden of Disease*. Harvard School of Public Health. Cambridge, MA. US, Harvard University Press. 1996.

2.   Smith A.L., Weissman M.M. Epidemiology, in *Handbook of Affective Disorders. 2nd Edition*. Ed. Paykel E.S. London, Churchill Livingston. 1992.

3.   Judd L.L. The clinical course of unipolar major depressive disorders. *Archives of General Psychiatry*, 1997, 54, 989-91.

4.   American Psychiatric Association. *Diagnostic and Statistical Manual of Mental Disorders*. Fourth Edition. Washington DC, American Psychiatric Association. 1994.

5.   World Health Organisation. *The ICD-10 Classification of Mental and Behavioural Disorders: Clinical Descriptions and Diagnostic Guidelines*. Geneva, Switzerland. 1992.

6.   Beck A.T., Rush A.J., Shaw B., Emery G. *Cognitive Therapy of Depression*. Guildford, New York. 1979.

7.   Nemeroff C.B. The neurobiology of depression. *Scientific American*, 1998, 278, 42-9.

8.   Paykel E.S. Depression and appetite. *Journal of Psychosomatic Research*, 1977, 21, 401-7.

9.   Liebowitz M.R., Quitkin F.M., Stewart J.W., McGrath P.J., Harrison W., Rabkin J., Tricamo E., Markowitz J.S., Klein D.F. Phenelzine 'v' imipramine in atypical depression: a preliminary report. *Archives of General Psychiatry*, 1984, 41, 669-77.

10.   Levitan R.D., Parikh S.V., Lesage A.D., Hegadoren K.M., Adams M., Kennedy S.H., Goering P.N. Major depression in individuals with a history of childhood physical or sexual abuse: relationship to neurovegetative features, mania, and gender. *American Journal of Psychiatry*, 1998, 155, 1746-52.

11. Gold P.W., Chrousos C.P. The endocrinology of melancholic and atypical depression: relation to neurocircuitry and somatic consequences. *Proceedings of the Association of American Physicians*, 1999, 111, 22-34.

12. Nierenberg A.A., Pava J.A., Clancy K., Rosenbaum J.F., Fava M. Are neurovegetative symptoms stable in relapsing or recurrent atypical depressive episodes? *Biological Psychiatry*, 1996, 40, 691-6.

13. Rosenthal N.E., Sack D.A., Gillin J.C., Lewy A.J., Goodwin F.K., Davenport Y., Mueller P.S., Newsome D.A., Wehr T.A. Seasonal affective disorder. A description of the syndrome and preliminary findings with light therapy. *Archives of General Psychiatry*, 1984, 41, 72-80.

14. Rosenthal N.E., Genhart M.J., Caballero B., Jacobsen F.M., Skwerer R.G., Coursey R.D., Rogers S., Spring B.J. Psychobiological effects of carbohydrate and protein-rich meals in patients with seasonal affective disorder and normal controls. *Biological Psychiatry*, 1989, 25, 1029-40.

15. Arbisi P.A., Levine A.S., Nierenberg J., Wolf J. Seasonal alteration in taste detection and recognition threshold in seasonal affective disorder: the proximate source of carbohydrate craving. *Psychiatry Research*, 1986, 59, 171-82.

16. Amsterdam J.D., Settle R.G., Doty R.L., Abelman E., Winokur A. Taste and smell perception in depression. *Biolological Psychiatry*, 1987, 22, 1477-81.

17. Steiner J.E., Rosenthal-Zifroni A., Edelstein E.L. Taste perception in depressive illness. *Israel Annals of Psychiatry Related Disciplines*, 1969, 7, 223-32.

18. Paykel E.S., Mueller P.S., De La Vergne P.M. Amitriptyline, weight gain and carbohydrate craving: a side effect. *British Journal of Psychiatry*, 1973, 123, 501-7.

19. Kupfer D.J., Coble P.A., Rubinstein D. Changes in weight during treatment for depression. *Psychosomatic Medicine*, 1979, 41, 535-44.

20. Harris B., Young J., Hughes B. Changes in appetite and weight during short-term antidepressant treatment. *British Journal of Psychiatry*, 1984, 145, 645-8.

21. Harris B., Young J., Hughes B. Comparative effects of seven antidepressant regimes on appetite, weight and carbohydrate preference. *British Journal of Psychiatry*, 1986, 148, 590-2.

473

22. Yeragani V.K., Pohl R., Aleem A., Balon R., Sherwood P., Lycaki H. Carbohydrate craving and increased appetite associated with antidepressant therapy. *Canadian Journal of Psychiatry*, 1988, 33, 606-12.

23. Balon R., Yeragani V.K., Pohl R., Merlos B., Sherwood P. Changes in appetite and weight during the pharmacological treatment of patients with panic disorder. *Canadian Journal of Psychiatry*, 1993, 38, 19-22.

24. Fernstrom M.H., Krowinski R.L., Kupfer D.J. Chronic imipramine treatment and weight gain. *Psychiatry Research*, 1986, 17, 269-73.

25. Stunkard A.J., Fernstrom M.H., Price R.A., Frank E., Kupfer D.J. Direction of weight change in recurrent depression: consistency across episodes. *Archives of General Psychiatry*, 1990, 47, 857-60.

26. Fernstrom M.H., Krowinski R.L., Kupfer D.J. Appetite and food preference in depression: effects of imipramine treatment. *Biological Psychiatry*, 1987, 22, 529-39.

27. Fernstrom M.H., Kupfer D.J. Imipramine treatment and preference for sweets. Appetite, 1988, 10, 149-55.

28. Kazes M., Danion J.M., Grange D., Pradignac A., Simon Ch., Burrus-Mehl F., Schlienger J.L., Singer L. Eating behaviour and depression before and after antidepressant treatment: a prospective, naturalistic study. *Journal of Affective Disorders*, 1994, 30, 193-207.

29. Stunkard A.J., Fernstrom M.H., Price R.A., Buss E., Frank E., Kupfer D.J. Weight change in depression: influence of "disinhibition" is mediated by body mass and other variables. *Psychiatry Research*, 1991, 38, 197-200.

30. Carter F.A., Bulik C.M., Joyce P.R. Direction of weight change in depression. *Journal of Affective Disorders*, 1994, 30, 57-60.

31. Shiori T., Kato T., Murashita J., Yamada N., Takahashi S. Changes in the frequency distribution pattern of body weight in patients with depression. *Acta Psychiatrica Scandinavia*, 1993, 88, 356-60.

32. Fernstrom M.H. Depression, antidepressants and body weight change. *Annals of the New York Academy of Science*, 1989, 575, 31-9.

33. Bloom F.E., Kupfer D.J. *Psychopharmacology: the fourth generation of progress.* New York, Raven Press. 1995.

34. Arborelius L., Owens M.J., Plotsky P.M., Nemeroff C.B. The role of corticotrophin-releasing factor in depression and anxiety disorders. *Journal of Endocrinology*, 1999, 160, 1-12.

35. Joffe R.T., Singer W. The effect of tricyclic antidepressants on basal thyroid hormone levels in depressed patients. *Pharmacopsychiatry*, 1990, 23, 67-9.

36. Halaas J.L., Gajiwala K.S., Maffei M., Cohen S.L., Chait B.T., Rabinowitz D., Lallone R.L., Burley S.K., Friedman J.M. Weight-reducing effects of the plasma protein encoded by the obese gene. *Science*, 1995, 269, 543-6.

37. Collin M., Hakansson-Ovesjo M., Misane I., Ogren S.O., Meister B. Decreased 5-HT transporter mRNA in neurons of the dorsal raphe nucleus and behavioral depression in the obese leptin-deficient ob/ob mouse. *Molecular Brain Research*, 2000, 81, 51-61.

38. Antonijevic I.A., Murck H., Frieboes R.M., Horn R., Brabant G., Steiger A. Elevated nocturnal profiles of serum leptin in patients with depression. *Journal of Psychiatric Research*, 1998, 32, 403-10.

39. Oppert J.M., Lahlou N., Laferrere B., Roger M., Basdevant A., Guy-Grand B. Plasma leptin and acute serotoninergic stimulation of the corticotropic axis in women who are normal weight or obese. *Obesity Research*, 1997, 5, 410-6.

40. Deuschle M., Blum W.F., Englaro P., Schweiger U., Weber B., Pflaum C.D., Heuser I. Plasma leptin in depressed patients and healthy controls. *Hormone and Metabolic Research*, 1996, 28, 714-7.

6.4. DEPENDENCE-LIKE FEATURES OF CARBOHYDRATES

Marie Reid and Richard Hammersley

6.4.1   Introduction

This section will critically evaluate the accuracy and utility of carbohydrate addiction as a description of some problematic eating behaviour. As we discussed in section 6.2, over the past 30 years the applications of addiction have widened to include behaviours other than consuming psychoactive drugs. During the same time period addiction research has become wary of using the word 'addiction' to mean a specific physiological state caused primarily by habitually consuming a substance. As also discussed in section 6.2, despite academic caution, society seems to have acquired a fondness for 'addiction' as an explanation of people's behaviour. In this context, there are a number of possible explanations for complaints of carbohydrate addiction, which this section will look at in turn. First, it is useful to consider whether there is a specific syndrome of 'carbohydrate addiction', whatever its aetiology and whatever it should be called. 'Addiction' is sometimes loosely applied to any behaviour that people do more than they believe that they should, while knowing it is bad for them in some sense. While this is perhaps a necessary condition for dependence (1), it is not sufficient. Dependence also involves other features, as discussed in section 6.2, broadly including clear psychological, social and health problems resulting from the behaviour and difficulties modifying the behaviour despite repeated attempts to do so.

6.4.2   Is Carbohydrate Addiction a Specific Syndrome?

The rising prevalence of obesity may be associated in part with over-consumption of convenience and fast foods (2), which are high in fat and carbohydrate, energy-dense, usually sweetened (even for savoury food), and highly palatable. Palatability can be increased by sweetness, mouthfeel and the rate at which people feel full. The latter two factors can be improved by high fat content. Chocolate products are the canonical sweet, high-fat foods. There is clear evidence that people can feel dependent upon chocolate, as reviewed in sections 4.2 and 4.3. This may in part be because research effort has mainly focused on chocolate, which has in turn fuelled the popular idea of being 'addicted' to chocolate, particularly in the media. If there are people comparably 'addicted' to other fat-carbohydrate mixtures, they have so far been less likely to be labelled as addicts.

People suffering from eating disorders may binge upon specific foods. Foods chosen may be carbohydrate-fat mixtures (CHOF), such as chocolate biscuits, or relatively pure carbohydrate (CHO), such as bread (3). Sufferers constitute a spectrum, as with substance abuse, from less to more severe forms of behaviour. It is feasible that some less severe sufferers may describe their behaviour as specific, addiction-like, cravings for specific foods. These will usually be foods that they restrain. Indeed, dependence cannot meaningfully occur without attempted or desired restraint (1). However, most clinicians would consider the specific foods used for bingeing and avoided during restraint to be the result of an eating disorder, not its cause.

People who literally depend on CHO, rather than CHOF mixtures, are not common. Perhaps this is due to their not being researched extensively, or being considered, rightly or wrongly, as having primary eating disorders rather than primary problems with CHO. At the anecdotal level, when, during the 1980s, the Coca Cola Company reformulated Coca Cola and withdrew the original formula, this unearthed a large number of consumers who objected, including many who reported consuming several litres of sugary (and caffeinated) soft drink per day. We know nothing about the rest of their diet, although it is likely that the energy in the soft drinks displaced energy from more nutritious sources. What is uncommon, or at least undocumented, is people subsisting primarily on sugars, or even on simple starches and sugars and reporting concerns about this. Most diets, even problem ones, also have fat content. The occasional spectacular case should not distract from this point. After all, dependency on carrots (4) and water (polydipsia) (5,6) have been documented, suggesting that almost any ingestive habit can become dependence for a small minority. As with other substance dependencies, polydipsia is associated with other psychiatric problems, including depression, learning difficulties and schizophrenia (6).

Sugar or simple CHO are rarely given blind. In most studies and everyday life people know what they are eating and can behave accordingly. This is based on what they expect and what they have learned about the results of eating. When CHO is given blind, there is no evidence of psychological effects on normal people strong enough to justify an analogy with drugs (7,8), and this appears to apply also to obese people (9).

The cautious and not thoroughly evidenced conclusion is that there is no specific syndrome of excessive consumption of CHO only. The problematic consumption of CHO almost always involves fat consumption too, and rather less is known about the psychological effects of fat consumption (10). The occasional exception can probably be subsumed under the general banner of eating disorders and restrained attempts to avoid certain foods. There are also some diets that specifically promote the avoidance of refined carbohydrates (11), suggesting that they have adverse 'addiction-like' effects (see also Duffy (12) for an earlier example), rather than simply being part of a palatable, widely available but unhealthy diet. Restraining intake of specific foods leads to craving and bingeing for some people (3). Addiction to CHOF mixtures seems more plausible, and addiction may be a useful metaphor or explanation with which to consider the excessive consumption of chocolate, or other such mixtures. Thus, in considering explanations for CHO addiction, we will focus primarily upon CHOF addiction.

We take 'carbohydrate-fat addiction' to refer to certain related phenomena, including the behaviour of some people, some people's explanations of their behaviour, and society's depictions of certain eating patterns. These phenomena do not entail any specific type of cause. For example, they do not guarantee that CHOF addiction is caused by specific physiological changes.

6.4.3   Explanations for the Phenomenon of 'Carbohydrate-Fat Addiction'

Reviews of the possible causes of eating disorders (3) still consist of a lengthy list of varied causes, which seem to have been derived by *ad hoc* hypothesis posing of the Popperian style. The same difficulty applies to addiction theories, although there have been more attempts to develop integrated approaches there. In considering possible explanations for CHOF addiction, we will review the plausibility of various different types of approach, rather than focusing on specific hypotheses.

6.4.3.1   *Physiological mechanisms*

There are a number of types of physiological mechanism that might explain CHOF addiction. We have reviewed some of these at length elsewhere (13), concluding that physiological mechanisms are unlikely to explain CHO or CHOF addiction. Here, we will recap the main issues and consider some other plausible mechanisms.

6.4.3.1.1 *Drug-like effects*

a)   Direct effects on mood

It has been suggested that CHO ingestion influences mood via serotonin metabolism (14). However, the mood effects of CHO are small and difficult to replicate, and do not convincingly follow the temporal dynamics that the serotonin hypothesis predicts. It remains possible that CHO can influence mood for people suffering from specific mood disorders, including seasonal affective disorder (SAD) and carbohydrate-craving obesity (13). However, CHOF is more commonly ingested that CHO and the mechanism of mood improvement may be reinforcement (15), rather than the serotonin mechanism.

Another possible explanation is that CHO can raise blood sugar when this is low. Raising blood sugar has larger effects on cognitive performance than on subjective mood (16,17), perhaps because cognitive measures are more precise than mood rating scales. People might become dependent on mood changes or performance enhancement. That an actual performance boost would not occur when CHO was ingested in a state of high blood sugar is not a problem, because it is known that people will habitually consume drugs even when only some episodes of consumption are reinforcing. Caffeine is a useful analogy. Caffeine enhances performance and people consume it deliberately for this reason. Yet it is likely that only the first cup of coffee (or equivalent) has measurable effects on performance (18). Nonetheless, people consume further caffeinated drinks to enhance performance, which may be explicable as a partial reinforcement effect. This might apply also to CHO ingestion. Caffeine 'dependence' can occur, but it is benign compared with dependence on other drugs (19). Again, CHO might be similar. The fat in CHOF is probably irrelevant to performance enhancement, or reduces the effect by slowing digestion. However, the addition of fat may enhance the attractiveness of CHOF to some consumers.

A more extreme hypothesis has been advanced by Heller and Heller (20), who propose that chronic hyperinsulinaemia is largely responsible for hunger, cravings and weight gain observed in obesity, as well as in many other health problems (21). Although these authors cite epidemiological data and animal work to support this hypothesis (20), we are not aware that it has been examined under controlled conditions with humans. Work such as that conducted by Benton and Owens (17) would be required to show that cravings and hunger were associated over time with specific changes in blood glucose and insulin levels. Nonetheless, Heller and Heller have a series of best-selling diet books.

b)   Reinforcement through sweet taste and high palatability

There is also evidence that sweet taste is reinforcing, even when non-nutritive sweeteners are used; so is the mouthfeel of some CHOF foods (22). If CHOF is highly reinforcing, then CHOF addiction could be created and sustained purely by standard learning mechanisms, without there being any specific neuropsychological results of ingesting CHOF (see also section 3.1).

Learning also plays a role in substance dependence (23-25). At the very least, users must learn to ignore the aversive effects of drugs (such as nausea for heroin or alcohol) and recognise the enjoyable effects. It is also important that conditioning can occur without awareness (although it can also occur consciously). The result can be that people develop habits that they do not fully understand and find it difficult to recondition. They may not be conscious of the specific stimuli that initiate the habitual response, which can be craving or thoughts that lead to drug or CHOF consumption. Furthermore, the stimulus - appraisal or cognitive response - response chain may occur very rapidly and be over before the person can assume conscious control over it (26). Moreover, people have difficulty in retrospectively identifying their chains of thought and may construct an account afterwards (27). In theory at least, learning theory could be applied to much longer chains of behaviour. For example, somebody could impulsively buy chocolate in the supermarket 'for the kids', take it home, then impulsively consume it, without necessarily having first formed a self-deceptive plan to buy and consume chocolate. To complicate matters, some people do seem to form such plans, and some of them lie about this afterwards.

Space precludes further discussion of learning theory (28; see also section 3.2), but it is worth noting that people tend to underestimate the power of learning alone to control behaviour and favour specific neuropsychological explanations instead. Another problem is that few researchers in human addiction or human nutrition are knowledgable about modern learning theory, and some crude paradigms have been applied, such as simple classical conditioning as a model for cue exposure (29). The implications of modern cognitive learning theory for addiction are just being explored (30-32).

c)   Tolerance

To the extent that CHOF or CHO has reinforcing mental effects, it is feasible that people could become tolerant of these and require increasing doses to achieve such effects. However, it is not clear that this would occur in practice. Glucose metabolism is not straightforward - people with high blood glucose are simply unaffected by additional CHO (17), and conditioned effects, such as the partial reinforcement of caffeine ingestion, discussed above, are not subject to tolerance. It is also possible that regular CHO consumption alters hunger and satiety so that only further CHO will satiate (21), causing cravings, but this has not been subject to empirical test. In a pilot study (33) we found that providing soft drinks in sugary or intensely sweetened forms over 7 days made no difference to mood beyond the second day; this is currently being explored further. Digestive tolerance to fat will be discussed separately. As yet, it is not clear that fat has direct mental effects, so tolerance to such is not relevant.

6.4.3.1.2   Non-drug-like effects

a)   Digestive adaptation

Another possibility, which is perhaps a form of tolerance, is that people's digestive processes adapt to eating CHOF and so they come to find other foods inadequately satiating. Sweetness and mouthfeel may play a role here. It is known that the gut adapts to a high-fat diet (34). A number of other adaptations could be postulated - for example, in glucose metabolism (20). Indeed, digestion could adapt in a number of ways to a high CHOF diet. The end result would be that low CHOF food might be digested differently, perhaps causing some discomfort and producing slow satiation. CHOF could therefore become the 'quick food fix' of choice, or feel like 'proper' or 'satisfying' food, compared with low-fat food, or fat and protein mixtures. Whether such mechanisms are powerful enough to create and sustain CHOF addiction remains to be established.

b)   Deficiencies/displacement

Another possibility is that the important causes of CHOF addiction involve what CHOF fails to provide rather than what it provides. High CHOF food can be deficient in vitamins, minerals and other nutrients. Eating high CHOF food may also displace other foods from the diet that may have beneficial effects because of their nutritional content. The resultant deficiencies might contribute to CHOF addiction in some way. Currently lacking is a clear mechanism that could link physiological deficiencies and psychological effects.

6.4.3.1.3   Conclusions for physiological mechanisms

The direct physiological effects of CHO or CHOF do not appear to be large and may be unlikely to sustain CHOF addiction without additional learning. As well as conditioning effects, which we have somewhat arbitrarily placed with physiological effects, there is also a variety of psychological effects that may contribute to CHOF addiction.

6.4.3.2   Psychological processes

The ways in which people think about food affects how and what they eat. It is often implicitly assumed in the study of human nutrition that people adapt and learn to eat whatever the environment offers. This view is superficially supported by the impressive abilities of hunter-gatherer cultures to utilise the foods available in their environment, and phrases such as 'the Mediterranean diet' also suggest that diets are determined by the environment. However, the comparative anthropology of nutrition suggests that food choice is more complex than simple adaptation to meet nutritional requirements. As Lindlahr (35) describes: 'You eat what you are', at least in conditions above starvation. Two forms of evidence are that, first, migrants often go to great effort to import or carry with them 'proper' food, which is subsequently adapted. Italian American cuisine is a good example. Italian immigrants did not simply abandon pizza, pasta, olive oil or wine, but instead started importing the key ingredients from Italy. Second, despite availability, people often reject devalued or taboo food. The different values placed on seafood in Britain and Spain is a contemporary example that has caused clashes over fishing rights. A less subtle example is the British revulsion towards horsemeat, widely enjoyed in France.

The general point, for understanding oddities and disorders of human eating, is that beliefs and attitudes influence everybody's food choices. Some beliefs are rational, some irrational. It is therefore likely that CHOF addiction will be caused in large part by the same mental and social processes, taken to extremes. The study of this is not yet well developed because research into eating problems has tended to pursue hypotheses based on specific physiological abnormalities or individual developmental psychopathology. This mirrors the fact that society tends to equate powerful effects, such as those underlying addiction, with biological effects. However, the success of cognitive-behavioural therapies for eating disorders suggests that the study of nutritional beliefs and attitudes will be fruitful for understanding normal and abnormal eating. The general psychological mechanisms discussed here are sufficiently powerful to explain CHOF addiction.

6.4.3.2.1 Cognitive-behavioural problems

Amongst the common but fallacious beliefs found amongst patients seeking help for obesity or eating disorders is that certain foods are particularly fattening. Until about 20 years ago, CHO foods were widely believed to be fattening and many diets for weight loss were low in carbohydrates. Since then, nutritional advice has refocused on high-fat foods in general and CHOF in particular. CHOF foods can easily be consumed in excess because they are energy-dense and palatable. However, some dieters and restrained eaters attempt to abstain from CHOF. This can lead to cravings for such foods and to planned or unplanned relapse, resulting in spiralling cycles of excessive restraint followed by over-consumption of CHOF, leading to weight gain, or extreme fears of weight gain.

Cognitive-behavioural approaches to treatment find that there are several common distortions of thinking that contribute to problems with food (3). These include setting impossibly high standards, such as avoiding fat almost entirely, and then, when the standards are not met, regarding this as a failure, which is evidence of low self-worth. Another tendency is that of having contradictory beliefs or goals that cannot simultaneously be accomplished, such as placing a high value on CHOF 'treats' while wanting also to be thin. Additionally, there is the indulgence in 'awfulising', where minor infractions of self-imposed standards are regarded as so terrible that they can lead on to major misbehaviours. For example, as it is terrible to eat ice cream at all, once started one might as well eat the whole litre. Finally, there is the assumption that other people make harsh judgements about one, without checking the reality of these assumptions. Do other people really notice if the dieter has gained (or lost) half a kilo?

From a cognitive behavioural perspective, CHOF addiction is a distressing psychological problem, but one that is caused by distorted thinking about food in general and CHOF in particular, rather than by any fundamental physiological mechanism. Indeed, one of the features of cognitive-behavioural therapies is to focus on tackling the existing problematic behaviours, rather than being overly concerned with the development and causation of the behaviours.

6.4.3.2.2   Social attribution

People describe themselves as addicted because it is socially functional to do so (36). This view of addiction as social attribution may under-emphasise the extent to which severe drug or alcohol dependence can be socially and personally dysfunctional - the type of problem that "12 step programmes to recovery" would regard as true addiction. Social attribution as a primary explanation of addiction has more appeal when the benefits and costs of a behaviour are more ambivalent. This is likely to be the case for CHOF addiction. Why do people describe themselves as addicted to CHO or CHOF? This has not been explicitly researched but generalising from Davies' theory (36), socially functional answers could include:

- To get recognition for the severity of their problem from family or health professionals.
- To justify consumption that they regard as excessive.
- To avoid taking responsibility for behaviour that they regularly enact, then regret.
- To apologise for behaviour that they regard as socially embarrassing or shameful.
- To provide an explanation of behaviour that sometimes goes against their prior intentions.

For drugs, the two main strands of evidence supporting the social attribution approach, as reviewed by Davies (36) are, first, that people attribute their substance use differently depending upon the set-up of the interview, describing themselves as more 'addicted' to professionals than to peers. Secondly, as people move through treatment, they talk about their behaviour in a more 'addicted' style, even though the behaviour (in the past) has not changed. This is normally considered to be the addict facing up to the 'truth' about his/her behaviour, but that presupposes a 'truth' whose main evidence originates in the reports of 'addicts'. Those who provide different accounts are 'in denial' or not yet facing up to their addiction.

A more objective view is that the addict's account is constructed to make sense of behaviour. The issue becomes one of functionality, not truth. The role of 'recovered addict' is often socially functional and viewed positively. However, it may be problematic to force all substance users into the mould of the addict. At the extreme, this can be highly dysfunctional. For example, needle exchanges for drug injectors remain rare in the USA because they are seen as sustaining addiction rather than encouraging abstinence, and also, addicts are not regarded as capable of controlling their behaviour and injecting safely. This view ignores the fact that many drug injectors can and do moderate their behaviour, and lack of implementation has resulted in many unnecessary deaths from AIDS and hepatitis (37). Similarly, waiting for heavy drinkers to admit their alcoholism before treating it denies treatment to those who may be unwilling to abstain and may delay treatment until serious physical damage has been caused.

Such problems are reasons to be cautious in promoting the view that CHOF (or other foods) are 'addictive' and therefore outside the person's volitional control and perhaps amenable to pharmacological interventions, or extreme measures such as avoidance of certain foods. Indeed, such rigid and extreme thinking appears to be a feature of disordered eating (see also section 7.4). Other approaches to eating disorders and obesity are also required.

6.4.3.2.3   Selective attention

Another related psychological explanation for CHOF addiction may be that the phenomenon is largely an artefact of general attribution errors (rather than the specific problems discussed above). Most important of these may be people's tendency to seek confirming evidence for their lay theories, to rely excessively on dramatic examples for evidence, and to actively ignore contradictory evidence. A lively review is given by Sutherland (38). For example, some dieters may forget the many times when they did not crave CHOF, notice the few times when they really wanted ice cream or chocolate, and remember their most extreme examples of overeating. They may then use this selected material to construct an account of their own behaviour that resembles CHOF addiction. The hypothesis associating sugar with hyperactivity in children is due to one such attribution error (39), with the apparent links being due to the association between sweets and time out or fun, as well as selective recall of events. Given that the media offer 'addiction' as a candidate explanation for eating behaviour, it is plausible that some people will use this explanation to account for their own or other people's behaviour. That the account can be made to fit, subject to the biases described here, does not of course mean that it is correct, or indeed functional.

6.4.3.3   Media influence

The role of the media in promoting CHOF addiction is to provide a source of pseudo-psychological vocabulary to talk about eating behaviour and to replicate, if not invent, society's fascination with and ambivalent attitudes to eating and body image (40). CHOF addiction, whatever its real basis, is part of that pseudo-psychological talk. Furthermore, the media tend to over-simplify scientific ideas, and 'addiction' is one of the great simplifying ideas about human behaviour. As with many other simplistic ideas, it neatly divides the world into good and bad. Sugar is bad, pasta is good, for example. It is harder to communicate the idea that it is a behaviour pattern that is problematic, rather than the intrinsic behaviour.

It is noticeable that journalists tend to take food much less seriously as a topic than drugs or alcohol. The latter tend to be sensationalised, but food problems tend to be trivialised. Pop explanations such as 'addiction' may nonetheless be seized upon by people who are concerned about their eating behaviour. It does not help that health professionals are often poorly informed about eating problems and sensible advice about them can be difficult to obtain. Thus, the media may contribute to the social construction of CHOF addiction, when the underlying problems are less straightforward.

6.4.3.4 *Feminist explanations*

A number of authors have discussed the complex interplay between femininity, eating, body image and personal control in a society that is only gradually becoming less patriarchal (40-43). Space precludes going into detail, but such accounts emphasise that women particularly have a structurally problematic relationship with food and eating. As was discussed in section 6.2, addiction is one explanatory device that conveniently packages a person's substance use problems as an individual psychopathology, without having to address more awkward issues about the contributions of family and society to such problems. For example, if women ought to - literally - love chocolate, as the adverts suggest, then it is easier to blame individual women if they learn to love it too much. If they take what was meant tongue in cheek too seriously, then there must be something wrong with them (see section 4.3 for historical background to this). Reid and Burr (44) suggest that eating disorders may be feminine addictions, which are created in part by the social problems of being a woman, while substance dependence involves different, more masculine issues. Taking 'addiction' to be a physiological disorder ignores these issues.

6.4.4 Conclusions

It appears unlikely that there is a specific syndrome of addiction to CHO. CHOF is commonly implicated in disordered eating, but it is again unclear that CHOF or CHO have specific physiological effects that might sustain dependence upon such foodstuffs. However, it is plausible that people can learn to consume CHO or, more commonly, CHOF for a variety of reasons that may indeed lead some people to become dependent upon CHOF. These reasons include beliefs and attitudes about food, including belief in the possibility of CHO/CHOF addiction. However, as far as we know at this time, CHOF dependence is usually part of a broader eating disorder, in the sense that the specific foods consumed and/or avoided do not make a fundamental contribution to the development or prognosis of the disorder. This is in contrast to, say, drug dependence, where it makes a considerable difference whether the person is dependent on heroin, alcohol or marijuana. Heller and Heller (21) have suggested that CHO addiction is responsible for obesity, the prevalence of which has risen very rapidly. Over-consumption of highly palatable, energy-dense CHOF mixtures probably plays a role in obesity (2), but labelling this problem addiction is unhelpful and controversial. Carbohydrate craving obesity may occur (14), but most overweight people are not CHO cravers.

The search for biological causes of 'addiction' may distract research attention away from an understanding of how general psychological and social processes can construct an addiction. These processes are sufficiently complex and powerful to explain why some people feel addicted to CHO, whether or not physiological mechanisms are also involved. There are clear disadvantages to framing eating disorders as addictions, although substance dependence and eating disorders have much in common (see also section 7.4). Only if 'addiction' is seen as a field of study, rather than as a well-defined medical condition, is the framing useful. Unfortunately, 'addiction' usually tends towards the latter, in so far as it is used to describe anything coherent at all.

6.4.5   References

1.   Orford J. *Excessive appetites: a psychological view of addiction*. Chichester, Wiley. 1985.

2.   Battle E.K., Brownell K.D. Confronting a rising tide of eating disorders and obesity: Treatment vs. prevention and policy. *Addictive Behaviors*, 1996, 21, 755-65.

3.   Gilbert S. *Counselling for eating disorders.* London, Sage. 2000.

4.   Cerny L., Cerny K. Can carrots be addictive? An extraordinary form of drug dependence. *British Journal of Addiction,* 1992, 87, 1195-7.

5.   Blum A., Tempey F.W., Lynch W.J. Somatic findings in patients with psychogenic polydipsia. *Journal of Clinical Psychiatry,* 1983, 44, 55-6.

6.   Deleon J., Verghese C., Tracy J.I., Josiassen R.C., Simpson G.M. Polydipsia and water-intoxication in psychiatric-patients - a review of the epidemiologic literature. *Biological Psychiatry,* 1994, 35, 408-19.

7.   Reid M., Hammersley R. The effects of sucrose on everyday eating in normal weight men and women. *Appetite,* 1994, 22, 221-32.

8.   Reid M., Hammersley R. The effects of carbohydrate intake on subsequent food intake and mood state. *Physiology and Behavior,* 1995, 58, 421-7.

9.   Reid M., Hammersley R.H. The effects of carbohydrates on subsequent food intake and mood state in obese and non-obese females. *Psychology, Health & Medicine,* 1998, 3, 299-313.

10. Reid M., Hammersley R.H. The effects of corn oil and sucrose on subsequent food intake. *British Journal of Nutrition,* 1999, 82, 447-55.

11. Heller R.F., Heller R.F. *The carbohydrate addict's diet: the lifelong solution to yo-yo dieting.* London, Cedar. 1992.

12. Duffy W.F. *Sugar blues.* Radnor P.A., Chilton. 1975.

13. Hammersley R., Reid M. Are simple carbohydrates physiologically addictive? *Addiction Research,* 1997, 5, 145-60.

14. Wurtman J.J. Carbohydrate craving. Relationship between carbohydrate intake and disorders of mood. *Drugs,* 1990, 39 (Supplement 3), 49-52.

15. Drenowski A. Changes in mood after carbohydrate consumption. *American Journal of Clinical Nutrition,* 1987, 46, 703.

16. Benton D. The impact of increasing blood glucose on psychological functioning. *Biological Psychology,* 1990, 30, 13-19.

17. Benton D., Owens D. Is raised blood glucose associated with the relief of tension? *Journal of Psychosomatic Research,* 1993, 37, 7, 723-5.

18. Robelin M., Rogers P.J. Mood and psychomotor performance effects of the first, but not of subsequent, cup-of-coffee equivalent doses of caffeine consumed after overnight caffeine abstinence. *Behavioural Pharmacology*, 1998, 9, 611-8.

19. Strain E.C., Griffiths R.R. Caffeine dependence – fact or fiction. *Journal of the Royal Society of Medicine*, 1995, 88, 437-40.

20. Heller R.F., Heller R.F. Hyperinsulinemic obesity and carbohydrate addiction – The missing link is the carbohydrate frequency factor. *Medical Hypotheses*, 1994, 42, 307-12.

21. Heller R.F., Heller R.F. Profactor-h (elevated circulating insulin) - the link to health risk-factors and diseases of civilization. *Medical Hypotheses*, 1995, 45, 325-30.

22. Rogers P.J. Behaviour: Dietary effects on mood and behaviour, in *Encyclopaedia of Human Nutrition Volume 1*. Eds Sadler M.J., Strain J.J., Caballero B. London, Academic Press. 1999, 156-63.

23. Eiser J.R. Smoking – The social learning of an addiction. *Journal of Social and Clinical Psychology*, 1985, 3, 446-57.

24. Siegel S., Allan L.G. Learning and homeostasis: Drug addiction and the McCollough effect. *Psychological Bulletin*, 1998, 124, 230-9.

25. Di Chiara G., Tanda G., Bassareo V., Pontieri F., Acquas E., Fenu S., Cadoni C., Carboni E. Drug addiction as a disorder of associative learning - Role of nucleus accumbens shell/extended amygdala dopamine. *Annals of the New York Academy of Science*, 1999, 877, 461-85.

26. Tiffany S.T. Cognitive concepts of craving. *Alcohol Research and Health*, 1999, 23, 215-24.

27. Hammersley R. A digest of memory phenomena for addiction research. *Addiction*, 1994, 89, 283-93.

28. Tarpey R. *Contemporary learning theory and research*. Maidenhead, McGraw-Hill. 1997.

29. Carter B.L., Tiffany S.T. Meta-analysis of cue-reactivity in addiction research. *Addiction*, 1999, 94, 327-40.

30. Schulze D., Jones B.T. The effects of alcohol cues and an alcohol priming dose on a multi-factorial measure of subjective cue reactivity in social drinkers. *Psychopharmacology*, 1999, 145, 452-4.

31. McCusker C.G., Gettings B. Automaticity of cognitive biases in addictive behaviours: Further evidence with gamblers. *British Journal of Clinical Psychology*, 1997, 36, 543-54.

32. Weinstein A., Feldtkeller B., Malizia A., Wilson S., Bailey J., Nutt D.J. Integrating the cognitive and physiological aspects of craving. *Journal of Psychopharmacology*, 1998, 12, 31-8.

33. Reid M., Hammersley R.H. Effects of blind substitution of asparatame-sweetened for sugar-sweetened soft drinks on appetite and mood. *British Food Journal*, 1998, 100, 254-9.

34. Covasa M., Ritter R.C. Reduced sensitivity to the satiation effect of intestinal oleate in rats adapted to high-fat diet. *American Journal of Physiology*, 1999, Reg I 46 (1) R279-R285.

35. Lindlahr V. *You are what you eat*. Toronto, Coles Publishing Company. 1980.

36. Davies J.B. *The myth of addiction*, 2nd edition. Reading, Harwood. 1998.

37. Lurie P., Drucker E. An opportunity lost: HIV infections associated with lack of a national needle-exchange programme in the USA. *Lancet*, 1997, 349: (9052) 604-8.

38. Sutherland S. *Irrationality*. London, Penguin. 1992.

39. Wolraich M.L., Lindgren S.D., Stumbo P.J., Stegink L.D., Appelbaum M.I., Kiritsy M.C. Effects of diets high in sucrose or aspartame on the behavior and cognitive performance of children. *New England Journal of Medicine*, 1994, 330, 301-7.

40. Wolf N. *The Beauty Myth*. London, Vintage. 1990.

41. Malson H. *The thin woman. Feminism, post structuralism and the social psychology of anorexia nervosa*. London, Routledge. 1998.

42. Orbach S. *Fat is a feminist issue*. London, Hamlyn. 1972.

43. Orbach S. *Hunger strike*. London, Faber. 1986.

44. Reid M., Burr J. Are eating disorders feminine addictions? *Addiction Research*. (In press).

6.5. FUNCTIONAL FOODS, MOOD AND CRAVING

France Bellisle

6.5.1   Introduction

The primary role of foods is to provide a variety of nutrients in sufficient amounts to cover the metabolic requirements of an individual. In this sense, all foods are functional and fulfil a vital role. In addition to this basic role of foods, there is growing evidence that numerous foods, food components and/or food ingredients, can modulate specific target functions of the body and exert beneficial physiological and psychological influence beyond basic nutritional effects. A recent consensus workshop (1) came to the conclusion that substances ingested as foods or with foods can act in two different directions and improve the health or well-being or quality of life of consumers: they can contribute to reducing the risk of disease (this is the case of antioxidants, for example) and they can enhance several body functions. The present chapter will deal with the latter type of function played by foodstuffs, and discuss how mood, arousal, and cognitive functions can be affected positively (or negatively) by the ingestion of specific foods.

6.5.2   General Notions

A food can be regarded as "functional" if it is satisfactorily demonstrated to affect beneficially one or more target functions in the body, beyond adequate nutritional effects, in a way that is relevant to an improved state of health and well-being and/or reduction of risk of disease. Functional foods must remain foods and they must demonstrate their effects in amounts that can normally be expected to be consumed in the diet: they are not pills or capsules, but part of normal food selection (1).

A functional food can be a natural food, a food to which a component has been added, or a food from which a component has been removed by technological or biotechnological means. It can also be a food where the

495

nature of one or more components has been modified, or a food in which the bioavailability of one or more components has been modified, or any combination of these possibilities. A functional food might be functional for all members of a population or for particular groups of the population, which might be defined, for example by age or by genetic constitution (1). Functional foods must be safe according to all standards of assessing food risk. The safety evaluation of micronutrients must take into account potential adverse effects of low intakes as well as effects from intakes that are too high (clinical toxicity). It is important to identify specific target groups of individuals who might present higher/lower susceptibilities to potential adverse effects and to consider that the effects of functional foods might be positive in some target groups and negative in others. The long-term consequences of the intake of functional foods must be considered as well as the immediate effects.

6.5.3   Functional Foods and Behaviour

There are numerous foods or food components that are not directly related to disease or to health in the traditional sense but, nevertheless, provide an important function in terms of changing mood or mental state. These foods, therefore, are involved in creating more a sense of "feeling well" than of "being well". Effects on behaviour, on emotional state, and on cognitive performance fall within this category.

The complexity and variability of human behaviour arise from the fact that behaviour is the cumulative outcome of two distinct sources of influence: biological factors (encompassing genetics, gender, age, body size, etc.) and the socio-cultural environment (including tradition, education, religion, economic status, etc.). As might be expected from the large number of complex factors involved, the effects of foods on behavioural and psychological functions are conspicuously varied, typically subtle and frequently interdependent. In all cultures, there is a host of anecdotal information of such effects. Scientifically established effects, however, are less numerous.

The effects of food components on cognitive state or mood are acute, immediate effects. They therefore provide a clear, immediate positive reinforcement to the consumer for their use. They can thus support motivated behaviour by the consumer who wants to modify deliberately his/her mood or mental status (2). They can give rise to cravings or self-medication (1). Functional foods can be regarded as instrumental to achieve a certain mood change or a certain level of arousal. The scientific evidence reviewed below does suggest deliberate alteration of mental state by the consumer but, as will become evident, numerous questions remain open to scientific exploration.

6.5.4   Cognitive Performance

The public is well aware that substances such as caffeine and alcohol can exert strong effects on mental alertness. Macronutrients (proteins, fats, and carbohydrates) influence mental performance, as demonstrated by scientific protocols. These experimental studies use validated instruments for assessing various dimensions of cognitive functioning: reasoning, perception, memory, attention, information processing, accuracy and speed of movement (2).

6.5.4.1   Meals and cognitive functions

Several studies have demonstrated a positive effect of breakfast on cognitive performance in the following hours. Reaction time, spatial memory and immediate word recall are impaired in subjects who have missed breakfast (3,4). A breakfast composed of cereals improves mood and spatial memory, as compared with a no-breakfast condition (5). Children appear more sensitive than adults to breakfast omission (6,7).

Although a few negative results have been reported, a majority of studies have shown that having breakfast (as opposed to no breakfast) and high energy breakfasts (as opposed to low energy ones) facilitate sustained attention, reaction time and memory. Although the mechanism for this effect is not elucidated, one interesting hypothesis is that cognitive performance could be related to blood glucose levels (8).

Unfortunately, these positive effects of food and energy following breakfast are not replicated following lunch. Having lunch (versus not having lunch) worsens attention and performance on reaction time tasks (9). Mental functions in the few hours following lunch are likely to be disturbed by a phenomenon called the "post-lunch dip", which is characterised by low alertness, and high fatigue (10). The appearance, intensity and the duration of the post-lunch dip are affected by lunch size, the consumption of alcohol, habits, and time of day (the post-lunch dip is maximum if lunch occurs between 1200 and 1400h, suggesting a circadian biological effect). The post-lunch dip can be reversed to a certain extent by ingestion of caffeine. The post-lunch dip, a clearly undesired effect in developed societies, could be a fruitful area of research for the development of functional foods.

Whether lunch contains high-fat or high-carbohydrate foods, post-lunch mental state is poor in the hours that follow, characterised by drowsiness, low cognitive efficiency, and increased lassitude (11,12). Following high-fat meals (versus high-carbohydrate), performance is slower but more accurate on selective attention tasks (13). Alertness is impaired and reaction time is lower after a high-fat lunch, as compared with a low-fat one (14). This is consistent with the observation that infusion of lipids into the duodenum of human subjects reduces alertness and performance in attention tasks (14). Psychomotor task performance is affected by neither previous nutrient nor energy intake (15).

Very few studies have examined the effects of food intake in the evening on subsequent mental performance. The effects are mixed, some functions being improved (logical memory) while others are not affected (attention, word recall, or word recognition) (16). Some complex functions can be worsened, such as visual search under high memory load (17). Consumption habits play a role since optimal performance is observed when the experimental meal is as close as possible to the subject's usual meal.

The effects of high-energy, high-carbohydrate afternoon snacks on various aspects of mental performance have been investigated (18-20). Compared with diet soft drinks, a high-carbohydrate snack is followed by improved memory and attention in the late afternoon. Again, it is suggested that the effects are due to a rise in blood glucose.

6.5.4.2   Nutrients and cognitive functions

Numerous studies have demonstrated that the ingestion of glucose has beneficial effects on cognitive performance. In laboratory animals, it is established that a high level of circulating glucose is associated with improved learning ability, in particular with increased memory. By contrast, learning and memory are impaired in rats fed a high-fat diet (21). Recent data suggest that glycaemic control and good glucose regulation in young men and women are associated with performance in tests involving memory (22). Individuals with poor glycaemic control have impaired immediate and delayed memory for words as compared with controls, but this difference disappears after the subjects are given a 50-g glucose load.

Short-term memory is improved by glucose in elderly subjects and in young adults (3,22-25). The rise in blood glucose that follows a glucose drink correlates with improved decision time in a reaction time task, faster information processing, better word recall, and improvement on a cognitive conflict task (26). This effect is not due to the correction of hypoglycaemia, since it is reproduced across a range of baseline blood glucose levels. Hypoglycaemia, however, is associated with slower reaction times. A recent study carried out in 80 adults confirmed that having breakfast and/or a glucose drink improves performance on a memory test (27): performance is positively associated with blood glucose level. Glucose improves memory in patients with Down's syndrome (28) and Alzheimer's disease (29,30).

The mechanisms mediating the memory-enhancing properties of glucose are not elucidated at the present time. They could include both peripheral and central processes. In particular, glucose could act as a cholinergic agonist and as an opioid antagonist (31), or else via its effects on insulin (32,33).

In recent years, the notion of "glycaemic index" has been proposed to replace the outdated and misleading concept of fast/slow carbohydrates, and even the more structure-based notion of simple/complex carbohydrates.

Nutrition experts now increasingly advise the public to select foods with low glycaemic index (34). Such carbohydrate foods induce a very modest rise in post-ingestive glucose. It remains to be seen whether high or low glycaemic index foods exert different effects on cognitive functions, in particular those that are enhanced following glucose load and/or that are improved when glycaemia is high.

Vitamins and minerals have also been studied in the context of cognitive performance. Supplementation of the diet with vitamins B6 and B12 and folic acid improves cognitive function and measures of intelligence in elderly subjects (35). In children, positive results have been reported, suggesting that multivitamin supplements improve performance on a cognitive test battery (36). Two studies have failed to reproduce this effect (37,38). It is possible that supplementation is more likely to produce improved performance in individuals with vitamin-deficient diets. Where the diet is deficient in several nutrients, children typically show poor performance on tests of non-verbal IQ (39). The potential effect could be very modest in well-nourished individuals.

In agreement with anecdotal observations, several studies have confirmed that intake of caffeine leads to improvement of cognitive performance, particularly reaction time, memory and psychomotor co-ordination (4,5,40). It has been hypothesised that the cognition-enhancing properties of caffeine could be due to its cholinergic action in the nervous system. In animals, significant improvements in learning performance have been seen with choline-enriched diets. Improvements in memory are sometimes reported in humans fed choline-rich diets (41); however most studies report no effect.

The habitual level of caffeine intake plays a role in the observed effects, although the direction of effects is not clear. Verbal memory is better in high caffeine users (42); verbal reasoning is worse in high users compared with low and moderate users (43); and high users perform more efficiently than low users in a reaction time task (42,44). Personality characteristics can also affect results: highly impulsive individuals perform better following caffeine, whereas the performance of persons with low impulsivity is impaired (45). Highly impulsive persons respond positively to caffeine in the morning, when their arousal level is low, as well as in the afternoon (46).

Alcohol has well-known deleterious effects on psychomotor performance and cognitive functions (47).

6.5.5   Arousal and Sedation

Some substances present in the usual diet potentially affect levels of arousal during waking hours and also sleepiness or sedation. Scientific studies have focused mainly on two particular substances: caffeine and the amino acid tryptophan.

It has been observed under several experimental circumstances, that high-carbohydrate meals tend to be followed by intense feelings of drowsiness, sleepiness, and calmness (48). Following a high-starch or a high-sugar meal, subjects report feeling lethargic, clumsy, dreamy, bored and mentally slow (10). It has been hypothesised that the dietary effects of large carbohydrate loads are caused by increasing the level of brain serotonin (5-hydroxytryptamine, 5-HT) (49). The hypothesis implies that carbohydrate loads induce changes in the plasma ratio of tryptophan:large neutral amino acid (LNAA). Circulating tryptophan exists in a free form and bound to blood albumen. After a high carbohydrate meal (which must contain almost no protein), the insulin that is released causes branched-chain amino acids to be taken up into tissues, particularly muscles. Insulin also reduces non-esterified fatty acids (NEFA) released into the plasma. Plasma NEFA concentration falls and albumen binding sites are liberated. Consequently, a high-carbohydrate meal elevates the tryptophan:LNAA ratio in the plasma. This, in turn, favours the uptake of tryptophan into the brain as the amino acids compete for the selective carrier across the blood brain barrier. Consequently, carbohydrate meals increase brain tryptophan. Since the enzyme tryptophan hydroxylase is normally not saturated with its precursor, the availability of tryptophan becomes the rate-limiting step in the synthesis of the neurotransmittor 5-HT. The logic of this argument is that high-carbohydrate meals enhance serotoninergic neurotransmission in the brain (50). The "tryptophan effect", however, is abolished by adding as little as 4% protein to the meal (51).

Tryptophan administration, which should produce the same effects as a pure carbohydrate load, produces feelings of fatigue, inertia, and decreased feelings of vigor, as assessed by rating scales (52). In both adults and children, tryptophan reduces sleep latency (53). Given this unequivocal effect, it is tempting to use tryptophan to modify arousal level. This idea has been used and kits are sold on the market to combat jet lag. Pills containing tryptophan taken before going to bed should facilitate sleepiness. Complementary pills containing tyrosine, an amino acid facilitating alertness, are to be taken in the morning. This treatment should, at least theoretically, help synchronise circadian rhythms more rapidly after a major change in the day-night cycle. No experimental evidence supports this hypothesis (54).

In agreement with the above-mentioned observations, drowsiness, sleepiness and calm are usually found to be more intense after high-carbohydrate than after high-protein meals (48). At lunch, both carbohydrates and proteins induce some drowsiness, but the effect is greater after a high-carbohydrate load (48,55,56). Any breakfast reduces fatigue in regular breakfast eaters; however, a carbohydrate-rich breakfast tends to reduce fatigue less than a protein-rich breakfast.

Caffeine is well-known as a potent psychostimulant (57-59). Caffeine increases alertness (4,5). It may also increase anxiety at high doses in susceptible individuals but its overall toxicity is minimal (60). A "withdrawal syndrome" has been reported: in regular consumers of caffeine, the cessation of intake is followed by adverse effects, such as headache, drowsiness and fatigue (61). Withdrawal responses vary between subjects, and depending on the duration of caffeine deprivation (62). After overnight deprivation (13 hours), subjects report feelings of tiredness, drowsiness, anger and dejection. After 7 days, they are more likely to report headache and mood deterioration. It is thus difficult to determine if experimental results on the effects of caffeine, often obtained after an overnight caffeine deprivation, are due to beneficial effects of the substance or to the correction of the negative consequences of short-term caffeine deprivation.

6.5.6 Food and Mood

It is clear that certain nutrients or substances consumed with or in foods and drinks exert a strong influence on mood and affective state. The most obvious of these substances is alcohol. A low dose of alcohol is likely to improve mood, disinhibit behaviour, and facilitate social contacts in most people (63). More alcohol has an increasingly disturbing influence, and large doses are associated with numerous physical, mental, and behavioural problems (47). For centuries, people have used alcohol as a mood enhancer, with variable degrees of success. While most liquids that are used as drinking substances serve hydroregulatory functions, alcoholic beverages have to do a great deal more with mood than with thirst.

The literature on alcohol and alcohol intake is vast and clearly exceeds the scope of the present chapter. Reviews are published at short intervals, updating knowledge of the various beneficial effects of moderate alcohol intake (on the cardiovascular system, for example) and the severe personal and social risks associated with excessive consumption (64,65).

Tryptophan deficiency has recently been linked to dysphoria-related alcohol abuse. Alcohol abuse may be a result of abnormal serotonergic activity in certain individuals since alcohol can mimic the central effects of serotonin (66). This hypothesis is purely speculative at this time, but the potential capacity of ethanol to modulate brain serotonin activity and alleviate depressive mood merits scientific attention.

Other nutrients have been implicated in behavioural distress and mood shifts. They can be used as "functional foods" inasmuch as individuals who are aware of their properties are tempted to self-medicate and deliberately use food or drinks to combat aversive mood states such as anxiety, frustration, or depression. Conversely, some foods can be avoided in order to protect oneself from their potential deleterious effects on moods or behaviour (67-69). Sugar, for example, has been blamed for disturbances of mood, sleep and cognitive performance (70).

One phenomenon that has received significant attention is the concomitant occurrence of dysphoria, a state of feeling unwell or unhappy, with a strong attraction for foods high in sugar or in starch. A syndrome called "carbohydrate craving" has been described in patients who report irrepressible impulses to ingest high-carbohydrate foods in various situations of tension (71-73). These patients, "carbohydrate cravers", describe themselves as anxious, tense, or depressed before a carbohydrate snack and peaceful and relaxed after (71). In agreement with this notion, preferences for sweet and starchy foods have been reported to increase during depressive episodes (74), premenstrual syndrome (75), bulimic episodes (55), seasonal affective disorder (76), and atypical depression (77), as well as during withdrawal from alcohol, caffeine and tobacco (78). Carbohydrate intake can provide a temporary elevation in energy (79) and mood (72,73), but this effect is not always observed (80). In healthy subjects, a high-carbohydrate breakfast improves mood by reducing fatigue and dysphoria (81).

According to the "carbohydrate craving" hypothesis, individuals would consume specific high-carbohydrate foods in order to improve their mood state. Any transient improvement in mood, however, is typically followed by a more prolonged period of increased anxiety, fatigue and depression (79,82) or even guilt (83), in a similar way as has been reported following alcohol intake (63). The motivation to alleviate the negative mood state is high and consumers respond to it by consuming more carbohydrates, or more alcohol. As such, it seems that the initial positive effect controls the consumer's behaviour rather than the ensuing negative consequence (84). This is consistent with well established laws of learning: an immediate positive reinforcement of behaviour is much more likely to control a subject's responses than more distant negative effects (see also section 3.2).

Central serotonergic imbalance has been linked to both disorders of food intake and affective behaviour. The scientific support for this hypothesis, however, is mixed. Tryptophan depletion in humans can lead to mild dysphoria (85), but this effect might be observed only in susceptible individuals, such as persons with a multi-generational history of major affective disorders (86). In several cases, dietary manipulations probably exert very little influence on the plasma tryptophan:LNAA ratio (87). There is some evidence, however, that diet can influence the tryptophan/LNAA ratio (88,89). Studies have failed to find carbohydrate versus protein effects on mood, despite significant changes in the tryptophan:LNAA ratio (68,90).

In addition, the existence of true "carbohydrate cravers" in the population has been repeatedly questioned. Self-labelled cravers of sweet foods do not consume an abnormally high proportion of high-carbohydrate, low-protein foods (91); they reportedly enjoy chocolate, ice cream, and other desserts, each of these deriving the highest proportion of their energy from fat (92). A study of French obese women failed to find even one individual who would correspond to the classic definition of a "carbohydrate craver" (93). A recent review highlights the inconsistencies in the literature about carbohydrate ingestion and psychological effects (94): they can be crucially affected by a host of factors including prior mood state of the subject, his/her habitual diet, expectations, etc. The potential variations in serotonin levels cannot alone account for the observed effects.

In free-living subjects, mood is not affected by food ingested in the last meal and does not predict nutrient choices in the next meal (95). This confirms that, in everyday life, the mixed nutrient content of meals does not allow the "tryptophan" effect to develop. It has been observed, however, that, over nine consecutive days, average mood states are associated with the proportion (but not the absolute value) of nutrients in the diet: high protein content correlates positively with depression while high carbohydrate content correlates negatively with it (95). Cause and effect relationships are difficult to identify in such studies of contemporary mood states and food choices.

Certain vitamin deficiencies have been implicated in psychiatric symptoms such as psychosis and depression. The classic example is pellagra, which results from severe niacin deficiency (96). Folate deficiency is characterised by insufficient levels of its metabolic precursor S-adenylmethionine. Since S-adenylmethionine may exert anti-depressant effects by raising brain serotonin levels, folate deficiency has been implicated in serotonin-related depressive episodes (97). In the absence of deficiency, however, there is no evidence that vitamin supplementation improves mood or is a potential treatment for behavioural problems (70).

The mere process of food ingestion may produce effects on moods. It was recognised long ago that restrictive, weight-reducing diets are associated with feelings of depression (98). Chronic dieting and "dietary restraint" are associated with several untoward mental states and attitudes (99,100). On a short-term basis, during a one-hour experimental hypoglycaemia induced by a glucose clamp technique, a negative mood state was reported by healthy young adults (101). This state was characterised by decreased hedonic tone and increased tension, in association with a relatively negative appraisal of career prospects. In everyday life, the negative affect induced by hypoglycaemia could constitute a strong stimulus to eat and restore glycaemia, whether the consumer is dieting or not.

Conversely, the intake of foods can be linked to the activation of endogenous opioid responses in the central nervous system. The oral ingestion of a light meal and the consequent stimulation of gastric function are associated with the increase in β-endorphin levels in humans (102). Endorphins are endogenous opioid substances involved in reward and pain perception. They could be increased in the post-meal period as a result of the normal processing of food in the digestive tract (103,104). There is evidence that the endogenous opioid peptide system modulates food preferences and cravings among obese persons and patients with bulimia nervosa (105). The opioid antagonist naloxone reduces snack eating in binge eaters and alters taste preferences in patients and controls. The most affected foods are high-fat items such as cookies or chocolate, suggesting a selective effect on highly rewarding foods (105).

The mere act of ingesting food might therefore be a means of reducing pain perception and altering mood state. Such a provocative hypothesis has attracted much scientific attention. At present, however, the literature remains confusing. Several experiments in isolated rat pups have shown that infusion of sugar into the oral cavity stops distress vocalisations, suggesting a calming, rewarding effect of sucrose (106,107). A palatable food reward (chocolate milk) appears to influence β-endorphin activity in rats, as evidenced by their behavioural response to the administration of the opioid antagonist naloxone. Hyperphagic obese rats are more tolerant to painful stimuli than lean controls, which suggests a higher level of opioid activity (108). In other studies, pain sensitivity has been shown to decrease after food deprivation (109) and to increase in rats with continuous access to a palatable sucrose solution (104). Sweet taste and milk flavour give rise to analgesia in rat and human newborns. Administering a sweet stimulus to a newborn human undergoing blood collection efficiently reduces the behavioural markers of pain perception (110).

There was no increase in circulating β-endorphin level in human subjects following the intake of a highly palatable meal (111), while high levels of β-endorphins have been found in patients with anorexia nervosa (112). Women who consume palatable foods under experimental meal conditions show increased pain tolerance, as measured using a pressure algometer, compared with controls receiving unpalatable foods, neutral foods, or nothing (113).

6.5.7   Conclusions

There is ample evidence that some foods, food components or food ingredients can exert an influence on various aspects of behaviour and mental functions. These effects are modulated by numerous non-nutritional factors such as time of day, age, gender, personality factors and consumers' expectations, etc. They also vary over time. One important factor determining the end effect is the context of food ingestion, in particular the culture where a specific effect is observed (94). Culture, which is the crucial factor determining food preferences and aversions in humans (114,115), is also the general context where an effect will be judged positive or negative (2).

A lot remains to be investigated: the exact circumstances where an effect can be expected, its time course, and its mechanisms. Research efforts have established constellations of partial, disconnected effects. They remain to be integrated, and clear causal relationships must be elucidated between nutritive and non-nutritive factors on the one hand and behavioural and cognitive responses on the other. This can be achieved only by concerted, long-term scientific investigation in humans, which will allow scientists to establish how foods can be used effectively to improve the consumer's sense of "feeling well".

6.5.8 References

1. Diplock A.T., Aggett P.J., Ashwell M., Bornet F., Fern E.B., Roberfroid M. Scientific concepts of functional foods in Europe: Consensus Document. *British Journal of Nutrition*, 1999, 81, Suppl. 1.

2. Bellisle F., Blundell J.E., Dye L., Fantino M., Fern E., Fletcher R.J., Lambert J., Roberfroid M., Specter S., Wentenhöfer J., Westerterp-Plantenga M.S. Functional food science and behaviour and psychological functions. *British Journal of Nutrition*, 1998, 80, Suppl. 1, S173-S193.

3. Benton D., Sargent J. Breakfast blood glucose and memory. *Biological Psychology*, 1992, 33, 207-10.

4. Smith A.P., Kendrick A., Maben A., Salmon J. Effects of breakfast and caffeine on cognitive performance, mood and cardiovascular functioning. *Appetite*, 1994, 22, 39-55.

5. Smith A.P., Clark R., Gallagher J. Breakfast cereal and caffeinated coffee: effects on working memory, attention, mood, and cardiovascular function. *Physiology & Behavior*, 1999, 67, 9-17.

6. Vaisman N., Voet H., Akivis A., Vakil E. Effect of breakfast timing on the cognitive functions of elementary school students. *Archives of Pediatric and Adolescent Medicine*, 1996, 150, 1089-92.

7. Tuttle W.W., Daum K., Larsen R., Salzano J., Roloff L. Effect on schoolboys of omitting breakfast: physiologic responses, attitudes and scholastic attainments. *Journal of the American Dietetic Association*, 1954, 30, 674-7.

8. Benton D. The impact of increasing blood glucose on psychological functioning. *Biological Psychology*, 1990, 30, 13-19.

9. Smith A.P., Miles C. The effects of lunch on cognitive vigilance tasks. *Ergonomics*, 1986, 29, 1251-61.

10. Smith A.P., Leekam S., Ralph A., McNeill G. The influence of meal composition on post-lunch changes in performance efficiency and mood. *Appetite*, 1988, 10, 195-203.

11. Lloyd H.M., Green M.W., Rogers P.J. Mood and cognitive performance effects of isocaloric lunches differing in fat and carbohydrate content. *Physiology & Behavior*, 1994, 56, 51-7.

12. Wells A.S., Read N.W. Influences of fat, energy and time of day on mood and performance. *Physiology & Behavior*, 1996, 59, 1069-76.

13. Smith A.P., Kendrick A., Maben A.L. Use and effects of food and drinks in relation to daily rhythms of mood and cognitive performance. Effects of caffeine, lunch and alcohol on human performance, mood and cardiovascular function. *Proceedings of the Nutrition Society*, 1992, 51, 325-33.

14. Wells A.S., Read N.W., Craig A. Influences of dietary and intraduodenal lipid on alertness, mood, and sustained concentration. *British Journal of Nutrition*, 1995, 74, 115-23.

15. Kelly T.H., Foltin R.W., Rolls B.J., Fischman M.W. Effect of meal macronutrient and energy content on human performance. *Appetite*, 1994, 23, 97-111.

16. Smith A.P., Maben A., Brockman P. Effects of evening meals and caffeine on cognitive performance, mood and cardiovascular functioning. *Appetite*, 1994, 22, 57-65.

17. Smith A.P., Miles C. The combined effects of occupational health hazards: an experimental investigation of the effects of noise, nightwork and meals. *Internal Archives of Occupational Environmental Health*, 1987, 59, 83-9.

18. Kanarek R.B., Swinney D. Effects of food snacks on cognitive performance in male college students. *Appetite*, 1990, 14, 15-27.

19. Kanarek R. Psychological effects of snacks and altered meal frequency. *British Journal of Nutrition*, 1997, Suppl. 1, S105-S120.

20. Hetherington M.M., Macdiarmid J.I. Chocolate addiction: a preliminary description and report of its relationship to problem eating. *Appetite*, 1993, 21, 233-46.

21. Greenwood C.E., Winocur G. Learning and memory impairment in rats fed a high saturated fat diet. *Behavioral Neural Biology*, 1990, 53, 74-87.

22. Messier C., Desrochers A., Gagnon M. Effect of glucose, glucose regulation, and word imagery value on human memory. *Behavioral Neuroscience*, 1999, 113, 431-8.

23. Manning C.A., Parsons M.W., Cotter E.M., Gold P.E. Glucose effects on declarative and nondeclarative memory in healthy elderly and young adults. *Psychobiology*, 1997, 25, 103-8.

24. Craft S., Murphy C., Wemsrom J. Glucose effects on complex memory and nonmemory tasks: The influence of age, sex, and glucoregulatory response. *Psychobiology*, 1994, 22, 95-105.

25. Korol D.L., Gold P.E. Glucose, memory, and aging. *American Journal of Clinical Nutrition*, 1998, 67, 764S-771S.

26. Benton D., Owens D. Blood glucose and human memory. *Psychopharmacology*, 1993, 113, 83-8.

27. Martin P.Y., Benton D. The influence of a glucose drink on a demanding working memory task. *Physiology & Behavior*, 1999, 67, 69-74.

28. Manning C.A., Honn V.J., Stone W.S., Jane J.S., Gold P.E. Glucose effects on cognition in adults with Down's syndrome. *Neuropsychology*, 1998, 12, 479-84.

29. Craft S., Zallen G., Baker L.D. Glucose and memory in mild senile dementia of the Alzheimer type. *Journal of Clinical and Experimental Neuropsychology*, 1992, 14, 253-67.

30. Messier C., Gagnon M. Glucose regulation and cognitive functions: Relation to Alzheimer's Disease and diabetes. *Behavioural Brain Research*, 1996, 75, 1-10.

31. Rodriguez W.A., Horne C.A., Padilla J.L. Effects of glucose and fructose on recently reactivated and recently acquired memories. *Progress in Neuropsychopharmacology and Biological Psychiatry*, 1999, 23, 1285-317.

32. Craft S., Newcomer J., Kanne S., Dagogo-Jack S., Cryer P., Sheline Y., Luby L., Dagogo-Jack A., Alderson A. Memory improvement following induced hyperinsulinemia in Alzheimer's disease. *Neurobiology of Aging*, 1996, 17, 12130.

33. Hoyer S. Models of Alzheimer's disease: Cellular and molecular aspects. *Journal of Neurotransmission (supplement)*, 1997, 49, Suppl., 11-21.

34. Brand-Miller J. L'index glycémique des aliments. *Cahiers de Nutrition et de Diététique*, 1997, 32, 42-7.

35. Goodwin J.S., Goodwin J.M., Garry P.J. Association between nutritional status and cognitive functioning in a healthy elderly population. *Journal of the American Medical Association*, 1983, 249(21), 2917-21.

36. Benton D. Vitamin-mineral supplements and intelligence. *Proceedings of the Nutrition Society*, 1992, 51, 295-302.

37. Crombie I.K., Todman J., McNeill G., Florey C.D., Menzies I., Kennedy R.A. Effect of vitamin and mineral supplementation on verbal and non-verbal reasoning of schoolchildren. *Lancet*, 1990, 311, 744-7.

38. Nelson M., Naiswith D.J., Burley V., Gatenby S.J., Geddes N. Nutrient intakes, vitamin-mineral supplementation and intelligence in British schoolchildren. *British Journal of Nutrition*, 1990, 64, 13-22.

39. Nelson M. Vitamin and mineral supplementation and academic performance in schoolchildren. *Proceedings of the Nutrition Society*, 1992, 51, 303-13.

40. Smith A., Kendrick A., Maben A., Salmon J. Effects of fat content, weight, and acceptability of the meal on postlunch changes in mood, performance, and cardiovascular function. *Physiology & Behavior*, 1994, 55, 417-22.

41. Bartus R.T., Dean R.L., Beer B., Lippa A.S. The cholinergic hypothesis of geriatric memory dysfunction. *Science*, 1982, 216, 408-17.

42. Jarvis M.J. Does caffeine intake enhance absolute levels of cognitive performance? *Psychopharmacology*, 1993, 110, 45-52.

43. Mitchell P.J., Redman J.R. Effects of caffeine, time of day and user history on study-related performance. *Psychopharmacology*, 1992, 109, 121-6.

44. Rogers P.J., Richardson N.J., Dernoncourt C. Caffeine use: is there a net benefit for mood and psychomotor performance? *Neuropsychobiology*, 1995, 31, 195-9.

45. Anderson K.J., Revelle W. Impulsivity, caffeine and proof-reading: A test of the Easterbrook hypothesis. *Journal of Experimental Psychology: Human Perception and Performance*, 1982, 8, 614-24.

46. Smith A.P., Rusted J.M., Savory M., Eaton-Williams P., Hall S.R. The effects of caffeine, impulsivity and time of day on performance, mood, and cardiovascular function. *Journal of Psychopharmacology*, 1991, 5, 120-8.

47. Hindmarch I., Kerr J.S., Sherwood N. The effects of alcohol and other drugs on psychomotor performance and cognitive function. *Alcohol & Alcoholism*, 1991, 26, 71-9.

48. Spring B., Chiodo J., Bowen D.J. Carbohydrates, tryptophan, and behavior: a methodological review. *Psychological Bulletin*, 1987, 102, 234-56.

49. Fernstrom J. The effect of dietary macronutrients on brain serotonin formation, in *Appetite and Body Weight Regulation*. Eds Fernstrom J.D., Miller G.D. Boca Raton, CRC Press, Inc. 1994, 51-62.

50. Fernstrom J.D., Wurtman R.J. Brain serotonin content: physiological dependence on plasma trytophan levels. *Science*, 1972, 173, 149-51.

51. Teff K.L., Young S.N., Marchand L., Botez M.I. Acute effect of protein or carbohydrate breakfasts on human cerebrospinal fluid monoamine precursor and metabolite levels. *Journal of Neurochemistry*, 1989, 52, 235-41.

52. Lieberman H., Corkin S., Spring B. Mood, performance and sensitivity: Changes induced by food constituents. *Journal of Psychiatric Research*, 1983, 17, 135-45.

53. Steinberg L.A., O'Connell N.C., Hatch T.F., Picciano M.F., Birch L.L. Tryptophan intake influences infants' sleep latency. *Journal of Nutrition*, 1992, 122, 1781-91.

54. Waterhouse J., Minors D., Atkinson G., Benton D. Chronobiology and mealtimes: internal and external factors. *British Journal of Nutrition*, 1996, 77 (Suppl. 1), S29-S38.

55. Rosenthal N.E., Hefferman M.M. Bulimia, carbohydrate craving, and depression: A central connection, in *Nutrition and the Brain, Vol 7*. Eds Wurtman R.J., Wurtman J.J. New York, Raven Press. 1986, 139-66.

56. Spring B., Maller O., Wurtman J., Digman L., Cozolino L. Effects of protein and carbohydrate meals on mood and performance: Interactions with sex and age. *Journal of Psychiatric Research*, 1983, 17, 155-67.

57. James J.E. *Caffeine and Health*. London, Academic Press. 1991.

58. Debry G. *Le café, sa composition, sa consommation, ses incidences sur la santé*. Nancy, Centre de Nutrition Humaine. 1989.

59.   Nehlig A., Daval J.L., Debry G. Caffeine and the central nervous system: mechanisms of action, biochemical, metabolic and psychostimulant effects. *Brain Research Reviews*, 1992, 17, 139-70.

60.   Stavric B. Methylxanthines: Toxicity to humans. 2. Caffeine. *Food Chemistry & Toxicology*, 1988, 26, 645-62.

61.   Silverman K., Evans S.M., Strain E.C., Griffiths R.R. Withdrawal syndrome after double-blind cessation of caffeine consumption. *New England Journal of Medicine*, 1992, 327, 1109-114.

62.   Richardson N.J., Rogers P.J., Elliman N.A., O'Dell R.J. Mood and performance effects of caffeine in relation to acute and chronic caffeine deprivation. *Pharmacology, Biochemistry & Behavior*, 1995, 52, 313-20.

63.   Lloyd H.M., Rogers P.J. Mood and cognitive performance improved by low dose of alcohol administered double blind. *Appetite*, 1995, 24, 280.

64.   Gurr M. Alcohol. *Health issues related to alcohol consumption. 2nd edition.* Brussels, ILSI Europe Concise Monograph Series. 1997.

65.   Rimm E.B., Williams P., Fosher K., Criqui M., Stampfer M.J. Moderate alcohol intake and lower risk of coronary heart disease: meta-analysis of effects on lipids and haemostatic factors. *British Medical Journal*, 1999, 319, 1523-8.

66.   Adams W.R., Kiefer S.W., Badia-Elder N. Tryptophan deficiency and alcohol consumption in rats as a model for disadvantaged human populations: A preliminary study. *Medical Anthropology*, 1995, 16, 175-91.

67.   Christensen L., Krietsch K., White B. Development, cross-validation, and assessment of the reliability of the Christensen Dietary Distress Inventory. *Canadian Journal of Behavioral Science*, 1989, 21, 1-15.

68.   Christensen L., Redig C. Effect of meal composition on mood. *Behavioral Neuroscience*, 1993, 107, 346-53.

69.   Rogers P.J. Food, mood and appetite. *Nutrition Research Reviews*, 1995, 8, 243-69.

70.   Kruesi M.J.P., Rapoport J.L. Diet and human behavior: How much do they affect each other? *Annual Review of Nutrition*, 1986, 6, 113-30.

71.   Wurtman J.J. The involvement of brain serotonin in excessive carbohydrate snacking by obese carbohydrate cravers. *Journal of the American Dietetic Association*, 1984, 84, 1004-7.

72.   Lieberman H.R., Spring B., Garfield G.S. The behavioral effects of food constituents: strategies used in studies of amino acids, protein, carbohydrates and caffeine. *Nutrition Reviews*, 1986, 44 (Suppl.), 61-9.

73.   Spring B., Lieberman H.R., Swope G., Garfield G.S. Effects of carbohydrates on mood and behaviour. *Nutrition Reviews*, 1986, 44s, 51-60.

74.   Fernstrom M.H., Krowinski R.L., Kupfer D.J. Appetite and food preference in depression: Effects of imipramine treatment. *Biological Psychiatry*, 1987, 22, 529-39.

75.   Wurtman J.J., Brzezinski A., Wurtman R.J., Laferrere B. Effect of nutrient intake on premenstrual depression. *American Journal of Obstetrics and Gynecology*, 1989, 161, 1228-35.

76.   Rosenthal N.E., Genhart M.J., Caballero B., Jacobsen F.M., Skwerer R.G., Coursey R.D., Rogers S., Spring B. Psychobiological effects of carbohydrate- and protein-rich meals in patients with seasonal affective disorder and normal controls. *Biological Psychiatry*, 1989, 25, 1029-40.

77.   Wallin M.S., Rissanen A.N. Food and mood: Relationship between food, serotonin, and affective disorders. *Acta Psychiatrica Scandinavica*, 1994, 377, 36-70.

78.   Rosenthal N.E., Genhart M.J., Caballero B., Jacobsen F.M., Skwerer R.G., Coursey R.D., Rogers S., Spring B.J. Psychobiological effects of carbohydrate- and protein-rich meals in patients with seasonal affective disorder and normal controls. *Biological Psychiatry*, 1989, 25, 1029-40.

79.   Thayer R.E. Energy, tiredness, and tension effects of a sugar snack versus modest exercise. *Journal of Personality and Social Psychology*, 1987, 52, 119-25.

80.   Reid M., Hammersley R. Effects of carbohydrate intake on subsequent food intake and mood state. *Physiology & Behavior*, 1995, 8, 421-7.

81.   Lloyd H.M., Rogers P.J., Hedderley D.I. Acute effects on mood and cognitive performance of breakfasts differing in fat and carbohydrate content. *Appetite*, 1996, 27, 151-64.

82. Milgram G.G. *The Facts About Drinking: Coping With Alcohol Use, Abuse, and Excessive Drinking.* New York, Consumers Union. 1990.

83. Macdiarmid R.I., Hetherington M.M. Mood modulation by food: An exploration of affect and cravings in "chocolate addicts." *British Journal of Psychology*, 1995, 34, 129-38.

84. Tamerin J.S., Mendelson J.H. The psychodynamics of chronic inebriation; observation of alcoholics during the process of drinking in an experimental group setting. *American Journal of Psychiatry*, 1969, 125, 886-9.

85. Young S.N., Smith S.E., Pihl R.O., Ervin F.R. Tryptophan depletion causes a rapid lowering of mood in normal males. *Psychopharmacology*, 1985, 87, 173-7.

86. Benkelfat C., Ellenbogen M.A., Palmour R.M., Young S.N. Mood-lowering effect of tryptophan depletion: Enhanced susceptibility in young men at genetic risk for major affective disorders. *Archives of General Psychiatry*, 1994, 51, 687-97.

87. Young S.N. Some effects of dietary components (amino acids, carbohydrate, folic acid) on brain serotonin synthesis, mood, and behaviour. *Canadian Journal of Physiology and Pharmacology*, 1991, 69, 893-903.

88. Goodwin G.M., Fairburn C.G., Cowen P.J. Dieting changes serotonergic function in women, not men: implications for the aetiology of anorexia nervosa? *Psychological Medicine*, 1987, 17, 839-42.

89. Schweiger U., Laessle R.G., Kittl S., Dickhaut B., Schweiger M., Pirke K.M. Macronutrient intake, plasma large neutral amino acids and mood during weight-reducing diets. *Journal of Neural Transmission*, 1986, 67, 77-86.

90. Deijen J.M., Heemstra M., Orlebeke J.F. Dietary effects on mood and performance. *Journal of Psychiatric Research*, 1989, 23, 275-83.

91. Schlundt D.G., Virts K.L., Sbrocco T., Pope-Cordle J., Hill J.O. A sequential behavioral analysis of craving sweets in obese women. *Addictive Behavior*, 1993, 18, 67-80.

92. Drewnowski A. Dietary fats: Perceptions and preferences. *Journal of the American College of Nutrition*, 1990, 4, 431-5.

93. Basdevant A., Craplet C., Guy-Grand B. Snacking patterns in obese French women. *Appetite*, 1993, 21, 17-23.

94. Reid M., Hammersley R. The effects of carbohydrates on arousal. *Nutrition Research Reviews*, 1999, 12, 3-23.

95. de Castro J.M. Macronutrient relationships with meal patterns and mood in the spontaneous feeding behaviour of humans. *Physiology & Behavior*, 1987, 39, 561-9.

96. Lipton M.A., Kane F.J. Psychiatry, in *Nutritional Support of Medical Practice, 2nd Edition*. Eds Scheider H.A., Anderson C.E., Coursin D. Philadelphia, Harper & Row. 1983, 562-80.

97. Young S.N. The use of diet and dietary compounds in the study of factors controlling affect in humans. *Journal of Psychiatry and Neuroscience*, 1993, 18, 235-44.

98. Stunkard A.J. The dieting depression: Incidence and clinical characteristics of untoward responses to weight reduction regimens. *American Journal of Medicine*, 1957, 23, 77-86.

99. Stunkard A.J., Messick S. Three-factor Eating Questionnaire to measure dietary restraint, disinhibition and hunger. *Journal of Psychosomatic Research*, 1985, 29, 71-83.

100. Herman C.P., Polivy J. Restrained Eating, in *Obesity*. Ed. Stunkard A.J. Philadelphia, Saunders. 1980, 208-25.

101. McCrimmon R.J., Frier B.M., Deary I.J. Appraisal of mood and personality during hypoglycaemia in human subjects. *Physiology & Behavior*, 1999, 67, 27-33.

102. Matsumura M., Fukuda N., Saito S., Mori H. Effect of a test meal, duodenal acidification, and tetragastrin on the plasma concentration of β-endorphin-like immunoreactivity in man. *Regulatory Peptides*, 1982, 4, 173-81.

103. Dum J., Gramsch C., Ferz A. Activation of hypothalamic β-endorphin pools by reward induced by highly palatable food. *Pharmacology, Biochemistry & Behavior*, 1983, 18, 443-7.

104. Roane D.S., Martin R.J. Continuous sucrose feeding decreases pain threshold and increases morphine potency. *Pharmacology, Biochemistry & Behavior*, 1990, 35, 225-9.

105. Drewnowski A., Krahn D.D., Demitrack M.A., Nairn K., Gosnell B.A. Taste responses and preferences for sweet high-fat foods: evidence for opioid involvement. *Physiology & Behavior*, 1992, 51, 371-9.

106. Blass E., Fitzgerald E. Milk-induced analgesia and comforting in 10-day-old rats: Opioid mediation. *Pharmacology, Biochemistry & Behavior*, 1988, 29, 9-13.

107. Blass E., Fitzgerald E., Kehoe P. Interactions between sucrose, pain and isolation distress. *Pharmacology, Biochemistry & Behavior*, 1987, 26, 483-9.

108. Ramzan I., Wong B.K., Corcoran G.B. Pain sensitivity in dietary-induced obese rats. *Physiology & Behavior*, 1993, 54, 433-5.

109. McGivern R.F., Berntson G.G. Mediation of diurnal fluctuations in pain sensitivity in the rat by food intake patterns: reversal by naloxone. *Science*, 1980, 210, 210-1.

110. Blass E.M., Watt L.B. Suckling- and sucrose-induced analgesia in human newborns. *Pain*, 1999, 83, 611-23.

111. Melchior J.C., Fantino M., Colas-Linhart N., Rigaud D., Petiet A., Laforest M.D., Fumeron F., Apfelbaum M. Lack of plasmatic beta-endorphin response to a gastronomic meal in healthy humans. *Physiology & Behavior*, 1991, 49, 1217-21.

112. Kaye W.H., Pickar D., Naber D., Ebert M.H. Cerebrospinal fluid opioid activity in anorexia nervosa. *American Journal of Psychiatry*, 1982, 139, 643-5.

113. Mercer M.E., Holder M.D. Antinociceptive effects of palatable sweet ingesta on human responsivity to pressure pain. *Physiology & Behavior*, 1997, 61, 311-8.

114. Zellner D.A., Garriga-Trillo A., Rohm E., Centeno S., Parker S. Food liking and craving: A cross-cultural approach. *Appetite*, 1999, 33, 61-70.

115. Rozin P. *Towards a Psychology of Food Choice*. Danone Institute, Brussels. 1998.

7. DIETING, EATING DISORDERS AND ADDICTION

7.1. DIETARY RESTRAINT AND CRAVING

Mike Green

7.1.1   Introduction

This chapter examines the complex relationship between food and craving from the perspective of the processes at work during the deliberate attempt to suppress those cravings. Given the current increase in rates of obesity in the developed world (1,2), 1994, it is of great scientific interest and importance (from the public health perspective) to understand the psychological and biological consequences that ensue from the deliberate restriction of food intake. These consequences may be either negative or positive, depending on the success or failure of attempted weight loss. As an additional marker of the importance of this phenomenon, it is estimated that, at any one time, 12% of women between the ages of 12 and 64 are following a weight loss programme (3), and that 90% have attempted weight-reducing diets at some time in their lives (4). The control (or lack of control) of food cravings is, therefore, of great importance.

The first part of the chapter will outline the main concepts of, and recent developments in dietary restraint theory, with emphasis on the role of the restriction of food cravings in the success of weight control. The second part will concentrate on the shared characteristics of dietary restraint and other craving-related states such as substance abuse disorders. The third section of the chapter will concentrate on the relevance of food cravings to a consideration of binge eating and bulimic psychopathology, in addition to a discussion of comparabilities and differences between these two phenomena.

7.1.2   Dietary Restraint

Dietary restraint has been defined as being the ".. tendency to control food intake consciously in order to prevent weight gain or to promote weight loss" (5). At the basis of this definition is the assumption that restraint involves the deliberate suppression of hunger cues and that dietary restraint, therefore, is analogous to other states of abstinence from pleasurable substances, such as attempted abstinence from tobacco or alcohol. It is possible to debate the validity of this analogy in terms of comparability of these states, since food is essential to life whereas alcohol and tobacco are not. It is the case, however, that very few of the cues that initiate feeding behaviour in the developed world actually result from physiological need states for food, and that situational cues may initiate feeding, irrespective of these needs. Anecdotal examples of this phenomenon include the cessation of hunger after the normal time of day at which an individual would eat lunch, even though that individual has not actually eaten lunch, and the feeling that, in a restaurant, one desires a dessert even after consuming a large amount of calories from the other courses consumed during the meal. Support for this hypothesis was demonstrated by Herman *et al.* (6) in a study during which both food-deprived and non-food-deprived participants were presented with video clips (a food-cue-related clip, an 'absorbing' non-food-related clip, or a neutral control video). It was found that the food-related video clip increased self-rated hunger for both food-deprived and non-deprived participants alike. This indicates that the mere presence of food (even in an abstracted form) is sufficient to initiate hunger in those individuals who are not currently in a metabolic state of food need.

The most widely investigated and comprehensive model of dietary restraint is that proposed by Herman and Polivy (7). This model (Fig. 7.1.1) proposes that individuals regulate their food intake according to a number of cognitively controlled boundaries or limits.

For unrestrained eaters, the cessation of eating occurs when the 'satiety boundary' is reached, whether this be for physiological or sensory factors (8). For restrained eaters, however, the cessation of eating behaviour is governed by the 'diet boundary'. As long as dietary restraint is not threatened or overwhelmed by excessive intake, restrained eaters are motivated to eat smaller amounts than unrestrained eaters, and will cease eating when their own idiosyncratic diet boundary is reached. For the restrained eater, it is this boundary that sets the limit of what constitutes permissible eating.

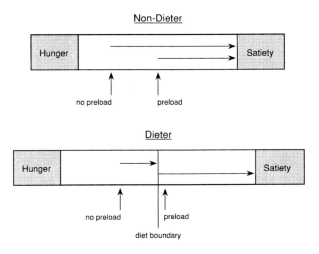

Fig. 7.1.1. The boundary model

Breaching of the diet boundary, according to Herman and Polivy's model, leads to a phenomenon known as 'counterregulation' or 'disinhibition' (Fig. 7.1.2). This has been likened to a laboratory analogue of binge eating (9).

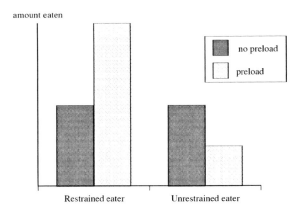

Fig. 7.1.2. The phenomenon of disinhibition

If, for a number of possible reasons, a restrained eater consumes amounts of food exceeding that permitted by the self-imposed diet boundary, it is hypothesised that a breakdown of restraint then occurs and the normally restrained eater will overindulge. The possible factors that may trigger this disinhibition of eating behaviour are numerous, and include (in naturalistic settings) situations in which the diet boundary of the restrained eater is forgotten owing to emotional agitation, intoxication or even otherwise normal pressures to overeat, such as social gatherings or being presented with overly large restaurant portions of food. In laboratory settings, this breaching of the diet boundary can be observed in situations in which restrained eaters are required to ingest a calorically dense preload, such as a milkshake, prior to an *ad libitum* taste test. In a classic demonstration of this phenomenon, Herman and Mack (10) gave subjects either one or two glasses of milkshake prior to their being required to rate the taste of a number of different ice creams. The subjects were told that they were allowed to eat as little or as much ice cream as they desired. It was found that, after ingestion of the milkshake preload, the non-restrained eaters consumed the ice cream to an amount that was inversely proportional to the size of the preload. That is, the larger the amount of milkshake consumed, the less ice cream was eaten. The restrained eaters, however, displayed the reverse pattern in that the larger the preload, the larger the amount of ice cream eaten.

This phenomenon of counter-regulatory eating is not necessarily related to the actual caloric content of the preload. Indeed, it has been found that manipulating participants' beliefs about the caloric content of a preload is sufficient to induce such disinhibition of eating control in restrained eaters (11). Disinhibition of eating amongst restrained eaters is not as simple a phenomenon as first conceptualised, and is mediated by a number of factors other than the caloric density of the administered preload. Specifically, there is evidence suggesting that disinhibition of eating behaviour is also mediated by mood state. For instance, it is reliably found that the induction of negative affective states such as depression or anxiety in restrained eaters results in crossing the diet boundary and, consequently, disinhibition (12). Unrestrained eaters, in contrast, respond to such inductions by eating less. Although this is a replicable finding, it is by no means the case that all studies have confirmed this relationship. Steere and Cooper (13) found that, contrary to the studies reviewed by Ruderman (12), restrained eaters actually reduced their food intake if they were both hungry and anxious. The relationship between dietary restraint and the disinhibition of eating behaviour following a breaching of the diet boundary is, therefore, not a simple one.

7.1.2.1 Recent developments in restraint theory

The pioneering work of Polivy and Herman in understanding the factors governing the maintenance or breakdown of dietary restraint tended to conceptualise restraint as a unitary phenomenon and (see below) even used the term 'restraint' interchangeably with dieting status. Recent work has challenged this view of restraint by asserting that it is not a unitary phenomenon and that the effects of dietary restraint on eating behaviour or subsequent behavioural effects of challenging that restraint rely on the precise nature of the type of dietary restraint exercised. Indeed, it has been found that successful exercise of dietary restraint is modified by other variables, such as the degree of self control (14). The major impetus behind such refinements in the dietary restraint model proposed by Herman and Polivy (7) has been a number of studies that show that not all restrained eaters respond to caloric preloads with a disinhibition of eating (15), and that, in general, there is a far greater variability in patterns of eating amongst restrained eaters than amongst unrestrained eaters (16).

One recent indication that dietary restraint is not a unitary phenomenon can be seen from the work of Joachim Westenhoefer and colleagues. They propose that there are two strategies of dietary restraint (rigid and flexible control), and that the successful exercise of weight control (and, by implication control over food cravings) is dependent on the style of restraint adopted. Westenhoefer (17) found that those individuals who engaged in highly regimented eating were more likely to engage in overeating than those who adopted a more flexible pattern of eating control.

Rigid restraint can be conceptualised as being an 'all or nothing' approach to eating behaviour and weight control. Individuals exhibiting such an eating style tend to diet frequently and, whilst they attempt to avoid tempting or forbidden foods, they do not overcompensate if they eat such foods. Flexible control is characterised by strategies that are associated with successful weight control. Such strategies may include permitting certain amounts of forbidden foods, which can be eaten without feelings of guilt or the planned compensation of food intake such that, if a large amount of food is eaten on one occasion, less food than normal is eaten during later eating occasions. These eating styles were defined by participants' responses on the Dietary Restraint and Disinhibition (a measure of overeating) subscales of the Three Factor Eating Questionnaire (TFEQ) (18). Flexible control has been associated with lower scores on the Disinhibition subscale of this questionnaire and rigid restraint associated with higher scores.

One implication of this distinction between flexible and rigid control of eating behaviour is that individuals exhibiting these two eating styles would behave differently in experimental settings where control over eating behaviour is challenged, such as the type of caloric preload study conducted by Herman and Mack (10). Experimental evidence indicates that this is, indeed, the case. For example, Westenhoefer *et al.* (19) carried out a study in which participants were required to eat ice cream *ad libitum* either following a milkshake preload or without such a preload. It was found that, relative to individuals exhibiting a self-reported rigid eating style, those with a self-reported flexible eating style consumed less ice cream following the preload. Those participants with a rigid eating style consumed the same amount of ice cream, irrespective of the presence or absence of a preload. From this result, it was concluded that "....high susceptibility to eating problems may be caused by rigid control of eating behaviour, whereas flexible control of eating behaviour may be a less problematic strategy of long-term weight control."

Further evidence to support this assertion can be seen in the finding that, during a weight reduction programme lasting one year, successful weight loss was predicted by higher baseline scores of flexible restraint, whereas rigid restraint was not predictive of weight loss (20). It has also been found that flexible restraint (as measured by responses on a modified version of the TFEQ) is negatively correlated with body mass index and is predictive of the symptoms of anorexia nervosa (an extreme example of successful dietary restraint), whereas rigid restraint was correlated with the symptoms of bulimia nervosa (unsuccessful restraint) and weight fluctuation (21). There is also evidence relating type of restraint to other aspects of psychological well-being in restrained eaters. Smith *et al.* (22) found that flexible restraint significantly correlated with the absence of overeating, lower body mass indices (BMI) and low levels of self-reported depression and anxiety. Strategies characteristic of rigid restraint, such as calorie counting, ceasing eating before satiation and deliberate dieting were associated with negative behavioural outcomes, such as weight cycling, increased BMI and overeating whilst alone.

A related development in restraint theory, which also stresses the degree of self-control utilised in the exercise of dietary restraint can be seen in the work of LeGoff *et al.* (23), who hypothesise that variability of eating patterns is an important factor modulating the success of dietary restraint. This work postulates the existence of two distinct eating styles in restrained eaters, these being termed 'anorexic' and 'bulimic'. The assumption is that very few of the environmental cues that initiate hunger (or food cravings) are related to physiological need. It is postulated that, to a large extent (at least in the developed world), hunger is initiated by a range of situational cues, which are, to a greater or lesser extent, associated with eating behaviour. An everyday example of this would be the feelings of hunger experienced as a person approaches the normal time of day at which they eat lunch. If, for some reason, they are prevented from eating lunch at this time, it is a common occurrence for these feelings of hunger to recede, even though the actual physiological need for food has increased.

It is hypothesised that an anorexic eating style is characterised by a very low degree of variability, with eating occurring only in a limited number of places and times of day, with a relatively limited range of portion sizes and food types. In contrast, the bulimic eating style is characterised as being highly variable, with no set meal or snack patterns, portion sizes or food types. As a result, individuals who exercise this 'bulimic' eating style are subjected to a far greater number of situational cues that may trigger feelings of hunger, and are, therefore, less successful in the exercise of dietary restraint.

LeGoff *et al.* (23) provided support for this hypothesis in a study that examined the salivary flow rates of clinically anorexic and bulimic patients when presented with food cues both at baseline and after 2 months of treatment. Both eating-disordered participants and non-disordered controls were exposed to a number of food odours whilst their salivary flow rates were measured. It was found that the anorexic subjects salivated less in the presence of food odours than either non-eating-disordered controls or the bulimic patients. The bulimic patients, however, salivated more than did the controls. Also of importance, it was found that salivary flow rate was significantly related to self-reported variability of eating patterns (assessed via dietary intake diaries) for all subjects. This second finding indicates that hunger sensations (as indicated by salivary flow) may be mediated by habitual variability in eating patterns. Further support for this idea that successful weight control relates to habitual variability in eating patterns can be seen in the results of a study conducted by Kirk and Hill (24). This study classified female participants as being either successful or non-successful dieters on the basis of past history of weight loss. Women who were classed as 'successful dieters' displayed a more invariable pattern of eating than those women classed as being 'unsuccessful dieters'. This work, whilst providing a tantalising glimpse of the way in which dietary restraint can be fractionated, is only preliminary. Further work needs to be done in order to replicate and extend these ideas concerning variability of eating patterns and their contribution to the success or failure of attempted dietary restraint.

What can be concluded from this work is that the attempt to control food cravings via the exercise of dietary restraint is strewn with a number of negative psychological and physical consequences. Recent work indicates that dietary restraint is not a unitary phenomenon and that behavioural strategies in the exercise of restraint (and, by implication, to control food intake) differ in terms of both the eventual success of weight control and their impact on other aspects of psychological well-being.

7.1.2.2   Relationship between dietary restraint and dieting to lose weight

Initially, the terms dieter and restrained eater were used fairly interchangeably. Indeed, Polivy and Herman define a restrained eater in terms of being a 'chronic dieter'. More recently, however, it has become evident that there are both conceptual and practical distinctions between merely exhibiting a habitual high level of dietary restraint and actively attempting weight loss by means of dieting. Conceptually, it is implicit that being on a diet involves a high level of dietary restraint, whereas a highly restrained eater can be attempting to maintain weight at a low, but stable level. Lowe (25) argues that the pattern of eating behaviour exhibited by restrained eaters stems from their past history of overeating and dieting, rather than their current dieting status, and that the two states have different effects upon eating behaviour. A number of studies have demonstrated that individuals classified as restrained eaters by the Restraint Scale questionnaire (26) do not differ in their natural caloric intake from unrestrained eaters (27,28). Dieting does, by definition, imply a restriction of caloric intake.

Support for this distinction between habitual restraint and current dieting behaviour can be seen in the study carried out by Lowe, Whitlow and Bellwoar (29). This study assessed *ad libitum* ice cream consumption following a preload or no preload of three groups (unrestrained non-dieters, restrained non-dieters and restrained current dieters). It was found that, as with previous studies, highly restrained non-dieters consumed more milkshake following the preload than without the preload. Restrained dieters displayed a different pattern of results in that, whilst they ate more than restrained non-dieters in the no-preload condition, they reduced their intake of ice cream following the preload. Further, partial support for this dieting/restraint distinction can be seen in the study of Hetherington and Rolls (30), who found that normal-weight current dieters did not demonstrate the disinhibition of eating behaviour following a high calorie preload characteristic of habitually restrained eaters.

Given these demonstrations of a distinction between dietary restraint and current dieting behaviour, Lowe (25) proposes a three-factor model of dieting behaviour that explains findings inconsistent with restraint theory. According to this model, the effects of dieting upon eating behaviour can be conceptualised according to these factors. The first is termed past 'Frequency of Dieting and Overeating' and may be analogous to weight cycling. The model postulates that such vulnerability to overeating (which accounts for the frequency of dieting behaviour and the persistent failure of attempted weight loss) is a causal factor in the vulnerability of restrained eaters to disinhibition. A number of investigators (5,7) have also maintained that past cycling of dieting and overeating does affect the ability of restrained eaters to perceive feelings of hunger and satiety accurately. In essence, this factor is hypothesised to be the variable that is comparable to Herman and Polivy's conceptualisation of restraint.

The second factor in Lowe's model is that of 'Current Dieting Status', and refers to ongoing efforts at weight reduction. Lowe conceptualises this factor as the cognitive effort expended in weight reduction, rather than in terms of negative energy balance or the actual weight lost over the course of a dieting episode. Evidence to support the distinction of this factor from habitual restraint is presented above, e.g. dieters' differential reactions to caloric preloading.

The third factor is termed 'Weight Suppression' and refers to the successful control of weight (and, by implication, hunger and food cravings) over time. Individuals exhibiting this behavioural style can also be conceptualised as being 'successful restrainers'. This ability to control weight successfully over time also exerts specific effects upon eating behaviour. For instance, individuals with high levels of habitual weight suppression eat significantly less than non-suppressers following a calorically dense preload (31). It is also hypothesised that the long-term successful control of weight, characteristic of weight suppressers, is associated with decreased cravings and an overall reduction in appetite - a hypothesis supported by the findings of Kleifield and Lowe (32).

These three factors may be mediated by a number of other variables, such as weight and sensory, psychological and physiological factors. In general, however, Lowe's (25) model comprises the first comprehensive theoretical model of how dieting differs from dietary restraint and how the factors that determine the success or failure of attempted weight loss in dieters is related to eating behaviour. Its relevance to the subject matter of the present chapter is to give a framework within which it is possible to examine the behavioural factors operating during successful and unsuccessful attempts to resist food cravings in order to modify body weight.

7.1.2.3   *Other negative consequences of dieting and dietary restraint*

Aside from the negative effects of dietary restraint on the regulation of eating behaviour outlined above, there are a number of adverse psychological consequences of such an eating style. Amongst non-clinically eating-disordered individuals, dietary restraint and dieting have been linked to negative psychological effects and impaired cognitive processing efficiency. For instance, it has been found that dieting behaviour is associated with mood swings (33), depression (34) and increased concern with body shape (35,36). High levels of dietary restraint have also been associated with distractibility, as measured by performance on a proof-reading task (37) and attentional biases towards food and body shape material following caloric preloading (38). When examining the evidence relating to impaired cognition resulting from food deprivation, however, an important distinction has to be made between intended weight loss that arises as a result of dietary restraint and self-esteem versus weight loss, which is induced as part of an experimental manipulation.

The earliest demonstration that caloric restriction might result in impaired cognition in non-eating-disordered individuals is that of the famous Minnesota Study of semi-starvation (39). In this study, subjects were voluntarily subjected to a dietary regime resulting in a loss of 25% of their original body weight over a period of 6 months. It was found that semi-starvation increased preoccupation with food, in addition to being associated with increased self-reported lethargy, irritability and (importantly from the perspective of the current review) failures in memory. These self-reported failures were not, however supported by the results of objective testing, although the lack of a non-starved control group indicates that any effect of starvation on memory could be confounded by practice effects.

Another, more recent, study also concluded that experimentally induced low-energy diets exerted negative effects upon cognitive function. Wing *et al.* (40) reported that the administration of a low-carbohydrate diet (549 kcal/day) over 28 days amongst obese subjects was associated with impaired performance on a trail-making task, relative to a group administered a low-fat diet (590 kcal/day). This interpretation can, however, be criticised on several grounds. Foremost of these is that, although β-hydroxybutyrate levels (a metabolic indicator of starvation) rose significantly over the whole 28 days of the diet, trail-making task performance was significantly impaired only at 7 days of dieting, compared with baseline. Subsequent measurements showed that trail-making performance was actually better than baseline, with performance after 28 days of low carbohydrate dieting improving relative to baseline. This was further confounded by marginally significant baseline differences between trail-making performances.

The present conclusion that induced weight loss *per se* does not significantly affect cognitive processing efficiency is supported by the study of Deijen *et al.* (41). This particular study found that, after a 3-week-long, experimentally induced weight-loss diet, dieters performed better than non-dieters on a measure of motor speed (two-finger tapping). Although the dieters performed less well than non-dieters on a memory scanning task, this difference was apparent only during morning test sessions, and not during the afternoon. There were no significant diet-related differences in performance on a continuous performance task, pattern comparison task or the Symbol-Digit substitution sub-test of the Weschler Adult Intelligence Scale (WAIS). In addition, more recent data (42) also found that caloric restriction of 30 days' duration did not significantly affect either mood or reaction times.

Dieting in a naturalistic setting has, however, been unequivocally associated with impaired cognition. For example, females who report that they are currently dieting to lose weight perform more poorly than non-dieters on a task of sustained attention (43), in addition to displaying poorer performance on immediate free recall and simple reaction time tasks (44). Further, performance has been demonstrated to be poorer, within the same individuals, when dieting than when not dieting (45), indicating that the phenomenon is related to dieting *per se*, rather than pre-existing individual differences between dieters and non-dieters. A number of supplementary studies in this series has revealed that these impairments are unlikely to be due to the gross physiological effects of food deprivation, since neither deprivation for periods of up to 24 hours (46) nor experimentally induced weight loss over a period of several months (47) significantly affects performance on the same task battery found to be sensitive to cognitive changes in naturalistic dieting. Rather, these impairments in task performance, which are characteristic of current dieting behaviour, appear to result from preoccupying thoughts preferentially consuming working memory capacity in a manner similar to that found with anxiety (48) and depression (49). Working memory (50) can be considered to be the basic cognitive system, which serves to remember the moment-to-moment rules of action and to allocate an individual's limited cognitive processing capacity to other, ongoing, tasks according to their relative importance. In the case of dieting, however, the nature of these preoccupying cognitions relate to body shape (51) and, importantly from the perspective of the present chapter, food cravings (as defined by self-reported 'desire to eat') (52).

An important aspect of this body of work is that it is consistently found that non-dieting, restrained eaters display a level of performance that is intermediate between that of current dieters and that of unrestrained non-dieters (44). Aside from supporting Lowe's (25) distinction between dieting and restraint, this finding also supports a threshold hypothesis of the relationship between dieting and impaired cognition. It is consistently found that non-dieting, restrained eaters are characterised by an enduring trait - preoccupation with body shape (26) - which can be assumed to impose some capacity restraint on working memory. When this is combined with the state-related feelings of hunger and food craving resulting from reduced caloric intake experienced during attempted weight loss (53), it is hypothesised that a threshold of preoccupation is crossed, whereby sufficient working memory capacity to perform efficiently the tasks presented to dieters in experimental settings is not available. This hypothesis is supported by the studies outlined above, which have demonstrated no clear effects of weight loss upon cognition in the absence of any pre-existing concerns with weight and body shape. The central conclusion that can be drawn from this work, therefore, is that the cognitive load imposed by food cravings and hunger (in addition to pre-existing concerns with body shape and self-esteem) in dieters is a causal factor in their impaired cognitive task performance.

7.1.3   Analogy between Dietary Restraint and other Addictive Behaviours

Earlier on in this chapter, an analogy was made between the exercise of dietary restraint and abstinence from pleasurable substances such as alcohol and tobacco. This, second, part of the chapter will explore the validity of this analogy further. Kassel and Schiffman (54) suggest a number of criteria whereby this analogy can be examined.

The first of these concerns the question of whether hunger and drug cravings reflect an underlying biological need. It is claimed that alcohol and tobacco cravings do not actually represent a biological need since, if that were the case, deprivation of these substances should increase craving as a function of time, and the ingestion of the craved substance should reduce craving. In the case of heroin (55), alcohol (56) and tobacco (57), although craving initially increases after deprivation, it subsides after a period of time. There is a similar argument to be made in the case of food cravings. Although some studies have found that subjective hunger ratings and energy intake are related to the energy content of an individual's stomach (58), in the long term, a number of studies have actually found that sustained low-calorie dieting actually leads to a diminution of self-reported hunger over time (59). As Kassel and Shiffman note, this phenomenon is strikingly similar to the drug literature in that, during periods of food deprivation, feelings of hunger initially increase but then decline over time. Indeed, a clinical example of this phenomenon can be seen in anorexia nervosa, where it has been found that the extreme states of starvation characteristic of this disorder are not associated with increased feelings of hunger (60) and that the ability to ignore internal hunger cues may be a risk factor for the development of anorexia (60). It can be seen from this evidence, therefore, that there is some validity in the analogy between hunger and drug cravings in that, to a limited extent, neither is an expression of physiological need.

The second criterion proposed by Kassel and Shiffman (54) for evaluating the analogy between hunger and drug cravings is that of the nature of the physiological correlates of both drug cravings and hunger. They conclude that there are no reliable correlates of either drug craving or hunger, although there is some evidence to suggest that alcohol craving (62) and hunger (63) are both associated with increased salivation. The third criterion is that of whether both drug craving and hunger can be mediated by internal regulatory mechanisms. Kassel and Shiffman conclude that, whilst it is probable that drug actions are regulated via neurotransmitter and neuroendocrine systems, conclusions regarding the mechanisms underlying drug cravings are speculative at present. Similarly, in the case of hunger, although it is commonly held that hunger and satiety are mediated via the hypothalamus, there is also a great deal of evidence (summarised above) indicating that hunger is mediated by a number of environmental, affective and cognitive factors that bear little relationship to the physiological need for food. Overall, Kassel and Shiffman conclude that there are sufficient comparabilities between drug cravings and hunger to justify the analogy between the two.

Assuming the validity of the analogy, it can therefore be assumed that models devised to explain the psychological processes that occur when drug cravings are manipulated will also serve as models to explain manipulations of hunger. One recent model that offers an explanatory framework for such changes was proposed by Tiffany (64). This model hypothesises that the urges and drug use patterns of addicts can be accounted for in terms of automatised action schema. According to this model, urges represent the operation of non-automatic processes, which may be activated either in support of drug use schemata or as a consequence of attempts to block those schemata. For instance, an abstinent smoker will experience urges for tobacco, which may be triggered by the sight or sensation of smoking-related cues, such as the presence of other individuals smoking. By virtue of the fact that these urges are processed in a non-automatic fashion, they will tend to consume processing resources, leading to fewer resources being available to deal with other demands on processing capacity. This model generates a number of testable hypotheses concerning the possible analogy between drug cravings and hunger. One such hypothesis would be that food deprivation results in greater cue-reactivity to food-related stimuli. Evidence to support this can be seen in the finding that food-deprived subjects exhibit greater degrees of self-reported food cravings during presentation of a food cue than in its absence (65).

Tiffany's cue reactivity model can also provide a theoretical framework to explain the previously mentioned cognitive processing impairments characteristic of dieting to lose weight. Conceptualising dieters as being comparable to abstinent drug users, the cognitive impairments found amongst dieters can be explained in terms of the constant state of cue reactivity that dieters experience through everyday exposure to food. This hypothesis is experimentally testable using a similar cue reactivity challenge to that used by Cepeda-Benito and Tiffany (66). It has been found that, when asked to imagine a scenario in which they are presented with their favourite food, both dieters and highly restrained non-dieters perform less well on a concurrent simple reaction time task than non-dieting unrestrained eaters (67). This finding is also interesting from the point of view of a threshold explanation of impaired cognitive processing in dieting outlined above. By making non-dieting, unrestrained dieters ruminate upon food, they then perform at a level comparable to that of current dieters. That is, by adding a state-based preoccupation with food to the pre-existing, trait preoccupation with weight and body shape found in restrained eaters, sufficient working memory capacity is taken up to impair task performance.

What can be concluded from the attempt to make an analogy between cravings for food and cravings for other pleasurable substances? Although there appear to be obvious differences between the two states, in that food is necessary for the maintenance of life whereas alcohol or tobacco are not, the analogy is strengthened by an appreciation of the crucial role played by external eating-related stimuli in the control of hunger and eating (68). Thus a simple depletion-repletion model of motivation fails to provide an adequate account of eating behaviour, and, like the appetite for drugs, the appetite for food is strongly influenced by external cues and is modified by cognitions and restraint. Drug use and eating share a biological basis, but are also cognitively controlled. Although alcohol and tobacco, for example, are taken in order to produce certain psycho-stimulant effects, and food is necessary for the maintenance of the proper biological functioning of an organism, the decision either to initiate or to abstain from drug use or limit food intake is one that is under conscious control.

7.1.4 Eating Disorders: Psychological Characteristics of Bulimics and Binge Eaters

This, final part of the chapter is concerned with extreme examples of the breakdown of dietary restraint resulting from food cravings. Specifically, this section will compare bulimic psychopathology and non-clinical binge eating, in terms of the degree of comparability of the characteristics of individuals who exhibit such behaviours. A distinction between bulimia nervosa and binge eating is an important one to make since, whilst both conditions entail the consumption of large amounts of food within a discrete period, it is only bulimia nervosa that is accompanied with a consequent attempt at purging the food ingested during that binge via vomiting, laxative or diuretic abuse.

7.1.4.1 *Characteristics of bulimia nervosa and non-bulimic binge eating*

Bulimia nervosa was first categorised as a psychopathology separate from anorexia nervosa in 1979 (69), although it was recognised as a distinct disorder as early as 1903 (70). The Diagnostic and Statistical Manual of the American Psychiatric Association (71) states the following criteria for a diagnosis of bulimia nervosa: "Bulimia nervosa is characterised by repeated episodes of binge eating followed by inappropriate compensatory behaviours such as self-induced vomiting, misuse of laxatives, diuretics or other medications, fasting or excessive exercise."

Binge eating is defined as being:

"1. Eating, in a discrete period of time (e.g. within any 2-hour period) an amount of food that is deliberately larger than most people would eat during a similar period of time and under similar circumstances.
2. A sense of lack of control over eating during the episode (e.g. a feeling that one cannot stop eating or control what or how much one is eating.)"

During such episodes of binge eating, extremely large amounts of food are consumed, typically in excess of 3,000 kcal, with this food being mostly high-fat or high-carbohydrate in nature (72). Evidence suggests that, as with the mechanisms that mediate the disinhibition effect characteristic of non-eating-disordered restrained eaters, bulimic binges are mediated by affective state. For instance, Cooper and Bowskill (73) found a strong relationship between an increase in negative mood state and the onset of bingeing in patients with bulimia nervosa. This has led to the suggestion that bingeing episodes are a compensatory behaviour, which have the effect of 'self-medicating' negative mood state and are, therefore, negatively reinforced by emotional relief (74). Although temporary emotional relief may be gained by the bulimic during a binge, it is commonly followed by emotional deterioration, feelings of guilt, disgust and low self-esteem. These feelings result in the consequent purging behaviour that is characteristic of bulimia nervosa. As a result of this purging behaviour, purging may improve mood, thus providing negative reinforcement. Thus, a vicious cycle of harmful behaviours is constructed, relying at their base for short-term self-medication of negative mood states. Binge eating amongst non-clinically eating-disordered individuals, however, can be conceptualised as being a different phenomenon, with different associated behavioural and psychological characteristics. Differences in binge eating amongst non-clinically eating-disordered individuals and that seen in bulimia nervosa arise from associated behavioural and psychological characteristics - in particular, post-binge purging.

It has been argued that bulimia nervosa represents the extreme end of a continuum of dietary restraint and that the bulimic binge-purge cycle is merely the clinical manifestation of dietary restraint (75). This continuum hypothesis would postulate that non-clinically eating-disordered examples of binge eating would share some characteristics of restrained eating and bulimia nervosa. Indeed, experimental evidence, reviewed by Guertin (76) indicates that this is so, which generally supports such a continuum hypothesis. This review examines the degree to which the eating behaviours of bulimia nervosa patients, non-clinical binge eaters and non-clinical, non-binge eaters share degrees of comparability. It was concluded that, overall, the results of the experimental work carried out to date generally support the continuum hypothesis proposed by Polivy and Herman. Specifically, the evidence reviewed suggests that bulimia nervosa sufferers and non-clinical binge eaters differ in the extent and frequency of bingeing episodes. With regard to the number of calories ingested during a binge, it has been found that bulimics consume between 1,000 (77) to 4,400 kcal (78) during the course of a binge. Non-bulimic, self-identified binge eaters, however, typically ingest between 605 (79) and 1,260 kcal (80) per binge. With regard to the frequency of binge-eating episodes, there are also differences between bulimic patients and non-bulimic binge eaters, with the finding that bulimics binge an average of ten times per week and non-bulimic binge eaters binge an average of four times per week (76). There are, however, a number of similarities between bulimic and non-bulimic binges, in terms of both the duration of a binge episode and the context in which they occur (76). It can be concluded, therefore, that, whilst there are consistent and replicably found differences between the eating patterns of bulimics and non-bulimic, non-binge eaters, some shared characteristics exist between the two groups, lending support to the continuum hypothesis.

7.1.4.2 *Relationship between bingeing and food craving*

It is a commonly held assumption that the primary reason for a food binge is the experience of food craving (81) and that extreme degrees of food craving are, therefore, a risk factor for the development of bulimia nervosa. Indeed, this would be one prediction of the continuum hypothesis outlined above. There is some evidence to suggest that women who experience food cravings also exhibit a number of other psychological features that may predispose them to the development of eating disorders. For instance, Gendall *et al.* (82) found that women who reported experiencing food cravings were also more likely to engage in binge eating, to be frequent dieters, to have a history of alcohol abuse or dependence, and to have more frequently exercised and used weight control pills, laxatives and vomiting to control weight than non-food cravers. All of these behaviours are considered to be risk factors for the development of an eating disorder. It has also been suggested that food cravings should be viewed in terms of a mood-regulation effect, with cravings for particular foods (particularly high-fat, high-carbohydrate foods such as chocolate) being viewed in terms of mood-improving experiences (83).

However, food cravings do not always result in binge eating. Whilst clear associations between food cravings and binge eating have been made (84), a number of studies have also indicated that the relationship between the two is not always clear. For instance, it has been found that food cravings are typically found in a far larger proportion of the general population than indicated by numbers of those who actually report binge eating (85). Recent work by Gendall and colleagues (86) has attempted to characterise the differences between food cravers who binge eat and those who do not. Specifically, it was found that the factors separating food cravers who did binge and those who did not binge were that bingeing food cravers displayed a higher body mass index (a measure of weight adjusted for height), a higher level of dietary restraint, more frequent diagnoses of bulimia nervosa, a higher likelihood of a prior incidence of clinical depression and social phobia, and a lower degree of self-directedness (see also section 7.3).

It can be stated, therefore, that there is a continuum of abnormal eating behaviour, from anorexia nervosa at the extreme end of the continuum to binge eating at the other. In addition, whilst it is assumed that food cravings or specific hungers play a mediating role in the degree to which individuals will fall on this continuum, the relationship is not simple. Specifically, it is argued that, whilst there are comparabilities between bulimia nervosa and non-bulimic binge eating, there are a number of differences between the two phenomena. These differences relate to the nature of eating patterns, the relationship between cravings for food and subsequent bingeing and the allied psychological states that determine whether craving for food is behaviourally manifested as a binge-eating episode.

7.1.5   General Conclusions

This chapter outlines and reviews research in the field of dietary restraint from the point of view of conceptualising restraint as an attempt to resist food cravings and hunger. In general, it is concluded that the attempt to resist these cravings in order to attempt weight control is not without psychological cost and that such attempts are frequently unsuccessful, especially when restrained eaters are challenged by the ingestion or even mere presence of food. It is also concluded that there is, to some extent, a valid comparison to be made between cravings for food and cravings for other substances, at least in terms of the psychological consequences of attempted abstention from those substances. Finally, it is concluded that food cravings are of great relevance to the consideration of eating disorders, in terms both of resisting those cravings and acting upon them.

7.1.6   References

1. Kuczmarski R.J., Flegal K.M., Campbell S.M., Johnson C.L. Increasing prevalence of overweight among US adults. The National Health and Nutrition Examination Surveys, 1960 to 1991. *Journal of the American Medical Association*, 1994, 272, 205-11.

2. Seidell J.C. Obesity in Europe. *Obesity Research*, 1995, 3 (suppl 2), 89s-93s.

3. Gregory J., Foster K., Tyler H., Wiseman M. *The Dietary and Nutritional Survey of British Adults*. London, H.M. Stationery Office. 1990.

4. Ogden J. Fat Chance: *The Myth of Dieting Explained*. London, Routledge. 1992.

5. Tuschl R.J. From dietary restraint to binge eating: Some theoretical considerations. *Appetite*, 1990, 14, 105-9.

6. Herman C.P., Ostovich J.M., Polivy J. Effects of attentional focus on subjective hunger ratings. *Appetite*, 1999, 33, 181-93.

7.   Herman C.P., Polivy J.A. Boundary Model for the Regulation of Eating, in *Eating and its disorders*. Eds Stunkard A., Stellar E. New York, Raven. 1984, 141-56.

8.   Rolls B.J., Rolls E.T., Rowe E.A. The influence of variety on human food selection and intake, in *The Psychobiology of Human Food Selection*. Ed. Barker L.M. Westport, CT, AVI. 1982, 101-22.

9.   Wardle J., Beinart H. Binge eating: A theoretical review. *British Journal of Clinical Psychology*, 1981, 20, 97-109.

10.   Herman C.P., Mack D. Restrained and unrestrained eating. *Journal of Personality*, 1975, 43, 647-60.

11.   Spencer J.A., Fremouw W.J. Binge eating as a function of restraint and weight classification. *Journal of Abnormal Psychology*, 1979, 88, 262-7.

12.   Ruderman A.J. Dietary restraint: A theoretical and empirical review. *Psychological Bulletin*, 1986, 99, 247-62.

13.   Steere J., Cooper P.J. The effects on eating of dietary restraint, anxiety and hunger. *International Journal of Eating Disorders*, 1992, 13, 211-9.

14.   Kirshenbaum D.S., Dykman B.M. Disinhibited eating by resourceful restrained eaters. *Journal of Abnormal Psychology*, 1991, 100, 227-30.

15.   Tomarken A.J., Kirshenbaum D.S. Effects of plans for future meals on counterregulatory eating by restrained and unrestrained eaters. *Journal of Abnormal Psychology*, 1984, 93, 458-72.

16.   Knight L.J., Boland F.J. Restrained eating: An experimental disentanglement of the variables of perceived calories and food type. *Journal of Abnormal Psychology*, 1989, 98, 412-21.

17.   Westenhoefer J. Dietary restraint and disinhibition: Is restraint a homogeneous construct. *Appetite*, 1991, 16, 45-55.

18.   Stunkard A.J., Messick S. The three factor eating questionnaire to measure dietary restraint, disinhibition and hunger. *Journal of Psychosomatic Research*, 1985, 29, 71-83.

19.   Westenhoefer J., Broeckmann P., Munch A.K., Pudel V. Cognitive control of eating behaviour and the disinhibition effect. *Appetite*, 1994, 23(1), 27-41.

542

20.   Pudel V., Westenhoefer J. Dietary and behavioural principles in the treatment of obesity. *International Monitor on Eating Patterns and Weight Control*, 1992, 1, 2-7.

21.   Shearin E.N., Russ M.J., Hull J.W., Clarkin J.F., Smith G.P. Construct validity of the three-factor eating questionnaire: Flexible and rigid control subscales. *International Journal of Eating Disorders*, 1994, 16, 187-98.

22.   Smith C.F., Williamson D.A., Bray G.A., Ryan D.H. Flexible vs. rigid dieting strategies: Relationship with adverse behavioural outcomes. *Appetite*, 1999, 32, 295-305.

23.   LeGoff D.B., Leichner P., Spigelman. Salivary response to olfactory food stimuli in anorexics and bulimics. *Appetite*, 1988, 11, 15-25.

24.   Kirk S.F.L., Hill A.J. Exploring the food beliefs and eating behaviour of successful and unsuccessful dieters. *Journal of Human Nutrition and Dietetics*, 1997, 10, 331-41.

25.   Lowe M.R. The effects of dieting on eating behaviour: A three factor model. *Psychological Bulletin*, 1993, 114, 100-21.

26.   Herman C.P., Polivy J. Restrained Eating, in *Obesity*. Ed. Stunkard A.J. Philadelphia, W.B. Saunders. 1980, 208-25.

27.   Laessle R.G., Tuschl R.J., Kotthaus B.C., Pirke K.M. A comparison of the validity of three scales for the measurement of dietary restraint. *Journal of Abnormal Psychology*, 1989, 98, 504-7.

28.   Klesges R.C., Klem M.L., Bene C.R. Effects of dietary restraint, obesity and gender on holiday eating behaviour and weight gain. *Journal of Abnormal Psychology*, 1989, 98, 499-503.

29.   Lowe M.R., Whitlow J.M., Bellwoar V. Eating regulation: The role of restraint, dieting and weight. *International Journal of Eating Disorders*, 1991, 10, 461-71.

30.   Hetherington M.M., Rolls B.J. Eating behavior in eating disorders: Response to preloads. *Physiology and Behavior*, 1991, 50, 101-8.

31.   Lowe M.R., Kleifield E. Cognitive restraint, weight suppression and the regulation of eating. *Appetite*, 1988, 10, 159-68.

32. Kleifield E., Lowe M.R. Weight loss and sweetness preferences: The effects of recent versus past weight loss. *Physiology and Behavior*, 1991, 27, 195-8.

33. Tiggemann M. Dietary restraint as a predictor of reported weight loss and affect. *Psychological Reports*, 1994, 75, 1679-82.

34. Smoller J.W., Wadden T.A., Stunkard A.J. Dieting and depression: A critical review. *Journal of Psychosomatic Research*, 1987, 31, 429-40.

35. Warren C., Cooper P.J. Psychological effects of dieting. *British Journal of Clinical Psychology*, 1988, 71, 247-61.

36. Green M.W., Rogers P.J. Selective attention to food and body shape words in dieters and restrained non-dieters. *International Journal of Eating Disorders*, 1993, 14, 515-7.

37. Herman C.P., Polivy J., Pliner P., Threlkeld J., Munic D. Distractibility in dieters and non-dieters: An alternative view of externality. *Journal of Personality and Social Psychology*, 1978, 36, 536-48.

38. Ogden J., Greville L. Cognitive changes to preloading in restrained and unrestrained eaters as measured by the Stroop task. *International Journal of Eating Disorders*, 1993, 14, 185-95.

39. Keys A., Brozek J., Henschel A., Mickelsen O., Taylor H.L. *The Biology of Human Starvation*. Minneapolis, University of Minnesota Press. 1950.

40. Wing R.R., Vazquez J.A., Ryan C.M. Cognitive effects of ketogenic weight reducing diets. *International Journal of Obesity*, 1995, 811-6.

41. Deijen J.B., Heemstra M.L., Orlebeke J.F. Dietary effects on mood and performance. *Journal of Psychiatric Research*, 1989, 23, 275-83.

42. Shukhitt-Hale B., Askew E.W., Lieberman H.R. Effects of 30 days of undernutrition on reaction time, moods and symptoms. *Physiology and Behavior*, 1997, 62, 783-9.

43. Rogers P.J., Green M.W. Dieting, dietary restraint and cognitive performance. *British Journal of Clinical Psychology*, 1993, 32, 113-6.

44. Green M.W., Rogers P.J., Elliman N.A., Gatenby S.J. Impairment of cognitive function associated with dieting and high levels of dietary restraint. *Physiology and Behavior*, 1994, 55, 447-52.

45. Green M.W., Rogers P.J. Impaired cognitive function during spontaneous dieting. *Psychological Medicine*, 1995, 1003-10.

46. Green M.W., Elliman N.A., Rogers P.J. Lack of effect of short-term fasting on cognitive function. *Journal of Psychiatric Research*, 1995, 29, 245-53.

47. Krestch M.J., Green M.W., Fong A.K.H., Elliman N.A., Johnson H. Cognitive effects of a weight reducing diet. *International Journal of Obesity*, 1997, 21, 14-21.

48. Darke S. Anxiety and working memory capacity. *Cognition and Emotion*, 1988, 2, 145-254.

49. Channon S., Baker J.E., Robertson M.M. Working memory in depression: An experimental study. *Psychological Medicine*, 1993, 23, 87-91.

50. Baddeley A.D. *Working Memory*. Oxford, Oxford University Press. 1986.

51. Green M.W., Rogers P.J. Impairments in working memory associated with spontaneous dieting behaviour. *Psychological Medicine*, 1998, 28, 1063-70.

52. Green M.W., Elliman N.A., Rogers P.J. Impaired cognitive performance in dieters: Failure of attentional focus or resource capacity limitation. *British Journal of Health Psychology*, 1997, 2, 259-67.

53. Hart K.E., Chiovari P. Inhibition of eating behavior: negative cognitive effects of dieting. *Journal of Clinical Psychology*, 1998, 54, 427-30.

54. Kassel J.D., Shiffman S. What can hunger teach us about drug craving? A comparative analysis of the two constructs. *Advances in Behavioral Research and Therapy*, 1992, 14, 141-67.

55. Glaser F.B. Letter: Psychologic vs. pharmacologic heroin dependence. *New England Journal of Medicine*, 1974, 290, 231.

56. Mathew R.J., Claghorn J.L., Largen J. Craving for alcohol in sober alcoholics. *American Journal of Psychiatry*, 1979, 136, 603-6.

57. Schiffman S.M. The tobacco withdrawal syndrome, in *Cigarette smoking as a dependence process, NIDA Research Monograph 23*. Ed. Kransegor N.A. Washington DC, U.S. Department of Health and Human Services. 1979.

58. de Castro J.M., Elmore D.K. Subjective hunger relationships with meal patterns in the spontaneous feeding behaviour of humans: Evidence for a causal connection. *Physiology and Behavior*, 1988, 43, 159-165.

59. Wadden T.A., Stunkard A.J., Day S.C., Gould R.A., Rubin C.J. Less food, less hunger: Reports of appetite and symptoms in a controlled study of a protein-sparing modified fast. *International Journal of Obesity*, 1987, 11, 239-49.

60. Szmukler G.I., Tantam D. Anorexia nervosa: Starvation dependence. *British Journal of Medical Psychology*, 1984, 57, 303-10.

61. Heilbrun A.B., Worobow A.L. Attention and disordered eating behaviour: Disattention to the turbulent inner sensations as a risk factor in the development of anorexia nervosa. *Psychological Reports*, 1990, 66, 467-87.

62. Monti P.M., Binkoff J.A., Abrams D.B., Zwick W.R., Nirenberg T.D., Liepman M.R. Reactivity of alcoholics and non-alcoholics to drinking cues. *Journal of Abnormal Psychology*, 1987, 96, 122-6.

63. Rogers P.J., Hill A.J. Breakdown of dietary restraint following mere exposure to food stimuli: Interrelationships between restraint, hunger, salivation and food intake. *Addictive Behaviors*, 1989, 14, 387-97.

64. Tiffany S.T. A cognitive model of drug urges and drug-use behaviour: role of automatic and non-automatic processes. *Psychological Review*, 1990, 97, 147-68.

65. Overduin J., Jansen A. Food cue reactivity in fasting and non-fasting subjects. *European Eating Disorders Review*, 1996, 4, 249-59.

66. Cepeda-Benito A., Tiffany S.T. The use of a dual-task procedure for the assessment of cognitive-effort associated with cigarette craving. *Psychopharmacology*, 1996, 127, 155-63.

67. Green M.W., Rogers P.J., Elliman N.A. Dietary restraint and addictive behaviours: The generalisability of Tiffany's (1990) cue reactivity model. *International Journal of Eating Disorders*, 2000, 27, 419-27.

68. Mela D.J., Rogers P.J. *Food, Eating and Obesity: The Psychobiological Basis of Appetite and Weight Control*. London, Chapman and Hall. 1998.

69. Russell G. Bulimia nervosa: An ominous variant of anorexia nervosa. *Psychological Medicine*, 1979, 9, 429-48.

70. Janet P. *Les obsessions à la psychasthénie*. Paris, 1903.

71. *American Psychiatric Association. Diagnostic and statistical manual of mental disorders*, 4th ed, 1994, Washington DC, APA.

72. Hetherington M.M., Altemus M., Nelson M.L., Bernat A.S., Gold P.W. Eating behaviour in bulimia nervosa: multiple meal analyses. *American Journal of Clinical Nutrition*, 1994, 60, 864-73.

73. Cooper P.J., Bowskill R. Dysphoric mood and overeating. *British Journal of Clinical Psychology*, 1986, 25, 155-6.

74. Mizes J.S. Bulimia: A review of its symptomatology and treatment. *Advances in Behaviour Research and Therapy*, 1985, 7, 91-142.

75. Polivy J., Herman C.P. Diagnosis and treatment of normal eating. *Journal of Consulting and Clinical Psychology*, 1987, 55, 635-44.

76. Guertin T.L. Eating behaviour of bulimics, self-identified binge eaters, and non-eating-disordered individuals: What differentiates these populations? *Clinical Psychology Review*, 1999, 19, 1-23.

77. Elmore D.K., de Castro J.M. Meal patterns of normal, untreated bulimia nervosa and recovered bulimic women. *Physiology and Behaviour*, 1991, 49, 99-105.

78. Mitchell J.E., Laine D.C. Monitored binge-eating behavior in patients with bulimia nervosa. *International Journal of Eating Disorders*, 1985, 4, 177-83.

79. Crowther J.H., Lingswiler V.M., Stephens M.A.P. The topography of binge eating. *Addictive Behaviors*, 1984, 9, 299-309.

80. Grilo C.M., Shiffman S., Carter-Campbell J.T. Binge eating antecedents in normal-weight, non-purging females: Is there consistency? *International Journal of Eating Disorders*, 1994, 15, 239-49.

81. Abraham S.F., Beaumont P.J. How patients describe bulimia or binge eating. *Psychological Medicine*, 1982, 12, 625-35.

82. Gendall K.A., Sullivan P.F., Joyce P.R., Fear J.L., Bulik C.M. Psychopathology and personality of young women who experience food cravings. *Addictive Behaviors*, 1997, 22, 545-55.

83. Hill A.J., Heaton-Brown L. The experience of food craving: A prospective investigation of healthy women. *Journal of Psychosomatic Research*, 1994, 38, 801-14.

84. Schlundt D.G., Virts K.L., Sbrocco K., Pope-Cordle J. A sequential behavioural analysis of craving sweets in obese women. *Addictive Behaviors*, 1993, 18, 67-80.

85. Bruce B., Agras W.S. Binge eating in females: A population based investigation. *International Journal of Eating Disorders*, 1992, 12, 365-73.

86. Gendall K.A., Joyce P.R., Sullivan P.F., Bulik C.M. Food cravers: Characteristics of those who binge. *International Journal of Eating Disorders*, 1998, 23, 353-60.

7.2. CRAVING AND BINGE EATING

Anita Jansen

7.2.1   Summary

In this chapter, a classical conditioning model of craving and binge eating is presented. The model states that the craving and excessive food intake of binge eaters is cue-controlled. According to the model, cues that reliably signal food intake, such as the sight, smell and taste of food, time of the day or even negative mood states and cognitions, may start to act as conditioned stimuli, which can easily trigger cue reactivity or conditioned responses. It is assumed that craving reflects the subjective experience of the learned responses. The main prediction flowing from this model is that cue reactivity (including craving) increases the probability of (excessive) food intake. The model also predicts that a decrease in the binge frequency will be reached when the craving for binge food is extinguished. Cue exposure with response prevention is indeed an effective way to extinguish craving; general findings are that, during cue exposure with response prevention, the craving first becomes strong and then slowly dies down. Preliminary data from mainly pilot studies also suggest that cue exposure is an extremely effective method for combating binges.

7.2.2   Introduction

Binge eating refers to the consumption of a large amount of food in a discrete period of time, during which a loss of control over intake is experienced (1). Mostly, high-calorie food is eaten during a binge, and the food is usually stuffed into the mouth. Between the binges, binge eaters often try to restrain their food intake. The most frequently identified proximal antecedents to binge eating are negative emotions, such as feeling depressed, hopeless, worried and dissatisfied, and appetitive cues that elicit craving, such as the sight, smell and taste of preferred food (2-5). Following the binge, a relief from negative feelings is sometimes reported (5), whereas others found an increase in negative feelings (3). A decrease in craving after the binge is a consistent finding (3,5).

Binge eating occurs in eating disorders and it has also been found to occur in about 12% of a normal female population sample (6). It is a main diagnostic criterion of bulimia nervosa and nearly half of the patients with anorexia nervosa (7,8), as well as 15-50% of the obese participating in weight-control programmes (9) are characterized by recurrent episodes of binge eating. Research criteria for Binge Eating Disorder were included in the DSM IV section 'criteria sets and axes provided for further study' (1). From the prevalence rates of the eating disorders (1), it might be deduced that about 2 to 8% of the female population suffer from clinically relevant binge eating episodes. Eating Disorders Not Otherwise Specified (EDNOS), apart from Binge Eating Disorder are considered to be much more common (10), but how common is currently unknown.

Thus, before and at the start of a binge, binge eaters usually report feelings of craving that could best be described as a strong desire for the binge food (1,3,6). The craving might be elicited by appetitive cues, but it might also follow from negative mood states or other cues. In the present chapter, attention will be focused on the relationship between cues, craving and binge eating. The first question is how the craving develops. The second question is how the craving can be reduced, and the final question is whether a reduction of craving results in less frequent binge eating.

7.2.3   Development of Craving

The intake of food activates physiological responses. Interestingly, a large number of studies show that the physiological responses brought about by food intake, e.g. insulin release, blood sugar increase and salivation, can be brought under the control of any stimulus predictive of food intake, such as odours, sounds, time of the day, eating-related situations, seeing, smelling, tasting and even thinking of food (11-13). Deutsch (14) showed that an initially neutral taste cue could elicit a glycometabolic effect in rats after pairing the taste with glucose administration in a classical conditioning paradigm. The author also found that rats learned to respond with a decline in blood sugar to a placebo after they were repeatedly injected with sugar. Conversely, after repeated intravenous injections of insulin (which are usually followed by a decline in blood sugar level), rats learned to respond with a rise in blood sugar level to a placebo (15). Many years ago, Mityushov demonstrated conditioned hypoglycaemia in dogs as well as humans after injections with intravenous glucose (16). In humans, it has also been found that the mere anticipation of food and sham feeding (i.e. the sight, smell, taste, chewing, or the swallowing of food without its entering the gastrointestinal tract), as well as cognitive processes (such as the thought of food or even hypnotic suggestion of food) elicit responses that prepare the organism for digestion, such as insulin release and salivary responses (17-21). These conditioned responses contribute to the body's internal homeostatic regulation. Also, eating behaviour can be triggered by cues that have been associated with food consumption: rats who had already eaten to satiety were found to eat a large meal when exposed to a tone that was previously associated with food consumption (22).

Food intake may thus, in terms of classical conditioning, be considered an unconditioned stimulus (US), whereas its metabolic responses are unconditioned responses (URs). Cues that reliably signal food intake, such as the sight, smell and taste of food, time of the day or even cognitions and negative mood states, may start to act as conditioned stimuli (CSs), which can easily trigger cue reactivity or conditioned responses (CRs). It is assumed that craving reflects the subjective experience of the learned responses and thus forms the subjective part of the cue reactivity. The main prediction flowing from this model is that cue reactivity (including craving) increases the probability of (excessive) food intake (12,23). In line with this, we found that food exposure elicited physiological changes that might be interpreted as a preparation for food intake (32). The gastric activity during food exposure was related to the amount eaten afterwards, whereas, in a second experiment, the amount of subjective craving for food determined how much one ate (24).

The classical conditioning model of craving and binge eating offers a unifying explanation for the motley collection of disinhibitors that have been identified in binge eaters. Eating a calorie-rich preload (appetiser or 'priming dose'), smelling a tasty 'preload', the perceived breach of a diet, thinking of binge food, being in a low mood or being anxious - all are cues or stimuli for binge eaters to overeat. For the sake of parsimony, one single mechanism that underlies each trigger to overeating should be looked for; all these disinhibiting stimuli could, hypothetically, be conditioned to the excessive intake of food. It is hypothesised that the variety of disinhibitors all act as conditioned stimuli with an identical consequence: binge eating. After systematic association of environmental and/or interoceptive cues with binge food intake, the cues reliably signal the food effects. The moment the cues are good predictors of intake, they acquire the ability to elicit autonomic and/or biochemical responses that are subjectively experienced as craving, which increase the likelihood of binge eating.

Findings on the eating behaviour of binge eaters indirectly support the learning model of craving and binge eating. Binge eaters usually alternate between binge eating and dieting episodes; a very common eating pattern is that they resist eating during the day and binge eat late in the afternoon or in the evening. Such an eating pattern facilitates classical conditioning: deprivation as well as eating large amounts (strong USs) within a limited and specific range of cues (CSs) both have the implication that the contingency between CS and US, and thus classical conditioning, will be strong. Strong conditioning is reflected in strong conditioned responses, and these conditioned responses (or cue reactivity) are supposed to be experienced as craving. Experimental studies indeed show that dieters overeat after exposure to cues that typically predict food intake, such as tasting a priming dose (appetiser or preload; see (25) for a classical experiment), and in recent studies it was found that they overeat after mere exposure to the smell of binge food (26-28). The exposure to food cues (tasting, eating or smelling the food) elicited a strong desire to eat in dieters.

Note, however, that direct tests of the classical conditioning model of craving and binge eating are still scarce and inconclusive. No support was found for an anticipative insulin response and blood sugar decline in obese binge eaters (29), or in normal unrestrained eating subjects after classical conditioning of sugar intake (30). Others, however, do report that highly restrained eaters show preparatory insulin responses (31), and some recent studies support the idea of cue reactivity in normal eaters as well as binge eaters and obese subjects as a method of priming the body to absorb and use the nutrients to ingest (19,24,32-35).

7.2.4   Reduction of Craving

The classical conditioning model of binge eating states that craving follows from probabilistic CS (cues) - US (binge eating) contingencies. The cues will elicit craving as long as they remain reliable predictors of substance use or, to put it differently, as long as the CSs are systematically reinforced by the US. The model predicts that the craving will extinguish when the CS-US bond is broken by prolonged and repeated non-reinforced exposure to the conditioned stimuli (cues that predict binge eating). Thus, for cue exposure, the subject should be exposed to the cues that predict the binge, but should be prevented from binge eating. The treatment inferred from the model is essentially the same as current treatments for anxiety disorders. For most individuals with phobias and obsessive compulsive disorders, *in vivo* exposure is highly effective in reducing fear and avoidance behaviour (36-38). Exposure therapy follows from the idea that the anxiety and avoidance behaviour are typically cue-controlled. During exposure, the subject is exposed to the feared cue (stimulus), and avoidance behaviour is prevented.

Like the association between cues and anxiety, the link between cues that indicate that a binge is forthcoming and the actual binge might possibly be eliminated by cue exposure with response prevention. During cue exposure with response prevention, the subject is exposed to the craving-eliciting cues and avoidance behaviour (bingeing) is prevented.

It is as yet unknown how many and which cues need to be included in the exposure for it to be effective - the broadest possible range of stimuli or solely a set of cues directly related to food, such as seeing, smelling and tasting favourite binge food (39). Studies on anxiety and addictions indicate that individually customised sets of cues are the best to use. When anxiety is involved, customised sets have proved to be the most effective (40), and research regarding alcohol indicates that the more likeness the cue has to the favourite beverage, the better the reactivity is (39). This means that, for the exposure to binge eating cues, all of the cues that play a part in binge eating are included: the exposure takes place at the usual binge time, at the customary bingeing spot (usually in the patient's home) and with the real bingeing food. Perhaps specific bingeing clothes, music, magazines must be included. Special attention must be paid to moods and thoughts that accompany the binge. Earlier, it was found that negative moods are important cues that elicit craving for a binge, and alcohol studies have indicated that negative mood induction magnifies the urge to drink (39,41). The goal of the exposure is to elicit a strong craving for the binge food. The patient is encouraged to go through the entire binge ritual as true to life as possible, to touch the food, to feel around in it, to grab it, to hold it to the nose and to smell it. If necessary, to increase the craving, the patient takes a lick or small bite. The objective always is to make the craving as strong as possible and, in pilot studies, it could be shown that cue exposure with response prevention indeeds elicits craving (42-45).

Cue reactivity and craving will be less, and the chance of extinction reduced, in cases of cognitive avoidance. Focusing the patient's attention on the cues and the reactions they cause may prevent cognitive avoidance. Anxiety research shows that concentrating on the cues and their effects results in a markedly stronger cue reactivity and greater extinction between the sessions than when the concentration is less (39). Note that the therapist is usually not part of a binge, he or she rather is a *safety signal:* a cue not to binge. Thus, eventually, his or her presence during the exposure is not wanted: the therapist moves behind the scene as quickly as possible. Our experience is that most patients can handle the exposure alone after three or four times.

If the exposure lasts long enough, the craving for food will slowly diminish, despite all attempts to keep it as strong as possible (42-45). In order to assess whether the exposure has been performed successfully (the craving becomes strong and then slowly dies down), the strength of the craving is registered on a regular basis, say every 10 minutes, by means of a 100-mm Visual Analogue Scale. According to some anxiety researchers (36,46,47), the duration of the confrontation is dependent on the speed at which the anxiety extinguishes. Once the anxiety has extinguished, there is no point in continuing the exposure; if the anxiety has not yet extinguished, the patient is in danger of its returning even more strongly the next time he/she is exposed to the cues (sensitisation). It is argued that exposures lasting from 50 to 90 minutes - no longer and certainly no shorter - are the most effective (37,39,40). Opiate studies indicate that exposure sessions lasting an hour are considerably more effective than 10-minute sessions: with 10-minute sessions, the craving did not expire until after 18 sessions, while 45-minute sessions resulted in extinction within six sessions (39).

However, de Silva and Rachman (48) showed that subjects who were given the opportunity to leave an anxious situation when their anxiety was 70 on a 100% scale profited as much from the exposures as subjects who were obliged to stay in the anxious situation until their anxiety had extinguished. Note that the opportunity to leave the anxious situation did not lead to more avoidance behaviour in the former group, so, in fact, their exposure sessions were no shorter. Others indeed found that short exposures were as effective as longer exposures in the extinction of anxiety and, contrary to what generally is believed, the short exposures did not lead to sensitisation (49-51).

Anxiety researchers have established that exposure will not succeed unless the sessions are repeated regularly at relatively short intervals. Five times a week is more effective than less frequent exposure (52). There is no reason to assume that this is any different for bingers.

7.2.5   Reduction of Craving and Binge Eating

The cue reactivity model predicts that treatments that fail to reduce craving and cue reactivity will have higher rates of relapse than treatments that are successful in the reduction of craving and cue reactivity. Outcome studies find indisputably that cognitive behaviour therapy (CBT), as it is originally described by Fairburn (53), is the most successful treatment for bulimia nervosa. A relevant question, however, is: why is CBT successful? What are the working mechanisms of the treatment? CBT is a multi-component treatment package including, amongst others, self-control techniques, self-monitoring, education, diet management, cognitive restructuring, problem solving, interpersonal training and relapse prevention. Looking closer at CBT, some of these procedures will break classically conditioned responses. A part of the diet management, for example, is the gradual introduction of feared foods in the diet and the establishment of normal eating patterns. Both decrease the probability relationship between binge cues and the intake of large amounts of binge food because the binge food is eaten more often and in a wider range of cues, whereas the introduction of small amounts of binge food in the diet in essence reduces the US. These procedures promote an extinction of cue reactivity and thus the urge to eat. Schulte, Künzel, Pepping and Schulte-Bahrenberg (54) found that the amount of *in vivo* exposure given in various multimodal anti-phobia treatments was the best predictor of success. From the present model, the same prediction may be made for anti-binge treatments (including CBT): treatments are effective to the degree in which they include exposure.

Outcome studies on exposure treatment for addictions and binge eating are scarcely out of the egg. In most studies, small subject samples were examined and a number of the research designs show methodological shortcomings. However, the preliminary data of alcohol cue exposure treatment (55,56) are promising, and several large controlled clinical trials are under way (39). Drummond and Glautier (55) found that subjects treated with cue exposure did better than controls (relaxation treatment) in terms of latency of relapse and quantity consumed; however, they found no differences between the groups in the number of abstinent subjects. Monti and colleagues (56), on the other hand, did find higher abstinence rates in a group treated with exposure and coping skills training as compared with a control group receiving the standard hospital treatment. Also, the urge to drink decreased more in the exposure group. Uncontrolled studies on cue exposure treatment in opiate and cocaine users show that cue exposure led to significant reductions in craving while the physiological cue reactivity did not extinguish (57), whereas the only randomised controlled trial showed that cue reactivity decreased in opiate-dependent subjects treated with cue exposure as well as in opiate-dependent subjects treated with group discussions of issues related to drug use (58).

All in all, the cue exposure studies show large reductions in (subjective) craving, whereas reductions in physiological cue reactivity and drug-taking behaviour sometimes, but not unequivocally, have been found. The evidence is stronger in the field of alcohol dependence than in opiate, cocaine and nicotine dependence (52). The modest success in opiate, cocaine and nicotine dependence might, however, be attributed to a lack of statistical power in most studies (59). In fact, cue exposure has not been given a fair test yet, and the positive findings from alcohol exposure studies should stimulate further research. The same goes for the field of the eating disorders. Six pilot studies on cue exposure in the treatment of binge eating were carried out, whereas, as far as the author knows, one large controlled trial is still under way (60) and one large controlled trial is finished (61).

The six pilot studies showed that cue exposure was successful in the extinction of craving; extinction took place within and between sessions. In most pilot studies, the exposure also led to large reductions in binge episodes (42-45,62,63).

The controlled study of Bulik et al. (61) was, however, less positive. The effectiveness of exposure with response prevention to a short cognitive behaviour therapy (CBT) programme was examined. All bulimic subjects were first treated with eight sessions of CBT, followed by a couple of exposure sessions. The exposure did not improve the results of the short cognitive behaviour therapy. However, the cognitive behaviour therapy was already very effective; an 80% reduction of binge eating and a 40% abstinence percentage was reached. These excellent results highlight a major problem, that is the design of the study reduced the chance of exposures having any success, owing to a ceiling effect. Therefore, the conclusions of the authors that exposures are not successful may be rather premature. Moreover, the data of Bulik et al. (61), say that exposure to cues that predict binges is more effective than exposure to cues that predict purging behaviour and it is also more effective than relaxation training. Unfortunately, Bulik et al. (61) did not report measures of physiological cue reactivity that were taken during overeating instead of during the exposure. It would have been informative to relate physiological cue reactivity during exposure at the end of treatment to the speed and seriousness of relapse after treatment. According to the cue reactivity model, the strength of the reactivity to cues that are associated with overeating will predict relapse.

The one controlled study that is underway is too small to yield specific conclusions as yet. Patients who announced for treatment in the Mental Health Center Maastricht and were diagnosed as suffering from bulimia nervosa, were given one of three cognitive or behavioural treatments. The treatments were short (15 hours in total) and they were pure, i.e., subjects were given only cognitive treatment, only cue exposure with response prevention or only diet management. Up to now, 41 patients randomly divided between the three conditions have been treated. The preliminary data show that the three pure treatments have been equally successful up to now, and that, at the one-year follow up, a mean binge frequency reduction of 87% was reached and an abstinence percentage of 61% (60).

All in all, the preliminary positive findings from pilot studies and the ongoing controlled outcome study suggest that cue exposure might be an effective treatment for binge eaters. Note, again, that, although the data are promising, they were derived from pilot studies with small subject samples and weak research designs. The only large controlled clinical trial that was published is not positive about the contribution of cue exposure with response prevention to CBT in the treatment of binge eating, but there are some methodological shortcomings of that study.

7.2.6   Conclusions

The present classical conditioning model of binge eating states that cues that reliably signal food intake, such as the sight, smell and taste of food, but also time of day, thoughts, mood states and other cues, may start to act as conditioned stimuli that trigger cue reactivity, i.e. autonomic or biochemical responding and craving. It is assumed that the learned cue reactivity increases the probability of (excessive) food intake. Although not many direct tests of the model have been published, findings on the eating behaviour of dieters and binge eaters directly and indirectly support the classical conditioning model of binge eating.

The cue reactivity model predicts that treatments that fail to reduce craving and cue reactivity will have higher rates of relapse than treatments that are successful in the reduction of craving and cue reactivity. Pilot studies on cue exposure with response prevention for binge eaters showed that the cue exposure was successful in the extinction of craving; extinction took place within and between sessions. In most pilot studies, the exposure also led to large reductions in binge episodes.

Despite the fact that there have been a number of small-scale, primarily uncontrolled short-term studies that suggest that cue exposure is an effective therapy for binge eating, for the time being there are two reasons why it should not be applied as the sole type of treatment. To begin with, there are no properly controlled data about the effectiveness of the treatment in either the short or the long term. Pilot studies suggest that cue exposure is an effective method for combating binges, but this must be confirmed through properly controlled, large-scale studies. Secondly, and certainly equally important, is the fact that most binge eaters not only suffer from binge eating; they attempt to prevent their weight from increasing through bizarre methods (such as not eating for days, intentionally regurgitating and using laxatives), have a low self-esteem and their way of thinking about their body weight and shape is dysfunctional. Whether these symptoms can be favourably influenced through cue exposure remains to be seen. Empirical research on the validity of the cue reactivity model should not be applied as the sole type of treatment, and, before conclusions about its effectiveness can be drawn, studies on the effectiveness of cue exposure should measure and report changes in all relevant symptoms, including general psychopathology, eating pattern, weight control methods, self-esteem, as well as body weight and shape concern.

7.2.7   References

1.   American Psychiatric Association. *Committee on Nomenclature and Statistics: Diagnostic and Statistical Manual of Mental Disorders. Fourth Edition.* Washington DC, American Psychiatric Association. 1994.

2.   Greeno C.G., Wing R.R., Shiffman S. Binge antecedents in obese women with and without binge eating disorder. *Journal of Consulting and Clinical Psychology*, 2000, 68, 95-102.

3.   Jansen A., van den Hout M., Griez E. Clinical and non-clinical binges. *Behaviour Research and Therapy*, 1990, 28, 439-44.

4.   McManus F., Waller G. A functional analysis of binge eating. *Clinical Psychology Review*, 1995, 15, 845-63.

5.   Stickney M., Miltenberger R., Wolff G. A descriptive analysis of factors contributing to binge eating. *Journal of Behavior Therapy and Experimental Psychiatry*, 1999, 30, 177-89.

6.   Bruce B., Agras W.S. Binge eating in females: a population-based investigation. *International Journal of Eating Disorders*, 1992, 12, 365-73.

7.   Polivy J., Herman C.P. Dieting and bingeing: a causal analysis. *American Psychologist*, 1985, 40, 193-201.

8.   Wardle J., Beinart H. Binge eating: A theoretical review. *British Journal of Clinical Psychology*, 1981, 20, 97-109.

9.   Marcus M.D., Wing R.R., Lamparski D. Binge eating and dietary restraint in obese patients. *Addictive Behaviors*, 1985, 10, 163-8.

10.   Fairburn C.G., Walsh B.T. Atypical eating disorders, in *Eating disorders and obesity. A comprehensive handbook*. Eds Brownell K.D., Fairburn C.G. New York, Guilford Press. 1995, 135-40.

11.   Rodin J. Insulin levels, hunger, and food intake: an example of feedback loops in body weight regulation. *Health Psychology*, 1985, 4, 1-24.

12.   Wardle J. Conditioning processes and cue exposure in the modification of excessive eating. *Addictive Behaviors*, 1990, 15, 387-93.

13.   Woods S.C. The eating paradox: how we tolerate food. *Psychological Review*, 1991, 4, 488-505.

14.   Deutsch R. Conditioned hypoglycemia: A mechanism for saccharin-induced sensitivity to insulin in the rat. *Journal of Comparative and Physiological Psychology*, 1974, 86, 350-8.

15.   Siegel S. Conditioning of insulin-induced glycemia. *Journal of Comparative and Physiological Psychology*, 1972, 78, 233-41.

16. Overduin J., Dworkin B.R., Jansen A. Introduction and Commentary to: M.I. Mityushov (1954) "Conditioned Reflex Secretion of Insulin". *Integrative Physiological and Behavioral Science*, 1997, 32, 228-46.

17. Jansen A., Boon B., Nauta H., van den Hout M. Salivation discordant with hunger. *Behaviour Research and Therapy*, 1992, 30, 163-6.

18. Johnson W.G., Wildman H.E. Influence of external and covert food stimuli on insulin secretion in obese and normal persons. *Behavioral Neuroscience*, 1983, 97, 1025-28.

19. Mattes R.D. Physiological responses to sensory stimulation by food: nutritional implications. *Journal of the American Dietetic Association*, 1997, 97, 406-12.

20. Powley T. The ventromedial hypothalamic syndrome, satiety and a cephalic phase hypothesis. *Psychological Review*, 1977, 84, 89-126.

21. Simon C., Schlienger J.L., Sapin R., Imler M. Cephalic phase insulin secretion in relation to food presentation in normal and overweight subjects. *Physiology and Behavior*, 1986, 36, 465-9.

22. Weingarten H.P. Conditioned cues elicit feeding in sated rats: a role for learning in meal initiation. *Science*, 1983, 220, 431-2.

23. Jansen A. A learning model of binge eating: Cue reactivity and cue exposure. *Behaviour Research and Therapy*, 1998, 36, 257-72.

24. Nederkoorn C., Smulders F., Jansen A. Cephalic phase responses, craving and food intake in normal subjects. *Appetite*, 2000, 35, 45-55.

25. Herman C., Mack D. Restrained and unrestrained eating. *Journal of Personality*, 1975, 43, 647-60.

26. Fedoroff I.C., Polivy J., Herman C.P. The effect of pre-exposure to food cues on the eating behavior of restrained and unrestrained eaters. *Appetite*, 1997, 28, 33-47.

27. Jansen A., van den Hout M. On being led into temptation: 'counterregulation' of dieters after smelling a 'preload'. *Addictive Behaviors*, 1991, 5, 247-53.

28. Rogers P.J., Hill A.J. Breakdown of dietary restraint following mere exposure to food stimuli: interrelationships between restraint, hunger, salivation, and food intake. *Addictive Behaviors*, 1989, 14, 387-97.

29. Karhunen L.J., Lappalainen R.I., Tammela L., Turpeinen A.K., Uusitupa M.I.J. Subjective and physiological cephalic phase responses to food in obese binge-eating women. *International Journal of Eating Disorders*, 1997, 21, 321-8.

30. Overduin J., Jansen A. Conditioned insulin and blood sugar responses in humans in relation to binge eating. *Physiology & Behavior*, 1997, 61, 569-75.

31. Teff K., Engelman K. Palatability and dietary restraint: effect on cephalic phase insulin release in women. *Physiology & Behavior*, 1996, 60, 567-73.

32. Nederkoorn C., Jansen A. (submitted). Cue reactivity and the regulation of food intake. *Eating Behaviors* (in press).

33. Karhunen L.J., Lappalainen R.I., Vanninen E.J., Kuikka J.T., Uusitupa M.I.J. Regional cerebral blood flow during food exposure in obese and normal-weight women. *Brain*, 1997, 120, 1675-84.

34. Nederkoorn C., Smulders F., Jansen A. Recording of swallowing events using electromyography as a non-invasive measurement of salivation. *Appetite*, 1999, 33, 361-9.

35. Vögele C., Florin I. Psychophysiological responses to food exposure: An experimental study in binge eaters. *International Journal of Eating Disorders*, 1997, 21, 147-57.

36. Emmelkamp P. *Phobic and Obsessive Compulsive Disorders: Theory, Research and Practice*. New York, Plenum Press. 1982.

37. Marks I.M. *Fears, phobias and rituals: panic, anxiety and their disorders*. Oxford, University Press. 1987.

38. Rachman S., Hodgson R. *Obsessions and compulsions*. New Yersey, Prentice Hall Inc., Englewood Cliffs. 1980.

39. Rohsenow D.J., Monti P.M., Abrams D.B. Cue exposure treatment in alcohol dependence, in *Addictive Behaviour. Cue exposure Theory and Practice*. Eds Drummond D.C., Tiffany S.T., Glautier S., Remington B. West Sussex, Wiley Series in Clinical Psychology. 1995, 169-96.

40. Foa E.B., Kozak M.J. Emotional processing of fear: exposure to corrective information. *Psychological Bulletin*, 1986, 99, 20-35.

41.   Cooney N.L., Litt M.D., Morse P.A., Bauer L.O., Gaupp L. Alcohol cue reactivity, negative-mood reactivity, and relapse in treated alcoholic men. *Journal of Abnormal Psychology*, 1997, 106, 243-50.

42.   Jansen A., van den Hout M., van Loof C., Zandbergen J., Griez E. A case of bulimia succesfully treated with cue exposure. *Behavior Therapy and Experimental Psychiatry*, 1989, 20, 327-32.

43.   Jansen A., Broekmate J., Heymans M. Cue exposure vs self-control in the treatment of binge eating: a pilot study. *Behaviour Research and Therapy*, 1992, 30, 235-41.

44.   Hansen A., de Haan E. De behandeling van bulimia nervosa met cue-exposure; ervaringen uit de praktijk [Treatment of bulimia nervosa with cue exposure; clinical experiences]. *Directieve Therapie [Directive Therapy]*, 1995, 15, 279-91.

45.   Kennedy S.H., Katz R., Neitzert C.S., Ralevsky E., Mendlowitz S. Exposure with response prevention treatment of anorexia nervosa-bulimic subtype and bulimia nervosa. *Behaviour Research and Therapy*, 1995, 33, 685-9.

46.   Eysenck H.J. Behavior Therapy, in *Theoretical Foundations of Behavior Therapy*. Eds Eysenck H.J., Martin I. New York, Plenum Press. 1987.

47.   Wilson G.T., O'Leary D. *Principles of Behavior Therapy*. Englewood Cliffs, NY, Prentice-Hall. 1980.

48.   de Silva P., Rachman S. Does escape behaviour strengthen agoraphobic avoidance? A preliminary study. *Behaviour Research and Therapy*, 1984, 22, 87-91.

49.   Van den Hout M.A., Merckelbach H. Over exposure [About exposure]. *Directieve Therapie [Directive Therapy]*, 1993, 13, 192-203.

50.   Kimmel H.D., Kearns W.D., Anderson D.E. Extinction instead of incubation following classical aversive conditioning in dogs. *Integrative Physiological and Behavioral Science*, 1992, 27, 356-70.

51.   Richards M., Martin I. Eysenck's incubation of fear hypothesis: an experimental test. *Behaviour Research and Therapy*, 1990, 28, 373-84.

52.   Drummond D.C., Tiffany S.T., Glautier S., Remington B. *Addictive Behaviour. Cue Exposure Theory and Practice*. West Sussex, Wiley Series in Clinical Psychology. 1995.

53. Fairburn C.G., Marcus M.D., Wilson G.T. Cognitive-behavioral therapy for binge eating and bulimia nervosa: a comprehensive treatment manual, in *Binge eating. Nature, assessment, and treatment*. Eds Fairburn C.G., Wilson G.T. New York, Guilford Press. 1993, 361-404.

54. Schulte D., Künzel R., Pepping G., Schulte-Bahrenberg T. Tailor-made versus standardized therapy for phobic patients. *Advances in Behaviour Research and Therapy*, 1992, 14, 67-92.

55. Drummond D.C., Glautier S. A controlled trial of cue exposure treatment in alcohol dependence. *Journal of Consulting and Clinical Psychology*, 1994, 62, 809-17.

56. Monti P.M., Rohsenow D.J., Rubonis A.V., Niaura R.S., Sirota A.D., Colby S.M., Goddard P., Abrams D.B. Cue exposure with coping skills treatment for male alcoholics: a preliminary investigation. *Journal of Consulting and Clinical Psychology*, 1993, 61, 1011-9.

57. Childress A.R., Ehrman R., Rohsenow D.J., Robbins S.J., O'Brien C. Classically conditioned factors in drug dependence, in *Substance Abuse: A Comprehensive Textbook*. Eds Lowinson J., Ruiz P., Millman R., Langrod J. Baltimore, Williams & Wilkins. 1992, 56-69.

58. Dawe S., Powell J.H. Cue exposure treatment in opiate and cocaine dependence, in *Addictive Behaviour. Cue Exposure Theory and Practice*. Eds Drummond D.C., Tiffany S.T., Glautier S., Remington B. West Sussex, Wiley Series in Clinical Psychology. 1995, 197-210.

59. Brandon T.H., Piasecki T.M., Quinn E.P., Baker T. Cue exposure treatment in nicotine dependence, in *Addictive Behaviour. Cue Exposure Theory and Practice*. Eds Drummond, D.C., Tiffany, S.T., Glautier, S., Remington, B. West Sussex, Wiley Series in Clinical Psychology. 1995, 211-27.

60. Jansen A. Towards effective treatment of eating disorders: nothing is as practical as a good theory. *Behaviour Research and Therapy*, in press.

61. Bulik C.M., Sullivan P.F., Carter F.A., McIntosh V.V., Joyce P.R. The role of exposure with response prevention in the cognitive-behavioural therapy for bulimia nervosa. *Psychological Medicine*, 1998, 28, 611-23.

62. Schmidt U., Marks I. Cue exposure to food plus response prevention of binges for bulimia: a pilot study. *International Journal of Eating Disorders*, 1988, 7, 663-72.

63. Schmidt U., Marks I. Exposure plus prevention of bingeing vs. exposure plus prevention of vomiting in bulimia nervosa. *The Journal of Nervous and Mental Disease*, 1989, 177, 259-66.

7.3. CHARACTERISTICS OF FOOD CRAVERS WHO BINGE EAT

Kelly A. Gendall and Peter R. Joyce

7.3.1   Introduction

Food cravings are reported by women with and without clinical eating disturbances (1), but have frequently been associated with conditions in which bouts of excessive or "binge" eating occur. Binge eating is defined as the consumption of a large amount of food within a discrete period of time, and is usually accompanied by feelings of lack of control (2). Like food cravings, binge eating occurs in both non-clinical and eating-disordered groups across all weight ranges (3,4), and non-pathological binge eating has been described as a fairly "widespread phenomenon" (5). In a review of studies on the epidemiology of bulimia nervosa, Fairburn *et al.* (6) found that the prevalence of binge eating ranged from 7% to 79% (mean 35.8%). In New Zealand samples, 43.6% of young female tertiary students (7) and 22.5% of 18- to 44-year-olds (8) have reported binge eating at some stage. In the Zürich Cohort Study, binge eating at some point in the past was reported by approximately three females to every male (9). Halmi *et al.* (10) reported that only marginally more females than males reported having had an episode of binge eating (68% versus 60%). However, in this study, twice as many females as males also said that they felt "miserable and annoyed" about binge eating (10).

Although "craving" for food is not the only factor antecedent to binge eating episodes, food cravings do appear to precede binge eating in vulnerable groups. Women with bulimia nervosa have described "craving" food as one of the most common antecedents to binge eating (11). Regular episodes of overeating in obesity, seasonal affective disorder, in individuals with premenstrual syndrome (12) and in "compulsive overeaters" (13) have also been attributed to "carbohydrate cravings".

While clear associations between craving, particularly for sweet food, and binge eating have been made (13,14), a number of observations also indicate that not all of those who experience food cravings also binge on the desired foods. First, although studies on food craving and binge eating are complicated by the definitions and criteria used (15), food cravings are generally reported by a greater proportion of individuals than is binge eating. Depending on sampling strategies and the definitions/criteria used for food craving, from 58% (16) to 98% (17,18) of women report food cravings. Yet binge eating has been estimated to occur regularly in only 12% (3) to 19% (19) of women. These figures suggest that not all of those who experience food cravings also binge eat. Second, in a group of "chocolate addicts" only 15% reported consuming an amount that could be considered a binge (three or more 60-g bars of chocolate each day). A further 60% reported consuming no more than one 60-g bar of chocolate per day, on average 25 times per month, implying that the majority of subjects could not be considered binge eaters (20).

7.3.2 Study into Food Craving and Binge Eating

Why is it that some individuals are able to satisfy food cravings with a "normal" amount of food, while in others food cravings precipitate, and perhaps are only satisfied by a binge? Given that binge eating is a distressing experience and is associated with bulimia nervosa and adiposity (21), we have specifically investigated the possible factors that differentiate food cravers who do and do not binge eat (22). Aside from this investigation, there are few published studies specifically examining the relationship between food craving and binge eating. Thus, the ensuing discussion will describe this study, its principal findings and, where relevant, data that have emerged from other studies.

7.3.2.1 *Description of the study*

The original investigation involved two groups of women: one group recruited through advertising and one group consisting of a random community sample. Because of selection bias associated with studying individuals recruited through advertisement, only the findings from the randomly selected group of women (who were serving as controls for a separate study (23)) will be discussed. The sample was obtained from the Christchurch (New Zealand) electoral roll, on which all adults are legally obliged to register. Of 109 individuals initially contacted, eight refused participation. The final sample of 101 women were between 18 and 46 years old. They completed the Diagnostic Interview for Genetic Studies (DIGS) (24,25) with a trained interviewer to determine the occurrence of lifetime affective, anxiety, substance use, and eating related disorders, including binge eating tendencies. Two clinicians independently reviewed the interviews to make a consensus decision on all psychiatric diagnoses. Participants also completed a series of self-report questionnaires, including the Temperament and Character Inventory (TCI) (26), the Three Factor Eating Questionnaire (TFEQ) (27) and the Parental Bonding Instrument (PBI) (28).

7.3.2.1.1 Assessment of food craving

Food craving was assessed during the structured interview using a Food Craving Questionnaire (FCQ) devised by the authors (16). Investigations into food cravings have tended to suffer from arbitrary definitions of the term "craving" and have also lacked established criteria or standard dimensions of measurement. In the past, assessment of food cravings has frequently encompassed only one question: "Have you ever experienced food cravings (i.e. an intense desire to eat a specific food)?" (18). Thus, in designing the FCQ, we attempted to determine the existence of carefully defined current or past food cravings, the nature and temporal patterns of the experience, and factors associated with craving episodes. Participants were asked if they had ever experienced "an uncontrollable desire to eat a certain food or type of food" and "a strong urge to eat a specific food", before being asked if they had ever experienced "a craving for food". This was to allow for a varied understanding of the concept and to avoid an initial emotive response to the term "craving"[1]. Any participant who responded positively to any one of these three initial questions completed the remaining questions in the section. Non-cravers were considered to be those who responded

---

[1] Kozlowski, Mann Wilkinson and Poulos (78) have recommended that the sole use of the term craving should be avoided and that questions relating to desires or urges should also be asked.

negatively to all three of the initial questions and those who craved only during pregnancy. In addition, those who reported only "mild" cravings were also categorised as non-cravers because "mild" craving was not compatible with our initial definition of craving as "a strong desire with a specific food or type of food". Individuals who reported "moderate" or "strong" cravings with two or more features of intensity were categorised as cravers. The features we had previously delineated as indicating intensity were a change in speed of consumption, level of difficulty resisting the craved food, and anxiety when the craved food was unavailable (16).

7.3.2.1.2 Assessment of binge eating

All women classified as cravers were grouped according to their binge eating status. Any participant who reported a history of i) having eaten what would be considered a large amount of food by an outside observer within a short period of time, and ii) feeling out of control during that eating episode was considered to be a "binge eater". A minimum frequency and duration of binge eating were not required for individuals to be categorised into the binge eating group. However, frequency and duration criteria were required for participants to receive a diagnosis of bulimia nervosa.

7.3.2.2 Prevalence of binge eating among food cravers

In this study, 17% of women categorised as food cravers met criteria for binge eating. Thus, the majority (83%) of women who experience food cravings do not appear to suffer from significant binge eating. Because of variations in definitions of binge eating and criteria used to classify individuals, it is difficult to compare this rate of binge eating among food cravers with rates of binge eating reported in general community samples from other studies (6-8). However, among women who reported no experiences of food cravings in this study, only 5% reported binge eating. This suggests that food cravers are at greater risk of experiencing episodes of binge eating than are non-cravers.

7.3.2.3 *Variables associated with binge eating in food cravers*

7.3.2.3.1 *Body weight*

The Body Mass Indices (BMI) of cravers who did and did not binge eat are shown in Table 7.3.I. Current and past highest BMI of cravers who binged were significantly elevated compared with those of cravers who did not binge. We have previously found that, compared with non-cravers, women who experience food cravings (including both those who do and do not experience binge eating) have a tendency towards higher current and maximum BMI (29). Comparison of only those cravers who did not binge with non-cravers revealed no significant differences between the groups in current and highest BMI. Thus, elevated BMI among women who experience food cravings appear to be due to the sub-group who binge eat.

TABLE 7.3.I
Characteristics of food cravers who do and do not experience binge eating[1]

Variable	Bingers	Non-bingers	Statistic[2]
N (%)	7 (17)	35 (83)	
Body Mass Index - current	32.7 ± 11.6	25.7 ± 6.5	5.1*
Highest	35.8 ± 10.6	27.0 ± 6.6	8.2**
Lowest	23.2 ± 3.9	20.6 ± 3.1	3.9
Ideal	22.7 ± 2.9	24.0 ± 2.7	0.4
TFEQ Scores - Total	27.9 ± 6.2	17.4 ± 8.8	8.9*
Cognitive restraint	7.9 ± 4.7	6.8 ± 4.8	0.3
Disinhibition	10.6 ± 3.6	5.9 ± 3.8	8.7 **
Susceptibility to hunger	9.4 ± 1.7	4.7 ± 2.7	19.3 ***

[1] Data shown are mean ± SD for continuous variables or N (%) for discrete variables.

P- values;   * = 0.05 - 0.01
                   ** = 0.001 - 0.01
                   *** = 0.0001 - 0.001

[2] Statistics are F-ratio for continuous variables and χ^2 for discrete variables.

BMI has been positively associated with binge eating in already overweight individuals (21) and in community-based samples (3). Bruce and Agras (3) have suggested that frequent binge eating is the aetiological factor in the relationship between binge eating and overweight. Telch *et al.* (21) have hypothesised that weight gain in binge eaters may be a function of repeated dieting and weight cycling patterns. Alternatively, binge eating may occur in response to dysphoria associated with incidental weight gains and thus be consequential to an elevated BMI. At present, the issue of whether the binge eating causes a high BMI, or whether those with a high BMI are more likely to binge, remains unclarified.

7.3.2.3.2 Dietary restraint

Cravers who binged had significantly higher total TFEQ, susceptibility to hunger and, in particular, disinhibition scores compared with cravers who did not binge eat (Table 7.3.I). As with BMI, we have previously found elevated TFEQ scores in food cravers as a group compared with non cravers (29). However, the cravers who did not binge had similar TFEQ scores to the non-cravers, suggesting that high total TFEQ, disinhibition and susceptibility to hunger scores in food cravers are attributable to the subgroup who binge eat. Restrained eaters are characterised by chronic weight concerns (cognitive restraint), by the tendency to overeat or "counter-regulate" under conditions antagonistic to self-control (disinhibition), and by an inclination to submit to external eating cues and reactivity to perceived hunger (susceptibility to hunger) (30). Correlations between dietary restraint and binge eating have been shown by a number of investigators (30). Several mechanisms by which dietary restraint predisposes to binge eating may operate: psychological frustration and deprivation may enhance the attractiveness of normally forbidden foods and vulnerability to loss of control; restriction-induced hyper-responsiveness to food-related stimuli may accelerate the rate of eating, delaying the emergence of satisfaction and prolonging the eating episode; and a high variability in intake may impair metabolism of ingested food (31). Although cognitive restraint was not elevated in the cravers who binged, the use of cognitively imposed limits to terminate eating may extinguish conditioned satiety cues and may be another mechanism by which dietary restraint contributes to binge eating in other groups. Where restraint leads to successful dieting and weight loss, biological mechanisms, such as reduced serotonergic function, may also predispose to binge eating (32). While it is possible that binge eating predisposes to dietary restraint - guilt or anxiety about the possibility of weight gain after binge eating may motivate the individual into a mode of restrained eating in an attempt to rectify the episode of overeating - it is more likely that dietary restraint precedes binge eating (33) and thereafter a self-perpetuating cycle operates (34).

7.3.2.3.3 Psychiatric diagnoses

Cravers who did and did not binge had similar rates of lifetime major depression, anxiety disorders, social and simple phobia and anorexia nervosa. However, significantly higher rates of bulimia nervosa and cannabis abuse/dependence were found in the cravers who binged compared with those who did not binge. This phenomenon will be discussed in detail in the following paragraphs.

7.3.2.3.4 Bulimia nervosa

Bulimia nervosa is an eating disorder characterised by recurrent episodes of binge eating followed by compensatory purging in efforts to avoid weight gain. By definition, therefore, it is not surprising that a diagnosis of bulimia nervosa was more likely to be met by cravers who binged (43%) compared with those who did not binge (0%) (F = 6.2, p = 0.001). It is important to note that, probably as a result of infrequent binge episodes or the absence of purging, not all of those cravers who binged also had bulimia nervosa.

It is worth stating here that the contribution that craving for foods makes towards triggering binge eating in bulimia nervosa has been an issue of some debate. Craving for specific food, is frequently cited as an antecedent to binge eating by patients with bulimia (11,35,36). The favourite types of food eaten during binge episodes, e.g. ice cream, cake, pastries, donuts, cookies, chocolate, breads/toast, cereal (37,38) by women with bulimia are similar to those foods craved by non-eating-disordered women (18,39). Probably owing to this preference for sweet/starchy foods during a binge, women with bulimia tend to believe they are particularly likely to crave and binge on carbohydrate-rich foods (40). However, according to DSM-IV (2) binge eating in bulimia is characterised more by a large energy content than by a craving for a specific nutrient. The concept that women with bulimia crave carbohydrates in particular has also been questioned, because the percentage of energy from carbohydrates in binge episodes is not necessarily higher than that of non-binge-eating episodes or freely selected diets (41-46). However, Van der Ster Wallin et al. (45) argued that the fundamental food choice during binges was carbohydrate-rich items. In addition, when the macronutrient content of binge episodes is measured in absolute amounts, protein intake is reduced, and the carbohydrate and sucrose intake is over twice that of fat, suggesting that sweet-tasting, highly palatable types of foods may be the "craved" items in bulimia (45,47).

Determination as to whether craving is indeed a feature of bulimia nervosa is complicated further by two factors. First, although the definition of craving requires that the desire to eat be strong and that it be for a specific food or type of food (39), no consistent definitions or criteria for craving have been used in studies of bulimia nervosa. The extreme lengths gone to in order to obtain binge foods, the difficulty experienced in resisting a binge and the anxiety experienced when binge eating is prevented (37) suggest that the drive to eat in bulimia almost certainly meets the requirements regarding strength. However, the categorical existence of craving in bulimia may depend on whether specificity criteria require craving be for a type of food (e.g. sweet-tasting) or for a nutrient (e.g. carbohydrate).

It is also possible that a number of food cravers who binge suffer from binge eating disorder (BED). Being a relatively new DSM-IV diagnosis (2), BED was not assessed by the instruments used in the study and it may be important to screen for this disorder in future studies. Individuals with BED are frequently obese and experience recurrent episodes of binge eating, which cause significant distress, but they do not engage in compensatory purging methods as in bulimia nervosa (48). An early report found that 77%

of individuals with what would now be considered to be BED, described craving for a particular food or type of food at least half of the time they binged (49). There are anecdotal reports of specific cravings for carbohydrate-rich foods in BED patients, and a controlled laboratory study has found their favoured binge foods to include desserts, candy and snack foods (50). Therefore, similar to the argument in bulimia nervosa, the specificity of cravings in BED may be more accurately described as being for highly palatable or sweet foods rather than being based on macronutrient composition.

7.3.2.3.5 Substance abuse/dependence

In light of high rates of comorbid substance abuse reported in women with BN (51-53), the observation of more frequent cannabis abuse/dependence in cravers who binged (29%) compared with those who did not (3%) is of interest (χ^2 = 7.0, p = 0.05). Although it has been argued that substances of abuse and food are used interchangeably as addictive substances (54,55), some third factor, such as a family background or impaired social adaptation, may predispose to extreme forms of consummatory behaviour. A strong appetitive drive or desire for sensory stimulation may also operate as one common variable that mediates the relationship between binge eating and substance abuse/dependence (56). In food cravers as a group (including those who do and do not binge eat), we have observed significantly higher rates of substance abuse/dependence and a trend towards higher levels of novelty seeking compared with non-cravers (29). The novelty-seeking trait on the TCI is characterised by excitability, impulsivity, and thrill seeking (57) and is itself strongly associated with alcohol abuse (58,59) and bulimia nervosa (56). However, novelty-seeking scores were not higher in cravers who binged than in cravers who did not binge; therefore, it is unlikely that this personality trait mediated the relationship between binge eating and drug abuse in food cravers. It is possible that the personality trait of low self-directedness (discussed below) mediated the relationship between binge eating and substances abuse in cravers (60).

7.3.2.3.6 Personality

The cravers who did and did not binge eat had similar scores on the TCI subscales of novelty seeking, reward dependence, harm avoidance, self-transcendence and persistence. Significantly lower scores on the character trait of self-directedness were observed in the binge eaters. Further analysis of the subscale scores for each of the higher-order traits revealed that, while the means of all facets of self-directedness were lower in binge eaters, SD4, low self-acceptance ($p = 0.01$), followed by SD5, the inability to act in accordance with long-term goals in tempting situations ($p = 0.07$), contributed most to this relationship.

Self-directedness is a character trait describing mature, self-sufficient, responsible, constructive, goal-oriented and well-integrated individuals. The facets of low self-directedness, the conviction that one's behaviour is determined by influences outside their control (SD1, blaming), a reactivity to current circumstances and immediate needs rather than an ability to delay gratification to achieve goals (SD2, lack of goal direction), a sense of helplessness and ineffectiveness when solving problems (SD3, inertia), low self-esteem and non-acceptance of one's physical and mental features (SD4, self-striving) and the manifestation of self-defeating habits that are inconsistent with long-term goals (SD5, bad habits) (61) are character variables that are compatible with a vulnerability to binge eating. Indeed, body dissatisfaction (62,63), an unstable self-concept (64), inadequate coping skills (65), a susceptibly to over-eat in the presence of disinhibitors (palatable foods, low mood, etc.) (66) and impulsivity (36), all features antithetical to self-directedness, have been found in binge eaters in other samples. In addition, characteristics associated with low self-directedness have been shown to be associated with substance abuse (60) and poor outcome after treatment for bulimia nervosa (67). The use of other instruments, such as the MMPI (68), may provide further insight into the personality characteristics of those food cravers who binge eat.

7.3.2.3.7 Parental characteristics

We did not observe any significant differences between cravers who did and did not binge on any of the PBI scales. To date, no other studies have examined other parental or family characteristics of the subgroup of food cravers who binge eat.

7.3.3   Treatment of Food Cravers who Binge Eat

Binge eating can have serious psychological and physiological consequences (69) and therefore treatment is warranted in affected individuals. No investigations have been made into the treatment of binge eating specifically in food cravers and it is conceivable that either the craving or the binge eating could be the target for treatment. With respect to treatments for binge eating, cognitive behavioural therapy and selective serotonin reuptake inhibitor medication (SSRI) have been found to be effective at reducing the frequency of binge eating in bulimia nervosa and, more recently BED (70-73). There is some evidence that the now-banned serotonin releasing agent d-fenfluramine reduces consumption of carbohydrate-rich snacks in obese "carbohydrate-cravers" (74-76). However, it is not clear whether these "carbohydrate" cravers were also binge eaters and, if so, whether d-fenfluramine also ameliorated binge eating in these individuals. With respect to treatments that potentially targets craving itself, some SSRI and opioid antagonising medications have been found to reduce cravings in individuals with substance abuse disorders (77). However, whether such medications could effectively reduce cravings for food is currently speculative.

7.3.4   Conclusions

Knowledge of the characteristics and patterns of binge eating in food cravers is, at present, elementary. Initial findings from a random sample of women suggest that slightly less than one in five women who experience food cravings appear also to experience binge eating. Food cravers who binge eat tend to be heavier, are more likely to meet criteria for lifetime bulimia nervosa and some forms of substance abuse, and are characterised by a high level of dietary restraint and low self-directedness. Future studies need to corroborate these initial observations, and studies including males may also be of interest. Relatively recent progress in the neurobiology of eating disorders also paves the way for investigations into the neurobiological basis of, and relationship between food craving and binge eating. The specific nature of craving and its role in triggering binge eating in bulimia nervosa and BED require more systematic and detailed investigation. Finally, treatment modalities specific to individuals in whom food craving precipitates binge eating remains to be investigated.

7.3.5   References

1.   Hill A.J., Heaton-Brown L. The experience of food craving: a prospective investigation in healthy women. *Journal of Psychosomatic Research*, 1994, 38(8), 801-14.

2.   American Psychiatric Association: Diagnostic and Statistical Manual of Mental Disorders. Washington DC, American Psychiatric Association. 1994.

3.   Bruce B., Agras W.S. Binge eating in females: A population based investigation. *International Journal of Eating Disorders*, 1992, 12, 365-73.

4.   Fairburn C.G., Hay P.J., Welch S.L. Binge eating and bulimia nervosa: Distribution and determinants, in *Binge Eating: Nature, Assessment and Treatment*. Eds Fairburn C.G., Wilson G.T. New York, Guilford Press. 1993, 123-43.

5.   Hawkins R.C., Clement P.F. Development and construct validation of a self-report measure of binge eating tendencies. *Addictive Behaviors*, 1980, 5, 219-26.

6.   Fairburn C.G., Beglin S.J. Studies of the epidemiology of bulimia nervosa. *American Journal of Psychiatry*, 1990, 147, 401-8.

7.   Welch G., Hall A. Is the prevalence of bulimia nervosa higher among tertiary education populations? *New Zealand Medical Journal*, 1990, 103, 476-7.

8.   Bushnell J.A., Wells J.E., Hornblow A.R., Oakley-Browne M.A., Joyce P.R. Prevalence of three bulimia syndromes in the general population. *Psychological Medicine*, 1990, 20, 671-80.

9. Vollrath M., Koch R., Angst J. Binge eating and weight concerns among young adults. Results from the Zurich Cohort Study. *British Journal of Psychiatry*, 1992, 160, 498-503.

10. Halmi K.A., Falk J.R., Schartz E. Binge-eating and vomiting: survey of a college population. *Psychological Medicine*, 1981, 11, 697-706.

11. Mitchell J.E., Hatsukami D., Eckert E.D., Pyle R.C. Characteristics of 275 patients with bulimia. *American Journal of Psychiatry*, 1985, 142, 482-5.

12. Wurtman J.J. Carbohydrate craving. Relationship between carbohydrate intake and disorders of mood. *Drugs*, 1990, 39 (Suppl. 3), 49-52.

13. Hetherington M.M., Macdiarmid J.I. Pleasure and excess: liking for and overconsumption of chocolate. *Physiology & Behavior*, 1995, 57(1), 27-35.

14. Schlundt D.G., Virts K.L., Sbrocco T., Pope-Cordle J., Hill J.O. A sequential behavioural analysis of craving sweets in obese women. *Addictive Behaviors*, 1993, 18, 67-80.

15. Fairburn C.G., Wilson T.G. Binge eating: Definition and classification, in *Binge Eating: Nature, Assessment and Treatment*. Eds Fairburn C.G., Wilson G.T. New York, Guilford Press. 1993, 3-14.

16. Gendall K.A., Joyce P.R., Sullivan P.F. The impact of definition on the prevalence of food cravings in a random sample of young women. *Appetite*, 1997, 28, 63-72.

17. Rodin J., Mancuso J., Granger J., Nelbach E. Food cravings in relation to body mass index, restraint and estradiol levels: A repeated measures study in healthy women. *Appetite*, 1991, 17, 177-85.

18. Weingarten H.P., Elston D. Food cravings in a college population. *Appetite*, 1991, 17, 167-75.

19. Heatherton T.F., Nichols P., Mahamedi F., Keel P. Body weight, dieting, and eating disorder symptoms among college students, 1982 to 1992. *American Journal of Psychiatry*, 1995, 152 (11), 1623-9.

20. Hetherington M.M., Macdiarmid J.I. Chocolate addiction: a preliminary description and report of its relationship to problem eating. *Appetite*, 1993, 21, 233-46.

21. Telch C.F., Agras W.S., Rossiter E.M. Binge eating increases with increasing adiposity. *International Journal of Eating Disorders*, 1988, 7(1), 115-9.

22. Gendall K.A., Joyce P.R., Sulivan P.F., Bulik C.M. Food cravers: characteristics of those who binge. *International Journal of Eating Disorders*, 1998, 23, 353-60.

23. Sullivan P.F., Bulik C.M., Fear J.L., Pickering A.F. Outcome of anorexia nervosa: A case-control study. *American Journal of Psychiatry*, 1998, 155(7), 939-46.

24. NIMH Diagnostic Centres for Psychiatric Linkage studies: Diagnostic Interview for Genetic Studies. version 1.0. Modified by Sullivan P.F., Bulik C.M., Fear J.L. Christchurch, New Zealand. 1992.

25. Nurneberger J.I., Blehar M.C., Kaufmann C.A., York-Cooler C., Simpson S.G., Harkavy-Friedmen J., Severe J.B., Malaspina D., Reich T.D. Diagnostic Interview for Genetic Studies: rationale, unique features and training. *Archives of General Psychiatry*, 1994, 51, 849-59.

26. Cloninger C.R., Svrakic D.M., Przybeck T.R. A psychobiological model of temperament and character. *Archives of General Psychiatry*, 1993, 50, 975-90.

27. Stunkard A.J., Messick S. The three-factor eating questionnaire to measure dietary restraint, disinhibition and hunger. *Journal of Psychosomatic Research*, 1985, 29(1), 71-83.

28. Parker G., Tupling H., Brown L.B. A Parental Bonding Instrument. *British Journal of Medical Psychology*, 1979, 52, 1-10.

29. Gendall K.A., Sullivan P.F., Joyce P.R., Bulik C.M. Psychopathology and personality of young women who experience food cravings. *Addictive Behaviors*, 1997, 22(4), 545-55.

30. Ruderman A.J. Dietary restraint: A theoretical and empirical review. *Psychological Bulletin*, 1986, 99(2), 247-62.

31. Tuschl R.J. From dietary restraint to binge eating: Some theoretical considerations. *Appetite*, 1990, 14, 105-9.

32. Cowen P.J., Anderson I.M., Fairburn C.G. Neurochemical effects of dieting: relevance to changes in eating and affective disorders, in *The Biology of Feast and Famine*. Eds Anderson G.H., Kennedy S.H. San Diego, Academic Press. 1992.

33. Polivy J., Zeitlin S.B., Herman C.P., Beal A.L. Food restriction and binge eating: a study of former prisoners of war. *Journal of Abnormal Psychology*, 1994, 103(2), 409-11.

34. Heatherton T.F., Polivy J. Chronic dieting and eating disorders: A spiral model, in *The Etiology of Bulimia Nervosa: The Individual and Family Context*. Eds Crowther J.H., Tennenbaum D.L., Hobfoll S.E., Parris Stephens M.A. Ohio, Hemisphere Publishing Corporation. 1990, 157-77.

35. Abraham S.F., Beumont P.J. How patients describe bulimia or binge eating. *Psychological Medicine*, 1982, 12, 625-35.

36. Pyle R.L., Mitchell J.E., Eckert E.D. Bulimia: a report of 34 cases. *Journal of Clinical Psychiatry*, 1981, 42, 60-4.

37. Hsu L.K.G. Experiential aspects of bulimia nervosa. *Behavior Modification*, 1990, 14, 50-65.

38. Kales E.F. Macronutrient analysis of binge eating in bulimia. *Physiology & Behavior*, 1990, 48, 837-40.

39. Weingarten H.P., Elston D. The phenomenology of food cravings. *Appetite*, 1990, 15, 231-46.

40. Russell G.F.M. Bulimia nervosa: an ominous variant of anorexia nervosa. *Psychological Medicine*, 1979, 9, 429-48.

41. Kaye W.H., Gwirtsman H.E., George T., Weiss S.R., Jimerson D.C. Relationship of mood alterations to binging behavior in bulimia. *British Journal of Psychiatry*, 1986, 149, 479-85.

42. Kissileff H.R., Walsh B.T., Kral J.G., Cassidy S.M. Laboratory studies of eating behaviour in women with bulimia. *Physiology & Behavior*, 1986, 38, 563-70.

43. Mitchell J.E., Laine D.C. Monitored binge eating behavior in patients with bulimia. *International Journal of Eating Disorders*, 1985, 4, 177-84.

44. Walsh B.T., Kissileff H.R., Cassidy S.M., Dantzic S. Eating behavior of women with bulimia. *Archives of General Psychiatry*, 1989, 46, 54-8.

45. Van der Ster Wallin G., Norring C., Holmgren S. Binge eating versus non purged eating in bulimics: is there a carbohydrate craving after all? *Acta Psychiatrica Scandinavica*, 1994, 89, 376-81.

46. Woell C., Fitcher M.M., Pirke K., Wolfram G. Eating behavior of patients with bulimia nervosa. *International Journal of Eating Disorders*, 1989, 8(5), 557-68.

47. Gendall K.A., Sullivan P.F., Joyce P.R., Carter F.A., Bulik C.M. The nutrient intake of women with bulimia nervosa. *International Journal of Eating Disorders*, 1997, 21(2), 115-27.

48. Nagle D.W., Johnson W.G., Carr-Nagle R.E., Engler L.B. Binge eating disorder and the proposed DSM-IV criteria: Psychometric analysis of the Questionnaire if Eating and Weight Patterns. *International Journal of Eating Disorders*, 1994, 16(2), 47-157.

49. Loro A.D., Orleans C.S. Binge eating in obesity: Preliminary findings and guidelines for behavioural analysis and treatment. *Addictive Behaviors*, 1981, 6, 155-66.

50. Yanovski S.Z., Leet M., Yanovski J.A., Flood M., Gold P.W., Kissileff H.R., Walsh B.T. Food selection and intake of obese women with binge-eating disorder. *American Journal of Clinical Nutrition*, 1992, 56, 975-80.

51. Bulik C.M., Sullivan P.F., Epstein L.H., McKee M., Kaye W.H., Dahl R.E., Weltzin T. Drug use in women with anorexia and bulimia nervosa. *International Journal of Eating Disorders*, 1992, 11(3), 213-25.

52. Reid L. *Opioids, bulimia and alcohol abuse and alcoholism.* New York, Springer-Verlag. 1990.

53. Suzuki K., Higuchi S., Yamada K., Komiya H., Takagi S. Bulimia nervosa with and without alcoholism: a comparative study in Japan. *International Journal of Eating Disorders*, 1994, 16(2), 137-46.

54. Scott D.W. Alcohol and food abuse: Some comparisons. *British Journal of Addiction*, 1983, 78, 339-49.

55. Yeary J. The use of overeaters anonymous in the treatment of eating disorders. *Journal of Psychoactive Drugs*, 1987, 19, 303-9.

56. Bulik C.M., Sullivan P.F., Weltzin T.E., Kaye W.H. Temperament in eating disorders. *International Journal of Eating Disorders*, 1995, 17(3), 251-61.

57. Cloninger C.R. A unified biosocial theory of personality and its role in the development of anxiety states. *Psychiatric Developments*, 1986, 3, 167-226.

58. Cloninger C.R., Sigvardsson S., Boham M. Childhood personality predicts alcohol abuse in young adults. *Alcoholism: Clinical and Experimental Research*, 1988, 12, 494-505.

59. Earleywine M., Finn P.R., Peterson J.B. Factor structure and correlates of the Tridimensional Personality Questionnaire. *Journal of Studies on Alcohol*, 1992, 53, 233-8.

60. Treece C., Khantzian E.B. Psychodynamic factors in the development of drug dependence. *Psychiatric Clinics of North America*, 1986, 9(3), 399-412.

61. Cloninger R.C., Przybeck T.R., Svrakic D.M., Wetzel R.D. *The Temperament and Character Inventory (TCI): A guide to its development and use*. St Louis, Missouri, Center for Psychobiology of Personality, Washington University. 1994.

62. Striegel-Moore R.H., Silberstein L.R., Rodin J. Toward an understanding of risk factors for bulimia. *American Psychologist*, 1986, 41(3), 246-63.

63. Striegel-Moore R.H. Etiology of binge eating: A developmental perspective, in *Binge Eating: Nature, Assessment and Treatment*. Eds Fairburn C.G., Wilson G.T. New York, Guilford Press. 1993, 144-72.

64. Schupak-Neuberg E., Nemeroff C.J. Disturbances in identity and self-regulation in bulimia nervosa: Implications for a metaphorical perspective. *International Journal of Eating Disorders*, 1993, 13(4), 335-47.

65. Hawkins R.C.I., Clement P.F. Binge eating: Measurement problems and a conceptual model, in *The binge-purge syndrome*. Eds Hawkins R.C.I., Fremouw W.J., Clement P.F. New York, Springer. 1984, 229-53.

66. Wardle J., Beinart H. Binge eating: A theoretical review. *British Journal of Clinical Psychology*, 1981, 20, 97-109.

67. Bulik C.M., Sullivan P.F., Joyce P.R., Carter F.A., McIntosh V.V. Predictors of one-year treatment outcome in bulimia nervosa. *Comprehensive Psychiatry*, 1998, 39(4), 206-14.

68. Hathaway S.R., McKinley J.C. *Minnesota Multiphasic Personality Inventory: Manual for Administration and Scoring*. New York, Psychological Corporation. 1967.

69. Lingswiler V.M., Crowther J.H., Stephens M.A.P. Emotional and somatic consequences of binge episodes. *Addictive Behaviors*, 1989, 14, 503-11.

70. Agras W.S. Pharmacology of bulimia nervosa and binge eating disorder: longer-term outcomes. *Psychopharmacology Bulletin*, 1997, 33(3), 433-6.

71. Fairburn C.G., Marcus M.D., Wilson G.T. Cognitive-behavioural therapy for binge eating and bulimia nervosa: A comprehensive treatment manual, in *Binge Eating: Nature, Assessment and Treatment.* Eds Fairburn C.G., Wilson G.T. New York, Guilford Press. 1993, 361-404.

72. Fluoxetine Bulimia Nervosa Collaborative Study Group: Fluoxetine in the treatment of bulimia nervosa. *Archives of General Psychiatry*, 1992, 49, 139-47.

73. Walsh B.T., Devlin M.J. Pharmacotherapy of bulimia nervosa and binge eating disorder. *Addictive Behaviors*, 1995, 20(6), 757-64.

74. Toornvliet A.C., Pijl H., Hopman E., Elte-de Wever B.M., Meinders A.E. Serotonergic drug-induced weight loss in carbohydrate craving obese patients. *International Journal of Obesity*, 1996, 20, 917-20.

75. Wurtman J.J., Wurtman R.J., Growdon J.H., Henry P., Lipscomb A., Zeisel S.H. Carbohydrate craving in obese people: suppression by treatments affecting serotonergic transmission. *International Journal of Eating Disorders*, 1981, 1, 2-11.

76. Wurtman J.J., Wurtman R.J., Mark S., Tsay R., Gilbert W.J.G. D-Fenfluramine selectively suppresses carbohydrate snacking by obese subjects. *International Journal of Eating Disorders*, 1985, 4, 89-99.

77. el-Guebaly N., Hodgins D. Substance related cravings and relapse: Clinical implications. *Canadian Journal of Psychiatry*, 1998, 43(1), 29-36.

78. Kozlowski L.T., Mann R.E., Wilkinson D.A. & Poulos C.X. "Cravings" are ambiguous: ask about urges or desires. *Addictive Behaviour*, 1989, 14, 443-5.

7.4. EATING DISORDERS AND ADDICTION

G. Terence Wilson and Janet D. Latner

7.4.1 Introduction

Eating disorders include anorexia nervosa, bulimia nervosa, and sub-threshold variations of these two disorders, called Eating Disorders Not Otherwise Specified (EDNOS) (1). Probably the most prominent and actively researched example of EDNOS is Binge Eating Disorder (BED), which is characterised by recurrent binge eating without the compensatory weight control methods (e.g. purging) that define bulimia nervosa. In contrast to bulimia nervosa, patients with BED who seek treatment are typically overweight or obese. It is important, however, to point out that obesity itself is not classified as an eating disorder. Neither Diagnostic and Statistical Manual version IV (American Psychiatric Association) (DSM-IV) nor its predecessor, DSM-III-R, classified eating disorders as a form of psychoactive substance abuse (2,3).

Likening the eating disorders to an addiction (i.e. psychoactive substance abuse) has been commonplace in both the eating disorders and substance abuse literatures (4). That there are apparent similarities between the two classes of disorder seems undeniable. For example, a loss of control over eating occurs during binge eating episodes; food can be consumed in response to negative emotion; patients report "cravings", and become preoccupied with food. However, these apparent similarities do not make eating disorders an addiction, and are more usefully and accurately explained by a very different conceptual framework.

7.4.2 Does Food Have Psychoactive Effects?

The critical assumption on which the addiction model of eating disorders rests is that food is a drug - either literally or functionally. As such, it can have psychoactive effects on mood and behavior in a manner comparable to that of alcohol and other addictive substances.

The hypothesis that food has psychoactive effects has been tested and found wanting. In their incisive analysis of this basic question, Haddock and Dill (2) concluded that the effects of food are very different from those of psychoactive substances such as alcohol. They observe that food constituents (with the possible exception of caffeine) do not interact directly with synaptic macromolecules or accumulate *in vivo*. Therefore, any effects on mood or behaviour are likely to be subtle and hard to detect. Even when various food substances are administered in large quantities and in pure form, they demonstrate little pharmacological effect (2).

7.4.3 Characteristics of Addiction

Addiction or chemical dependency, as it is often called, is characterised by the phenomena of tolerance, physical dependence, and withdrawal reactions. We are unaware of any credible scientific evidence establishing that these phenomena apply to eating disorders.

7.4.3.1 *Physical dependence*

Citing a physical dependence on food as evidence for a food addiction in eating disorder patients is meaningless, as it would imply that all animal species are similarly addicted, based on their biological dependence on food. This argument is analogous to claiming that the need for sleep reflects an addiction to this behaviour. The obvious biological consequences of food hardly make it an addictive substance, just as the biological effects of activities such as sex, sleep, and exercise do not make these behaviours physiologically addictive. Starvation, or the withdrawal of food, produces a specific constellation of physiological and psychological symptoms, including irritability and distractibility, preoccupation with food and weight, and binge eating. These can develop in food-deprived bulimia nervosa patients (5) as well as in healthy food-deprived males (6). Identifying and addressing these symptoms (through the elimination of strict dieting) is essential for treatment, but they are not equivalent to drug withdrawal effects.

7.4.3.2   Craving

Selective cravings for particular foods or food categories are often cited as evidence that individuals who crave them are addicted to food. For example, so-called carbohydrate craving has received attention as a possible contributing cause of bulimia nervosa and binge eating disorder. The notion of carbohydrate craving is based on the premise that carbohydrates increase the transport of tryptophan, relative to other large neutral amino acids (LNAAs), into the brain. This increase enhances serotonin synthesis, which in turn is thought to reduce negative affect. Although tryptophan depletion may be a trigger for increased eating in patients with bulimia nervosa (7), there is no evidence that carbohydrates or tryptophan repletion relieve negative mood. Turner et al. (8) found that mood ratings in bulimia nervosa patients remained the same even after they consumed a 1,200 kcal carbohydrate drink. Jansen et al. (9) also found a near-zero correlation between carbohydrate intake and mood in bulimia nervosa patients.

More recently, Toornvliet et al. (10) completed an experimental analysis of the psychological and metabolic responses of obese patients with so-called carbohydrate craving to carbohydrate, fat, and protein-rich snacks. In an effort to test the hypothesis that carbohydrate-craving (CC) obese patients are a unique subgroups of obese individuals, they divided patients into two groups: 9 CC obese patients, and 17 non-CC obese control patients. The CC patients, by definition, included those who consumed 30% or more of their total intake from snacks that were nearly pure carbohydrate. At least 40% of their total daily carbohydrate intake came from these snacks.

To test the hypothesis that CC patients consume carbohydrate as a kind of self-medication to alleviate depressive symptoms, each group was given three different liquid snacks on three different days - a carbohydrate-rich snack, a fat/carbohydrate-rich snack, and a protein-rich snack. Mood, performance, and glucose and insulin levels were assessed before and after each snack. The results showed no carbohydrate-specific or patient-specific effects on either the subjective or physiological measures used. Although anger and fatigue scores were higher for CC patients at baseline, mood did not change significantly in these or control patients after any of the snacks. Performance on a cognitive task improved equally after administration of all three snack types in all patients. Glucose and insulin responses to the snacks also did not differ between the groups. These findings occurred despite a substantial rise in the ratio of plasma tryptophan levels to other LNAA levels in all subjects after carbohydrate and fat snacks and a decline in this ratio after protein. The steep rise in tryptophan:LNAA ratio therefore failed to produce the predicted elevation in mood. Based on these data, the authors concluded that it is "useless to maintain the concept of carbohydrate craving for subdividing obese patients".

Another fundamental problem with the carbohydrate craving hypothesis is that most carbohydrate-rich foods do not even increase tryptophan levels. Only foods that are nearly pure carbohydrate ($\leq$4%) will allow a rise of brain tryptophan levels (11), and very few foods contain proportions of protein this small. However, even if tryptophan were to increase, the ratio of tryptophan to the other LNAAs would need to increase between 50% and 100% to have a significant impact on serotonin synthesis; this amount of change cannot occur in a normal diet (2). Other problems with the tryptophan model of carbohydrate regulation remain (see also sections 4.2 and 6.5). For example, the level of carbohydrate intake consumed over extended periods of time is actually not tightly controlled, suggesting the absence of a regulatory system. Furthermore, serotonin releasers such as fenfluramine do not produce a selective suppression of carbohydrate intake as the model predicts (12).

Drewnowski (13) has argued that it is taste responsiveness and hedonic responses that play a central role in the selection of food, rather than an effect of foods on serotonin levels. Hedonic response to carbohydrates, most positive when they are paired with fats (13), may be mediated by endogenous opioid peptides. Beta-endorphin levels in bulimia nervosa patients were not found to rise in response to glucose ingestion (14). However, there is evidence that opioid antagonists such as naltrexone reduced the intake of palatable foods in normal males (15). In BED patients, the opioid antagonist naloxone reduced taste preferences, particularly for sweet high-fat foods, and total caloric intake (16). In a double-blind, placebo control study, Mitchell *et al.* (17) found that naloxone decreased food intake during binge eating episodes in bulimia nervosa patients but had only modest effects in reducing binge eating frequency. In a study with no placebo control group, naltrexone at high doses reduced binge and purge frequency more than a lower dose of naltrexone over a 6-week period (18). Alger *et al.* (19) found no effect of naltrexone on binge eating in normal weight and obese patients. It appears that, although opioid antagonists may mediate taste response to palatable foods, this mediation is not specific to carbohydrates, as the serotonergic model would predict. Naltrexone was found to have no effect on macronutrient selection in women with bulimia nervosa (20). The theory that taste response is mediated by opioid peptides is distinct from theories proposing that the brain is able to regulate macronutrient selection (and craving), which require that efferent signals relate to the metabolic consequences of ingested food rather than its sensory properties (21).

Numerous studies have examined the intake of bulimia nervosa patients throughout the day and during binges and meals. Most studies have found that no particular macronutrient (e.g. carbohydrate) is predominant, and therefore, they provide little evidence that patients are using carbohydrates to regulate brain serotonin levels. Over the course of the day, proportions of energy intake from carbohydrate are no different between bulimia nervosa patients and control subjects, whereas fat intake is somewhat higher and protein intake lower in patients (22). Similarly, as meal size and 24-hour caloric intake increase in bulimia nervosa patients, the percentage of food consumed as fat, but not carbohydrates, increases (23).

During binge episodes, the proportions of carbohydrate and fat consumed by bulimia nervosa patients are similar to those of control subjects given instructions to binge eat (24). Patients also consume similar proportions of carbohydrate during binges and non-binges (9,24). Yanovski and her associates (25) found no difference between BED patients and weight-matched controls in the percentage of energy from carbohydrate they consumed when instructed to binge eat. Walsh *et al.* (24) and Yanovski *et al.* (25) did find higher proportions of fat intake and lower proportions of protein intake in the binge episodes of patients. Only one study has shown a slightly higher proportion of intake from carbohydrates during the binge episodes of patients with bulimia nervosa (26). However, in this Swedish study, patients also consumed significantly more fat during binges compared with other eating episodes.

Generally, the most outstanding difference between patients and controls is in the amount of food consumed, not in the proportions of macronutrients selected (27). Bulimia nervosa patients consume approximately three times as much food as control subjects during binge episodes (28) and over a 24-hour period (22,23).

7.4.3.3   Loss of control over eating

Patients with bulimia nervosa or BED experience a periodic loss of control over eating and may be preoccupied with food. The most parsimonious explanation for these phenomena is patients' excessive dietary restraint that triggers binge eating through its biological and psychological sequelae (29) (see also section 7.1). Caloric restriction in animals elicits hyperphagia when palatable foods are presented, and this overeating can persist even months after the caloric deprivation has ended (30).

Psychological aspects of food restriction can also trigger overeating and reported loss of control. Bulimia nervosa patients categorise different foods as "safe" or "forbidden" (31) and, once a forbidden food is eaten, patients may believe they have violated a dietary rule and then overeat (5). Marlatt and Gordon (32) have termed this reaction the "abstinence violation effect" in the context of alcohol abuse. Of the foods consumed by bulimia nervosa patients during binge eating episodes, 69% contained individuals' forbidden foods; 15% of non-binge-eating bouts contained these foods (31). One major reason that bulimia nervosa patients report craving carbohydrate may be that they have tried to limit their carbohydrate intake. In 74% of patients, the onset of binge eating is preceded by a failure to maintain a carbohydrate-restricted diet (33). Woell and colleagues (34) have suggested that society's shifting perception of healthy or dangerous foods can influence the categories of foods that bulimia nervosa patients consider forbidden. Foods consumed during binges often contain a combination of sweet and fat ingredients, but, depending on the most popular current target, patients may perceive and report their binges to consist primarily of fat or primarily of carbohydrate (34). For example, currently the popular media has increasingly been representing carbohydrates as unhealthy and fattening; this trend is reflected among patients referred recently for treatment. When interviewed about their dietary rules and restrictions, patients report trying to avoid carbohydrates and sugar. They also report binge eating on these foods. This pattern probably reflects the tendency to binge on foods that are restricted at other times as well as the tendency to perceive binges as consisting of forbidden foods.

The difference between the addiction model of loss of control and the evidence-based cognitive-behavioural model (35) can be illustrated in the following case vignette from Wilson (36):

Carolyn had suffered from bulimia nervosa for 10 years. She was preoccupied with controlling her body weight and shape by rigid dieting. She skipped meals and avoided specific "forbidden foods," especially ice cream. But once or twice a week she lost control and binged. As part of her cognitive-behavioral treatment (CBT)*, I encouraged her to cease dieting, eat three regular meals each day, and deliberately consume some previously "forbidden foods." Carolyn insisted that she could not eat ice cream without binge eating. She believed that ice cream *per se* automatically triggered loss of control over eating. I encouraged her to test this firmly held belief. I suggested an alternative explanation for her binge eating. She had binged after eating ice cream in the past because, by violating her rigid diet, guilt combined with her actual hunger to cause loss of control.

Carolyn decided that she could not trust herself to keep ice cream in her house, but did agree to make plans with her teenage daughter to go out for ice cream during the afternoon. Our goal was to change the biological and psychosocial conditions under which she ate ice cream. Instead of being hungry, she would have eaten lunch. Instead of being

---

alone and feeling vulnerable as in the past, she would have the support and pleasure of being with her daughter, with whom she was emotionally close. Carolyn ate the ice cream, experienced no loss of control, and came away empowered by the event.

* see ref 36.

The point of this case illustration is that loss of control occurs within an emotional and psychosocial context. It is far more complex than a physiological reaction to specific foodstuffs.

7.4.4   Conceptual Limitations of the Addiction Model

The addiction model of eating disorders focuses too narrowly on binge eating. The reason is obvious - this symptom, marked by loss of control over food (substance) intake, most closely resembles psychoactive substance abuse. But it is now well-established that binge eating is but one facet of bulimia nervosa. The cognitive behavioural model of the factors that maintain bulimia nervosa details how binge eating is largely a product of rigid and unhealthy dietary restraint. The latter is driven by the need to lose weight, which is a function of negative self-evaluation and dysfunctional concerns about body weight and shape (35). Given this conceptual model of what maintains bulimia nervosa, there simply is no comparable phenomenon in substance abuse disorders. As Fairburn (37) points out, binge drinking in alcoholics is not triggered by a rigid commitment to sobriety or because they fear intoxication.

Another problem with the addiction model is that it lumps together the different eating disorders. This lack of differentiation is inevitable given the assertion that eating disorders are simply one expression of a higher-order form of substance abuse; however this assertion opposes the data, not to mention common sense. There are important differences among the eating disorders. For example, roughly half of anorexia nervosa patients restrict food intake without binge eating or purging. Essentially, they starve themselves. To what psychoactive substance, then, are they addicted? Turning logic on its head, the answer is the absence of food (38). The illogicality of this debased meaning of addiction is highlighted in the case of a patient with anorexia nervosa who binges and purges. In this single case, the person must be said to be addicted both to food and its absence (39).

Binge eating characterises both bulimia nervosa and BED, but there are several important differences between the two eating disorders. BED is characterised by significantly lower levels of dietary restraint than bulimia nervosa (40). Whereas the onset of binge eating in bulimia nervosa is linked to dieting, many BED patients report binge eating well before initiating dieting (41). Consistent with this difference, the majority of BED patients seeking treatment are overweight or obese (42). Unlike bulimia nervosa, a significant minority of BED patients are males. The natural course of the two disorders differs, with BED far more likely to remit over time (43). And they respond differently to treatment. Both cognitive behaviour therapy and antidepressant medication have been shown to have specific treatment effects in bulimia nervosa (44). In contrast, in BED, CBT is no more effective than alternative psychological interventions, and antidepressant medication is not reliably more effective than pill placebo (45). The addiction model neither predicts nor explains these differences.

Despite the absence of empirical support and its conceptual weaknesses, the addiction model of eating disorders appears to be alive and well. It is adopted by many practitioners in the US, especially those with experience in 12-step programmes for the treatment of substance abuse. An indication of the influential nature of the addiction model can be gleaned from the recently published *Practice Guideline for Eating Disorders* from the American Psychiatric Association (46). This Guideline makes explicit reference to the addiction model as a treatment option. It cautions that there is no scientific evidence on 12-step treatments derived from the addiction model, and recommends against the "sole initial" use of 12-step programmes for both anorexia nervosa and bulimia nervosa. Nonetheless, the inclusion of the addiction model in the *Practice Guideline* is noteworthy.

Why, given the disconfirming experimental evidence, does the addiction model continue to flourish? Haddock and Dill (2) point out that the more general belief in the putative psychoactive properties of food has proved resistant to the accumulation of unsupportive scientific findings. They illustrate this phenomenon with the example of the alleged negative impact of sugar on hyperactivity, a relationship that has not been shown to hold up in carefully controlled research.

Attributing problems to an "addiction" exploded on the cultural scene in the US during the 1980s and 1990s (47,48). In her trenchant critique of this development, Kaminer (47) pointed out that "what were once billed as bad habits and problems are now considered addictions". The Oxford English Dictionary defines "addiction" as habitual behavior, as in an addiction to watching too much television. But this descriptive sense was abandoned and replaced by the notion of addiction as a disease state (48).

Explaining unwanted or puzzling behavior in terms of a disease state enjoys popular appeal. But in the case of eating disorders, as in other areas, simply relabelling the problem does not advance our understanding; nor has it led to a treatment that has been shown to be effective. The term "addiction" needs to be explained itself, let alone being used to explain another complex biopsychosocial problem such as eating disorders (39). Furthermore, it is important not to forget that the validity and utility of the disease theory have been challenged even in the area of chemical dependency (32,49).

7.4.5   Implications for Treatment

Proponents of the addiction model of eating disorders typically use a 12-step approach to treatment, which is basically the same programme of recovery as is used in Alcoholics Anonymous (AA). The words "food" and "compulsive overeating" are substituted for AA's "alcohol" and "alcoholism" (50). Based on the treatment of substance abuse, this approach calls for continual dietary restraint and the avoidance of certain foods thought to be toxic, rigid eating patterns, a heightened sense of powerlessness, and a reinforcement of dichotomous thinking patterns (51). For example, abstinence is a major goal of participants in Overeaters

Anonymous (OA) (52), and this often involves the complete elimination of certain foods from the diet, such as refined sugar or flour.

There is no scientific evidence supporting the use of 12-step programmes or abstinence from certain food groups as an effective treatment method for bulimia nervosa or BED. Moreover, the prescriptions of recovery programmes based on the addiction model of eating disorders contradict some key elements of what is now known about the maintenance of binge eating (28). Specifically, abstaining from specific types of food is a rigid dietary rule that serves only to maintain the disorder. CBT, the most effective treatment for bulimia nervosa (44) aims to replace strict dieting with regular and flexible meals and snacks that increase the controlled intake of previously forbidden foods. The addiction model would predict that this cognitive-behavioural approach could not possibly be effective, and, if forbidden foods actually have toxic elements, should be harmful. The long-term effectiveness of CBT provides clear disconfirmation of a key prediction of the addiction model.

Some 12-step programmes have attempted to replace the principle of abstinence from particular foods with abstinence from binge eating and purging (52,53). Whereas this revision makes the 12-step approach more compatible with evidence-based treatments for eating disorders, it does not add substantively to these existing treatments. Social support and other valuable but generic features of 12-step groups are not unique to this approach.

Individuals have minimal control over their body shape and weight. Therefore, eating disorders patients in CBT should be guided towards an acceptance of their shape and weight once they have made nutritionally sound and psychologically adaptive lifestyle changes (54). This principle is reflected in a core tenet of Alcoholics Anonymous, the Serenity Prayer: "God, grant me the serenity to accept the things I cannot change, the courage to change the things I can, and the wisdom to know the difference." Developing a balance between acceptance and change does not include patients' turning over control to some higher power or acknowledging their powerlessness over food. Increasing acceptance in CBT is an active process of self-affirmation and empowerment (54).

7.4.6   Comorbidity of Eating and Substance Abuse Disorders

To argue against the addiction model of eating disorders is not to gainsay the comorbidity of eating and substance abuse disorders. Several studies, including both community and clinical samples, have now shown that the two disorders do co-occur more frequently than would be expected. Substance abuse is higher among individuals with eating disorders than in the population at large (55). Furthermore, eating disorders appear to be more prevalent in patients who abuse alcohol (56). This evidence of a crossover effect between the two sets of disorders suggests a real association. The challenge is to identify the mechanisms responsible for this co-occurrence.

One model that has been advanced to explain the comorbidity between eating and substance abuse disorders is that they are different expressions of the same underlying biological or genetic vulnerability. The addiction model is one form of this "common cause" view. However, several different lines of evidence fail to provide empirical support for the model.

First, the link between eating and substance abuse disorders is not a specific one. Substance abuse in clinical samples occurs at least as frequently among patients with other psychiatric disorders such as anxiety disorders (57) as it does among those with eating disorders. Moreover, evidence has consistently shown that the comorbidity of both anxiety disorders and mood disorders with eating disorders is higher than that of substance abuse (55,58).

Second, the pattern of familial transmission of the two sets of disorders is inconsistent with the notion of a common causal factor. First-degree relatives of patients with eating disorders have higher rates of substance abuse disorder than community controls (59). Garfinkel *et al.* (55) found the same relationship in a community sample of women with bulimia nervosa. A case-control study of the development of bulimia nervosa found that alcohol problems in parents emerged as a specific risk factor for bulimia nervosa, providing further evidence of a familial association between the disorders (60).

Nevertheless, the evidence indicates that the familial aggregation of substance abuse in bulimia nervosa probands is independent of bulimia nervosa (61). The association obtains only in those bulimia nervosa patients who also report substance abuse (59). Consistent with this conclusion, Kendler *et al.*'s (62) analysis of female twins revealed that the genetic risk factors for bulimia nervosa and alcohol abuse/dependence were different.

If a common underlying mechanism causes both sets of disorders, there should be a reciprocal relationship in familial transmission, with higher rates of eating disorders in the first-degree relatives of alcoholics. Schuckit *et al.* (63) completed a large, well-controlled study of 2,283 women and 1,982 men with alcohol dependence in which they analysed the prevalence of both anorexia nervosa and bulimia nervosa in the alcoholic probands and their first-degree relatives. The results revealed "no indication of a high level of familial crossover between eating disorders and alcohol dependence. The data did not reveal a significantly higher rate of eating disorders among the relatives of primary alcoholics or among those of primary and secondary alcoholics combined than among the relatives of comparison subjects".

Finally, the common cause model must predict that the two disorders would alternate within the same person (28). For example, eliminating bulimia nervosa might increase the substance abuse unless the underlying problem was resolved. No evidence exists showing that this happens when bulimia nervosa is successfully treated even over a 5-year follow-up (64). To our knowledge, no published study has prospectively assessed the possible emergence of an eating disorder in patients successfully treated for substance abuse disorder.

Strober *et al.* (65) have reported that the presence of binge eating in anorexia nervosa predicted the onset of substance abuse disorder over a 10-year longitudinal study. This finding is intriguing on several counts. It replicates other studies indicating that the association with substance abuse disorder is confined to anorexia nervosa patients who binge or purge rather than those who simply restrict their eating (66). In addition, the later development of substance abuse disorder occurred more frequently in those patients who initially showed binge eating at the time of intake, and not in those who subsequently began to binge eat. This finding is difficult to interpret. It does not necessarily indicate that both disorders are expressions of a common cause. It is consistent with the view that the presence of one disorder predisposes to the development of another (67). Several other studies have shown that eating disorders precede the development of substance abuse disorders, but not vice-versa (68).

7.4.7   Clinical Recommendations

Given the association between eating disorders and psychoactive substance abuse, women seeking treatment for eating disorders should be routinely screened for the presence of substance abuse. Similarly, women in treatment primarily for substance abuse problems should be assessed for disturbances in eating.

In those cases where both eating and substance abuse disorders co-occur, we recommend that the latter be treated first. A sustained focus on changing eating or eliminating binge eating is difficult if not impossible if there is a serious drug or alcohol problem. Once the substance abuse problem is under control, attention can then be directed to the eating problem. If the alcohol or drug abuse is not severe, it may be possible to treat the two problems at the same time.

It is not uncommon for patients with bulimia nervosa to report a prior history of substance abuse. It does not appear that such a history is a negative prognostic indicator for success in treating the eating disorder itself (44).

7.4.8   Conclusions

The available evidence argues against viewing eating disorders as a form of addiction. Furthermore, the addiction model fails in conceptualising the clinical features of eating disorders and in accounting for the important differences among anorexia nervosa, bulimia nervosa, and BED. Perhaps its greatest weakness has been the failure to generate a demonstrably effective treatment. In marked contrast, cognitive behaviour therapy, which derives directly from a conceptual model that is fundamentally at odds with the addiction model, has been shown to be effective in numerous controlled clinical trials (44).

Studies of both clinical and community samples have revealed some form of association between eating and substance abuse disorders. The precise nature of this co-occurrence is unknown, although it does not appear to be a specific association. One possibility is that they are different expressions of the same underlying vulnerability, be it biological or psychological. The addiction model can be viewed as one form of this "common cause" interpretation. However, the available evidence neither supports the common cause view in general nor the addiction model in particular. The addiction model would seem to have little to offer in identifying the mechanisms responsible for the association between eating disorders and substance abuse. Future family-genetic studies and sophisticated risk factor research will be needed to uncover the mechanisms that account for the association between the two sets of disorders.

7.4.9   References

1.   American Psychiatric Association. *Diagnostic and statistical manual of mental disorders.* (4th ed.). Washington, DC, American Psychiatric Association. 1994.

2.   Haddock C.K., Dill P.L. The effects of food on mood and behavior: Implications for the addictions model of obesity and eating disorders. *Drugs and Society,* 2000, 15, 17-47.

3.   Rounsaville B.J., Spitzer R.L., Williams J.B.W. Proposed changes in DSM-III substance use disorders: Description and rationale. *American Journal of Psychiatry,* 1986, 143, 463-8.

4.   Vandereycken W. The addiction model in eating disorders: some critical remarks and a selected bibliography. *International Journal of Eating Disorders,* 1990, 9, 95-101.

5.   Polivy J. Psychological consequences of food restriction. *Journal of the American Dietetic Association,* 1996, 96, 589-92.

6.   Keys A., Brozek J., Henschel A., Mickelson O., Taylor H.L. *The Biology of Human Starvation.* Minneapolis, University of Minnesota Press. 1950.

7. Weltzin L.K., Fernstrom M.H., Fernstrom J.D., Neuberger S.K., Kaye W.H. Acute tryptophan depletion and increased food intake and irritability in bulimia. *American Journal of Psychiatry*, 1995, 152, 1668-74.

8. Turner M., Foggo M., Bennie J., Carroll S., Dick H., Goodwin G.M. Psychological, hormonal and biochemical changes following carbohydrate bingeing: A placebo controlled study in bulimia nervosa and matched controls. *Psychological Medicine*, 1991, 21, 123-33.

9. Jansen A., Van den Hout M.A., Griez E. Does bingeing restore bulimics' alleged 5-HT-deficiency? *Behaviour Research and Therapy*, 1989, 27, 555-60.

10. Toornvliet A.C., Pijl H., Tuinenburg J.C., Elte-de Wever B.M., Pieters M.S., Frolich M., Onkenhout W., Meinders A.E. Psychological and metabolic responses of carbohydrate craving obese patients to carbohydrate, fat and protein-rich meals. *International Journal of Obesity*, 1997, 21, 860-64.

11. Teff K.L., Young S.N., Blundell J.E. The effect of protein or carbohydrate breakfasts on subsequent plasma amino acid levels, satiety and nutrient selection in normal males. *Pharmacology Biochemistry and Behavior*, 1989, 34, 829-37.

12. Fernstrom J.D. Carbohydrate ingestion and brain serotonin synthesis: Relevance to a putative control loop for regulating carbohydrate ingestion, and effects of aspartame consumption. *Appetite*, 1988, 11 (Suppl.), 35-41.

13. Drewnowski A. Human preferences for sugar and fat, in *Appetite and body weight regulation: Sugar, fat and macronutrient substitutes*. Eds Fernstrom J.D., Miller G.D. Boca Raton, CRC Press. 1994, 137-47.

14. Getto C.J., Fullerton D.T., Carlson I.H. Plasma immunoreactive beta-endorphin response to glucose ingestion in human obesity. *Appetite*, 1984, 5, 329-35.

15. Yeomans M.R., Gray R.W. Effects of naltrexone on food intake and changes in subjective appetite during eating? Evidence for opioid involvement in the appetizer effect. *Physiology and Behavior*, 1997, 62, 15-21.

16. Drewnowski A., Krahn D.D., Demitrack M.A., Nairn K., Gosnell B.A. Taste responses and preferences for sweet high-fat foods: Evidence for opioid involvement. *Physiology and Behavior*, 1992, 51, 371.

17. Mitchell J.E., Laine D.E., Morley J.E., Levine A.S. Naloxone but not CCK-8 may attenuate binge-eating behavior in patients with the bulimia syndrome. *Biological Psychiatry*, 1986, 21, 1399-1406.

18. Jonas J.M., Gold M.S. The use of opiate antagonists in treatment of bulimia: A study of low-dose versus high-dose naltrexone. *Psychiatric Research*, 1988, 24, 195-9.

19. Alger S.A., Schwalberg M.J., Bigaouette J.M., Howard L.J., Reid L.D. Using drugs to manage binge-eating among obese and normal weight patients, in *Opioids, bulimia, and alcohol abuse and alcoholism*. Ed. Reid L.D. New York, Springer-Verlag. 1990.

20. Soll E., Thomas B., Mitchell J.E., Morley J. Lack of effect of naloxone on selection of nutrients by bulimic women. *American Journal of Psychiatry*, 1989, 146, 803.

21. Wurtman R.J., Wurtman J.J. Carbohydrate craving, obesity and brain serotonin. *Appetite*, 1986, 7 (Suppl.) 99-103.

22. Hetherington M.M., Altemus M., Nelson M.L., Bernat A.S., Gold P.W. Eating behavior in bulimia nervosa: Multiple meal analyses. *American Journal of Clinical Nutrition*, 1994, 60, 864-73.

23. Weltzin L.K., Hzu L.K.G., Pollice C., Kaye W.H. Feeding patterns in bulimia nervosa. *Biological Psychiatry*, 1991, 30, 1093-110.

24. Walsh B.T., Hadigan C.M., Kissileff H.R., LaChaussée J.L. Bulimia nervosa: A syndrome of feast and famine, in *The biology of feast and famine*. Eds Anderson G.H., Kennedy S.H. New York, Academic Press. 1992, 3-20.

25. Yanovski S.Z., Leet M., Yanovski J.A., Gold P.W., Kissileff H.R., Walsh B.T. Food intake and selection of obese women with binge eating disorder. *American Journal of Clinical Nutrition*, 1992, 56, 975-80.

26. van der Ster Wallin G., Noring C., Holmgren S. Binge eating versus nonpurged eating in bulimics: Is there a carbohydrate craving after all? *Acta Psychiatrica Scandinavica*, 1994, 89, 376-81.

27. Walsh B.T., Kissileff H.R., Cassidy S.M., Dantzic S. Eating behavior of women with bulimia. *Archives of General Psychiatry*, 1989, 46, 54-8.

28   Walsh B.T. Binge eating in bulimia nervosa, in *Binge eating: Nature, assessment, and treatment*. Eds Fairburn C.G., Wilson G.T. New York, Guilford Press. 1993, 37-49.

29.   Fairburn C.G. Eating disorders, in *The science and practice of cognitive behaviour therapy*. Eds Clark D.M., Fairburn C.G. Oxford, Oxford University Press. 1997, 209-42.

30.   Hagan M.M., Moss D.E. Persistence of binge-eating patterns after a history of restriction with intermittent bouts of refeeding on palatable food in rats: Implications for bulimia nervosa. *International Journal of Eating Disorders*, 1997, 22, 411-20.

31.   Kales E.F. Macronutrient analysis of binge eating in bulimia. *Physiology and Behavior*, 1990, 48, 837-40.

32.   Marlatt G.A., Gordon J. *Relapse prevention*. New York, Guilford Press. 1985.

33.   Lacey J.H., Coker S., Birtchnell S.A. Bulimia: Factors associated with its etiology and maintenance. *International Journal of Eating Disorders*, 1986, 5, 475-87.

34.   Woell C., Fichter M.M., Pirke K.M., Wolfram G. Eating behavior of patients with bulimia nervosa. *International Journal of Eating Disorders*, 1989, 8, 557-68.

35.   Fairburn C.G., Marcus M.D., Wilson G.T. Cognitive-behavioral therapy for binge eating and bulimia nervosa: A comprehensive manual, in *Binge eating: Nature, assessment, and treatment*. Eds Fairburn C.G., Wilson G.T. New York, Guilford Press. 1993, 361-404.

36.   Wilson G.T. Eating disorders and addiction. *Drugs & Society*, 1999, 15, 87-101.

37.   Fairburn C.G. *Overcoming Binge Eating*. New York, Guilford Press. 1995.

38.   Brumberg J.J. *Fasting girls: The emergence of anorexia nervosa as a modern disease*. Cambrige, Harvard University Press. 1988.

39.   Wilson G.T. The addiction model of eating disorders: A critical analysis. *Advances in Behaviour Research and Therapy*, 1991, 13, 27-72.

40. Wilfley D.E., Schwartz M.B., Spurrell E.B., Fairburn C.G. Using the Eating Disorder Examination to identify the specific psychopathology of binge eating disorder. *International Journal of Eating Disorders*, 27(3), 259-69.

41. Mussell M.P., Mitchell J.E., Weller C.L., Raymond N.C., Crow S.J., Crosby R.D. Onset of binge eating, dieting, obesity, and mood disorders among subjects seeking treatment for binge eating disorder. *International Journal of Eating Disorders*, 1995, 17, 395-401.

42. Marcus M.D. Binge eating in obesity, in *Binge eating: Nature, assessment and treatment*. Eds Fairburn C.G., Wilson G.T. New York, Guilford Press. 1993, 77-96.

43. Fairburn C.G., Cooper Z., Doll H.A., Norman P.A., O'Connor M.E. The natural course of bulimia nervosa and binge eating disorder in young women. *Archives of General Psychiatry*, 2000, (57), 659-65.

44. Wilson G.T., Fairburn C.G. Treatment for eating disorders, in *Treatments that work: A review of the outcome studies*. Eds Nathan P.E., Gordon J.M. New York, University Press. 1998, 501-30.

45. Wilfley D.E., Cohen L.R. Psychological treatment of bulimia nervosa and binge eating disorder. *Psychopharmacology Bulletin*, 1997, 33, 437-54.

46. American Psychiatric Association. *Practice guideline for the treatment of eating disorders*. Washington, DC, American Psychiatric Association. 2000.

47. Kaminer W. Chances are you're codependent too, in *New York Times Book Review*. 1990, February 11, 1.

48. Peele S. *Diseasing of America: addiction treatment out of control*. Massachusetts, Lexington Books. 1989.

49. Fingarette H. *Heavy drinking: the myth of alcoholism as a disease*. Berkeley, University of California Press. 1988.

50. Anonymous. Overeaters Anonymous. *Journal of the American Medical Association*, 1984, 251, 468-9.

51. Bemis K.M. Abstinence and nonabstinence models for the treatment of bulimia. *International Journal of Eating Disorders*, 1985, 4, 407-37.

52. Weiner S. The addiction of overeating: Self-help groups as treatment models. *Journal of Clinical Psychology*, 1998, 54, 163-7.

53. Johnson C.L., Sansone R.A. Integrating the twelve-step approach with traditional psychotherapy for the treatment of eating disorders. *International Journal of Eating Disorders*, 1993, 14, 121-34.

54. Wilson G.T. Acceptance and change in the treatment of eating disorders and obesity. *Behavior Therapy*, 1996, 27, 417-39.

55. Garfinkel P.E., Lin E., Goering P., Spegg C., Goldbloom D.S., Kennedy S., Kaplan A.S., Woodside D.B. Bulimia nervosa in a Canadian community sample: Prevalence and comparison of subgroups. *American Journal of Psychiatry*, 1995, 152, 1052-8.

56. Higuchi S., Suzuki K., Yamada K., Parrish K., Kono H. Alcoholics and eating disorders: Prevalence and clinical course. *British Journal of Psychiatry*, 1993, 162, 403-6.

57. Kushner M., Sher K.J., Beitman B. The relationship between alcohol problems and the anxiety disorders. *American Journal of Psychiatry*, 1990, 147, 685-95.

58. Bushnell J.A., Wells J.E., McKenzie J.M., Hornblow A.R., Oakley-Browne M.A., Joyce P.R. Bulimia comorbidity in the general population and in the clinic. *Psychological Medicine*, 1994, 24, 605-11.

59. Kaye W.H., Lilenfeld L.R., Plotnicov K., Merikangas K.R., Nagy L., Strober M., Bulik C.M., Moss H., Greeno C.G. Bulimia nervosa and substance dependence: Association and family transmission. *Alcohol: Clinical and Experimental Research*, 1996, 20, 878-81.

60. Fairburn C.G., Welch S.L., Doll H.A., Davies B.A., O'Connor M.E. Risk factors for bulimia nervosa. *Archives of General Psychiatry*, 1997, 54, 509-17.

61. Lilenfeld L.R., Kaye W.H., Greeno C.G., Merikangas K.R., Plotnicov K., Pollice C., Rao R., Strober M., Bulik C.M., Nagy L. Psychiatric disorders in women and bulimia nervosa and their first-degree relatives: Effects of comorbid substance dependence. *International Journal of Eating Disorders*, 1997, 22, 253-64.

62. Kendler K., Walters E., Neale M., Kessler R., Heath A., Eaves L. The structure of the genetic and environmental risk factors for six major psychiatric disorders in women: Phobia, generalized anxiety disorder, panic disorder, bulimia, major depression and alcoholism. *Archives of General Psychiatry*, 1995, 52, 374-83.

63. Schuckit M.A., Tipp J.E., Anthenelli R.M., Bucholz K.K., Hesselbrock V.M., Nurnberger J.I. Anorexia nervosa and bulimia nervosa in alcohol-dependent men and women and their relatives. *American Journal of Psychiatry*, 1996, 153, 74-82.

64. Fairburn C.G., Norman P.A., Welch S.E., O'Connor M.E., Doll H.A., Peveler R.C. A prospective study of outcome in bulimia nervosa and the long-term effects of three psychological treatments. *Archives of General Psychiatry*, 1995, 52, 304-12.

65. Strober M., Freeman R., Bower S., Rigali J. Binge eating in anorexia nervosa predicts later onset of substance use disorder: A ten-year prospective, longitudinal follow-up of 95 adolescents. *Journal of Youth and Adolescence*, 1996, 25, 519-26.

66. Strober M. Family-genetic perspectives on anorexia nervosa and bulimia nervosa, in *Comprehensive textbook of eating disorders and obesity*. Eds Fairburn C.G., Brownell K. New York, Guilford Press. 1995, 212-8.

67. Wonderlich S.A., Mitchell J.E. Eating disorders and comorbidity: Empirical, conceptual, and clinical implications. *Psychopharmacology Bulletin*, 1997, 33, 381-90.

68. Wilson G.T. Binge eating and addictive disorders, in *Binge eating: Nature, assessment and treatment*. Eds Fairburn C.G., Wilson G.T. New York, Guilford Press. 1993, 97-120.

INDEX

INDEX